ENGINEERING MANAGEMENT

[For the Students of B.E./B. Tech. and also useful for MBA, PGDBM and Subject-specific Courses of Professional Societies such as The Institution of Engineers (India)]

Dr. A.K. GUPTA

M.Sc. (Maths), Ph.D. (OR), MBA

Director
The Institution of Engineers (India)
8, Gokhale Road
Kolkata 700 020

S. CHAND
PUBLISHING
empowering minds

S Chand And Company Limited
(ISO 9001 Certified Company)
RAM NAGAR, NEW DELHI - 110 055

S Chand And Company Limited

(ISO 9001 Certified Company)

Head Office: 7361, RAM NAGAR, QUTAB ROAD, NEW DELHI - 110 055
Phone: 23672080-81-82, 66672000 Fax: 91-11-23677446
www.schandpublishing.com; e-mail: **helpdesk@schandpublishing.com**

S. CHAND
PUBLISHING
empowering minds

Branches:

Ahmedabad	:	Ph: 27541965, 27542369, ahmedabad@schandpublishing.com
Bengaluru	:	Ph: 22268048, 22354008, bangalore@schandpublishing.com
Bhopal	:	Ph: 4209587, bhopal@schandpublishing.com
Chandigarh	:	Ph: 2625356, 2625546, 4025418, chandigarh@schandpublishing.com
Chennai	:	Ph: 28410027, 28410058, chennai@schandpublishing.com
Coimbatore	:	Ph: 2323620, 4217136, coimbatore@schandpublishing.com (Marketing Office)
Cuttack	:	Ph: 2332580, 2332581, cuttack@schandpublishing.com
Dehradun	:	Ph: 2711101, 2710861, dehradun@schandpublishing.com
Guwahati	:	Ph: 2738811, 2735640, guwahati@schandpublishing.com
Hyderabad	:	Ph: 27550194, 27550195, hyderabad@schandpublishing.com
Jaipur	:	Ph: 2219175, 2219176, jaipur@schandpublishing.com
Jalandhar	:	Ph: 2401630, jalandhar@schandpublishing.com
Kochi	:	Ph: 2809208, 2808207, cochin@schandpublishing.com
Kolkata	:	Ph: 23353914, 23357458, kolkata@schandpublishing.com
Lucknow	:	Ph: 4065646, lucknow@schandpublishing.com
Mumbai	:	Ph: 22690881, 22610885, 22610886, mumbai@schandpublishing.com
Nagpur	:	Ph: 2720523, 2777666, nagpur@schandpublishing.com
Patna	:	Ph: 2300489, 2260011, patna@schandpublishing.com
Pune	:	Ph: 64017298, pune@schandpublishing.com
Raipur	:	Ph: 2443142, raipur@schandpublishing.com (Marketing Office)
Ranchi	:	Ph: 2361178, ranchi@schandpublishing.com
Sahibabad	:	Ph: 2771235, 2771238, delhibr-sahibabad@schandpublishing.com

First Edition 2007
Revised Edition 2010
Reprints 2012, 2013 (Twice)
Reprint 2017
Reprint 2018

ISBN : 978-81-219-2812-0   **Code** : 1010B 330

PRINTED IN INDIA

By Vikas Publishing House Pvt. Ltd., Plot 20/4, Site-IV, Industrial Area Sahibabad, Ghaziabad-201010 and Published by S Chand And Company Limited, 7361, Ram Nagar, New Delhi-110 055.

PREFACE

In this information-centric era, there is a need for engineers/technocrats, who can communicate intelligently and knowledgeably on the *home ground* of all functions of the organization. Considerable efforts have been expended in providing the means for this educational process. We are now beginning to witness the advent of the engineer who not only has an understanding of the alternative disciplines but whose thought-processes actually emulate those of the indigenous experts. These skills, which the engineers embrace in addition to their core skills, are those which equip them to be effective and successful managers. There are three major factors upon which every engineer-manager must focus: operational processes; management style; and organization structure.

Management concepts are receiving renewed emphasis. Fundamental ideas of planning, organizing, leading and controlling are central to management and engineering education. Apart from exciting opportunities in information technology, there is strong competitive pressure for zero defect products, customer service, on time delivery and lower costs. Therefore, present engineering education system demands study of various aspects of management irrespective of any specific engineering discipline.

It is this level of overall understanding and competence, the contents of this book are developed as an introductory text for students studying engineering/management course. The entire text is divided into 13 logically well-planned chapters. The contents of the book meet the requirements of over 1200 engineering colleges/institutes, including IITs, NITs, Deemed Universities. The structure of the book also caters to courses of BBA, MBA, PGDBM and subject-specific course(s) as prescribed by universities, institutions and non-formal courses being conducted by the professional societies such as The Institution of Engineers (India). The contents provide diverse mixes of text. Each chapter is followed by a number of self-assessment questions—theoretical and numerical.

The text is thoroughly revised and many solved/unsolved questions are added. Multiple choice/ short questions, covering the entire text, are added at the end.

Literature from other sources and from many disciplines have been freely consulted for this book. I express my gratitude to all such sources and authors, many of them have been listed in the bibliography. My wife, Mrs. Alka Gupta, deserves special mention for her forebearance, patience and support. I express my gratitude to Shri Navin Joshi, Vice President (Publishing), Shri R.S. Saxena, Adviser and Shri S.K. Bagal, Regional Manager of Kolkata Branch Office, whose constant persuasion has enabled me to complete the text inspite of many hindrances.

Any suggestion for improving contents of the text from teachers, students, and professionals would be gratefully acknowledged.

Dr. A.K. GUPTA

CONTENTS

The Challenge of Management

1.1 Introduction

The word *management* has the same wide connotation as the manipulative instinct of man. It started with the first man as he was born in an environment irrelevant to his existence. Nature was benevolent/ hostile by chance or accident over which he had little *managerial control*. This was the beginning of a war which continued unabated through the ages. Newton's First Law of Motion states that every body continues in its state of rest or of uniform motion unless it is compelled by some external force to act otherwise. This *external force* is indeed *management* that breaks all forms of inertia. It sifts and manipulates the direction; controls and monitors the speed; and makes certain that minimum of efforts, i.e., *force* (resources and inputs) will suffice to fulfil its aim. It is striking that even the short dictionary connotation embraces the concept lucidly and fairly comprehensively: to manage is to contrive successfully; to manipulate. In this wider connotation, every human being is a manager.

1.2 Definitions

All definitions of management agree on the essence, i.e., its universality. Management, succinctly, is the exercise of drawing the *straight line* from what you are and where you are; to what you want to be; where you want to go. The *straight line* connotes the economy in time and means—material and human, and the freedom from kinks, distortions and aberrations, in the journey from the starting point to the destination.

Urwick defines management as the art of directing human activities. Management is considered as the art and science of making decisions. It is the process of relating resources to goal accomplishment. Other views on management exist in literature are:

- It is the process of planning, organising, staffing, leading and influencing people, and controlling.
- Management is the complex of continuously coordinated activity by means of which any undertaking/administration/public or private service conducts its business.   *(ILO)*
- Management is guiding human and physical resources into a dynamic, hard-hitting organization until that attains its objectives to the satisfaction of those served, and with a high degree of morale and sense of attainment on the part of those rendering the service.

  (Lawrence A. Appley)

- It is the art and science of organising and directing human efforts applied to control forces and utilise the material of nature for the benefit of mankind.   *(ASME)*
- Management is the process or form of work that involves the guidance or direction of a group of people towards organizational goals/objectives.   *(Rue & Byars)*
- It is the art of coordinating resources: men, machine, material, money, market, information and knowledge.
- The process of optimising human, material, and financial contributions for achievement of organizational goals.   *(Pearce and Robinson, 1989)*
- Getting things done by other people.   *(Mary Parker Follett, 1941)*

• The process of planning, organising, leading and controlling the efforts of organization members and of using all organizational resources to achieve stated organizational goals.

(Mescon, Albert and Khedouri, 1985)

1.3 Elements of Management

The following *nine* elements of management, necessarily present in all forms, are presented in sequential order in which the management process is conceived, evolved and implemented:

• There has to be a horizon—a universe, an ambit within which the management must perform. This ambit may be large or small but it ought to be properly defined.

• There must be an organization, which gives the *body* to the management. It crystallises, carves out a shape and form for the management, which otherwise might look like an amorphous heap. The organization may be elaborate and complex or it may be simple.

• There is a universal need for planning, implementation and monitoring.

• Any management must properly equipped with its staff.

• Management needs leadership and direction.

• *Communication* is the life blood of the management process.

• There is the need for all-pervasive coordination.

• Management requires constant evaluation, monitoring or control.

• Innovation, a pride of place in competitive management success.

1.4 Management Thoughts

Some of the earliest illustrations of 'management thought' are provided by the Egyptians, Hebrews, Romans, the Roman Catholic Church, and the writings of select individuals. These thoughts have been employed almost since the dawn of time. A short review of management history reveals that many of the ideas and concepts used by today's managers were actually developed and applied by their historical predecessors (Table 1.1).

Table 1.1 Chronology of Managerial Accomplishments

Approximate Period	Management Thought/Concept	Accomplishments and Their Contributors
5000–1600 BC	Planning and control; material scheduling systems; organizational hierarchy	Pyramids: transportation system for huge objects; marketing of metal alloys
2000–1700 BC	Minimum wage; written receipts for control purposes	Code of Hammurabi
1491 BC	Planning, organizing, controlling; participative managements, span of control	Moses; exodus of Jews from Egypt
600 BC	Production control; incentive wage payments	Nebuchadnezzar, colour coding of raw materials for specific production lots
500–325 BC	Systems approach; specialization, scientific methods used; motion study; material handling techniques; use of the staff principle	Mencius; Cyrus; Plato; Socrates: Alexander the Great; development of trading companies; development of military organizations
300 BC–AD 284	Scalar principle of organization; job descriptions; performance standards; written plans, unity of command	Roman Empire; Cato; Jesus Christ; Diocletian
500–AD 1400	Decentralized operations; centralized authority; scalar control; double-entry book-keeping; traits of leaders	Growth of feudalism
1400–AD 1436	Various financing methods; use of ledgers	Partnerships; joint ventures; growth of international business

Approximate Period	Management Thought or Concept	Accomplishments and Their Contributors
1436–AD 1600	Cost accounting; large-scale manufacuturing; inventory control methods; system of checks and balances for internal control; personnel techniques; standardization of parts; beginning of use of assembly lines	The Arsenal of Venice; first large industrial plant; financial, personnel, accounting, and warehousing techniques refined
1700–AD 1785	Application of the principle of specialization; accountability of performance; location planning; payback computations; beginning of classical economic thought	England's Industrial Revolution; use of printing press; factory system of production; Adam Smith
1785–AD 1820	Market research; forecasting; site location; machine layout studies; interchangeable parts; incentive payments; concern for workers	Steam engine; milling machines; James Watt and Matthew Boulton; Robert Owen; Eli Whitney
1820–AD 1891	Development of management theory; description of functions of management; use of organization charts; motion studies refined; worker fatigue studies; shop management principles; wage incentive plans	Development of digital computer; growth of railways; continued industrial development by use of specialization and division of labour, foundations of scientific management; Henry Metcalfe; Henry Towne; Frederick Halsey; Charles Babbage
1900–AD 1920	Scientific management; functional organization; principles of management; time and motion studies; research on production methods; Gantt charts; training programmes for workers; application of psychology to management; economic lot size theory; office management concepts; efficiency engineering	Huge growth in productivity; revolutionary methods in the workplace; Frederick Taylor; Frank and Lillian Gilbreath; Henry Gantt; Hugo Munsterberg; Walter Dill Scott; Harrington Emerson; Henri Fayol; Max Weber
1920–AD 1940	Modern birth of human relations in industry; social responsibility of management; group dynamics; theories of motivation and communication; principles of organization	Hawthorne studies; Elton Mayo; Mary Parker Follett; Oliver Sheldon; James Mooney; Chester Burnard

There are three major schools of management thought—*quantitative school, management process school*, and *behavioural school*. The accomplishments of several contemporary writers in each of the three schools of thought are given in Table 1.2.

Table 1.2   Contemporary Contributors to Management

Contributor	Year	Contributions
Quantitative School		
Russell Ackoff	1956, 1963	• Developed modern theories in operations research and quantitative applications to business
Howard Raiffa and Robert Schlaifer	1965, 1967	• Contributed to statistical decision-making theory under conditions of uncertainty • Used strategy analysis to study competitive markets
Herbert Simon	1955, 1960, 1965	• Developed the field of decision theory by use of quantitative models of human behaviour

Contributor	Year	Contributions
Norbert Weiner	1949	• Wrote on information sciences, economics and decision-making, forming a theoretical base for study of organizations globally change • Developed theories of cybernetics used for modelling operations of the firm • Applied systems analysis to the study of organizations
Management Process School		
Alfred Chandler	1966	• Described relationship of strategy formulation to managerial functions of planning, organizing, and controlling
Ernest Dale	1952, 1960, 1967	• Analysed functions of management
Peter Drucker	1954	• Developed concepts of management by objectives, managerial planning, and the importance of knowing the real objectives of the firm • He is considered as the father of management
Harold Koontz and Cyril O'Donnell	1955	• Made the most comprehensive modern statements of management principles and the most significant attempts to unravel semantic problems in the literature
Behavioural School		
Chris Argyris	1957, 1962, 1964	• Studied organizations to determine the effect of management practices on individual behaviour and personal growth • Described conflicts between organizational goals and personal goals • Prescribed resolution techniques
Rensis Likert	1961, 1967	• Described four "systems" of management • Conducted research in effective leadership styles
Abraham Maslow	1954, 1964	• Developed major theory of individual motivation known as hierarchy of needs • Considered as the founder of humanism in modern organizations
Douglas McGregor	1960, 1967	• Described Theory X and Theory Y assumptions of human behaviour • Laid groundwork for coordinating human effort in complex organizations

Each of the three schools of thought provides a different emphasis. The quantitative people tend to be heavily economic and efficiency oriented; the management process people are generalists; and the behaviourists are most interested in psychological behaviour. Now, two obvious questions that arise are: What does the future promise? Will there be a unification of these three basic approaches to management or will everyone maintain his/her own current position? The answer appears to lie in the first-half of the second question due to the following reasons:

(*a*) Semantics: everyone is saying the same thing but using different terminology.

(*b*) There are different definitions of management.

(*c*) Tunnel vision causes each group to see its own point of view only.

Figure 1.1 represents the current state of management theory.

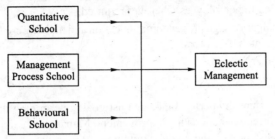

Fig. 1.1   Synthesis of modern management theory and concepts

Most managers are drawing together what they know about management, taking what is most appropriate, and disregarding the rest, thus transcending the arguments of different schools of thought and entering an eclectic stage.

1.5 Functions of Management

Key functions of management are planning, organising, motivating and controlling.

1.5.1 Planning

Planning involves advance decisions related to *what*, *when*, *why*, *how*, and *who*. It involves:
- Self-appraisal to determine the current position.
- Study of environment around organization.
- Specifications of goals and objectives and means to achieve them.
- Framework of policies, procedures, standards and anticipated course of actions.
- Forecasting.
- Resources to achieve the forecast.
- Revision of plans and adjustments in changed situations.
- Coordination of processes involving planning.

Thus, planning function of a manager includes activities which lead to the definition of ends and the management of appropriate means to achieve the defined end.

1.5.2 Organising

Organising involves those activities of the management that are performed to translate the required activities of plans into a structure of task, authority and responsibility. This framework includes people, task, resources, and performance in respect to the organizational goals. Sub-functions of organising are:
- Defining the nature and content of each job in the organization.
- Setting the base for grouping the jobs together.
- Deciding the size of groups.
- Delegating authority to assigned managers.

1.5.3 Directing and Motivating

Directing and motivating stimulate the organization to undertake actions along the plan. Major ingredients for directing are leading, coordination, communication, influencing and team work. Directing and motivating channelise the organizational behaviour for attainment of corporate goals. It involves:
- Communication and explanation of objectives to the subordinates.
- Assign the performance standards.
- Helping subordinates through proper guidance and personal interaction to meet the standards of performance.

- Reward for better performance both financially and written appreciation.
- Praise and censuring the employees wherever required.
- Management of change through proper communication and building confidence among different layers of management and workers.
- Coordination in the entire process.

1.5.4 Controlling

Controlling relates to measure the performance against goal, determining the causes of deviations from goals, and taking corrective actions for improvement. Managers are required to assure that the actual outcomes are consistent with the planned outcomes. It involves:

- Standard of performance.
- Information related to gaps in standard and attained performance.
- Corrective actions to bridge the identified gaps.

Control function is useful for (*a*) short-range corrections through better directing, (*b*) moderate corrections through re-engineering benchmarking, and (*c*) long-term corrections through re-defining goals and new planning endeavour.

The management process, involving *four* managerial functions, is shown in Fig. 1.2 as an integration of manager's functions.

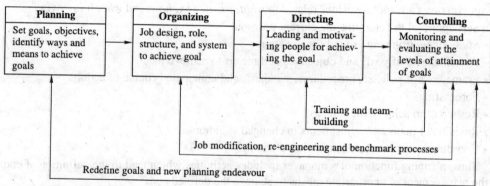

Fig. 1.2   Integration of manager's functions in the management process

1.6 Types of Management

The management is segmented into *three* distinct layers in an organization. These layers are top management, middle management and lower (operating) management (Fig. 1.3). Top management

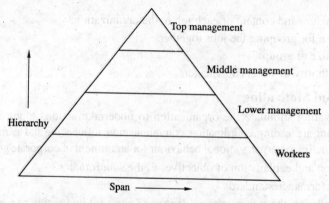

Fig. 1.3   Levels of management in an organization

consists of Chairman; Managing Director, President, Vice-President; and similar other positions; middle management involves heads of departments, divisional heads, general managers, etc; lower management includes workers like supervisor, foreman, superintendent and other operating personnel.

The activities of different types of management are different in proportions. For example, top management is more focussed on planning strategic issues but less involved in directing function. On the other hand, lower management is more focussed on directing and less on planning (Fig. 1.4). The skills needed for different levels of management is also different (Fig. 1.5). While less technical and personnel skill is required at top, more of these skills are required at lower level. On the contrary, more conceptual and decision-making skills are required at top level. For total quality management, more commitment is needed at top level while more efforts in team-building are required by lower management. Middle management is expected to facilitate the continuous improvement.

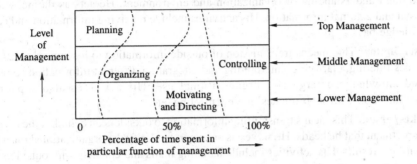

Fig. 1.4   Time spent (%) by each level of management

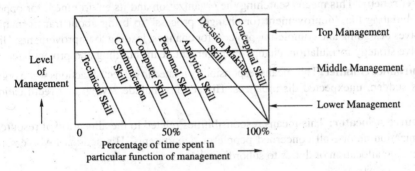

Fig. 1.5   Skill needed at different levels of management

1.7 Role of the Manager

A manager's role is to organise, supervise and control people so that there is a productive outcome to work. Organization of one type or another are essential for productive work because they bring people together with raw materials and equipment in order to achieve a variety of goals. By combining people's talents and energy with resources, very often more can be achieved than by individuals working on their own. Organizations, whether they are companies, educational institutions, industries, hospitals or even football teams, will all have objectives. These objectives/goals may be expressed in terms of profits, market share, educational achievements, health or winning games. Every organization will have a plan to achieve the objectives in order to make sure that they have the right people doing the right job with the best possible equipment at the right time.

Managers are the people responsible for helping organizations to achieve their objectives and for creating and implementing their plans. Based on Mintzberg (1973), one can identify *three* roles for managers.

1.7.1 Interpersonal Role

- **Figurehead:** It means symbolic-head. His activities include ceremony, status requests and solicitations.
- **Leader:** It means responsible for motivating and activating the subordinates. His activities include responsibility for staffing, training, subordinate's team building, etc.
- **Liaison:** It means maintaining a self-developed network of outside contacts and information. His activities include interactions with outsiders, responding to mails, external board work, etc.

1.7.2 Informational Roles

- **Monitor:** This means seeking and receiving a wide variety of special information to develop a thorough understanding of organization and environment. He acts as the nerve centre of internal and external information. His activities include receiving information and creating a knowledge-base.
- **Disseminator:** This means transmission of outside information to his subordinates. His role includes filtering, clarifying, interpreting and integrating different information so that value-added knowledge emerges for organizational use. His activities also support verbal communication with subordinates' review meeting, etc.
- **Spokesperson:** This means transmitting information to outsiders on behalf of the organization or department that he heads. He serves as an expert to clarify the organizational plan, policies, actions and results. His activities include handling mails and contacts with outsiders.

1.7.3 Decisional Roles

- **Entrepreneur:** This means searching the organization and its environment for opportunities and initiating the "improvement (or change) process" to bring about transformation. This involves designing and completing projects for changes, leading to improvements. His actions involve strategy formulation, change-management, team-building and project handling.
- **Disturbance Handler:** This means responsibility related to corrective actions when organization faces sudden, unexpected disturbances. His actions include review and rectification of the crisis.
- **Resource Allocator:** This means responsibilities related to the allocation of resources of the organization among all concerned people or departments. His actions involve scheduling, budgeting, allocation of duties to subordinates, authorization, etc.
- **Negotiator:** This means representing the organization at major negotiations. His actions include bringing advantage to the organization during the process of negotiation.

During recent years, the organizations are undergoing major changes. Managers' roles have also widened due to the advent of information technology and its impact on the way things are managed. Therefore, the managers have additional role as *Knowledge Leaders*. Thus, the fourth role is:

1.7.4 Knowledge Leadership Role

- **Knowledge team builder:** This means that the managers should create teams that have expertise in certain areas. This is done through regular updating of knowledge through seminar, journal, internet-search and adoption of technology. His activities include finding right people, who can share same expertise in building knowledge-base.
- **Sustaining and maintaining knowledge:** This is related to knowledge management. His activities include documenting and sharing the expertise among group members. If an individual leaves the organization, the knowledge should stay with other members of the group.

Managers' role have also diversified to the area of *change-management*. Change meant for improvement is the *key-mantra* these days. There are three modes of change in the organization: continuous improvement, benchmarking and re-engineering. This has been identified as the fifth role for the contemporary managers.

1.7.5 Change Handler

- **Continuous improvement supporter:** This means the route of marginal or gradual improvement. It is the path which TQM also advocates. Managers' role is to develop a quality culture and teambuilding. Problems are identified and solved for small but gradual improvement. The role of the manager is to tell everybody that there exists a better way of doing the thing which we are doing now.

- **Benchmarking Leader:** Benchmarking involves identifying "best-practices" or world-class performers in your area and identification of gap between world-class and your organization. This gap is bridged through systematic planning and leadership. Manager's actions involve identification of benchmark, building teams to make changes and evaluation of performance during the change.

- **Re-engineering Leader:** Re-engineering is the total, radical redesign of the system. Managers have a great role to play as they have to prepare resources (including subordinates) for a total transformation. Unlike continuous improvement, which is gradual, and benchmarking, which is moderate, re-engineering is dramatic transformation and thus requires careful handling of situation and resources. The risks are higher in re-engineering. Therefore, its management is more difficult as compared to other two change processes.

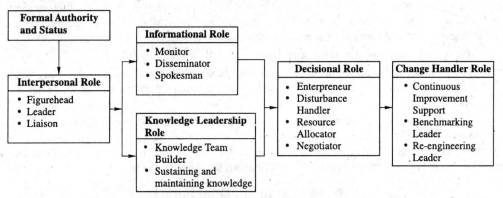

Fig. 1.6 Roles of manager [modified and enlarged in scope from: Henry Mintzber, 1973, *The Nature of Managerial Work*, Harper & Row Pub NY, pp 93-94]

1.8 The Management Challenge

The management challenge is to maintain control over the processes of an organization while at the same time leading, inspiring, directing and making decisions on all types of matters. The challenge for modern managers is to deal with this tension between operating the present systems, structures and processes and the need to change in order to survive.

Organizations, whether they are commercial companies or non-profit institutions, have to meet customer demands if they are to succeed. This is obvious with motor car companies and high street shops, but is now also true in the non-profit sector for organizations such as schools, universities, hospitals, museums and state-owned zoos. As customer needs alter, so the business must change by anticipating customer wants, leading these where appropriate as well as responding to them. The emphasis today is on a focus on the customer so that all managers are concerned with leading their organization, section, unit or team to enable work to be carried out successfully in response to the needs of their market. As society and the economy develop and as managers are promoted from junior to middle and senior levels, the requirement to be flexible, creative, innovative and able to absorb and communicate new ideas becomes of increasing importance.

This view of modern management suggests that it is about change because in order to meet their objectives, organizations need to focus on their customers through a marketing culture. This is as true of a professional football team as of a multinational company, a hospital trust or a small business. Management of a kind is required in the smallest task; in a one-person business, that one person will have to combine all the qualities of management as well as working at an operational level. Above all, in one way or another, the individual running a one-person business must satisfy the customers through the quality of the work and the service provided. The larger an organization the more specialised management can become, while at the highest level there will need again to be a convergence of skills, although on a different plane.

1.9 Management as a Science

The science of management is based today on the view that 'what can't be measured isn't worth doing'. This is a view supported by Professor Sir Roland Smith, but even this apparently 'up-to-date' theory has been described by John Harvey-Jones as out of date. This is partly because of the echoes thrown forward from the 1960s when there was a management view that everything could be measured and that success would follow improvements in systems of measurement, particularly accountancy. The modern version of this theory has been greatly encouraged by developments in information technology which has vastly increased the potential for measurement. Although all managers have to accept the need for business accounts and the application of statistics in making decisions, at the same time managers must consider the derivation and accuracy of the numbers presented to them. At times it may be sensible to override all the facts and figures that are available; for example, Sony produced the Walkman against the evidence of market research which suggested that the product would not be successful. This example does not invalidate market research, but puts it in its place as one of a number of factors in the management decision-making process.

Managers have to operate in the situation in which they find themselves:

'The difficulty is that there can never be any single correct solution to any management problem, or any all-embracing system which will carry one through a particular situation or period of time.'
(John Harvey-Jones, 1993)

The fact is that over the years management styles and fashions change and business environments alter. As a subject of study and analysis management can be seen as a mongrel form of social science, borrowing as necessary from other social sciences, and because it is concerned with people and their behaviour there is an element of unpredictability about the whole process.

Self-assessment Questions

1. What is understood by the term *management*? Explain lucidly.
2. Define the term *management* as viewed by Mary Follett; Mescon, Albert and Khedouri; and ASME. What are the similarities in these three definitions?
3. Briefly explain different elements of management by which it is conceived, evolved and implemented.
4. Examine briefly the evolution of management thought from the early times to the modern times. Also, name some of the earliest contributors and their accomplishments in the process of development of management thought.
5. What are the major schools of management thought? Give chromonological accomplishments of same contemporary writers in each of the three schools of thought.
6. What are the functions of management? Explain each of them in detail.
7. Explain the role of management, citing a live practical example of an industry.
8. How are management functions integrated? Explain with an appropriate diagram.
9. Define different levels of management. Elaborate the functions of each level of management.
10. How a manager play an effective role in an organization? Present your case with an appropriate example.
11. 'Managers are responsible for helping organizations to achieve their objectives and for creating and implementing their plans.' Comment on this statement.
12. Discuss the role of knowledge leadership and change handler of a manager in an organization.
13. What is re-engineering? How is it transform the organization?
14. How can management challenge be faced by the manager is an organization?
15. Explain whether management is a science or art. Justify your views with the theory postulated by John Harvey-Jones.

2

Organization Planning, Design and Development

2.1 Introduction

Organizations are formed whenever the pursuit of an objective calls for the joint efforts of two or more individuals. One can identify the following major components in the definition of an organization:

(a) Organizations are composed of individuals and groups of people;

(b) Organizations seek the achievement of shared objectives through division of labour; and

(c) Organizations are integrated by information-bound decision processes to coordinate the resulting tasks.

Thus, organization can be defined as follows:

- It is the grouping of activities necessary to attain organization objectives and assignment of each grouping to a manager with authority necessary to supervise it.

(Koontz and O'Donnell)

- Organization is the process of identifying and grouping work to be performed, defining and delegating responsibility and authority, and establishing relationships to enable people to work most effectively together in accomplishing objectives. *(Allen)*

- Organization is a system, having an established structure and conscious planning, in which people work and deal with one another in a coordinated and cooperative manner for the accomplishment of recognised goals.

Hence, the organization has (*i*) a system, (*ii*) well established structure, (*iii*) people to work and deal with each other in coordinated and cooperative manner, (*iv*) grouping of work, (*v*) established relationship for authority and delegation, (*vi*) attainment of common goals, (*vii*) internal structure for performance, (*viii*) defined role and responsibility of each person, and (*ix*) a constituent of (*a*) division of labour, (*b*) identification of the source of authority, and (*c*) establishment of enterprise relationship.

Organizations are developed around the concept that a complex task can be sub-divided into simpler components by means of division of labour. The design of a structure to attain the organization goals requires addressing two primary issues: how to perform the division of labour, and how to coordinate the resulting tasks.

2.2 Principles of Healthy Organization

The following *fourteen* principles help to form a good organization. These are:

1. **Principle of organizational objective:** It should be consistent, well-defined and aim at achieving high production with customer focus, growth and survival.

2. **Principle of division of work and specialisation:** It requires focus on specialisation and assignment of specific work to an individual.

3. **Principle of parity between authority and responsibility:** Responsibility rests with a person for completing the assigned task. It is also called as *accountability*. Authority is vested in the

superior of the organization to extract work from subordinates. It is necessary to maintain a balance between authority and responsibility.

4. **Principle of functional task:** Each employee must be assigned specific task, role, relationship and job-related activities.

5. **Principle of scalar chain:** Scalar chain means that there should be a continuous line of authority from top of the organizational pyramid to the lower levels. The chain provides a superior-subordinate relationship, and is useful in the delegation of authority down the chain. It is also possible to maintain effective communication between different layers of the organization.

6. **Principle of unity of command:** There should be only one source of authority for each subordinate, i.e., one subordinate-one boss. This is required for fixing responsibility for the result and to maintain discipline.

7. **Principle of balance:** Proper balance is required to be maintained in issues such as line *vs*, staff, centralisation *vs* decentralisation, unity of command *vs* specialisation, vertical hierarchy *vs* span of control, etc.

8. **Principle of flexibility:** In an organization design, there must be in-built flexibility to withstand the red-tapism, excessive control, complicated procedure, etc.

9. **Principle of delegation:** Delegation is for empowering the subordinates to achieve results.

10. **Principle of efficiency:** Considering system view of the organization (input-processing-output framework), the maximization of output and minimization of input will improve the efficiency.

11. **Principle of continuity:** Survival and existence, despite turbulence in market forces, should be the aim of an organization. Thus, the organization must look at long-term goals rather than mere profit-making and short-term goals.

12. **Principle of cooperation:** There is need to evolve proper code of conduct, business rules, conflict resolution mechanism, and cooperation to work as a team in the organization and solve the functional goals of the organization as one unit.

13. **Principle of coordination:** Proper coordination is needed to work in one direction to achieve the corporate goal. Effective communication, regular meetings, etc. are helpful in this direction.

14. **Principle of span of control:** A superior can supervise limited number of subordinates. Narrow span of control is useful for complex jobs whereas wider span of control is useful for routine jobs. Span of control is determined on the basis of (*a*) capacity and the ability of the superior, (*b*) capability and skill of the subordinate, (*c*) nature and importance of work to be supervised, (*d*) clarity of plans and responsibility, (*e*) level of decentralisation.

Graicunas defined *three* types of relationship between superior and subordinates: (*a*) direct single relationship among all subordinates, (*b*) direct group relationship, and (*c*) cross-relationship. The Graicunas formula is given in Table 2.1.

Table 2.1 Graicunas Formula for Span of Control

No. of Subordinates	Formula: $n\left(\dfrac{2^n}{2}+n-1\right)$
1	1
2	6
3	18
4	44
5	100
6	222

No. of Subordinates	Formula: $n\left(\dfrac{2^n}{2}+n-1\right)$
7	490
8	1,080
9	2,376
10	5,210
11	11,374
12	24,708
13	53,704
14	1,14,872
15	2,45,974
16	5,24,534
17	11,14,329
18	23,59,612
19	49,81,090
20	1,04,86,154

From the table, it indicates that superior-subordinate relationship increases substantially as the number of subordinates increases. With five subordinates, it is 100; and with six, it is 222. With 10 subordinates, relationships become 5210, which are difficult to handle effectively. Therefore, maximum six subordinates are recommended in a common type of organization.

2.3 Organization Planning

Organization planning defines or reshapes the organization structure for

(a) clarifying objectives, roles and relationships;

(b) determining the management resources required now and in the future; and

(c) providing information on job requirements so that the right people can be appointed, adequate training can be given, and payments to staff are commensurate with their relative levels of responsibility and value to the organization.

The organization structure is the framework for carrying out the task of management. The overall task has to be divided into a variety of activities, and means have to be established for the direction, coordination and control of these activities.

2.3.1 Techniques

Organization planning uses following *two* main techniques:

1. **Organization analysis:** This is the process of defining the objectives and activities of the organization in the light of an examination of its external environment and internal circumstances.

2. **Organization design:** The information provided by the organization analysis is used to define the structure of the organization, the function of each major activity, and the roles and responsibilities of each management position in the structure. The aim of organization design is to enable collective effort to be explicitly organised to achieve specific ends. The design process leads to a structure consisting of units and positions, between which there are relationships involving the exercise of authority, communication, and exchange of information.

2.3.2 Method

The stages followed in an organization planning exercise are shown in Fig. 2.1. The initial stages of defining overall aims and purposes, defining and classifying objectives and conducting an external analysis of factors affecting the organization are described separately. The remaining stages are described under the following headings:

- Organization Analysis,
- Organization Design, and
- Planning and Implementation.

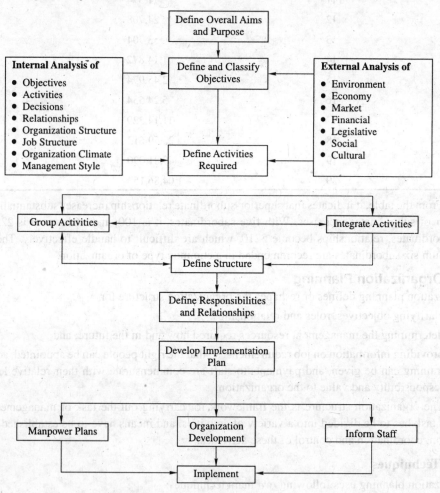

Fig. 2.1   Organization planning programme

Organization Analysis

Organization analysis examines:

1. **Objectives:** To find out what they are and how clearly they are defined and understood at all levels.
2. **Activities:** To establish what work is done and what work needs to be done by the organization to achieve its objectives.
3. **Decisions:** To study where and by whom the key decisions are made and how work is delegated and decentralized.

4. **Relationships:** To define what interactions and communications take place between people in the organization so that an assessment can be made of the extent to which the grouping of activities, lines of communication and information systems facilitate effective management and coordination.

5. **Organization structure:** To find out:
   - How activities are grouped together;
   - The spans of control of senior and middle managers (span of control is the number of subordinates reporting directly to one superior); and
   - The number of levels in the management hierarchy.

6. **Job structure:** To determine the content of individual jobs in terms of duties, responsibilities and authorities. The aim is to establish the degree to which tasks are logically and clearly allocated and to indicate whether job holders have been given sufficient responsibility and authority and are clear about what they are expected to achieve.

7. **Organization climate:** To get a feel of the working atmosphere of the company with regard to teamwork and cooperation, commitment, communications, creativity, conflict resolution, participation, and confidence and trust between people.

8. **Management style:** To find out what sort of approach to management is being practised in the organization especially at the top, *e.g.*, closed, authorization, open, or democratic.

9. **Management:** To establish
   - the extent to which the existing organization has been built round the personalities, strengths and weaknesses of the key people in it; and
   - the availability of the quality of people required to facilitate necessary changes in the organization structure.

2.3.3 Organization Structure

The organization structure may be defined as the allocation of work roles and administrative mechanisms that creates a pattern of interrelated work activities, and allows that organization to conduct, coordinate, and control its work activities. Thus, this structure is not only a hierarchical allocation of responsibilities, but also encompasses all the managerial processes towards realization of the tasks undertaken by the organization. Usually these processes give rise to formal managerial systems, among which one can cite the strategic and operational planning systems, the communication and information system, the motivation and reward system, and the management control system.

The study of the organization structure must give proper attention to the complex web of relationships and mutual conditioning between structure and other elements of the organization. The purpose is to identify and briefly describe the principal components of an organization, in order to position the notion of structure in its relation with other decision supporting systems of the firm: the organization structure, the planning system, the management control system, the information and communication system, and the evaluation and reward system (Fig. 2.2).

Changes in any one of these systems call for an immediate adjustment of the other related systems to obtain a sound balance of the overall managerial process. For instance, the switch from a functional to a divisional organization structure calls for a comprehensive review of the accounting process (which is the primary layer of the management control system), thorough change in the character of managerial accountabilities reflected in the reward system, a basic modification of the planning system, and a full review of the organization's information system.

The primary thesis is that a proper organization structure should recognize the strategic positioning of the firm, as well as facilitate its operational efficiency. It is not only the planning function that deals with strategic and operational matters but also the control process. Moreover, managers should be rewarded on achieving both strategic and operational commitments, and the information system should report the annual realizations in both modes.

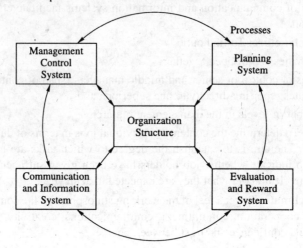

Fig. 2.2   Management systems: structure and processes

2.3.4 Organizational Archetypes

There are three archetypes that represent distinct forms of organization structures: *functional*, *divisional*, and *matrix*. They are important design anchors because they have been extensively tested and studied, and their advantages and disadvantages are relatively well-known. In practice, most organizations present combinations of these three archetypes, resulting in what is designated as a *hybrid* organization.

Functional and Divisional Organizations
Functional and divisional forms constitute the classical opposite archetypes for the organization design.

The functional form is structured around the *inputs* required to perform the tasks of the organization. Typically, these inputs are functions or specialities, such as finance, marketing, production, engineering, research and development, and personnel.

The divisional form is structured according to the *outputs* generated by the organization, most commonly the products delivered. However, other types of outputs could serve as a basis for divisionalisation, such as programmes and projects. Also, markets, clients, and geographical locations could serve as criteria for divisionalisation.

The nature of differentiation in functional and divisional forms of organizations lies in terms of orientation towards goals, orientation towards time, and perception of the formality of the organization. Major differentiations in functional and divisional organizations are given in Table 2.2.

Table 2.2   Differentiation in Functional and Divisional Organizations*

Dimensions of Differentiation	Functional Organization	Divisional Organization
Goal orientation	More differentiated and focused	Less differentiated and more diffused
Time orientation	Less differentiated and shorter-term	More differentiated and longer-term
Formality of structure	Less differentiated, with more formality	More differentiated with less formality

Source: AH Walker and JW Lorsch. 'Organizational Choice: Products vs Function.' *Harvard Business Review,* November-December 1968.

The characteristics of functional and divisional organizations are summarised in Table 2.3.

Table 2.3 Characteristics of Functional and Divisional Organizations*

Characteristic	Functional Organization	Divisional Organization
Differentiation	Less differentiation except in goal orientation	Greater differentiation in structure and time orientation
Integration	Less effective	More effective
Conflict management	Confrontation, but also 'smoothing over' and avoidance; rather restricted communication pattern	Confrontation of conflicts; open, face-to-face communication
Effectiveness	Efficient, stable production; less successful in capabilities	Successful in improving plant capabilities, but less effective in stable production
Employee attitudes	Prevalent feeling of satisfaction, but less stress and involvement	Prevalent feeling of stress and involvement, but less satisfaction

*Source: Ibid.

The functional and divisional forms of organization have their own set of advantages and disadvantages. The functional structure facilitates the acquisition of specialized inputs. It permits pooling of resources and sharing them across products or projects. The organization can hire, utilize and retain specialists. However, the problem lies in coordinating the varying nature and amount of skills required at different times. The divisional, or product, organization, on the other hand, facilitates coordination among specialists; but may result in duplicating costs and reduction in the degree of specialization. Thus, if a functional structure is adopted, projects may fall behind; if product/project organization is chosen, technology and specialization may not develop optimally. Therefore, the need for a compromise between the two becomes imperative. For example, Auto Maintenance Group and the Central Maintenance Workshop are organized on a product basis. They would find the quality of workmanship improved if the organization becomes a functional one.

Matrix Organization
A matrix organization employs a multiple command system that includes not only a multiple command structure, but also related support mechanisms and associated organizational culture and behaviour pattern. A matrix organization is not desirable unless: (*i*) the organization has to cope with two or more critical sectors (functions, products, services, areas); (*ii*) the organizational tasks are uncertain, complex and highly interdependent; (*iii*) there are economies of scale. All three conditions need to be present simultaneously before a matrix is indicated.

Ideally, the matrix organization induces: (*i*) the focusing of undivided human effort on two (or more) essential organizational tasks simultaneously; (*ii*) the processing of a great deal of information and the commitment of the organization to a balanced reasoned response; and (*iii*) the rapid deployment of human resources to various projects, products, services, clients, or markets.

Each archetype has its own set of advantages and disadvantages. Compromises are possible in the context of organization's environment, technology, culture and aspects of human behaviour.

2.3.5 Symptoms of an Inadequate Organization Structure

The organization structure is a framework with two primary roles: to support the full-fledged implementation of strategic programmes, and to permit the normal conduct of the firm's operating activities.

External and internal changes call for a continuous adjustment of the organization structure, in order to ensure an optimum handling of strategic and operating activities. However, practice has shown that, despite these adjustments, organizations need a comprehensive overhaul from time to time. As a structure grows older, it usually lacks the flexibility to accommodate new strategic and operational demands. The managerial team should maintain an eye on signs of stress that evidence an inadequate structure, because keeping it longer than necessary may impair the normal growth and development of a firm.

Some of the most common symptoms that can be traced to an inadequate organization structure are:

1. Lack of opportunities for development. This is usually the case with functionally-oriented organizations.
2. Insufficient time devoted to strategic thinking due to:
    (*a*) too much concentration on operational issues;
    (*b*) excessive decision-making at the top; and
    (*c*) overworked key personnel.
3. Intensive antagonistic environment. The motivational and reward system should be in tune with the given structure. An antagonistic environment may be signalling a problem of balance between structure and processes.
4. Lack of definition in portfolio business planning, neglect of special markets, and inappropriate setting for maximizing growth and profit. These are among the clearest evidence of an organization structure that cannot accommodate the new strategic positioning of the firm.
5. Lack of coordination with sister divisions. This points to a failure of integrating mechanisms.
6. Excessive duplication of functions in different units of the firm. The differentiation among units is not well established. Some re-definition of tasks or fusion of some units might be advantageous.
7. Excessive dispersion of functions in one unit of the firm. Determine whether the differentiation of tasks warrants the segmentation of this unit.
8. Poor profit performance and low return expectations. The organization structure cannot escape a major revision in a situation like this.

2.4 Organization Design

The organization design is a dynamic process, yet most of the models and concepts are static. Some of the limitations of a static model can be overcome by focusing on the stagewise process of development of an organization and by management of transitions from one stage to another.

Mintzberg conceptually describes an organization as typically having five basic parts as shown in Fig. 2.3.

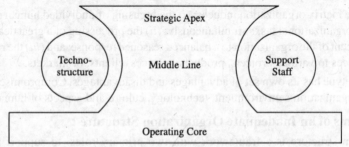

Fig. 2.3 Five basic parts of an organization

(*Source:* H Mintzberg, *The Structuring of Organizations*, Englewood Cliffs, New Jersey, 1979)

1. Operating core.
2. Strategic apex.

3. Middle line.

4. Technostructure.

5. Support staff.

These five basic parts of an organization are briefly examined below:

Operating Core: This part consists of those who perform the basic work relating to production or services. They secure inputs for production, transform inputs into outputs, distribute the outputs or provide direct services. Since other parts of the organization are meant to protect the operating core, standardization is generally attempted first at this level.

Strategic Apex: The strategic apex comprises people having overall responsibility of the organization, namely, the chief executive and other top-level managers. They have the responsibility to set goals, prepare plans, and develop strategies to implement plans and accomplish goals. They have to manage the relationship with environment. They also have to oversee the operations and provide direction and control. Work at this level is more abstract and conceptual and involves less of routine to permit any standardisation. Mutual adjustment is the favoured mechanism for coordination among the managers of the strategic apex.

Middle Line: It is the linking pin between the strategic apex and the operating core. The chain runs from senior managers down to the first-line supervisors. The chain of authority could be scalar (single line from top to bottom) or matrix (some subordinates having to report to more than one superior). A middle level manager has to function like a chief executive in managing his own section/ department/unit. The nature of job, however, changes as the middle line descends in the chain of authority. The job becomes more detailed and elaborate, less abstract and aggregated, more focused on the work flow itself.

Technostructure: Technostructure is made up of analysts whose job is to control, stabilize and standardize patterns of activity in the organization. In a fully developed organization, the technostructure is at work at all levels of the hierarchy. At the lowest level of manufacturing, analysts standardize the operating work flow in scheduling production, carrying out time-and-method studies, and in studying systems of quality control. At the middle level, they seek to standardize intellectual work (e.g. training, research studies on operations, attitudes, etc.). At the strategic apex level, they aid top management in designing strategic planning and control systems.

Support Staff: Support staff are engaged in large organizations to encompass more and more boundary activities, such as running an industrial canteen or hospital, in order to reduce uncertainty, and control their own affairs. The support units can also be found at various levels of hierarchy.

2.4.1 Design Parameters

To make organizations establish firm patterns of behaviour, organizations use formal and semi-formal methods, called *design parameters*, to differentiate and coordinate work activities. The choice and configuration of design parameters determine the structure of the organization. Basically, there are four design parameters:

1. Design of positions:
    - job positions
    - job specialisation
    - behaviour formalisation
    - training
    - indoctrination.
2. Design of the superstructure:
    - unit grouping
    - unit size.

3. Design of lateral linkages:
  - planning and control systems, and
  - liaison devices.
4. Design of decision
  - system set-up, and
  - vertical and horizontal decentralisation.

Centralization may be related to other design parameters. Behaviour formalization often exists when there is centralization. Training and indoctrination lead to decentralisation. Liaison devices are used in decentralised organizations, while planning and control systems are preferred in centralised organizations.

Mintzberg hypothesizes that 'effective structuring requires a consistency among the design parameters and contingency factors'. The design contingency factors are age, size of the organization, technical production system, environment and the organization's power system.

2.4.2 Shape of the Organization and the Design Process

The design is influenced by a number of critical variables such as size, technology, environment, social changes, etc. The design process involves both science and art. The organization design does not evolve purely by principles alone. (Chief executives also influence the shape of an organization).

Allen suggests the seven-step sequence for setting the design process into action:
1. Identify the major objectives of the firm and derive the primary line functions needed to accomplish the objectives.
2. Organize from the top down by establishing a scalar chain of authority and responsibility.
3. Organize from the bottom up by integrating the activities of each function.
4. Decide the management positions needed for each activity.
5. Identify positions in group related work.
6. Check groupings to ensure balance in the distribution of resources.
7. Check whether spans of control are appropriate.

Peter Drucker provides fresh perspective and lists a four-step sequence:
1. Determine desired results.
2. Determine key result areas.
3. Determine when activities could be integrated and when they should be kept separate.
4. Assign appropriate coordinative responsibility and authority.

Organization design thus requires that careful attention be given to three levels of problems and issues:
1. Mission should be consistent with environment.
2. Structure and process should be consistent with mission.
3. Individual problem solving should facilitate structure and process.

2.4.3 Organizational Guidelines

Although there are no absolute principles for designing organizations, there are certain guidelines that may be used, with discretion, in evolving the optimum solution to any organizational problem. The guidelines are:
1. **Allocation of work:** In order to get work done it is necessary to determine the activities required and group them logically into specific areas. Besides the objectives for each management post the responsibilities and authorities for planning, organizing, directing and controlling the work of the organization as a whole and of each constituent part should be clearly defined.

2. **Unity of command:** Unless there are exceptional circumstances, no person should report to more than one direct superior, or else friction and confusion will occur.

3. **Span of control:** There is a limit to the number of people a manager can control, although this limit will depend upon the nature of the job. But while it may be undesirable in general terms for a senior manager to have more than six or seven people reporting to him or her for distinct areas, it might be equally undesirable to have only one or two subordinates. 'One-over-one' relationships cause confusion and overlap, and with only two subordinates, managers can get overinvolved with one or the other or both.

4. **Levels of management:** Too many levels of management can cause communication difficulties, delays in decision making and creation of superfluous posts.

5. **Coordination:** In the design process, the need to achieve effective coordination and integration of activities must always predominate.

6. **Communications:** Organizations must provide suitable channels for clear and rapid communications.

7. **Flexibility:** Whatever structure is produced or evolved, it must be able to cope with change and expansion.

2.4.4 Organization Planning and Implementation

The planning and implementation process ensures that:

1. Changes are introduced smoothly on a staged basis to avoid disruption and provide time for new positions to be filled by training the existing managers or recruiting new ones.

2. Manpower plans are drawn up to develop, train and recruit the managers required—now and in the future.

3. Organization development programmes are introduced to help the new or revamped organization operate successfully.

4. Staff are kept informed about what is happening, why is it happening, where is it going to happen and how it affects them.

Benefits

The benefits of organization planning derive mainly from the initial analytical process. This stage defines any problems that may exist and leads directly to the provision of optimum solutions.

2.5 Organization Development
2.5.1 Definition

Organization development (OD) is concerned with planning and implementation of programmes designed to improve the effectiveness with which an organization functions and responds to change. It is based on scientific awareness of human behaviour and organization dynamics. It is directed towards more participative management and integration of individual goals with organization goals. OD is intended to create an internal environment of openness, trust, mutual confidence and collaboration and help the members of the organization interact more effectively. Thus, the organization is able to cope effectively with external forces in the environment.

2.5.2 Objectives of Organization Development

The four basic objectives of OD are stated as follows:

1. Improved organizational performance as measured by profitability, market share, innovativeness.

2. Better adaptability of the organization to its environment.

3. Willingness of members to face organizational problems and find creative solutions to these problems.

4. Improvement in internal behaviour patterns.

2.5.3 Characteristic Features of OD

Organization development programmes are usually characterized by three main features:

1. They are managed, or at least strongly supported, from the top but make use of third parties or 'change agents' to diagnose problems and hence manage change by various kinds of planned 'interventions'.
2. The plans for OD are based upon systematic analysis and diagnosis of the circumstances of the organization and the changes and problems affecting it.
3. They make use of behavioural science to improve the way the organization copes with such processes as interaction, communications, participation, planning and conflict. Typical activities include:
   (a) Introducing new systems or structures;
   (b) Working with teams on team development;
   (c) Working on inter-group relationships either defining roles or resolving conflict; and
   (d) Educational activities for improving personal skills concerned with relationships between people.

2.5.4 Models of Organization Development

There are three popular models of OD. They are Kurt Lewin's unfreezing, changing and freezing model; Griener's sequential process; and Leavitt's system model.

Lewin's Unfreezing, Changing and Freezing Model
This model can be divided into three stages.

Stage 1: *Unfreezing.* Creating the need for change, motivating the people for change and minimizing resistance to change.

Stage 2: *Changing.* Transition from old behaviour to experimentation with new behaviour in terms of cognitive redefinition through identification (information from a single source) and scanning (information through multiple sources).

Stage 3: *Re-freezing.* Stabilising and integrating the change by reinforcing the new behaviours and integrating them into one's personality, as well as in formal and interpersonal relationships.

Larry Griener's Sequential Process Model
According to this model, change is in terms of certain sequential stages (Fig. 2.4). The process of change is initiated by external pressure or stimulus on the top management motivating them to take action. The succeeding stages of intervention by a change agent are: diagnosis of the problem, invention of a new solution, experimentation with the new solution and reinforcement from positive results.

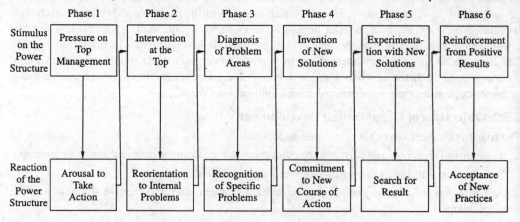

Fig. 2.4   Organization development sequential stages

HJ Leavitt's System Model

The model focuses on the interactive nature of various sub-systems in a change process. Organization is a system of four interacting sub-systems: task, structure, people and technology. Change in any one of the sub-systems tends to have consequences for other sub-systems. Hence, OD effort should not only focus on the intended change but also on the effects of change on other sub-systems. Change can be brought out in any of the sub-systems depending upon the diagnosis of the situation. The planned change may be interpersonal training of the required type or technological change or structural or task modification (Fig. 2.5).

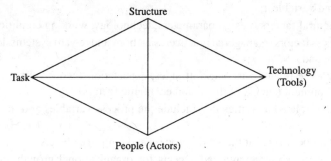

Fig. 2.5 Planned change in four interacting sub-systems

(*Source:* HJ Leavitt, *New Perspectives in Organization Research*, John Wiley & Sons, New York, 1964).

2.5.5 Organization Development Action Research Process

The success of an organization development programme depends upon the thoroughness and accuracy of the initial analysis and diagnosis of problems and opportunities faced by the organization. This should lead to a definition of the objectives of the programme and the preparation of action plans. A model of this process is shown in Fig. 2.6.

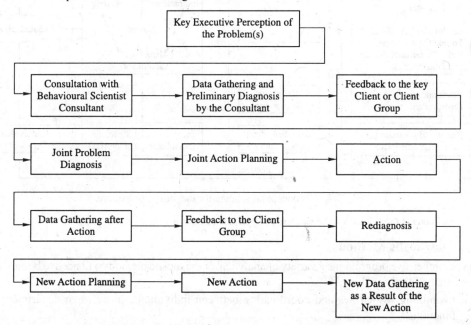

Fig. 2.6 Organization development action process

[*Source:* W French, *Organization Development Objectives, Assumption and Strategies* (California Management Review, Vol. 12, 1969, p. 26)].

The action plan begins with the *perception of the problem* in the organization or with the felt need for a change at the top management level. This sets the stage for intervention by a change agent (external/internal). The change agent should be unbiased, realistic and objective in the assessment of the problem. The change agent gathers data by the interview method or the questionnaire method or by a combination of both, for diagnosis of specific problems and assessment of the ability of the organization to function effectively. The data is then discussed with some of the top executives and the problems are identified. For identification of the problem, certain standard diagnostic procedures may be adopted. Any standardized diagnostic procedure takes into account the following:

1. Background variables:
    (*a*) Structural factors (design parameters, technology, working conditions, etc.);
    (*b*) Process factors (managerial practices, sanctions and reward systems, leadership behaviour, etc.); and
    (*c*) Employee-related variables (attitudes, expectations, work values, and the organization environment (social, political and economic factors).
2. Organization-related activities that include the process variables and the expected employee behaviour.
3. The resultant behaviour at the work, process and employee levels.
4. Resultant of the above-mentioned aspects for organizational growth and development and individual satisfaction.

A detailed diagnostic procedure is shown in Fig. 2.7.

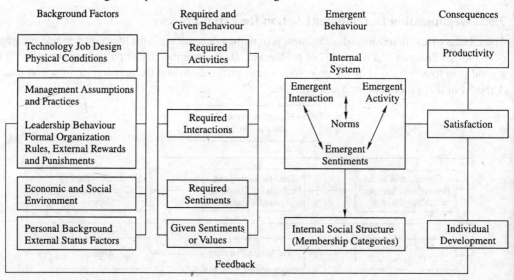

Fig. 2.7   A conceptual scheme for diagnostic procedure

(*Source:* A Turner, *A Conceptual Scheme for Describing Work Group Behaviour*).

2.5.6 Diagnostic Methods

In a comprehensive programme, a variety of analytical or diagnostic methods will need to be employed. These methods may include:

1. Examining work roles and coordinating between individuals, or between departments and functions.
2. Evaluating procedures for planning, coordinating, allocating resources, setting performance standards, monitoring performance, output quality or cost.
3. Analysing information systems and information flows.

4. Collecting and analysing feedback on operational problems, on attitudes, morale or job satisfaction.
5. Assessing leadership styles and relationships within or between work groups.
6. Reviewing rewards and incentives and opportunities for personal development or career progression.
7. Investigating internal procedures for negotiating terms and conditions of employment, or for resolving conflicts and disputes.

In programmes involving a study of work organization, it may also be necessary to use such techniques as process analysis, task analysis, activity analysis, method study or operational research to analyse work flows or procedures for planning and controlling operations. Studies of this type are best carried out by small multidisciplinary teams which include members with expertise in appropriate technology, operational research and organization development. In specialist industries and services, expert teams can make useful contribution to the development of structures, systems and procedures which are properly matched to the technological requirements of the enterprise.

Underlying all structural and procedural issues there is, in every organization, a 'culture', and 'atmosphere', a set of values which is partly reflective of the style of leadership within the institution itself, and partly of the society within which the institution operates. Technology is a major factor in determining structure and systems, but social and cultural factors are the main determinants of organizational style.

The most important and intangible of these factors are concerned with leadership, motivation and team work. All organization development programmes focus on the role of leadership, the use of teams as the agents of change, and the use of learning and feedback.

The action intervention stage is the pay-off stage in the OD process. Hence, choosing the appropriate intervention, the sub-system and the organizational level, is important for bringing effective change.

2.5.7 Planning the Programme

After the diagnosis has been completed, it is then necessary to:
- Define the objectives of the programme—as specifically as possible;
- Establish criteria to enable measuring the ultimate effectiveness of the programme and monitoring its progress during intermediate stages; and
- Prepare the action plan.

The plan will have to consider which of the various organizational development processes should be used. These include team development activities, inter-group relations, work and educational programmes. A typical approach would be to begin with a general education programme such as sensitivity training, Coverdale, or Blake's grid, continue with on-the-job team building or intergroup relations, as required, and add further educational programmes to follow up the initial activities. Such a sequence is illustrated in Fig. 2.8.

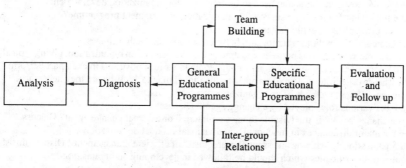

Fig. 2.8 Organization development programme

2.5.8 Characteristics of a Successful OD Programme

Richard Beckhard of the Massachusetts Institute of Technology in his essay on organization development lists eight characteristics of a successful OD programme:

1. It is a planned programme which involves the whole of an organization, or a relatively autonomous unit within an organization.
2. It is not a programme to improve managerial effectiveness in the abstract. It is designed to create organizational conditions which will directly help the institution to accomplish a specific strategy.
3. The senior management of the organization is personally committed to the goals of the programme.
4. It is a long-term effort, because two or three years are usually required for any significant organizational change to be planned, implemented, and its benefits realized and rewarded.
5. The programme is action-oriented. In this respect, an organizational development programme differs from a training programme in which the individual is left to transfer any knowledge or skill acquired, because the programme is designed from the outside to generate action by those involved.
6. Particular emphasis is placed on changing perceptions, attitudes and behaviour, and not solely on structural or procedural change.
7. It relies on some form of experience-based learning through which participants can examine the present situation, define new goals, and explore new ways of achieving them.
8. The basis of all programmes are the groups or teams from which the organization is constructed.

No discussion of an organization, or of organization development, can be concluded without reference to the character and quality of its people. People create organizations; successful organizations develop capable people who keep organizations flexible and responsive to changing needs and goals.

Self-assessment Questions

1. Define organization. Discuss the issues involved in divisional versus functional choice in the design of an organization.
2. What do you understand by organization Planning? Briefly explain the two main techniques of organization planning.
3. Draw a schematic diagram, explaining the stages followed in an organization planning exercise.
4. What is organization analysis? Outline the major factors that need to be considered in organization analysis.
5. Name the three different types of organization structures. Explain their merits and demerits.
6. Define the organization structure with a diagram. Enumerate the characteristics of functional and divisional/product organizations.
7. Outline the most common symptoms of an inadequate organization structure.
8. What is organization design? Critically examine the interrelationship between the five basic parts of an organization.
9. What are the major design parameters that determine the structure of the organization? Discuss one of them in detail.
10. List the seven-step sequence for setting the process of organization design into action.
11. Briefly explain the guidelines that may be followed to evolve an optimum solution to any organizational problem.
12. Define organization development and enumerate the objectives of an OD programme.
13. Explain the characteristic features of OD.
14. Examine some of the models of OD. Which model do you think would be more appropriate for Indian industries?
15. Outline the diagnostic methods that need to be employed for organization development.
16. What are the salient features of a successful organization development programme?
17. Explain the principles of healthy organization.
18. What is Graicunas formula for relationship between superior and subordinates.
19. Examine the interrelationships between and among the five parts of an organization, giving typical job titles as in your organization. Study the functions which people in various positions in each part perform.
20. Explain what is organizational analysis and organizational diagnosis. Why are they necessary?
21. What are the different methods of an organization analysis? Discuss.
22. What are the various roles played by a change agent? Discuss.
23. What is a change agent? Is it advisable to have an internal or external change agent? Discuss.
24. Outline the major differences in functional and divisional/product organizations.
25. 'Sound organisation structure is an essential prerequisite of efficient management'. Discuss this statement and point out various principles which should be followed in developing an organisation.
26. Differentiate between mission, goal and objective.

Management Planning and Control

3.1 Introduction

Planning is the essence of management. Conceived as a process, planning embraces a series of steps:

- Analysing factors affecting the future
- Forecasting the future environment
- Aims and objectives to be attained
- Policy-making, establishing programmes and procedures
- Decision-making and selection amongst alternatives
- Preparation and installation of plans.

Therefore, planning is a process of visualising intelligently appraising the future needs and purposes, identification and evaluating the opportunities and risks. It is a dynamic and continuous activity which must protect the changing conditions both from within and outside. Without planning, the management has no control over the economic forces.

According to Koontze and O' Donnell, "The managerial function of control is the measurement and correction of the performance of activities of subordinates in order to ensure that the objectives of an organization and the plans devised to attain them are being accomplished." Thus, control is aimed at results and not at people.

Plans can be effectively achieved in most organizations only with good controls. Therefore, planning is always prerequisite for controlling. Planning seeks to set goals and programmes and control seek to secure performance in accordance with plans.

3.2 Management Planning

As the word indicates, planning is the opposite of *improvising*. It is an organised foresight with corrective hind sight.

3.2.1 Analysing factors affecting the future

A plan provides a spring board from the present. The planner should start looking into the conditions which affect the organization's future opportunity. These conditions are: (a) environment, (b) internal conditions, and (c) obligations of the organization. In essence, an organization must be prepared and able to change the course of its business to meet customer demands and to find improved ways of service through better products, quality, and value.

3.2.2 Forecasting

Business forecasting is the calculation of probable events to provide for the future. This is possible on the basis of study with respect of environment. The forecast would include (a) estimates of general conditions in the total economy; (b) estimates of specific conditions in the total economy which affect the organization's business; (c) estimates of total demand for the products sold by the organization; (d) estimates of markets for the organization's current and/or prospective product line;

(*e*) estimates of sales possibilities; and (*f*) estimates of activities at peak, normal and below-normal conditions for short and long periods.

3.2.3 Aims and objectives

As the whole organization is expected to set aims and objectives, so must each department, section or division. One of the recognised methods of managing business is managing by objectives or by results. There is a hierarchy of objectives in an organization. The structure of planning starts at the top level. Each department in turn directs its efforts towards its own set of goals. Each sub-division of the department has its own objectives. Thus, the hierarchy can be built up by coordinating plans of different departments and with overall programme of the organization. Any conflict between different departments should be reconciled. Broad major objectives are normally multiple. It is, therefore, important to focus the attention of individual members of the organization on the objectives that are meaningful to them. A useful approach, as suggested by Peter Drucker, is "*management by objectives* in which objectives are supplied to every area where performance and results directly and vitally affect the survival and prosperity of business."

3.2.4 Policy-making, Programmes and Procedures

Policy is a general statement to serve as guide for the action of managers. It communicates top management's thinking to the employees of the organization and to suppliers, customers and the public. Policy-making cannot be delegated to subordinates.

Procedures state exactly the actions required to be taken. Procedures are useful where high degree of regularity is desired in frequently recurring events. A good procedure ensures that the work will/can be done by a person who is not as skilled as the individuals laying down the procedure.

Rules are specific instructions in regard to what may/may not be done, e.g., *no smoking in the plant* or *safety shoes must be worn in the plant*. Penalty may be given for not conforming the rules.

Programme is a definite plan of work made in proper sequence and in conformity with objectives, on the basis of laiddown policies and procedures.

Following *ten* elements are included in some degree or other in any management planning activity:

- Organization planning
- Product planning
- Facility planning
- Operations planning
- Material supply and inventory planning
- Financial planning
- Commercial planning
- Production planning
- Human resource planning
- Development planning.

3.3 Classical Principles of Management

Urwick (1949) gathered together classical principles of management, which are based on a combination of experience and philosophy rather than rigorous research and have thus been widely criticized. In fact, he produced a new synthesis based on the work of such people as Taylor, Fayol and Follett. Management principles gathered by Urwick have attracted criticism on the following grounds:

(*a*) There exists a common set of principles applicable to management in all types of situations This underlying assumption has been frequently challenged.

(*b*) Experiences based on which the principles were derived no longer exist and hence such principles have little or no validity for the contemporary organizations operating in the modern business environment.

Thus, changes in our ideas about management have conspired with the march of events to destroy the credibility of the classical management principles. The main changes which have affected the managerial role and altered it beyond recognition during the last three decades include:

(*a*) The impact of the computer, and more recently of the microprocessor, on information processing tasks in production and administration;

(*b*) The rapid pace of technological changes and the consequent fast speed with which manufacturing processes and products are becoming obsolete;

(*c*) The growth of international trade and the associated intensification of competition, together with the growth of multinational corporations and the impact on business of unstable exchange rates;

(*d*) The greater impact of legislation on business activity in such fields as employment protection, consumer protection, environmental care, health and safety, etc.;

(*e*) Changes in social climate leading to demands for employee participation in decision-making; and

(*f*) High rates of inflation.

These and other factors have brought about a geometric increase in the complexity of the management task and as a consequence of which decisions cannot be taken easily today in the light of just a few classical kind of principles or guidelines, however clearly they might have been enunciated in the past.

3.4 Modern Management Principles

The main propositions, principles/guidelines governing management, which command widespread agreement today, are:

- Management is the process of getting things done by other people.
- Management as an activity is universal but does not take the same form in all situations.
- The organization is a complex as well as an open system.
- The organization is composed of technical and social sub-systems.
- Appropriate and timely innovation is a necessity for sustainable survival of the organization.
- There is no one single best way to organise a business.
- Knowledge—product knowledge, process 'know-how' or knowledge of the market—is the essence of competition.
- Small is beautiful, Entrepreneurial drive, creativity, adaptability, and innovation are stifled alike by the bureaucratic system of administration and control which characterize large, monolithic organizations. Effective management structures, therefore, involve autonomous profit centres, served rather than directed by a small headoffice team.
- Management is a process involving a mix of rational, logical decision-making and problem-solving activities and intuitive, judgemental activities.

3.5 Management Movement

Management is recognized as a distinct and identifiable discipline directed towards achievement of established objectives by emphasizing the most efficient utilization of human effort and facilitating resources. The resulting sequence of events and their impact on the economy is known as the *management movement*. Management *moved* into the affairs of men as a means for maximizing the total productivity of labour, land and capital. The concepts and events which generated the cumulative forces for the management movement were:

(*a*) The concept of division of labour and factory system instead of the 'self-sufficiency' concept of craft labour and commerce, influenced the social and economic climates. The factory system developed from the need for: (*i*) large outputs of standardized products for expanded markets; (*ii*) complex operations which necessitated sizeable investments in fixed plant, mechanised processes, and power; and (*iii*) an assembly of workers under a definite organizational discipline.

(*b*) Economic prosperity from opportunities for freedom of choice in private enterprise ventures.

(*c*) The concept of 'social darwinism' permitted a system of ruthless competition which resulted in the success of the fittest who survived. The impact of the tenets of 'social darwinism' on the decision-making values of businessmen unleashed their 'achievement motives' and produced a dynamic climate for innovation and change in the economy.

(*d*) The personal ownership incentive has been a powerful force in motivating workers to participate in the management movement for increased productivity and a growing national product.

(*e*) The impact of technology produced necessary changes the management philosophies. Managers were challenged to find proper methods for augmenting human effort with the help of technological aids available. Industrial organizations increased in size, complexity, and productivity.

(*f*) The diversification of products within an enterprise and decentralization of production operations resulted in decentralization of management functions.

(*g*) The concept of scientific management introduced in the early part of the twentieth century provided the trigger which released the composite forces in the environment to initiate and sustain the management movement. For the first time in history, entrepreneurial and professional managers had a logical conceptual framework for resolving problems and achieving the objectives set for business enterprises.

Before discussion about the functions and activities of general management, it is important to distinguish between the meanings of "*management*" and "*administration*". The definitions given to "*management*" are many. Two of them are as follows:

• A social process entailing responsibility for effective and economical planning and regulation of the operations of an enterprise, in fulfillment of given purposes or tasks, such responsibility involving:

(*a*) Judgement and decision in determining plans and in using data to control performance and progress against plans; and

(*b*) The guidance, integration, motivation and supervision of the personnel composing the enterprise, and carrying out its operations.   —*E.F.L. Brech*

• Managing is the art of getting things done through and with people in formally organized groups.   —*Harold Koontz*

The essence of these two definitions should be able to create the definition that '*Management is the art or skill of directing human activities and physical resources in the attainment of pre-determined goals*'.

The word "*administration*" is used both to describe the activity of implementing policy decisions and regulating the day-to-day operations of several sections of an organization. The word is also used to describe the very senior functions in public service such as the administrative responsibility of the Indian prime minister. The word, of course, is concerned with implementing of policy but its freedom of action is limited by the decisions of policy laid down by those charged with the responsibility of setting and planning of general objectives. In view of the above discussion it may be said that administration is part of management and is rarely taken to be involved in policy-making decisions.

3.5.1 The Practice of Management

The practice of management as a skill is quite distinct from the other skills that a member of the management team might possess. For example, a production manager has technical skills and knowledge about the production processes and materials his department uses, but the application of such skills and knowledge does not necessarily imply that the production manager is employing management skills too.

It is seen that the ability to manage is an attribute different from any technical skill and knowledge which a person has in his own area of specialization. A successful manager can take advice from technical or functional experts, to arrive at conclusions or decisions considering the information given to him. One school of management throught states that a manager needs no specific skills and can, therefore, switch from one job to another and still be a successful manager. For example, requirement to hold a particular post in the IAS cadre is not technical know-how about the functions of the department one heads, but rather the ability to organize and direct the resources available and make competent decisions based on the advice received from the technical experts.

3.6 General Management

3.6.1 Definition

General management is a practice that plans, organizes, directs and controls a number of interrelated operations and supporting services in order to achieve defined objectives. It is a discipline requiring the use of a number of managerial skills rather than a technique in itself. But the skills of general management and the effectiveness with which the activities are directed and controlled to achieve the desired result are dependent on the understanding and use of a wide range of management techniques.

3.6.2 Functions of General Management

The four functions of general management are:

(*a*) **Planning:** Deciding where the organization should be going and how it should get there. This requires the appraisal of external and internal changes and constraints, forecasting, setting objectives, developing strategies and policies and preparing action plans.

(*b*) **Organizing:** Deciding who does what. This requires the definition and grouping of activities, defining responsibilities, and establishing means of communication, coordination and control.

(*c*) **Directing:** Ensuring that people know what to do and when to do it, and exercising leadership to get individuals to work to the best of their ability as part of a team.

(*d*) **Controlling:** Measuring and monitoring results, comparing results with plans and taking corrective action when required.

These functions and the continuous feedback that is received as a result of control mechanisms and planning, organizing and directing activities are shown in Fig. 3.1 schematically.

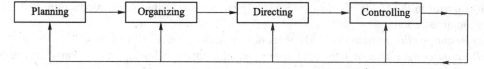

Fig. 3.1   Four functions of general management

3.6.3 General Management Activities

General management controls *two* main activities:

Line Activities

In a commercial enterprise, these comprise:

- *Business generation:* Innovation (new product development), marketing and selling.
- *Demand satisfaction:* Manufacturing the product to meet demand and distributing it to the customer. Feedback from the customer in the form of new orders and reactions to the product will affect the business generation activities.

Staff or Service Activities

These ensure fulfilment of line activities by means such as:

- Giving a sense of direction through planning and budgeting.
- Providing finance and the means of planning and controlling expenditure.
- Providing manpower in the quantities and qualities required.
- Providing management services and management support activities which include information technology, operations research, work study and other activities designed to improve the efficiency and effectiveness of the organization.

The relationships between these activities are shown in Fig. 3.2.

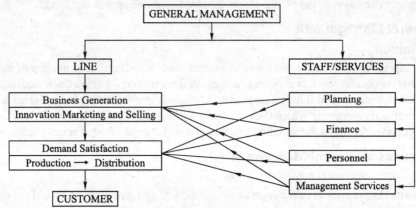

Fig. 3.2   Activities of general management

3.6.4 Techniques Used in General Management

The purpose of management techniques is to assist in the process of decision-making. Essentially, however, they are used to support, not supplement, the exercise of business judgement which is the key attribute of effective general management. A few techniques, such as operations research, are specifically designed for this purpose. Others are associated with the main processes of general management and provide guidance on the application of those processes and in solving problems related to them.

The main areas in which techniques are deployed in general management are:

(a) *Planning* in the fields of marketing, sales, production, project management, distribution, finance, manpower, corporate sector and other organizations.

(b) *Control* in the fields of finance (especially costs), marketing, sales, production, and salary administration.

(c) *Resource allocation* in the fields of capital, cash, manpower and facilities.

(d) *Resource development* in the fields of people, information technology, extension of automation, mechanization and improved techniques of manufacturing and distribution.

(e) *Management science* especially operations research, to assist in planning, resource allocation, problem solving, and decision-making.

(f) *Corporate effectiveness,* improving the efficiency and effectiveness of corporate operations.

The two key areas amongst the above in which management techniques help general management are planning and control—the initiation of the process of general management and the monitoring of performance to ensure that the planned results are achieved.

3.6.5 The Structure of Modern Management

As a result of 'management movement', the structure of modern management is shown in Fig. 3.3 and has the following three divisions:

- *Capital* (mainly shareholders)

- *Management* (largely salaried)
- *Labour.*

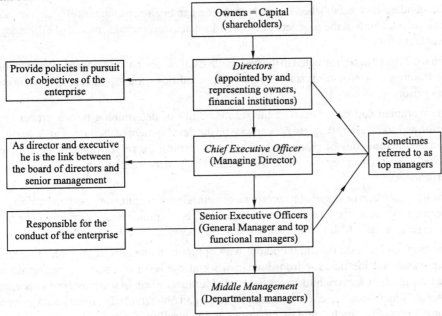

Fig. 3.3 The structure of modern management

3.6.6 The Need for Managerial Expertise

Managers, particularly senior executives of a company, are often concerned with planning the future of their organization, and setting objectives; when they are members of the Board of Directors they are responsible for formulating policies and making the final decision on corporate planning and strategy. However, the planning and strategy is ineffective without the work of the functional departments. Thus, at the functional level management expertise has to be coupled with technical expertise, because it is not necessary that a highly qualified person will necessarily turn out to be a good functional manager. For example, a competent production supervisor may not prove a success if promoted to the position of production manager which call for more managerial skill. In fact long years in a purely technical capacity can narrow the view of many people and it often demands a total change of attitude and outlook to become a competent functional manager requiring a certain amount of managerial skill. Here the term 'technical' is used in its widest sense and includes such areas as accountancy, marketing, production, personnel, purchasing and so on.

3.7 Scientific Management

The management concepts and practices which the engineers had innovated and introduced were earlier known by several names, such as 'efficiency engineering', 'rationalism', 'Taylorisrn', and 'the science of management'. Scientific management, however, became the accepted term which identified the new concept of management in the *management movement,* and which distinguished the progressive management practices from the traditional practices known as 'conventional management' or 'systematic management'.

3.7.1 Original Aims of Scientific Management

As the concept of scientific management was developing in the early part of the twentieth century, the following aims were stated:

(a) Industrial processes can be reduced to units that are amenable to scientific observations and experiments. The operations of workmen can be reduced to fundamental motions to ascertain the longest, shortest, and average time required for each motion. From such experimentation, data can be obtained to derive a standard time for the performance of each operation.

(*b*) The standard time established for each operation can be used as the task for each workman to achieve. Each unit of the product can be produced at a designated standard of efficiency and at a standard cost.

(*c*) The workmen can be instructed in the best methods of achieving the standard. The responsibility for training and providing standard working conditions must be accepted by foremen or supervisors.

(*d*) The workmen can be relieved of the responsibility of determining how a process is to be performed and thereby they can concentrate on the development of their manual dexterities. The managerial functions of planning and controlling must be responsible for determining the process and for routing the work. Workmen do not need to plan; they can concentrate on performance.

(*e*) The workmen can be inspired to accept new methods and acquire dexterity in carrying out the specifications to achieve performance standards. The inspiration to workmen can be provided by wage systems which permit them to share the benefits from increased productivity.

The emphasis was on maximum output with optimum human effort through the methods of separating waste and inefficiency from human work at the level of operative performance. The scientific management approach to the utilization of human efforts in work assignments embodied these concepts which became central to management: (*i*) an objective; (*ii*) a managerial process such as planning, organizing, motivating or directing, and controlling for achieving the objective; and (*iii*) the intelligent use of people for the performance of work projects.

3.7.2 Continuing Trend of Scientific Management

The basic concepts of scientific management have endured and developed into modem management theories, philosophies, and expanded conceptual frameworks for managerial problem-solving.

Although scientific management in the USA emerged from operating management, its values and basic concepts are now applied universally to all levels of management and fields of industrial enterprises. A process of management has developed that can be applied to the firm as a whole or to any divisionalized or functional segment of it. Thus,

(*a*) Goals or objectives must be set which are compatible with the economic, social, technological, and political environment.

(*b*) Policies to act as guides to managerial decision-making and behaviour must be formulated.

(*c*) Planning is essential to the efficient and effective achievement of the objectives.

(*d*) Organizing is needed to effect the plans by establishing the relationship between work, people, and work environment.

(*e*) Motivating or directing the people in the organization to effect the plans is required, to realize the objectives.

(*f*) Controlling the performance of the people in the organization is essential to achieve the objectives in conformance with the plans.

As the concept of identifiable functions of management that could be combined and integrated into a process of management for the achievement of predetermined results became established, contributions from other disciplines provided a boost to development of *management movement*.

3.7.3 Taylor's Scientific Management

F W Taylor (1856-1915), who is known as the father of scientific management, introduced the concept of management as a science. At Midvale Steel Company, Taylor was involved with developing *one best way of doing work*. His focus was on maximisation of worker productivity. His approach includes:

(a) Develop one best way of doing things, (b) Standardise the method, (c) Select the worker, best suited to perform the task, and (d) Train them in most efficient manner for performing the task.

Taylor defined four principles of management:

(a) Develop a science for each element of an individual work, thus replacing rule-of-thumb method.

(b) Scientifically select, train, teach and develop a worker.

(c) Cooperate with workers to ensure work in accordance with management principles.

(d) Divide responsibility between management and labour—Management plans, organises and controls. Management takes overall work for which it is better fitted than workers.

Taylor's principles has some offshoots:

(a) Enforced worker discipline gives more output.

(b) Management should not expect extraordinary work with ordinary days wages.

Taylor's work was followed by many others—Henry Gantt, Gilberth, etc. Many sub-fields like time study, motion study, work study, operations research, industrial engineering, etc. were evolved.

3.7.4 Criticism to Scientific Management

(a) Fails to appreciate the social context of work and higher needs of workers.

(b) Managers called it unwarranted interference in managerial prerogatives.

(c) Workers resisted it. In Taylor's testimony in 1912, he said that unions are really not needed.

(d) Fails to acknowledge the variance among individuals.

(e) Fails to recognize the ideas and suggestions of workers.

3.8 Administrative Management

In classical organization theory, it was believed that managerial practice fell into certain patterns that could be identified and analysed. Henri Fayol (1841-1925) was a contemporary of Taylor, but was interested in the management of large groups of people rather than organizational functions. He had suggested following *fourteen* principles of management:

(a) **Division of work:** Division of work aims at producing more and better work with the same effort. It is accomplished through reduction in the number of tasks to which attention and effort must be directed.

(b) **Authority and responsibility:** Authority means the right to give orders. Responsibility is associated with authority. Whenever authority is exercised, responsibility arises simultaneously.

(c) **Discipline:** Discipline means following rules, obedience and respect for the agreements between the firm and its employees. Discipline also involves sanctions judiciously applied in the organization.

(d) **Unity of command:** Employee should receive orders from *one* superior only.

(e) **Unity of direction:** Each group of activities should have one objective and should be unified by having one plan and one head.

(f) **Subordination of individual interest to general interest:** The interest of one employee or group of employees should not take precedence over that of the company or broader organization.

(g) **Remuneration:** To maintain the loyalty and support of workers, all employees must receive a fair wage for services rendered in the organization.

(h) **Scalar chain:** The scalar chain is the chain from top management ranging from the ultimate authority to the lowest ranks. Communication follows this chain.

(i) **Order:** Everything should be in right place at right time.

(*j*) **Stability of tenure of personnel:** High turnover increases inefficiency. A manager who stays for long is always preferred.

(*k*) **Centralization:** Centralization is the degree to which subordinates are involved in the decision-making. It belongs to the natural order of things. Proper proportion of centralization is needed for each situation.

(*l*) **Equity:** It is the kindness and fairness to subordinates.

(*m*) **Initiative:** This means allowing to originate and carry out plans to ensure its success.

(*n*) **Esprit de corps:** This means team spirit, harmony, and unity within the organization.

Further he insisted that management was a skill like any other so that managers were not born, but made. This was a major change and formed the basis of many modern attitudes.

During the same time, a comprehensive view was being developed by Max Weber (1864-1920) in Germany. His ideas were based on the structure of the organization, or the 'bureaucracy', which was characterised by:

• A clear definition of authority and responsibility.
• A chain of command.
• Selection based on qualifications, training and examination.
• Appointed officials working for fixed salaries.
• Strict rules, disciplines and controls.

Weber wanted to depersonalise management in order to promote a uniformity which would provide for the fair and equal treatment of all workers. His 'bureaucracy' was designed to provide stability and certainty in an organization and his model of management has contributed to organizational thinking over the last 100 years, particularly in large national and multinational companies.

3.9 Engineering Management

Engineering management is the art and science of planning, organizing, allocating resources, directing and controlling activities which have a technological component. This definition identifies a management speciality and also identifies specific activities which are integral to the full practice of various engineering and scientific disciplines. The practitioners of engineering management, known as 'Engineering Managers', generally claim an identification with some field of engineering/science or a related area which is also rooted in mathematics and physical sciences. Engineering management differs from industrial engineering, to which it is most closely related, by its greater focus on 'people' problems rather than on system design, which, of course, also includes people along with material and equipment. On the management side, it differs from general management in its requirement that practitioners be competent in some technical field. Engineering managers may be found occupying top, middle and supervisory management positions. They may be found working wherever a blend of managerial and technical knowledge is required, whether or not the primary business of the organization is technological in content.

The first real move towards recognition of this speciality as a separate profession took place in the USA in 1979 when a group of interested people from government, industry, and universities organized the American Society for Engineering Management. This society was expected to be influential in advancing engineering management in both theory and practice and in maintaining a high professional standard among its members. In India, there is no such society at present, but existence of such a society would lead to increased recognition of engineering management as an important profession in the future.

A typical engineering organization is shown in Fig. 3.4. Here the span of control for the engineering manager is four line supervisors. This arrangement is manageable and controllable; a number greater than seven will increase the control problem significantly.

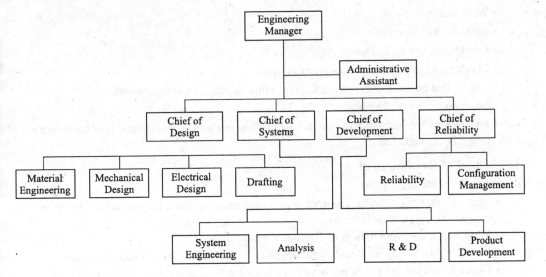

Fig. 3.4 A typical engineering organization

The scope and responsibilities of each of the four engineering areas reporting to the engineering manager are given below:

3.9.1 Chief of Systems

The responsibilities of the Chief of Systems are to:

- Convert customer requirements into a workable system, optimized for best performance.
- Provide system schematics.
- Create detailed requirements for component design.
- Analyse system performance.
- Analyse component performance.
- Interface with customers to assure them that system performance meets all customer requirements.

3.9.2 Chief of Design

The responsibilities of the Chief of Design are to:

- Evolve component hardware concepts that meet system requirements.
- Create design layouts and manufacturing drawings.
- Maintain weight control.
- Conduct structural design analysis.
- Assure that proper interface control is maintained to meet customer installation requirements.
- Review test procedures to ensure that the test programme thoroughly exercises the equipment that has been designed.

3.9.3 Chief of Reliability

The functional responsibilities are to:

(a) *Reliability*

- Perform system and component reliability analysis.
- Perform safety and hazard analysis.
- Assist in failure analysis to assure that failures are understood and that corrective action is complete and precludes recurrence of the problem.

- Write failure reports.
- Review test procedures.

(b) *Configuration Management*

- Create specifications and draw tree diagrams.
- Ensure that engineering documentation defines hardware configurations.
- Write engineering changes.
- Interface with customers to assure them that field retrofits or modifications of hardware are all properly documented.

3.9.4 Chief of Development

Responsibilities are to:

- Manage other engineering resources to provide a sound engineered product within engineering cost and schedule requirements.
- Maintain engineering liaison with manufacturing areas.
- Maintain day-to-day technical communications with customers and subcontractors.
- Direct resolution of problems occurring during manufacture, development, and in-service operation of the hardware.

Persons engaged in 'Engineering Management' may have educational background other than engineering, but they must be qualified by education and/or experience to make sound decisions involving technical work.

3.10 Manufacturing Management

Manufacturing management is concerned with the production of a product within the limits of cost, quality, and time established by the marketing and financial policies of the organization. It finds its roots in *scientific management* and the division of labour. It utilizes the techniques of applied engineering fundamentals fully, in the measurement and control of work and of human activity. In its earliest form, manufacturing management was mainly concerned with production. With the advent of scientific management in the early 1900s, management of production began to grow in scope to include all the functions related to manufacturing of a product.

3.10.1 Scope of Manufacturing

Over the years, many auxiliary management and engineering services have been introduced in the manufacturing industries to support production (or line) management. Rather than performing these auxiliary functions itself, in most companies the line management (while retaining ultimate accountability) depends upon the advice, guidance, or services of specialized staff departments. Most typically these services include:

(a) **Industrial Relations:** It caters to job placement, training, labour-union negotiations and retirement. It aids in establishing and administrating pay practices. In general, its objective is to develop a cohesive, well motivated, and effective workforce.

(b) **Costing and Budgeting:** It may report to manufacturing management either directly or indirectly. The manufacturing manager employs it to plan the financially related aspects of his operation, such as the establishment of operating budgets, and to accumulate and control production and related costs.

(c) **Production Planning:** It furnishes production schedules and machine loading programmes, and expedites work as it flows through the plant.

(d) **Inventory Control:** It works closely with marketing and finance to determine when and how much inventory should be accumulated.

(e) **Industrial Engineering:** It is the means by which engineering principles are applied to manufacturing problems. Typically, this function deals with work measurement, work methods, wage incentives, and standard costs. In most plants, it also encompasses material handling, plant layout, production machinery specifications, and manufacturing engineering.

(*f*) **Plant Maintenance:** It deals with the upkeep and repair of production equipment, buildings, and plant services.

(*g*) **Plant Engineering:** It is concerned with the design, construction, and installation of plant facilities and services.

(*h*) **Quality Control:** Its responsibility includes inspection and test of in-process and finished products, utilizing statistical techniques in order to control product manufacture within the specified quality limits.

(*i*) **Purchasing:** Although manufacturing management does not always supervise the procurement function, it exerts considerable influence upon the purchase of materials, supplies, services, equipment, and facilities as they facilitate or impede the production process.

(*j*) **Traffic:** It is generally concerned with scheduling of raw materials into the plant, and delivery of finished goods from the plant warehouse to either regional warehouses or to the customer's facility.

(*k*) **Product Design:** It normally lies between the realm of manufacturing and marketing, although each area exerts some influence on product design.

3.10.2 Measures of Effectiveness

The measure of how well manufacturing management performs its function is often a simple comparison between the profits generated and the capital put into the manufacturing operation. For instance, if an automatic lathe is purchased for Rs 100,000 and if it helps save Rs 25,000 per year as a result of its increased output, the rate of return is expressed as 25 per cent. Conversely, this investment may be described as having a "four-year payback."

When this rate of return principle is applied to *all* input costs—labour, materials, machinery, utilities, building facilities—and compared with total value of product output, it is probably the most comprehensive measure of the effectiveness of manufacturing management performance.

Other performance measures include those of material—or equipment—utilization, delivery schedule conformance, budget adherence, extent of operating cost reduction, reduction in rejects, labour productivity, and state of employee morale (as indicated by attitude surveys, accident records, number of grievances, extent of tardiness and absenteeism, and strikes).

3.10.3 Productivity and Automation

The main objective of manufacturing management is that of improving productivity of the capital invested in the operation, and of materials, machinery, and manpower. Traditionally, this improvement is achieved through replacement or modernization of existing equipment and facilities with more efficient ones. Either approach has an ultimate effect on the increased productivity of the total manpower employed.

Attaining greater return from existing resources usually takes the form of *method improvement* or *work simplification* designed to reduce the *total* cost of operation or the *net* cost per unit of production. Replacement of manual methods or obsolete equipment is dependent upon the investment of capital in new facilities that produce at faster rates, perform new operations, finish to higher specifications, or provide any of a number of improved services.

Replacement of human activity by machinery is termed *mechanization*. As the rate of mechanization accelerates, machinery and processes become more complex, and those employing the principles of *feedback* and utilizing highly sophisticated controls, are said to be automated. Both automation and cost reduction are employed by the management to reduce inputs or increase outputs, or both, in order to improve manufacturing productivity.

3.11 Systems Management

A *system* is an orderly arrangement of interdependent activities and related procedures which implements and facilitates the performance of a major activity of an organization.

A *policy* is a basic precept which guides administrative action and defines the authority and the respective relationships required to accomplish the objectives of the organization. (Policies are more fluid or changeable than objectives since they are subjected to external and internal changes in conditions; they relate to all levels of the organization, and are the product of managerial decision-making).

A *procedure* is a series of logical steps by which all repetitive business action is initiated, performed, controlled and finalized. A procedure establishes the required action, who is required to act, and when the action is to take place. (Its essence is a chronological sequence and its implementation is translated into results or actions).

A procedure is also a medium of communicating managerial policy decisions, applying to routine or repetitive areas of operations, to all concerned parties.

3.11.1 History

Systems concepts and techniques have existed from the beginning of organized human effort. But as an organized field in itself, present-day concepts and techniques of systems stem largely from the efforts of the early *scientific management* pioneers—FW Taylor, Frank and Lilian Gilbreth, Henri Fayol, and their associates. There is thus a close similarity between the application of *work simplification* and measurement concepts by systems personnel to clerical operations in the office and by industrial engineers to the work of the shop. This accounts also for the affinity of interest, between the office manager and the systems function, in techniques for controlling the flow of paperwork and measuring clerical work.

The basic responsibilities of the systems function cover a spectrum of tasks ranging from reducing clerical costs, improving timeliness of management reports, to meeting new and more sophisticated management information requirements.

The scope of the systems function today, however, goes far beyond that of simply systemizing clerical office operations and preparing procedures to govern them. It concerns itself with the overall complex interrelationship of organization structure, functional divisions of responsibility, and the optimum flow of management information—in fact, with the dynamics of the total administrative process in modem organizations.

The principal systems approaches to organization and management theory are summarized in Table 3.1. The dates referred to are those of the publications which first mentioned the theory/study concerned.

Table 3.1 Developments in Systems Approaches

Year	Research/Theory	Theorist(s)
1951	Socio-technical systems	Trist and Bamforth
1958	Open systems/work design	AK Rice
1961	Mechanistic/organic management structure. Environment and structure	Burns and Stalker
1965	Technology and structure	Woodward
1965	Types of environments	Energy and Trist
1966	Systems approach to organizations	Katz and Kahn
1967	Environment and structure—Contingency theory of organizations	Lawerence and Lorsch
1968/69	Environment, technology and structure—multidimensional approach	Pugh, Hickson and others

3.11.2 Functional Responsibilities of Systems Management

Many systems staff perform all or most of the following functional responsibilities:

(*a*) **Organizational analysis:** The development of close interrelationships between organization structure, effective administrative systems and optimum management information flow. This may include developing the organizational structure for new functions, reviewing the existing organizational structure in the light of changing organizational objectives, and preparing and issuing of organization charts and functional statements of responsibilities.

(*b*) **Systems analysis and design:** Periodic surveys of functional activities and study of administrative problems; the application of concepts and techniques of work simplification to the design of systems which will facilitate integration of business data flow throughout the organization and assure accurate feedback of information to management; and conducting feasibility studies on the application of new techniques and equipment ranging from office reproduction equipment to more intricate data transmission equipment and electronic computers.

(*c*) **Management audits:** A combination of organizational analysis and systems surveys to determine the effectiveness of specific operating functions.

(*d*) **Development of written policies and procedures:** The development of written administrative guidelines for operating personnel, including the initiation, coordination, maintenance and classification of these guidelines into appropriate manuals. These may include broad policy statements, inter-functional procedures crossing departmental lines, intra-functional procedures applicable only within a single department, and special supplementary managerial bulletins of a more temporary nature. In some companies, the systems staff is also responsible for the preparation of supplementary job instructions for major tasks involved in a procedure.

(*e*) **Forms design and control:** The design of appropriate formats to assist in proper transmission of data, and forms control measures to eliminate excess clerical data handling, with the recognition that forms are one of the main media for transmitting business data.

(*f*) **Reports analysis and control:** The design of reports to assure accurate and timely feedback of the relevant information in the form and details needed by various levels of operations and the elimination of redundant reporting.

(*g*) **Records management:** The development of records retention schedules and records storage facilities, to assure protection of vital records and to facilitate information retrieval from stored records.

(*h*) **Work measurement:** The analysis and measurement of clerical work and development of clerical work standards.

(*i*) **Office equipment selection:** The selection of suitable office tools for use in systems designed to optimize the efficiency of office operations. This includes conducting feasibility studies on applications of electronic data processing equipment and data transmission devices.

(*j*) **Office layout:** The best grouping of related and interdependent functions commensurate with optimum utilization of space.

A system can be closed or open. A closed system is self-sufficient and self-regulatory and has no interaction with the environment in which it exists (Fig. 3.5). The feedback from the output triggers a control mechanism which then regulates the input to bring back the output to the desired level.

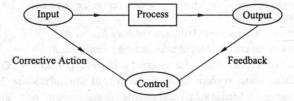

Fig. 3.5 A closed system

An open system interacts with the environment in which it exists. Figure 3.6 shows an open system. The organization here acts as an open system along with its subsystems which are its various divisions and departments. At the same time, the organization itself is a subsystem of the environmental system within which it operates.

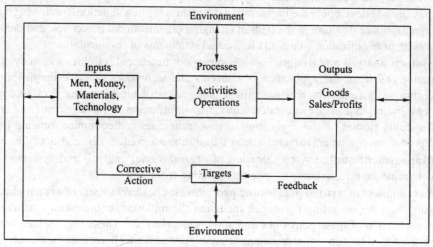

Fig. 3.6   An open system

The importance of the systems concept to the manager is that it helps him identify the critical sub-systems in his organization and their interrelationship with each other and the environment. This dynamic newer approach is sometimes referred to as 'the total systems concept' or by such terms as *integrated systems, management information systems, integrated information systems,* etc.

Self-assessment Questions Set-I

1. (*a*) Examine critically the contribution of FW Taylor towards the development of management thought.
   (*b*) Brief the contribution of FW Taylor towards scientific management.
2. Explain in detail the classical principles of management.
3. Outline the modern management principles which command widespread agreement in today's changed environment. 'These principles are flexible'. Discuss.
4. What do you understand by management movement? Outline the salient features of management movement.
5. Define general management, and enumerate its functions. Illustrate with a neat diagram.
6. Describe the main techniques employed in general management. Explain the key areas in which management techniques help general management.
7. What are the characteristic features of modern management? Also, discuss the recent trend in the field of management.
8. What is scientific management? Discuss the original aims of scientific management.
9. Discuss the major steps involved in applying the concepts of scientific management.
10. List out the latest trends in scientific management.
11. Define 'Engineering Management'. Explain the role of the 'Engineering Manager' in a research and development organization.
12. What are the responsibilities of the 'engineering manager' in the organization you are working with? Give a flowchart of the organization.
13. What is manufacturing management? Define its auxiliary functions.
14. How can one measure the effectiveness of manufacturing management?
15. The main objective of manufacturing management is to improve 'productivity'. Comment on this statement.
16. How is mechanization useful in improving the productivity of men and machines? Discuss.
17. How is the term 'system' defined in the systems approach to management? Also, differentiate between an 'open system' and a 'closed system' utilizing neat sketches.

18. What are some selection processes/techniques that a manufacturing organisation should adopt? Discuss.
19. How do forecasting and decision-tree techniques help in planning and decision-making in an organisation?
20. What are the basic concepts of systems management? Outline the developments in systems approaches.
21. Define functional responsibilities of systems management.
22. What is planning and control? How can it be executed effectively in a small scale enterprise to maximize its output?
23. Explain management by planning in detail. Outline the ten elements of management planning.
24. Discuss Taylor's scientific management and its offshoots.
25. Explain *fourteen* principles of management put forth by Henry Fayol.
26. What are the characteristics of bureaucracy developed by Max Weber?

3.12 Corporate Planning

3.12.1 Aims of Corporate Planning

Corporate planning is the systematic process of developing long-term strategies to achieve defined objectives of a firm. The aims of planning are to:

- Define and plan the long-term future of the firm as a whole.
- Increase the rate of growth of the firm in the long run.
- Ensure that the firm can meet the challenge of change and can profit from new opportunities.

Corporate planning consists of the following stages:

(a) **Setting objectives:** Which define what the company is and what it is setting out to do, in terms of growth in sales revenue and profit, and in terms of return on capital employed.

(b) **Preparing long-range forecasts:** Based upon present strategies, these will identify any gaps between the objectives and targets as set at stage 1 and indicate the extent to which new or revised strategies are required.

(c) **Defining broad strategies:** To achieve objectives, bearing in mind any gaps revealed by the analysis at stage 2.

(d) **Creating:** Financial, marketing, capital investment, acquisition, diversification and product development plans to implement strategies.

(e) **Monitoring results:** Against the plans and amending strategies or taking corrective action as necessary.

The first *three* stages—objectives, forecasts and strategies—are carried out in the light of a SWOT analysis which conducts:

- Internal appraisals of the **strengths** and **weaknesses** of the company; and
- External appraisals of the **opportunities** and **threats** facing the company now and in the longer term.

These processes are illustrated in Fig. 3.7.

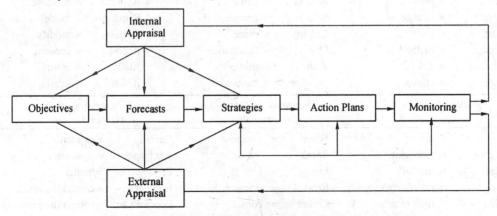

Fig. 3.7 The process of corporate planning

3.12.2 Benefits of Corporate Planning

Corporate planning enables the company to:

- Clarify its objectives.
- Understand where it may go if no action is taken.
- Take a systematic look at the future and decide the best course to take—in the full knowledge of how uncertain the future is.
- Appreciate the internal and external factors that have to be taken into account in planning for the future—strengths and weaknesses, threats and opportunities.
- Provide a strategic framework within which more detailed action plans can be made and which, having been defined, can readily be modified in the light of changes in the environment and feedback from results.

3.12.3 Planning Practices in Indian Organizations

In India, in general, organizational planning processes and plans focus on the short-run, and in particular, on short-term projections of monthly, weekly and daily operating data. Planning documents consist mostly of sales forecasts and some kind of operating budgets. However, these are prepared more for control purposes than for future planning.

The research study on the objectives of a sample of 65 out of the 251 giant companies listed by the Research Bureau of *Economic Times,* revealed that only 45 per cent of these had explicitly defined objectives and 55 per cent did not have expressed objectives. Out of 45 per cent, 17 per cent felt that their objectives were confidential and did not warrant to be divulged. This evidence indicates that the Indian business organizations, specially the large-sized ones, do realize the need and urgency of planning their operations over a longer period of time. However, many organizations still consider planning over longer periods a waste of effort primarily because of a larger measure of uncertainties prevailing in the Indian environment.

3.13 Management Functions

Management functions are divided into three distinct activities of *directing, implementing,* and *evaluating.* These three functions have many sub-elements which are broken down and briefly identified as shown in Table 3.2.

Table 3.2 Management Functions

Directing Plan (Design)		Implementing Staff (Administer)		Evaluating Control (Regulate)	
Forecast	= project	Recruit	= enlist	Appraise	= evaluate
Innovate	= change	Select	= choose	Standard	= model
Objective	= results	Employ	= place	Correct	= modify
Procedure	= method	Orient	= familiarize	Report	= account
Challenge	= risk	Train	= discipline	Audit	= assure
Budget	= allocate	Develop	= mature	Reward	= satisfaction

Organize (Structure)		Communicate (Convey) Understanding		Problem-Solve (Untangle)	
Jobs	= duties	Write	= compose	Define	= explain
Delegate	= represent	Speak	= tell	Analyse	= separate
System	= network	Listen	= hear	Prevent	= hinder
Span	= no. of workers	Read	= interpret, print	Feedback	= correct the initial
Authority	= right to act	Conter	= consult	Feedforward	= correct the expected
Policy	= guide	Gesture	= demonstrate	Solve	= answer

Schedule (Time-table)		Do (Complete)		Decide (Settle)	
Work sequence	= series	Survey	= watch	Information	= original data
Priorities	= precede	Command	= order	Participate	= involve
Time	= calendar	Motivate	= induce	Question	= inquiry
Programme	= tasks	Negotiate	= bargain	Options	= alternatives
Coordinate	= blend	Operate	= make	Agree	= conform
Overview	= total periphery	Perform	= accomplish	Resolve	= clear up

These functional sub-elements, like the major management functions, are highly interrelated. The performance of one element does not cease entirely before the next is begun. They act simultaneously, and affect each other. When the manager utilizes them in right combinations at the right time, optimum results are obtained.

Management recognizes the discreteness of functions, operations, and activities, but proceeds to bridge and interrelate them as necessary to keep the organization moving. Management synthesizes individual functions and activities within systems to bring about the total organization.

The twelve departmental operations have many sub-elements, which are broken down and briefly identified as follows:

Finance	Marketing	International Operations	Programme Management
Profits = gain	Sales = orders	Licensing = permitting	Matrix = geometric array
Investments = capital in use	Pricing = charges	Imports = foreign inputs	Life cycle = longevity
Cash-flow = available money	Advertise = communicate	Exports = local outputs	Configuration = phases
Accounting = record	Distribute = deliver	National = local hires	Baselines = time control
Engineering	**Operations**	**Systems and Data Processing**	**Materials**
Projects = undertakings	Methods = procedure	Information = organized data	Schedule = time table
Design = devise	Production = manufacture	Programming = sequencing	Purchase = buy
Develop = expand	Inventory = stock	Computers = calculators	Warehouse = store
Test = prove	Facilities = equipment	Documentation = valid information	Handling = moving
Quality Control	**Human Resources**	**Public Relations**	**Legal Questions**
Standards = criteria	Employment = hire	Image = symbol	Contract = negotiated agreement
Inspections = surveillance	Labour relations = cooperation	Giving = grants	Patents = exclusive rights
Assurance = confidence	Development = mature	Govt. relations = political cooperation	Litigation = lawsuit
Audits = certify	Compensation = reward	Community relations = social cooperation	Legal forms = compliance

These operational sub-elements, unlike sub-elements of managerial functions, are highly exclusive. They are 'pockets of specialization'. Each one is independent because of the unique knowledge of what each is composed of. These sub-elements need to be bridged and coordinated, and this is accomplished through the synthesizing nature of the highly related managerial functions. Thus, the practice of management involves the ability to apply managerial functions and sub-functions in a synthesizing process with organization operations so as to achieve desirable expectations.

3.14 Management Control

Management control is the process of assuring the efficient accomplishment of set objectives of an enterprise. In the turbulent environment faced by management, control is necessary to anticipate problems, measure performance against standards, take corrective actions for deviations from plans and, if necessary, modify plans.

The primary responsibility for exercising control rests with every manager charged with the execution of plans. As Henry Fayol said, "In an undertaking, control consists in verifying whether everything occurs in conformity with the plans adopted, the instructions issued and principles established. Its object is to point out weaknesses and errors in order to rectify them and prevent recurrence. It operates on things, people, actions." The major prerequisites of control are: a plan, and a structure. The more clear and complete the plan is, the more effective the control can be: plans become the standards by which the actions are measured. Similarly, the more clear and complete the organization structure is the more effective the control can be. The following are the five basic characteristics for an effective control:

(a) Appropriate,
(b) Strategic,
(c) Acceptable,
(d) Reliable and objective, and
(e) Cost-effective.

3.14.1 The Control Process

The control process involves four basic elements:

(a) Establishing standards of performance,
(b) Measuring performance,
(c) Comparing actual results with standards, and
(d) Correcting deviations.

This sequence of events is diagrammatically shown in Fig. 3.8, which shows how each element is linked to form a continuous process ending *either* in the achievement of targets *or* in the modification of plans as a result of feedback (Fig. 3.9).

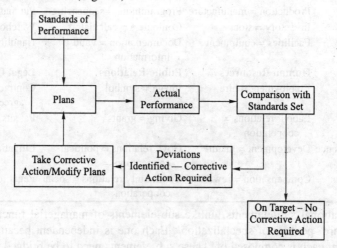

Fig. 3.8 The control sequence

First, the standards of performance need to be verifiable and clearly stated. e.g. in units of production or in sales volumes. In case standards are qualitative rather than quantitative, it is preferable for them to be expressed in terms of end-results rather than in terms of methods. Second, the measurement of performance depends heavily on the relevance, adequacy and timely availability of information. The supply of such information comes from a variety of sources within the organization.

The single-most important source is the management accounting department, which is responsible for the regular production of operating statements, expenditure analyses, profit forecasts, cash flow statements and other relevant control information. Third, when comparing actual results with performance, most organizations require action to be taken only when the deviation against standards is significant. Otherwise, no action is taken and no reference upwards is asked for. This is sometimes called the 'management by exception' principle. Fourth, control is not just a matter of identifying progress, it is also a matter of putting right what may have gone wrong. Hence, the importance of directing part of the control process to the implementation of appropriate corrective action.

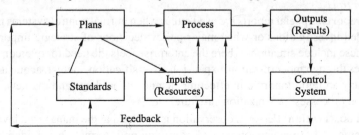

Fig. 3.9   Feedback in the control systems

The information generated by control systems is known as feedback. Feedback is usually produced on results, i.e., on the outputs of the system. Actual performance is recorded and the information fed back to the managers responsible for achieving the target performance. Early feedback is essential for accurate control, especially where unexpected deviations have occurred. Where deviations occur, feedback may indicate the need for a change in the process or its inputs or possibly, a change in the basic plans or original standards.

3.14.2 Methods of Management Control

Arthur Bedeian (1986) discusses nine methods of management control and classifies them into three categories based on their frequency of use:

   (*a*) **Constant controls:** Self-control, group control, policies/procedures/rules;

   (*b*) **Periodic controls:** Management information systems, external audits and budgets; and

   (*c*) **Occasional controls:** Special reports, personal observation and project controls.

Constant Controls

   (*a*) **Self-control:** Self-control means reporting to work on time, discharging duties and responsibilities properly and respecting the rights of others in the organization. Self-control can be promoted among employees through training in behaviour modification.

   (*b*) **Group control:** Group control can aid or hinder the formal authority. Organizations would do well to develop and use group control processes in order to reinforce formal authority. In some organizations, group control processes help increase output and improve quality, whereas in others they result in restricting output. Some examples of reinforcing group control processes to achieve organizational goals are quality circles, quality of worklife programmes, and work re-design experiments.

   (*c*) **Policies/procedures/rules:** These are managerial control mechanisms and are effective in controlling individual and work group behaviour.

Periodic Controls

   (*a*) **Management information systems:** These systems convert data from internal and external sources into information and communicate that information in an appropriate form to managers at all levels to enable them to make timely and effective decisions for planning, directing and controlling the activities for which they are responsible.

(*b*) **External audits:** The annual financial audit by an outside accounting firm is called an external audit. In India, for public sector undertakings, such an audit is performed by the Comptroller and Auditor General of India. Large companies, such as Tata Steel, have in the past sought to have a social audit to find out how well they have been discharging their social obligations.

(*c*) **Budgets:** Budgets deal with the future allocation and utilization of various resources for different activities of an enterprise over a given period of time. Budgets are also used for measuring/ evaluating the standards of performance. The expected results are expressed in numerical terms.

Occasional Controls

(*a*) **Special reports:** Special reports are used either when normal control systems point to the need for detailed investigations or when major policy decisions of strategic importance are being taken. These include situations where the enterprise feels the need for overcoming the existing difficulties through modernization, expansion, diversification, merger, acquisition, etc. Special reports play an important role in effecting changes in products and markets, technology and production processes, organization structure, etc.

(*b*) **Personal observation:** Personal observation is essential at the managerial level to know what is happening in an organization instead of relying on information provided by others. First-hand knowledge has to be critical to be effective.

(*c*) **Project controls:** For controlling specified projects of an organization, various methods have been developed such as the network analysis using programme evaluation and review technique (PERT). From this method, it is easy to determine the current status of a project, stimulate alternative plans, and undertake scheduling and controlling activities.

3.14.3 Management Control Options

In an organization, the management has three options in the area of exercising control:

(*a*) Centralization or delegation;

(*b*) Formal or informal; and

(*c*) Direct or indirect.

In centralization, the control is exercised by the chief executive or by the top management (comprising a few individuals). Others in the lower rungs of hierarchy cannot act on their own, thereby exhibiting lack of functional autonomy at operating levels. On the contrary, delegation manifests transfer of decision-making authority downwards and outwards within the framework of formal structure.

Formalization refers to establishing written policies, procedures, rules, etc. which prescribe the do's and don'ts. Formalization is effective in large organizations operating in conditions of stability. In today's environment complete formalization may not be desirable and practicable. The control should be flexible enough and reviewed periodically to keep it appropriate to the current changing situation. Direct control requires high quality managers who will properly understand and apply managerial principles, functions, techniques and philosophy, make few mistakes and initiate corrective actions themselves wherever necessary. Indirect control requires close supervision of subordinates' activities, tracing deviations in their activities and getting them to correct their practices. The higher the quality of managers and their subordinates, the less will be the need for indirect controls.

3.14.4 Management Control Strategies

John Child (1984) suggested the following four control strategies in an organization:

(*i*) **Personal Centralized Control**

    (*a*) Centralized decision-making.

    (*b*) Direct supervision.

    (*c*) Personal leadership.

    (*d*) Reward and punishment reinforce conformity to personal authority.

(*ii*) **Bureaucratic Control**

    (*a*) Splitting the task into definable elements.

    (*b*) Formal methods, procedures and rules.

    (*c*) Budgetary and standard cost-variance accounting controls.

    (*d*) Technology designed to limit variation in conduct of tasks with respect to pace, sequence and possibly physical methods.

    (*e*) Routine decision-making delegated within prescribed limits.

    (*f*) Reward and punishment systems reinforce conformity to procedures and rules.

(*iii*) **Output Control**

    (*a*) Jobs and units designed to be responsible for complete outputs.

    (*b*) Specification of output standards and targets.

    (*c*) Use of 'responsibility accounting' systems.

    (*d*) Delegation of decisions on operational matters.

    (*e*) Reward and punishment linked to attainment of output targets.

(*iv*) **Cultural Control**

    (*a*) Development of strong identification with management goals.

    (*b*) Semi-autonomous working; few formal controls.

    (*c*) Strong emphasis on selection, training and development of personnel.

    (*d*) Rewards oriented towards security of tenure and career progression.

The appropriateness of strategies varies from organization to organization.

Self-assessment Questions Set-II

1. Define the managerial process of planning, its aims and the likely benefits.
2. List the various stages of corporate planning. Explain the process of corporate planning with the help of a neat sketch.
3. Discuss the role of planning practices in Indian organizations in the light of changed circumstances.
4. Outline the management functions and their functional sub-elements. How are these interrelated? Which functions among them do you consider more important and why?
5. What are the management functions towards discharging various departmental operations? Give a detailed account of various sub-elements of departmental operations and their coordination among themselves.
6. What is the relationship between control and planning?
7. Discuss the role of feedback in a control system.
8. In defining the basic principles of management, often planning and control are considered as two separate and distinct functions. How far can they be regarded as independent of one another?
9. What are the basic elements in the management control process? Explain the control sequence with a neat diagram.
10. Examine the management control methods and the strategies used in an engineering organization.
11. Explain various methods of management control and management control options.
12. Why is management control necessary when everything is going as planned?
13. Write a short note on 'social audit'.

3.15 Skills of the Manager

Skill is the ability to apply knowledge effectively and readily in the performance of a particular physical/ mental task. Mere knowledge does not make the skill; rather skill is the ingenuity with which knowledge is used to guide thought, analysis, and judgements in responding to conditional needs in a variety of complex situations. Managers exercise this ability with varying degrees of competency and proficiency. (Knowledge is defined here as 'stockpiles' of valid information and facts organized from past experiences with specific problems). There are six general categories of skills as illustrated in Fig. 3.10, which a modern manager must possess. These are briefly described as follows:

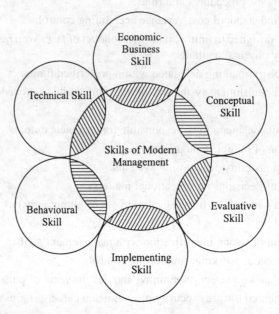

Fig. 3.10   Skill categories of modern management

3.15.1 Technical Skill

This skill requires the proficient use of the specialized information, methods, processes, procedures, and techniques involved in the technology of the product or services of the company or industry. Examples include:

(a) Ability to sense and forecast trends in the growth and development of the organization's technology,

(b) Ability to communicate and understand technical terms of organizational specialists, and

(c) Ability to exploit new knowledge to innovate services or products.

3.15.2 Behavioural Skill

This skill is primarily the utilization of knowledge to understand people as they conduct themselves. Such an understanding promotes working with others cooperatively and effectively as a natural and continuous activity. It requires an awareness of attitudes and beliefs held by individuals and groups and how these govern their goal-reaching processes. Examples include:

(a) Ability to sense people's needs and drives, and relate them to planned accomplishments;

(b) Ability to coordinate various power groups; and

(c) Ability to empathize with various lifestyles.

3.15.3 Conceptual Skill

This skill is the ability to utilize the existing knowledge in order to acquire additional knowledge. It is purposeful risk-taking for creating new conditions. Exploring, questioning, and probing are some of the tools that cut across established areas of a business. Conceptual skill is interdisciplinary, since it involves the ways in which various functions of systems depend on other systems, as well as the way changes in any one part affect all the others. Examples include:

(a) Ability to generate alternatives from present and past experiences;

(*b*) Ability to see the whole from the given constituent parts; and

(*c*) Ability to predict ends from certain beginnings even without an orientation.

3.15.4 Implementing Skill

This skill involves the ability to get work done on a day-to-day, programme-to-programme basis, or the ability to concentrate just enough resources of time, money, and effort to initiate an activity, conduct the activity and bring it to a successful end. Achievement and accomplishments are the principal dimensions for employing this skill. Examples include:

(*a*) Ability to sense and make use of pace, sequence, and time;

(*b*) Ability to work a task to completion with intensified drive; and

(*c*) Ability to foresee barriers and pursue circumventing steps.

3.15.5 Economic-business Skill

This skill is the utilization of knowledge to understand a business enterprise operating in a market for the sale of goods and services. It involves the manner in which an enterprise uses scarce and limited resources to meet changing and unpredictable demands. It involves the strategy of production, distribution and consumption of goods and services with maximization of output and minimization of input. Examples include:

(*a*) Ability to move ahead, as a member of an organization, towards coordinated ends;

(*b*) Ability to undertake a pursuit of gain in the market-place in the face of risk and uncertainty; and

(*c*) Ability to compete for positive results in the free enterprise system.

3.15.6 Evaluative Skill

This skill is the ability to appraise the value or the degree of worth of a process or accomplishment. This skill tends to be quantitative, since its basic idea is 'how much'. Examples include:

(*a*) Ability to analyse a complex mass of information into numerics and quantities;

(*b*) Ability to measure deviation, variation, and drift from prescribed directions; and

(*c*) Ability to initiate feedback corrections to reduce variance within prescribed times.

The separation of skills into these six broad areas is useful only for analysis and discussion. In practice, these skill areas are so closely interrelated that it is difficult to determine where one ends and the other begins. Capable practitioners become more generalists than specialists since they deal with segments of skills from each of the six broad areas. Practitioners cannot know everything contained in each of the six areas, yet they must have the insight and perception to extract from each the degree of the skill that is needed to achieve results in their jobs. As defined earlier, a skill is the effective utilization of knowledge. Practitioners must be alert to the generation of new knowledge in each of the six categories and assess the manner in which they can exploit it to improve the specific nature of their practice.

3.16 Responsibilities of Management

The responsibilities of management may vary from one organization to another. In general, there is a common core of six prime responsibilities.

3.16.1 Advancing the Technology of the Organization

Technology, basically, is the knowledge of ways of doing things. It is a body of formal information, containing concepts, principles, processes, methods, and techniques, that an organization exploits to develop products and services. Thus, there exists machine technology, food processing technology, electronic technology, and hundreds of others. As companies grow, utilization of the technology to the limits diminishes the potential for new products and services. Therefore, the work of management is to expand these limits with new knowledge and new information, while carrying out normal business and managerial functions.

3.16.2   Perpetuating the Enterprise

The work of management is to grow, think, expand, change, but *never terminate*! It is the prime duty of management to assure the firm's survivability. Although maximization of profit is a desirable goal, it is not as critical as the avoidance of losses as that can bring the firm to an end. This is the greatest indictment of management and the greatest measure of ineffective performance. Management must invest its time and effort to develop replacements, and its successors in turn must assume the responsibilities of perpetuating the firm. People may come and go, but the firm must continue to march ahead.

3.16.3   Giving Direction to the Firm

This responsibility of management always occupies the forefront of executive attention. It involves initiating plans, operating programmes, making decisions, evaluating, and controlling within a coordinated system that delivers results. Executives who grasp the reins and give directions to the firm assume work burdens of analysis and stress not often found in the society. This particular responsibility alone can fault a firm or an executive, and often does both.

3.16.4   Increasing Economic Performance

Economic performance is by far the most critical responsibility of management. In many ways it is the measure of how well other responsibilities are executed. Profits are needed for both the inventors of the firm and the economy of which the firm is a part. Profits support government, health, education, labour markets, and the community lifestyle in general. The work of management is the production o   f goods and services at prices and costs the market is able and willing to pay. Since the economy demands better products and increased services, increased economic performance is a critical responsibility.

3.16.5   Satisfying Employees

The work of management is to create jobs within the firm that offer rewarding and satisfying experiences to employees. Each job must be satisfying in itself rather than just a step in the promotion ladder to another job. Rewards should include something more than just salaries and financial benefits. They should include the excitement of the challenge of innovations, the recognition of important achievements, the sense of independence, the use of personal discretion and the satisfaction of participating in decision making. This satisfaction must permeate all levels from managers to supervisors and all other employees.

3.16.6   Contributing to the Community

The work of management often turns away from its own company towards the community of which it is a part. This attention to government, labour markets, health services, educational institutions, or social agencies is part of the relationship between the company and the community, and should be one of cooperation and contribution. This relationship requires mutual development and cultivation of values, people, services, policies, and resources. Profit-making for a firm is crucial for the community, as it is the basis for taxes, employment, charity, and affirmative action.

Evaluating how well an organization executes its prime responsibilities is not as easy as it might seem. If the firm existed solely to make a profit, then the evaluation of its responsibility would be easy. The plurality of responsibilities, however, requires other measures of evaluation. Some of these are suggested in Table 3.3.

Table 3.3 The Mission of Management

Prime Responsibilities	Some Evaluative Measures
1. Advancing the technology	Research reports; new product introduction rate; patents granted; R & D budgets; feasibility study reports; professional presentations.
2. Perpetuating the enterprise	Break-even points; cash flow; equity; liabilities; current rario; debt-equity ratio; bad debt losses.
3. Giving direction to the firm	Mission statements; goal formation; objective setting; long-range plans operational plans; strategic plans.
4. Increasing economic performance	Profits; return on investment; productivity, operating costs; price-earnings ratio; sales per employee.
5. Satisfying employees	Turnover, absenteeism; average remuneration per employee; benefits ratio; grievance rate; suggestion submittal rate.
6. Contributing to the community	Taxes; employment levels; donation policies; grants; affirmative action plans; executive participation.

3.17 Hidden Practices of Management

The real world of management is not orderly, well-defined, or clear in terms of its practices. It is a jungle of ideas, methods, techniques, and divergent philosophies that one might be tempted to call a mess. Textbook principles of organization, authority, command, and strategies for getting results comprise a logical and persuasive set of assumptions. The real world of management, however, is loaded with confusion, stress, uncertainty, politics, trial-and-error, frustration, disappointment, and emotional disturbances, and in many cases is a maze of 'the rat race of survivability'. The real world of management contains upheavals, redirections, and realignments because of new threats, new vibrations, new conflicts, new concerns.

An attempt has been made to list some of the hidden practices of management to gain insight into the management world that exists today:

(a) Managers role-play cooperative behaviour when they accept orders from more than one boss, often from no-authority staff.

(b) Managers get things done through people by using the powers of coercion and sanctions, by threatening exposure, or by cutting off benefits.

(c) Managers make up their minds early on important matters requiring decisions, and use the participative process to gain support and affirmation.

(d) Managers attempt to get work done through people but often find themselves doing the work.

(e) Managers are reluctant to fire employees because of threats of litigation, and adverse reactions from unions.

(f) Managers almost never have authority to commensurate with their responsibilities, and often depend on the actions of many people who cannot be controlled.

(g) Managers work long hours and are often underutilized in the process.

(h) Managers are expected to show no feelings from personally imprisoned frustrations, anxieties, and hostilities, even to the point of becoming emotionally exhausted.

(i) Managers often delay solving problems or dealing with dilemmas because the delay often produces solutions not originally available.

(j) Managers practise cooperation and often compromise to avoid the insecure finality of win-loss judgements.

(k) Managers manage work routines that are uninteresting, boring, and damaging to professional growth.

(*l*) Managers give in to unions because strikes are costly, and to assume "all the way" costs often brings the firm to a point of disaster.

(*m*) Managers have naive career expectations about loyalty and devotion to their organizations, and assume the price they are paying is the price to get ahead.

(*n*) Managers have, as their legacy, mediocre employees because of faulty selection and hiring, poor training and development, or inability to effect transfers or order discharges.

(*o*) Managers find themselves unwillingly involved in white-collar crimes often generated by upper levels of management.

3.18 Managerial Effectiveness

Competence implies standards. Standards are effectiveness factors. The following fifteen standards are those that make management practices effective at all levels in the organization (Fig. 3.11).

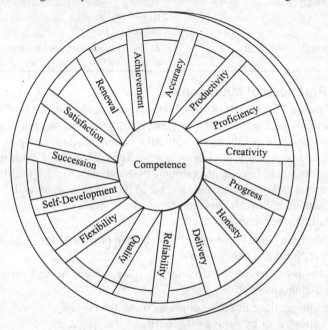

Fig. 3.11 Competence wheel of management

3.18.1 Achievement

Bringing to a successful end or accomplishing a planned set of expectations or intended results. Keep one's goals before him continually, to live with them so that they motivate and direct one's behaviour.

3.18.2 Accuracy

Acting and deciding correctly, i.e., without errors or faults that form barriers to getting results the first time. One may err the first time but never the second, for the same reason under the same conditions.

3.18.3 Productivity

Consuming minimal resources and costs while reaching for the highest possible level of performance and results. One is ready and willing to take reasonable risk, realizing that such performance stretches under conditions of minimal costs which involve some degree of probability.

3.18.4 Proficiency

Working smartly, drawing on talent training, experience, and practice. One should invest his time and energy in full measure to develop proficiency and skill to be able to harvest the benefits of opportunities.

3.18.5 Creativity

Generating alternatives that bring about innovative and unique thought processes, projects, and directions. One is certain that there is a better way to do just about everything when one has learnt how to harness the flow of creative ideas.

3.18.6 Progress

Advancing and bettering past and present conditions to enhance the quality of work life and achieve satisfaction in the organization. One is aware that it is impossible to stand still in a world of change, thereby one gives high priority to growth and advancement.

3.18.7 Honesty

Showing fairness, truth, and justice in working and responding to the needs of people, the organization, and the government. One comfortably tosses the ball to others in the team, knowing that they will play honestly and openly.

3.18.8 Delivery

Shipping goods or services at the time agreed upon with customers, clients, or buyers.

3.18.9 Reliability

Displaying consistent judgement, character, performance, or results that encourage confidence. It is known that people depend on you, and that drift and doubt must be controlled.

3.18.10 Quality

Attaining a grade or attribute distinct from others on the same level. One makes super performance a personal mission, for every task that is undertaken and for every achievement that is pursued.

3.18.11 Flexibility

Moving to new areas because of changed conditions in commitments and work processes. One is able to go over, around, and occasionally under obstacles, but never halt when obstacles appear.

3.18.12 Self-development

Growing to expand and advance perceptions, attitudes, talents, and skills for meeting new and formidable challenges. One can accomplish just about anything he sets out to do, because he can assimilate the skills and talents needed.

3.18.13 Succession

Developing successors for key positions who will advance the firm to a better stage than that at which they found it. One must pass the baton to the new runner with new energy, new thrusts, and new enthusiasm.

3.18.14 Satisfaction

Setting up conditions in the workplace and attaining quality of work life that would give satisfaction to employees in the organization. Satisfaction yields smooth work, better relations, and helps achieve greater heights. This enjoyment produces a new perspective and imparts a fresh outlook.

3.18.15 Renewal

Restoring lost and unused ideas, perceptions, understanding and skills so as to bring a manager back to his/her former position of competence.

3.19 Self-evaluation of Managerial Approaches

A. Goals, Objectives and Responsibilities

1. Take time to clearly understand expectations.

2. Assure expectations are attainable.
3. Sufficient discussions with boss on responsibilities.
4. Good follow-up on details as well as major aspects of work.
5. Frequency of changing completed work.

B. Performance Knowledge

1. Processes of performance are clearly understood both by the superior and the subordinate.
2. Superior makes concrete suggestions on how to improve performance and skills.
3. Superior shares his or her experience to improve performance.
4. Superior provides opportunity for education and training.
5. Frequency of discussions on future aspirations.

C. Communications

1. Superior communicates information.
2. Freedom to discuss all issues of performance.
3. Discussions permit two-way clarity and agreement.
4. Method of communications fits the type of discussions.
5. Superior asks you for suggestions.

D. Evaluation of Performance

1. Superior clearly communicates negative evaluation of performance.
2. Superior clearly communicates positive evaluation of performance.
3. Frankness in discussion on accuracy and amount of performance contribution.
4. Awareness and recognition of continuation by all who effect recognition and benefits.
5. Each completed job leads to progressive opportunities.

3.20 Checklist for a Competent Manager

Following points may ensure the competency of a manager:

1. Consistently exceed goals and objectives.
2. Show ways in which employees can improve.
3. Display a positive and constructive attitude.
4. Surround yourself with competent subordinates.
5. Relate level and amount of rewards to level and amount of performance.
6. Work in a system of priorities that yields payoff.
7. Show respect for others even if there is disagreement.
8. Continually reach for higher standards of performance.
9. Refrain from repeating unfavourable remarks about others.
10. Encourage new ideas and new ways of doing things.
11. Show interest in helping inexperienced people.
12. Discipline subordinates where warranted.
13. Avoid wasting time on unimportant things.
14. Keep in mind high tolerance of uncertainty in moving ahead.
15. Can orally persuade and convince.
16. Speak well of the organization, fellow managers and subordinates.
17. Impart guidance to subordinates.

18. Allow a competitive spirit in the group.
19. Encourage striving for excellence.
20. Accept development as a personal responsibility.
21. Show concern over things that can be improved.
22. Complete significant projects in time.
23. Continually raise questions that indicate search for knowledge and improvement.
24. Exhibit complete knowledge about the organization and job
25. Write simple, clearly, briefly, and persuasively.
26. Offer help to colleagues in their problems.

3.21 Managing Change

The purpose of change is to move an organization from its present status to a different one which is more desirable in meeting its objectives. In managing this process, the gap between the starting point and desirable conclusion needs to be identified. The usual steps are:

- **Vision:** A process of reminding everybody and clarifying to everybody the direction of the organization: *where we are going.*
- **Strategy:** Outlining how this is to be achieved through the development of objectives and goals; *how we are going to get there.*
- **Monitoring change:** Progress is measured in order to observe and encourage change; *this is how far we are now.*

Different stages of changes require different strategies. It may be better to work more slowly through the stages by developing a programme for change in order to establish long-term commitments. The programme for change will include:

- **Leadership:** A person who provides a clear statement of the vision and objectives.
- **Coherence:** Agreement on the operational tasks and goals consistent with the strategic view.
- **Communication:** Provision of clear and appropriate information to the relevant people about what is happening and why it is happening.
- **Timing:** Decisions on when to take action.
- **Structure:** A structured approach which moves logically through an understanding of the forces for change to the agreement on the management of the change process.

This programme will inevitably contain traps for managers. Active participation will help people to understand how the change will affect them and to come to terms with it. Employees need to be helped to say 'good goodbyes' to old practices, and are moving on. In this process, it is essential that managers are clear about objectives, and that these are SMART:

S : Specific about what to be accomplished
M : Measurable differences must be identified
A : Attainable targets should be established
R : Result output oriented change is desirable
T : Time limits should be established.

3.21.1 Continuous Change

People in organizations are often unwilling or unable to alter long-established attitudes and behaviour. A change in management style or attitude or a change in working practices may be seen as a violation of people's self-image or an indication of inadequacy. It is difficult to introduce change without suggesting a criticism of previous styles and methods. If it is suggested to a work unit that they should do things in a different way, they will immediately wonder what is wrong with their present operating method. There is an implied criticism, however diplomatically the suggestion is worded. If change can be perceived as a continuous process it may be possible to avoid this problem, because it will become part of working practices.

If change is seen to be a short-term process, after a brief period of doing things differently people may return to their earlier practices. In order to avoid this, a three-step model can be applied to the change process:

- **Unfreezing:** The need for change is made so obvious that individuals and teams can easily recognise and accept it.

- **Leadership:** Managers foster new values, attitudes and behaviour through the process of identification and internalisation.

- **Refreezing:** The new practices are locked into place by supporting and reinforcing mechanisms so that they become the new norm.

This process can be used to improve an organization's response to continuous change. This can be seen as:

> '*a top management-supported, long-range effort to improve an organization's problem solving and renewal processes, particularly through a more effective and collaborative diagnosis and management of organization culture.*'   (*French and Ball, 1984*)

This involves consultation right across the organization, and one part of the change process is decentralising management by transferring ownership of the problem to the lowest possible level. Decentralisation, flatter management organization and decisions taken at the point of action can increase both the ability to change and the speed with which change can be accomplished. Managers have to look at every way in which an organization conducts itself in order to find the most productive and efficient processes.

Through this approach it is possible to institutionalise change so that it becomes a continuous process instead of a set piece every five years. This is the modern management view based on observation of Japanese management practices. For example, the concept of 'just-in-time' production involves close and flexible working between manufacturer, supplier and purchaser. Japanese car manufacturers can be seen as specifiers and assemblers rather than manufacturers in the old sense, whereas General Motors in the USA has aimed at a high degree of vertical integration, controlling the manufacturing process from raw material to final product and customers. The 'just-in-time' process recreates the producer/customer relationship at every stage so that there is an urgency at each point. This may be a difficult feeling to transfer to departments and sections of a large organization.

The Japanese have been determined to have continuous incremental development and believe that this is most likely where there is a direct link with the customer. In an organization which is managed vertically, that is with a chain of control running from the raw material to the retail outlet, there is a vast amount of capital invested before the person nearest to the ultimate customer is reached. However, strong the links may be in this chain, the final and crucial link with the consumer may not be sufficiently strong to control the weight of expectations of the rest of the company. In large, vertically controlled companies, the people nearest to the ultimate customer may have difficulty in controlling everything that stands behind them. Rigidities tend to build up and pressures generate the wrong way. The 'just-in-time' philosophy may operate effectively in this type of organization, but only if managers encourage close working between supplier and customer at every level and then leave them to resolve all the day-to-day problems, rather than pushing decisions up the line to others who will not feel the urgency of the situation.

Self-assessment Questions Set-III

1. Define managerial skill. Explain various categories of skills of modern management illustrating with a neat diagram.

2. Outline the prime responsibilities of management, explaining some evaluative measures of each responsibility.

3. List out some of the hidden practices of management that have become a part of the new era of society.

4. What are the standards that make management practices effective at all levels in the organization? Illustrate by drawing a competence wheel of management.

5. Do you think management is practised in a professional manner in India? Discuss in detail.

6. List out the salient points for self-evaluation of managerial approaches.

7. What are the check points for a competent manager? On the basis of these check points, how would you evaluate that a manager is competent?

8. Are managers in the public sector faced with different challenges to those which face managers in the private sector?

9. How far the continuous change influences for change in organizations?

10. Distinguish between management and administration. How far is this distinction justified in your opinion.

11. Define management systems. Discuss its advantages and disadvantages briefly.

Human Resource Planning and Management

4.1 Introduction

Human resource management concerns the human side of enterprises and the factors that determine workers' relationships with their employing organizations. It is a wide-ranging subject that covers, among other things, management/worker communications; elements of work psychology; employee relations, training and motivation; organization of the physical and social conditions of work; and personnel management.

Everyone, who has control over others, shares in human resource management. Accordingly, individual manager plays a vital role in this important function.

4.1.1 Human Resources Management (HRM) and Personnel Management

In contrast with 'personnel management' which deals with the practical aspects of recruitment, staff appraisal, training, job evaluation, etc., HRM has a *strategic* dimension and involves the total deployment of all the human resources available to the firm (Guest, 1987; Legge, 1989). Personnel management is practical, utilitarian and instrumental, and mostly concerned with administration and the *implementation* of policies. Human resources management, in contrast, encompasses such broader matters as:

- **The aggregate size of the organization's labour force** in the context of an overall corporate plan (how many divisions and subsidiaries the company is to have, design of the organization, etc).
- **How much to spend on training the workforce**, given strategic decisions on target quality levels, product prices. volume of production and so on.
- **The desirability of establishing relations with trade unions** from the viewpoint of the effective management control of the entire organization.
- **Human asset accounting**, i.e., the systematic measurement and analysis of the costs and *financial* benefits of alterative personnel policies (e.g. the monetary consequences of staff development exercises, the effects of various salary structures, etc.) and the valuation .of the human worth of the enterprise's employees.

The strategic approach to HRM involves the integration of personnel and other HRM considerations into the firm's overall corporate planning and strategy formulation procedures. It is proactive, seeking constantly to discover new ways of utilizing the labour force in a more productive manner, thus giving the business a competitive edge. Practical manifestations of the adoption of a strategic approach to HRM might include:

- Incorporation of a brief summary of the firm's basic HRM policy into its mission statement.
- Explicit consideration of the consequences for employees of each of the firm's strategies and major new projects.

- Designing organization structures to suit the needs of employees rather than conditioning the latter to fit in with the existing form of organization.
- Having the head of HRM on the firm's board of directors.

More than ever before, human resource managers are expected to contribute to productivity and quality improvement, the stimulation of creative thinking, leadership and the development of corporate skills.

Further differences between personnel management and HRM are as follows:

1. HRM is concerned with the wider implications of the management of change and not just with the effects of change on working practices. It seeks proactively to encourage flexible attitudes and the acceptance of new methods.

2. Aspects of HRM constitute major inputs into organizational development exercises.

3. Personnel management is (necessarily) reactive and diagnostic. It *responds* to changes in employment, law, labour market conditions, trade union actions, government codes of practice and other environmental influences. HRM, on the other hand, is *prescriptive* and concerned with strategies, the initiation of new activities and the development of fresh ideas.

4. HRM determines general policies for employment relationships within the enterprise. Thus, it needs to establish within the organization a *culture* that is conducive to employee commitment and co-operation. Personnel management, on the other hand, has been criticized for being primarily concerned with imposing *compliance* with company rules and procedures among employees, rather than with loyalty and commitment to the firm.

5. Personnel management has short-term perspectives; HRM has long-term perspectives, seeking to *integrate* all the human aspects of the organization into a coherent whole and to establish high-level employee goals.

6. The HRM approach emphasizes the needs:

    (*a*) for direct communication with employees rather than their collective representation;

    (*b*) to develop an organizational culture conducive to the adoption of flexible working methods;

    (*c*) for group working and employee participation in group decisions; and

    (*d*) to enhance employees' long-term capabilities, not just their competence at current duties.

4.2 Human Resource Planning

4.2.1 Definition

Human resource planning (HRP) is the comparison of an organization's existing labour resources with forecast labour demand, and hence the scheduling of activities for acquiring, training, redeploying and possibly discarding labour. It seeks to ensure that an adequate supply of labour is available precisely when required. Specific human resource planning duties include:

- Estimation of labour turnover for each grade of employee and the examination of the effects of high or low turnover rates on the organization's performance.
- Analysis of the consequences of changes in working practices and hours.
- Predicting future labour shortages.
- Devising schemes for handling the human problems arising from labour deficits or surpluses.
- Introduction of early retirement and other natural wastage procedures.
- Analysis of the skills, educational backgrounds, experience, capacities and potentials of employees.

Effective HRP should result in the right people doing the right things in the right place at precisely the right time. The process of human resources planning is illustrated in Fig. 4.1.

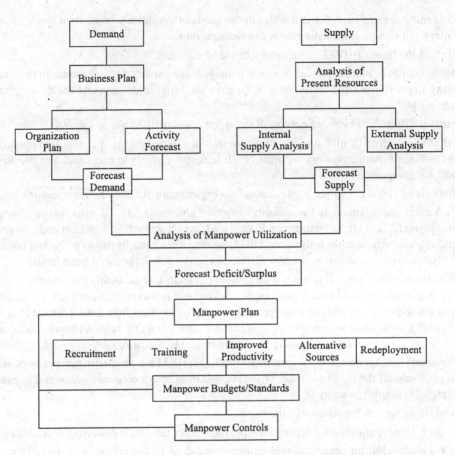

Fig. 4.1 The process of human resource planning

HRP should help management in making decisions concerning recruitment, the avoidance of redundancies, training and staff development, and the estimation of the costs of employing labour. Sometimes redundancies can be avoided through the preparation of '*skills inventories*' (i.e., detailed listings of all the competencies, work experiences and qualifications of current employees—even those characteristics not relevant to present occupations). The purpose of a skills inventory is to inform management of all the jobs that existing employees might be capable of undertaking.

4.2.2 Recent Trends in Human Resource Planning

Human resource planning deals with anticipating staffing requirements, taking into account current and likely future demand for skills, and the probable availability of individuals with such skills. It means that this definition deals with policies and programmes that are used in coordinating supply and demand in order to attain the goals desired.

While it has frequently been stated that human resources are a nation's and an organization's most valuable asset, there has been, paradoxically, a relative lack of attention to this critical resource. Financial planning, product planning, physical facilities planning, market planning and the like are probably more advanced in most organizations than is manpower planning.

The recent trend towards greater emphasis on human behaviour and social awareness will probably accelerate interest in manpower planning in all governmental, institutional, and business organizations. The bureaucratic and mechanistic emphasis on the non-human physical systems and economic goals will have to give way, partially, to concern about people as part of systems.

The nation's human resource requirements in the twentyfirst century can be expected to reflect both the growth in demand for skills and the changes in occupations and their distributions arising out of emerging national goals in a technological dynamic and socially aware society. Even in a stable organization, the normal replacement process usually requires some estimate of its future workforce. In a large and dynamic organization, this need becomes considerably more compelling, and the task more difficult.

Human behaviourists have indicated that large and bureaucratic organizations have characteristics that have been deleterious to human growth and development. Some such characteristics are: impersonality of interpersonal relations, few avenues for improving skills, limited opportunity for expressing opinions, emphasis on conformity and regulations, inflexibility of the organization to change, etc. Part of a human resource planning concept involves an enlightened viewpoint as regards employees, including: treating each person as a unique and valuable individual, providing avenues for improving skills, encouraging the growth and maturation of each individual, primary concern with human rather than physical systems, flexibility within the organization, etc.

The planning of human resources in an organization should not only be based on a desirable social goal, but also facilitate the organization's economic goals related to:

(*a*) The need for greater, more creative contributions to productivity in the face of rising costs and stiffer competition;

(*b*) The need for more broadly skilled managers at the top of the organization, and a stable executive succession; and

(*c*) The need to plan and assimilate changes in status, work, and relationships of employees.

4.2.3 Aims and Activities

The aims of human resource planning are to ensure that the organization:

- Obtains and retains the quantity and quality of human resources it needs.
- Makes the best use of its human resources.
- Is able to anticipate the problems arising from potential surpluses or deficits of human resources.

4.2.4 The Process of Human Resource Planning

Human resource planning consists of six interrelated areas of activity:

(*a*) **Demand forecasting:** Estimating the future needs of human resources by reference to corporate and functional plans and forecasts of future activity levels.

(*b*) **Supply forecasting:** Estimating the supply of human resources by reference to analysis of current resources and future availability, after allowing for wastage.

(*c*) **Determining human resource requirements:** Analysing the demand and supply forecasts to identify future deficits or surpluses.

(*d*) **Productivity and cost analysis:** Analysing human resource productivity, capacity utilization and costs in order to identify the need for improvements in productivity or reductions in cost.

(*e*) **Action planning:** Preparing plans to deal with forecast deficits or surpluses of human resources, to improve utilization and productivity or to reduce human resource costs.

(*f*) **Human resource budgeting and control:** Setting human resource budgets and standards, and monitoring the implementation of human resource plans against them.

Although these are described as six separate areas, they are, in fact, closely interrelated and often overlap.

4.2.5 Demand Forecasting

The 'manpower demand' implies manpower required to fulfil certain physical targets for Gross Domestic Produce (GDP) or industrial output or socio-cultural status. Demand forecasting is the process of estimating the future quantity and quality of manpower required. In practice, however, manpower demand implies functional/technological requirement of manpower necessary to perform a given task by the target date.

Rationale for Manpower Forecasts

The basic need for making manpower forecasts arises on account of the long gestation period involved in the production of skilled professional people. Manpower forecasts made well in advance, facilitate planning of education/training in the effort to ensure that manpower required is available at the time when it is needed.

The second reason is the observed imperfections in the labour market. Markets for manpower with long lead time for production are characterized by cobweb cycles, because of long lags in the supply side and short notices on the demand side. It is expected that manpower forecasts would facilitate correction of labour market distortions.

The third reason is the shortage of skilled category of manpower at a particular period of time. Manpower forecasts would help avoid such a situation by facilitating anticipation of skill shortages, and planning skill supplies as per the requirement.

Types of Manpower Forecasts

Some of the major types of forecasts could be categorized depending on the purpose for which forecasts are made:

(a) **Short-term forecasts:** Short-term forecasts are primarily made to facilitate estimation of financial provision for wages/salaries in the programmes/projects initiated or likely to be initiated in the immediate future. These are normally made for a period not exceeding two years. Short-term forecasts are useful at the company level.

(b) **Medium-term forecasts:** Medium-term forecasts are made in those offices which are concerned with advising ministers or preparing contingency plans to meet the 'twists and turns of economic circumstances.' The horizon for planning is about two to five years.

(c) **Long-term forecasts:** Long-term forecasts are useful in the field of educational planning, specially for highly skilled professional categories of manpower. Also, they are useful in the preparation of corporate plans, incorporating productivity changes, technological changes and organizational development. These forecasts are usually made for periods of over five years. The actual period of each forecast varies from situation to situation.

(d) **Optimizing forecasts:** Optimizing manpower forecasts are those which are obtained as solutions to an optimizing model in which numbers demanded of various categories of manpower are so determined that either the end benefits are maximized, or the cost of resources used in achieving a predetermined end objective is minimized.

(e) **Onlookers' forecasts:** Onlookers' forecasts are derived by assuming that the factors influencing manpower demand would behave in the future in the same way as they did in the past. These forecasts are obtained applying a rule of thumb or professional judgement, or with the help of an explicitly specified model, or any combination of the three.

(f) **Policy conditional forecasts:** Policy conditional forecasts are determined by the policy towards the factors which influence the demand for manpower. Similar to the onlookers' forecast, such manpower forecasts are based on a rule-of-thumb, or professional judgement, or an explicitly specified model, or any combination of the three.

(g) **Macro and micro forecasts:** At the macro level, manpower demand forecasts are needed as a basis for educational planning, choice of location of industries, size of industries and technology, and for determining priorities for creating and/or expanding economic and social infrastructure. The manpower demand forecasts may, therefore, need to be indicative in facilitating appropriate action, and are required to be comprehensive. The methodologies of macro manpower demand are, therefore, complex and often expensive because of the nature of techniques used and database required.

Micro level manpower demand forecasts are made at the enterprise or company level. At this level, the forecasts are needed for planning, recruitment, promotion and training. Forecasts, at this level will, therefore, have to be precise and in greater detail. A well defined manpower information system built up on the basis of personal history card of each individual employee is a pre-requisite for making detailed and precise forecasts at the enterprise or company level.

Macro Forecasting

The following five manpower demand forecasting techniques are used at the macro level in different countries:

(*i*) Employer's opinion method,

(*ii*) Normative method,

(*iii*) Component method,

(*iv*) International comparisons method, and

(*v*) Mediterranean regional project (MRP) method.

(*i*) **Employer's opinion method:** In this method, employers are asked to give their assessment of future manpower needs in different categories in their respective establishments. Aggregating the demand of all employers and making allowances for death, retirement, migration and occupational mobility, it is possible to arrive at the future manpower demand in each skill category. This method is more useful in making short-term manpower forecasts than in making medium-term and long-term forecasts. However, the technique is known to be severely constrained even as a means of making short-term forecasts. For instance, where markets for goods and services are characterized by stiff competition, employer's forecasts of manpower cannot be aggregated.

(*ii*) **Normative method:** This method uses norms for employing manpower to produce goods and services. The norms are usually expressed as ratios between manpower employed and the volume of goods and services produced. These ratios are based either on the existing situation or on the desirable situation. Examples of the ratios are employment-output ratio, teacher-student ratio, employment-value added ratio, medical doctor-population ratio, and engineer-technician ratio. This approach has two basic limitations. First, the method assumes that the norms are stable over a period of time. This can be overcome if it is possible to predict changes in the norms between the base year and target year. Second, it uses a uniform norm for all components of a production process. This limitation can be overcome if different norms for different components are used.

(*iii*) **Component method:** In this method, any one category of manpower requirement is sub-divided into its various components and then separate norm appropriate to each component is used in arriving at a forecast of manpower requirements for each component. Forecasts for all components are then aggregated to arrive at an estimate of future manpower requirements.

(*iv*) **International comparisons method:** This method, though not very popular, sometimes facilitates the use of stable norms. There is a considerable subjective evaluation of international experiences in using the international comparisons method which is not always easy to justify on objective considerations.

(*v*) **MRP method:** The MRP method is designed to forecast manpower requirements in educational categories so that the forecasts are rendered directly relevant to educational planning exercises.

Micro Forecasting

The following three steps are involved in micro manpower forecasting, which is essentially an estimation of manpower needs for a specified or anticipated workload structure:

(*a*) Evolving manning norms based on an analysis of workload structure, (*b*) Forecasting workloads, and

(*c*) Relating workloads to manning norms.

(*a*) **Evolving manning norms:** Here the work of an organization is first divided into functions and the functions are then sub-divided into tasks and into work groups associated with each task. For each work group: (*i*) the levels and the number of positions at each level, (*ii*) job descriptions of each position by level, and (*iii*) the performance of incumbents to each position by level *vis-á-vis* job expectations are analysed. Based on this analysis, the number of levels and the number of positions required at each level, skill gaps of incumbents to each position, and their education/training and experience requirements are worked out. The manning norms thus estimated for each work group are discussed with the employers and employee unions to arrive at a set of desired manning norms for the organization as a whole, relevant to the present workload pattern. Changes in the workload pattern—either due to technological change, or better manpower utilization or both—may result in a different set of manning norms for the organization.

(*b*) **Forecasting workloads:** Work consists of a variety of tasks, the relative magnitudes of which vary with time. To arrive at a forecast of total workload, one way is to predict the workload of each task separately and then aggregate the workloads of all tasks. If the tasks are numerous, then this procedure is tedious. It is, however, possible that several tasks are inter-correlated. Hence, dimensionality of the problem may be reduced. When all the tasks are perfectly correlated, in a rare case, it would suffice to take just one task or an average of all tasks for projection purposes. In case the tasks are not perfectly correlated, dimensionality of the problem may be reduced using either of the two statistical techniques: Principal Component Analysis and Factor Analysis.

In principal component analysis, linear transformation of numerous tasks are divided into a smaller number of indices (principal components) such that (*i*) the indices are all uncorrelated among themselves, and (*ii*) all the indices together summarize the information contained among the numerous tasks. Principal components are then projected to arrive at the forecast of workloads.

In factor analysis, some smaller number of factors are identified which are capable of explaining the behaviour of the numerous tasks. Predicting the behaviour of individual factors, forecasts of workload under each task can then be made, thereby arriving at the forecast of the total workload. In both the methods it is presumed that the character of work in each task will not change significantly during the forecast period, though technological change/manpower utilization can change the character of work in anyone or more tasks.

(*c*) **Relating workload to manning hours:** If workload 'W' can be forecast by the methods discussed above and if productivity 'P' of workers, given as the ratio of workload to workers, can be estimated based on *a priori* information on factors affecting productivity, then manpower forecasts in terms of numbers required in future can be obtained as W/P.

Database for Manpower Demand Forecasting

Database plays an important role in manpower forecasting as it determines the methodologies that can be adopted and methodological refinements that can be effected. Data requirements for manpower demand forecasting are discussed below separately at the macro and micro level.

(*a*) *Database for the macro level:* It is desirable to have comparable data on the following items spanning a number of years in the past:

    (*i*) Population statistics,

    (*ii*) Data on economic parameters, and

    (*iii*) Information on technologies.

(*b*) *Database for the micro level:* A well-defined manpower system is needed for micro forecasting at the enterprise level. The system may have the following modules:

    (*i*) **Personal data module:** Identification particulars, educational particulars, privileges (handicapped, SC/ST, etc.).

    (*ii*) **Recruitment module:** Data for recruitment, grading in aptitude tests, grading in leadership tests, overall grading, job preferences and choices, if any.

    (*iii*) **Job experience module:** Placement history, grade promotions, tasks performed, significant contribution, etc.

    (*iv*) **Performance appraisal module:** Performance appraisal at each job held, job experience with job description, communication rating of behaviour in a group, commitment to corporate goals, etc.

    (*v*) **Training and development module:** Type of training received at each level, individual evaluation and assessment of training *vis-á-vis* jobs currently being performed, etc.

    (*vi*) **Miscellaneous module:** Record of compensation and benefits received, health status, information relating to personal problems which calls for the attention of authorities, security needs, etc.

Manpower information system is based on personal history records of each individual employee within the enterprise and is updated annually.

4.2.6 Supply Forecasting

Manpower is the skilled component of labour force irrespective of the level of skill attained. Manpower supply is then the totality of manpower employed and manpower unemployed but the latter is without jobs.

Dimensions of Manpower Supply

The following four dimensions of manpower supply exist in the literature on manpower planning:

    (*a*) Stock and flow,

    (*b*) Quantity and quality,

    (*c*) Occupation and education, and

    (*d*) Macro and micro.

    (*a*) **Stock and flow:** Stock denotes the manpower supply at a particular point of time such as a target date of an economic plan, whereas flow refers to manpower supply over a period of time, say, over a five year plan period.

    (*b*) **Quantity and quality:** Quantitatively, manpower supply indicates the number of persons available with the requisite qualifications/skills both employed and unemployed, as well as those seeking jobs. Qualitative dimension indicates the characteristics of manpower supply such as specialization, duration and quality of training, length of job-related experience, and aptitude and motivation.

    (*c*) **Occupation and education:** Occupation is a description of functions. An occupation does not necessarily indicate education/training/skill requirements to perform the expected functional roles. Some occupations are uniquely related to a given profession—such as physicians—and some occupations do not have a precise relationship with education. In the latter case, manpower supply is more complex. Engineering is one such occupation which falls under this category. In case of engineers, manpower supply would be:

    • Number of engineers with degrees from engineering colleges.

    • Number of engineers with diplomas, equivalent to degree holders in engineering, from professional engineering societies such as the Institution of Engineers (India), the Institute of Chemical Engineers, and the Institution of Electronics and Telecommunication

Engineers. The characteristics of this category of engineers are that they are expected to be in the engineering profession.

- Number of engineering graduates in other occupations.
- Number of engineers without engineering degree (self-trained).

Since reliable occupation-education information is extremely difficult, manpower supply forecasts are generally made by broad categories of educational qualifications.

(d) **Macro and micro forecasts:** Macro level manpower supply for the future consists of: (i) current position of manpower; (ii) additions to current stock by way of new entrants or re-entrants; and (iii) subtractions due to death, retirement, migration, mobility, and withdrawal from labour force.

Micro level manpower supply comprises: (i) external supply caused by recruitment; and (ii) internal supply resulting from transfers, promotions, and redundancies.

Macro Forecasting

At the macro level, there are two methods of making manpower forecasting: direct method and indirect method.

Direct method: The direct method relies on census count of all persons for which manpower supply is estimated. Generally, census count can be obtained from the population census. The basic limitation of this method is that the census counts are infrequent, thereby they cannot be used in any forecasting exercise. Apart from this, the census is known for enumeration biases such as under count, misreporting and classification biases.

Indirect method: This method estimates manpower supply by cumulating economically active component of institutional turnover, the relevant period after making adjustment for all factors causing manpower attrition. Estimation of manpower by the indirect method involves the following six steps:

(a) Estimating active life span,

(b) Determining base period,

(c) Forecasting annual institutional turnover,

(d) Estimating attrition rate,

(e) Obtaining cumulated turnover adjusted for attrition, and

(f) Estimating manpower supply.

(a) **Active life span:** It is defined as the span of life over which an individual is active in any given profession or occupation. Active life span varies with the occupation and also varies from individual to individual within an occupation. Therefore, active life span is estimated for an average individual in each occupation. Estimation of two parameters for knowing the average active life span of any occupation is essential: (i) Average age at entry into the occupation; and (ii) Average age at retirement from the occupation. The difference between the average age at retirement and the average age at entry is then the average active life span.

(b) **Determining base period:** Manpower stock as of a target date comprises manpower of all vintages starting from the persons who have just entered to those who are on the verge of retirement. Hence, the base year is obtained by subtracting the number of years in the active life span from the target year. For example, assuring an active life span of 44 years for engineers (from 21 to 65 years of age) and the target year as 1999, then the base year will be 1955 (1999-44).

(c) **Forecasting annual institutional turnover:** Here past trends in enrolment are extrapolated to cover the target year, using suitable trend forecasting methods. The forecasts of enrolments thus obtained are then converted into forecasts of turnover, with the help of observed trends in annual rates of completion of the concerned educational level.

(*d*) **Estimating attrition rate:** Attrition in the manpower supply relevant to any category of education may be caused by the following four factors—death, retirement, migration, and occupational mobility. The combined effect of these four factors is called the *attrition rate*. Since impact of occupational mobility is difficult to estimate, usually, average impact of death, retirement and migration is estimated to obtain the attrition rate. In the Indian context, for example, an annual attrition rate of 2 per cent is used for engineering degree holders, out of which 0.8 per cent is attributable to death and retirement and 12 per cent to migration.

(*e*) **Obtaining cumulated turnover adjusted for attrition:** Given the base year of manpower supply (p_0), manpower supply in the first year (p_1) after the base year is obtained as

$$p_1 = p_0 \frac{(1-a)}{100} + y_1$$

where a is the attrition rate and y_1 the institutional turnover in the first year after the base year. Similarly, manpower supply in the second year (p_2) after the base year will be

$$p_2 = p_1 \frac{(1-a)}{100} + y_2$$

where y_2 is the institutional turnover in the second year after the base year.

Proceeding in the same manner, manpower supply in the target year (say t years after the base year) will be

$$p_t = (p_t - 1) \frac{(1-a)}{100} + y_t$$

where $p_t - 1$ is the manpower supply in the year prior to the target year.

(*f*) **Estimating manpower supply:** Manpower supply is the labour-force component of the cumulated and adjusted turnover. Further adjustment to cumulated and adjusted turnover is, therefore, warranted to account for withdrawals from the labour-force of persons with the requisite education/training:

Manpower supply in the target year

= Cumulated turnover adjusted for attrition × Labour-force participation rate.

Micro Forecasting

Micro level forecasting for manpower supply comprises external and internal supplies.

External manpower supply forecasting arises primarily through recruitment which is necessarily meant to augment internal supply. Another source of external supply is through deputing personnel from other organizations which takes place largely in government organizations and parastatals.

Forecasting of internal supply is crucially dependent on the analysis of wastage and internal movements, with a view to obtaining estimates of wastage and patterns of internal movements. Estimate of wastage is determined using the following methods:

(*i*) **Analysis of wastage**

$$\text{Annual manpower wastage} = \frac{\text{Manpower leaving in a year}}{\text{Average manpower in position}} \times 100.$$

(*ii*) **Stability index**

$$\text{Stability index} = \frac{\text{Manpower with one year service at time } t}{\text{Manpower in position at time } t-1} \times 100.$$

(*iii*) **Modified stability index**

$$\text{Modified stability index} = \frac{\text{Total service of manpower employed at the time of analysis}}{\text{Total possible service had there been no manpower wastage}} \times 100.$$

(*iv*) **Cohort analysis:** Manpower cohort in an organization is a group of staff which is more or less homogeneous and comprises persons who joined the organization at the same time. This analysis is useful in analysing the forecasts of wastage of specific groups of manpower who have similar characteristics and who also join at a particular time of the year such as graduate engineers, management trainees and computer professionals. Disadvantages of this analysis are: (*a*) In case of many cohorts, it is not possible to find year-wise wastage from a cohort for forecasting; (*b*) Size of the cohort is not known; and (*c*) If the manpower is relatively stable-Government Jobs and Public Sector Undertakings—the length of time over which a cohort must be followed can become too unwieldy to attempt any reliable forecast.

(*v*) **Census method:** In this method, a snapshot of the total situation is taken at a particular time and data on leavers with completed length of service is obtained. Based on such data, it is possible to estimate the proportion of manpower joining at a given point of time who will survive to a specified length of time.

Internal movements are of two types—vertical and horizontal. Vertical movements are caused by either promotion or demotion. Horizontal movements are between locations or divisions within the same category or level of manpower which are caused by transfers. For analysing and forecasting internal movements, the Markov chain model is usefully employed. It calls for the estimation of transition probabilities—a most difficult task relevant to each vertical and horizontal movement. Once the estimates of transition probabilities are made, they can be applied to any intake of fresh batch of recruits to forecast internal supplies as well as wastage by grade and length of service. It is also not necessary to keep transition probabilities constant in forecasting future supplies.

Database for Manpower Supply Forecasting

Since database requirements for macro and micro level forecasting are different, database needed for these forecasts are discussed separately.

(*i*) *Database for macro level:* Data on the following items is desirable for macro supply forecasting:

    (*a*) Age at entry and at exit,

    (*b*) Annual enrolment and turnover,

    (*c*) Attrition rates,

    (*d*) Retirement age,

    (*e*) Migration,

    (*f*) Morality, and

    (*g*) Labour-force participation rates.

(*ii*) *Database for micro level:* A detailed manpower information system is required for internal supply forecasting. It comprises the following modules:

    (*a*) **Personal data module:** Identification particulars, educational particulars, privileges (handicapped, SC/ST, etc.);

    (*b*) **Recruitment module:** Date of recruitment, grading in aptitude tests, grading in leadership tests, overall grading, job preferences and choices, if any;

    (*c*) **Job experience module:** Placement history, grade promotions, tasks performed, significant contributions, etc.;

    (*d*) **Performance appraisal module:** Performance appraisal of each job held, job experience evaluated with job description, communication rating, rating of behaviour in a group, commitment to corporate goals, etc.;

    (*e*) **Training and development module:** Type of training received at each level, individual evaluation of training received *vis-à-vis* jobs currently being performed, etc.; and (*f*) **Miscellaneous module:** Record of compensation and benefits received, health status, information relating to any personal problem which calls for the attention of the authorities, security needs, etc.

4.2.7 Determining Human Resource Requirements

Human resource requirements are determined by relating the supply to the demand forecasts and establishing any deficits or surpluses of manpower that may exist in the future. The reconciliation of demand and supply forecasts shows how many people may have to be recruited or made redundant and this forms the basis for the manpower plan proper—drawing up recruitment campaigns and training programmes or preparing for redundancy.

Human resource planning is not only concerned with obtaining people, but also concerned with how efficiently they are used. The raw assumptions built into the supply and demand forecasts need to be reconsidered to know if there is any scope for satisfying future demands by improved manpower utilization and controlling costs.

Staffing

The kinds of questions usually addressed to staff planning include the following:

(*a*) How many employees, by type, are needed to meet objectives?

(*b*) Are such employees available within the organization?

(*c*) How many people, by type, must be recruited and by what time periods?

(*d*) How should these employees be allocated to the various components of the organization?

(*e*) What is the best way to recruit and select the required personnel to assure the best quality for the positions available?

(*f*) What type of education and training is required to satisfy the needs of the organization and the individual?

(*g*) What kind of career programme is available for each individual?

(*h*) How can the work be designed to strike a desirable balance between productivity and employee satisfaction?

(*i*) How can the work environment be developed to provide maximum motivation to employees towards achievement of the organization goals?

From these discussions, the following principles are suggested:

(*a*) Management should not overlook the qualifications of its existing employees to fill anticipated work openings. It should think of its employees in terms of their potential rather than only in terms of their existing skills.

(*b*) Education and training should be thought of as being continuing processes, rather than one-time or spasmodic events.

(*c*) Human resource planning itself is a continuing activity. It must be sufficiently long-range to be able to provide the proper manpower resources in the right place, in the right amount, and at the right time. Because all planning is subject to uncertainties, the manpower plan should be flexible and adaptable to changes in conditions.

(*d*) Each organization must tailor its staffing plan to its particular needs, planning processes and policies.

(*e*) Human resources planning is highly dependent on good information. Consequently, the first requirement for the development of a planning programme for staffing is the establishment of an information base which will permit meaningful forecasting.

(*f*) Planning should not be performed in an ivory tower, but should involve all those affected. Involvement is necessary to assure all possible meaningful inputs, and to obtain acceptance of the plans.

(g) The plan should be subject to appraisal to determine its effectiveness and to strengthen the planning process.

(h) The planning should be action-oriented to accomplish specific tasks and to attain specific goals.

(i) The plan should emphasize broad and comprehensive goals, rather than minute and excessive details.

Some efforts are currently being made to improve human resource planning by use of a variety of computerized models. It appears that these efforts have either been of a research nature or are still being evaluated for effectiveness in an operational sense.

4.2.8 Manpower Productivity and Cost

Manpower planning is just as concerned with making the best use of people as with forecasting and obtaining the numbers required. An increase in activity levels can be catered for by improving productivity as well as by recruiting more staff. This means looking at productivity and manpower costs as well as the possibility of treating human resources as assets, rather than liabilities to be invested in, maintained and allocated on the same rational basis that is used for all other assets.

Productivity

Fundamentally, productivity represents the output of goods and services which can be obtained from a given input of employees. Within the firm, productivity should be monitored by using such measures as manpower costs per unit of output, manpower costs as a ratio of sales value, sales value per employee, tons of product handled per man-hour, or labour costs as a percentage of added value (the difference between production costs and sales value). Internal and external comparisons may then reveal areas where improvement is required by mechanization, automation, improved management or other means.

Manpower Costs

Manpower costs can be grouped under the following seven headings:

(i) **Remuneration costs**

 (a) Pay—basic, bonuses, profit-sharing, overtime and shift payments, merit pay, other supplementary pay;

 (b) Direct fringe benefits—pensions, life insurance, holidays, car, luncheon vouchers/subsidized meals, share ownership schemes, housing schemes, housing assistance, education loans; and

 (c) Statutory costs—national insurance and pension fund contributions, training costs (offset by grants), employer's liability towards insurance.

(ii) **Recruitment costs**

 (a) Preparation of job specifications and advertisements;

 (b) Advertising and general promotional activities;

 (c) Sifting through applications, interviewing, and corresponding with applications;

 (d) Selection testing;

 (e) Medical examinations; and

 (d) Induction.

(iii) **Training costs** (offset, where applicable, by grants)

 (a) Remuneration and expenses of trainees and trainers;

 (b) Preparing and maintaining training programmes;

 (c) Training materials, equipment and premises; and

 (d) Lower efficiency of trainees until fully trained.

(iv) **Relocation costs**

 (a) Travel, accommodation and disturbance allowances;

(b) Housing assistance; and

(c) Hostel charges.

(v) **Leaving costs**

(a) Loss of production between leaving and replacement;

(b) Statutory redundancy payments, less rebates; and

(c) *Ex gratia* payments.

(vi) **Support costs**

(a) Indirect fringe benefits—social and sports facilities, medical, welfare, rehabilitation and convalescent schemes, canteens, preferential purchase schemes, house magazines, library;

(b) Long-service awards;

(c) Suggestions schemes;

(d) Safety facilities; and

(e) Car parking.

(vii) **Personnel administration costs:** Personnel department costs, other than those allocated under other headings.

It may be difficult to collect and allocate expenses under all these headings, but the more detailed the analysis, the better the control that can be exercised over manpower costs.

4.2.9 Action Planning

The manpower plan should be prepared on the basis of an analysis of manpower requirements and a study of the implications of the information on productivity and costs. The main elements, depending on circumstances, will consist of:

(i) **The recruitment plan** which will set out:

(a) the numbers and types of people required and periods when needed;

(b) any special supply problems and how they are to be dealt with; and

(c) the recruitment programme.

(ii) **The re-development plan** which will set out programmes for transferring or re-training existing employees.

(iii) **The redundancy plan** which will indicate:

(a) who is to be redundant and where and when;

(b) the plans for re-development or re-training, wherever not covered in the re-development plan;

(c) the steps to be taken to help redundant employees find new jobs;

(d) the policy for declaring redundancies and making redundancy payments; and

(e) the programme for consulting with unions or staff associations and informing those affected.

(iv) **The training plan** which will show:

(a) the number of trainees or apprentices required and the programme for recruiting or training them;

(b) the number of existing staff who need training or re-training and the training programme; and

(c) the new courses to be developed or the changes to be made to existing courses.

(v) **The productivity plan** which will set out:

(a) Programmes for improving productivity or reducing manpower costs by such means as:

• improving or streamlining methods, procedures or systems.

• mechanization or automation.

• productivity bargaining.

• training.

- use of financial incentives: payment by result schemes, bonuses, profit-sharing.
- development of other methods of improving motivation and commitment, organization development programmes, redesigning jobs, increased participation.

(*b*) Productivity or efficiency targets such as:
- remuneration or total employment costs as a percentage of sales revenues;
- sales per employee;
- net profit after tax as a percentage of remuneration costs;
- remuneration or labour cost per unit of output;
- labour costs as a percentage of added value; and
- standard hours as a percentage of actual hours worked.

(*vi*) **The retention plan** which will describe the actions required to reduce avoidable wastage under the following headings:

(*a*) **Pay problems:** Increasing pay levels to meet competition; improving pay structures to remove inequities, altering payment systems to reduce excessive fluctuation; introducing procedures to relate rewards more explicitly to effort or performance;

(*b*) **Employees leaving to further their career prospects:** Providing better career opportunities and ensuring that employees are aware of them; extending opportunities for training; adopting and implementing 'promotion from within' policies and introducing more systematic and equitable promotion procedures; deliberately selecting employees who are not likely to want to move much higher than their initial job;

(*c*) **Employees leaving due to conflict:** Introducing more effective procedures for consultation, participation and handling grievances; improving communications by such means as briefing groups; using the conflict resolution and team-building techniques of organization development, programmes; re-organizing work and the arrangement of offices or workshops to increase group cohesiveness; educating and training management in approaches to improving their relationships with employees;

(*d*) **The induction crisis:** Improving recruitment and selection procedures to ensure that job requirements are specified accurately and that the people who are selected fit the specification; ensuring that candidates are given a realistic picture of the job, pay and working conditions; developing better induction and initial training programmes;

(*e*) **Shortage of labour, improving recruitment:** Selection of and training for the people required; introducing better methods of planning and scheduling work to smooth out peak loads;

(*f*) **Changes in working requirements:** Ensuring that selection and promotion procedures match the capacities of individuals to the demands of the work they have to do; providing adequate training or adjustment periods when working conditions change; adapting payment by result systems to ensure that individuals are not unduly penalized when engaged on short runs only; and

(*g*) **Losses of unstable recruits:** Taking more care to avoid recruiting unstable individuals by analysing the characteristics of applicants which are likely to cause instability and using this analysis to screen results.

In each of the six areas of manpower planning it will be necessary to estimate the costs involved for assessment against the potential benefits. It will also be necessary to indicate who is responsible for implementing the plan, reporting on progress and monitoring the results achieved.

A firm's success is closely tied to the strength of its various key departments. The innovation, desire, and discipline shown by various departments can make or break the firm. Management must be visible and must allow subordinates to make decisions. The growth of people is an essential part of the secret of success of a firm.

1. What do you understand by human resource planning? Enumerate its aims and activities.
2. Explain the process of human resources planning with a neat sketch. Discuss various aspects of manpower demand forecasting.
3. Outline the various types of manpower forecasts. Briefly explain the macro and micro level manpower demand forecast.
4. Why is a database necessary for manpower demand and supply forecasting? Discuss its salient features.
5. What is manpower supply forecasting? Explain the four dimensions of manpower supply.
6. Review the various factors involved in macro level manpower supply forecasting. What is attrition in the manpower supply?
7. Explain the meaning of external and internal supplies in micro level supply forecasting.
8. What is Cohort analysis? Explain the manpower cohort in an organization.
9. What are the essential factors involved in determining human resource requirements?
10. How is staff planning being done in research and development organizations?
11. Explain the importance of manpower productivity and manpower costs in the process of manpower planning.
12. What are the main elements of action planning in an analysis of manpower requirements?
13. 'A firm's strength is the strength of its various key departments'. Discuss this statement in detail with some real-life examples.

4.3 Human Resource Management Systems

Such systems involve identifying information which relates to the job itself such as grade, qualifications and experience required, and also identifying information relating to individual employees.

Figure 4.2 shows a total concept of a human resource management information system.

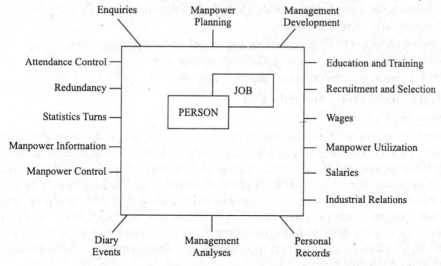

Fig. 4.2   Human resource management information system—a total concept

Such separation between people and jobs has the advantage of making it possible to undertake a matching of jobs and people to identify areas of imbalance.

4.3.1 Manpower Control

Management implies control. In practice, all organizations have some method of manpower control. The control procedure shown in Fig. 4.3 may be regarded as a framework within which the manager can develop his own system. The manager will have practical difficulties in trying to develop any system, particularly if it crosses established principles in the organization. For instance, the cost aspect will probably be covered in part by established financial procedures, but whether these will be adequate for manpower control may be less certain. Another problem may relate to the previous practices of the organization. Where rigid establishment control has been operated, with consequent for going beyond the norms, it is likely that only a flexible open system which relies more on managerial judgement will meet with immediate success.

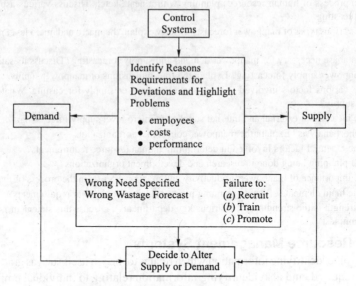

Fig. 4.3   Framework for manpower control

In addition, the control procedure should have the following features:

(*a*) Flexibility to meet new situations,

(*b*) It should relate to planning, objectives and procedures of the organization,

(*c*) It should relate to financial and productivity criteria, and

(*d*) It should result in action to solve identified problems.

4.3.2 Recruitment Policy and Selection

Recruitment and Recruitment Policy

Recruitment is the process of identifying the prospective employees, stimulating and encouraging them to apply for a particular job in an organization. Policy formulating is an essential managerial function. It is a complicated process which may involve all levels of employees. While formulating a policy, values and objectives of different groups involved should be kept in view so as to raise efficiency of working relationships in an organization. In addition, the recruitment policy shall have to be in line with the manpower requirements in order to attain the objectives of the organization. The recruitment process involves five different elements: (*a*) a recruitment policy; (*b*) a recruiting organization; (*c*) a forecast of manpower requirements; (*d*) development of manpower sources; and (*e*) techniques for utilizing these sources.

The recruitment policy states the objectives, and provides a framework for implementation of the recruitment programme in the form of procedures. A recruitment policy may include issues such as promotion within, or transfer from, the organization (as quotas are usually fixed in government and public sector organizations as also quotas for certain minority groups). While the recruitment system is a function related to the personnel function, in principle, recruitment should remain a line responsibility.

There is a need to constantly review and improve the methods of recruitment in view of the changing times and demand. A sound recruitment programme necessarily involves appraisal of each source, and the techniques, from the viewpoint of relative quality of personnel which it has provided.

The valuation procedures should consist of existing employees in terms of their jobs—success, evaluation of source from which good and poor employees were recruited and the methods used in assessing the relative values.

The overall aim of the recruitment and selection process should be to obtain at minimum cost the number and quality of employees required to satisfy the manpower needs of the company. There are three stages of recruitment and selection:

(a) **Defining requirements:** Preparing job descriptions and specifications; deciding terms and conditions of employment.

(b) **Attracting candidates:** Reviewing and evaluating alternative sources of applicants, inside and outside the company; advertising; using agencies and consultants.

(c) **Selecting candidates:** Sifting through applications, interviewing, testing, assessing candidates; offering employment, obtaining references; preparing terms of reference of employment.

The flow of work and the main decisions required to be taken in a recruitment and selection procedure are shown in Figs. 4.4 and 4.5, respectively. The numbers and categories of manpower required should be specified in the recruitment programme, which is derived from the manpower plan. In a large organization, it is useful to have a form for requisitioning staff as shown in Fig. 4.6.

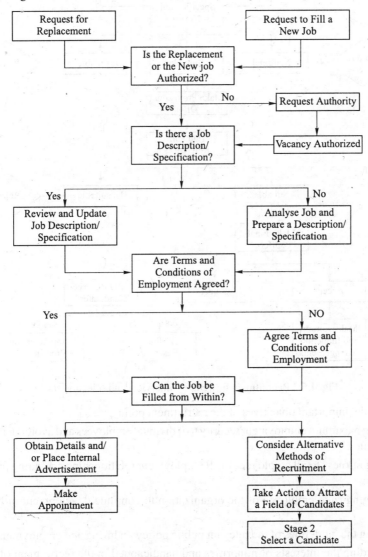

Fig. 4.4 Recruitment flowchart—preliminary stages

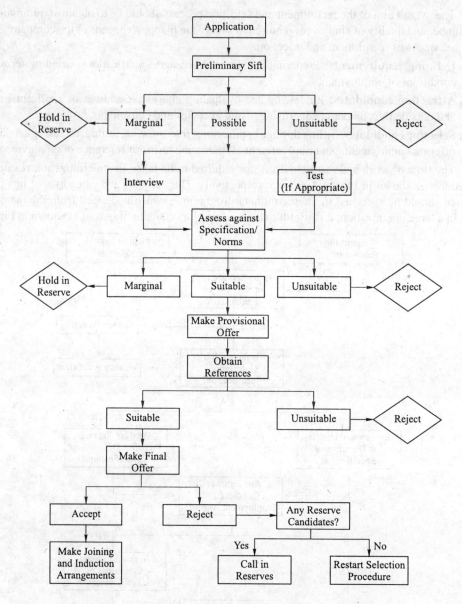

Fig. 4.5   Recruitment flowchart—interview and selection stages

Some of the important objectives of the recruitment policy are:

(*a*) Providing maximum employment security to individual employees and avoiding frequent lay-off or lost time;

(*b*) Assuring fairness to all employees in all employment relationships, including promotions and transfers;

(*c*) Encouraging each employee of the organization to continue development of his talents and skills;

(*d*) Following the guidelines of the relevant public policy on hiring and employment relationship;

(*e*) Safeguarding the interests of minorities and handicapped in the recruitment of personnel;

(*f*) Assuring employees interest in their personal goals and employment objectives;

STAFF REQUISITION

To	From	Department	Date
Personnel Department			

	REQUIREMENTS
Job title	Permanent ❏ Temporary ❏
Salary grade	Date needed
	If temporary, specify the period
	from to
Brief outline of main duties	Education and qualifications required
	Experience required
	Special skills, mental or personality requirements
	Age limits (if any)
	Who will supervise the employee?
	Whom will the employee supervise?

IF A REPLACEMENT, COMPLETE THE FOLLOWING:

Employee replaced	Job title	Salary	Date terminated
Reason for termination			
Performance			Would you re-engage?
❏ Above average ❏ Satisfactory ❏ Unsatisfactory			❏ Yes ❏ No

IF INCREASE IN ESTABLISHMENT, COMPLETE THE FOLLOWING:

What has created the need for an increase?

Explain why it is not possible to avoid this increase by organizational or other rearrangements.

Increase in establishment approved   Signed   Date

Fig. 4.6 Staff requisition form

(*g*) Avoiding cliques usually developed because of employment of a large number of members belonging to a particular community or the like; and

(*h*) Encouraging strong and responsible trade union(s).

These objectives may differ from one organization to another depending on their size, location, constituents of their manpower, philosophy of the management, social circumstances, etc.

Methods of Recruitment

Broadly, methods of recruitment can be divided into three categories: (*a*) Direct methods; (*b*) Indirect methods; and (*c*) Third-party methods.

(*a*) **Direct methods:** These methods include sending recruiters to educational and professional institutions;

(*b*) **Indirect methods:** These methods cover advertising in newspapers, trade and professional journals, technical journals, and on television; and

(*c*) **Third-party methods:** These include commercial and private employment agencies, state or public employment agencies, placement offices of schools, colleges and professional associations, recruiting firms, management consulting firms, indoctrination seminars for college professors, trade unions, temporary help agencies, casual labour sources, and the process of deputation.

Selection Process and Tests

The selection process involves the following *seven* steps:

   (*a*) Preliminary screening of applications,

   (*b*) Review of application forms,

   (*c*) Physical examination,

   (*d*) Checking references,

   (*e*) Psychological testing,

   (*f*) Interview, and

   (*g*) Internal promotion programme.

      Selection tests can be put into *four* categories:

   (*a*) Achievement or intelligence tests,

   (*b*) Aptitude or potential ability tests,

   (*c*) Personality tests, and

   (*d*) Interest tests.

Interviewing

The purpose of a job interview is to obtain information. Therefore, applicants should be put at ease as quickly as possible and hence into a frame of mind in which they will disclose the maximum amount of information about themselves. Uncomfortable, ill-at-ease candidates will not be as frank as those who are relaxed, confident and in full control of their responses. Accordingly, candidates should be interviewed promptly at the appointed time or, if delay is inevitable, apologies should be offered. Interruptions from telephone calls, secretaries, etc., disturb concentration and should be avoided.

      The following rules should be followed when conducting interviews:

1. Opening remarks should be supportive and uncontroversial.

2. Questions which simply ask for repetition of information already provided in application forms should be avoided. Rather, the interviewer should seek supplementry information to probe in depth the candidate's potential.

3. Detailed notetaking by interviewers is inadvisable because of its disturbing effects on the interviewee. Candidates should be assessed immediately after their interviews. Otherwise, important points in earlier interviews will be forgotten in the final end-of-session appraisal.

4. Open-ended questions such as 'what made you decide to do that?' or 'why did you enjoy that type of work?' are usually more productive in obtaining information than direct queries. Generally-worded questions invite the candidate to discuss feelings, opinions and perceptions of events. Simple yes/no questions will not draw out the candidate's opinions. Interviewers should not make critical or insensitive remarks during the interview.

5. Interviewers should not compare candidates with themselves.

6. Only job-relevant questions should be asked.

7. The 'halo effect', i.e., assuming that because a candidate possesses one desirable characteristic (smart appearance or a good speaking voice, for example), then he or she must be equally good in all other areas, must not be allowed to influence the selection.

8. 'Revealing' questions should not be asked. A revealing question discloses attitudes and beliefs held by the questioner. An example would be 'I like watching football, don't you?'

9. Inappropriate criteria must not be applied. This could involve, for example, males who interview females associating attractive physical appearance with work ability, or appointing people the interviewer knows socially.

10. Interviewers should not behave in a pompous manner. This wastes time and contributes nothing to the quality of the interview.

11. Interview panels should be as small as possible. Overlarge panels create unhelpful dramatic atmospheres, and panel members might ask irrelevant and disconnected questions.

Induction and Placement

The induction and placement programme simply proposes that new recruits shall be made to feel and develop themselves as a part of the organization as early as possible. It primarily consists of three steps:

(a) **General orientation by the staff:** The employee is given general information about the history and operations of the firm. The purpose is to help an employee build up some interest in the organization;

(b) **Specific orientation by the job supervisor:** The employee is shown the department and his place of work, the location of facilities and is told about specific practices and customs of the organization. The aim is to enable the employee to adjust to his work and environment; and

(c) **Follow-up orientation:** The purpose is to find out whether the employee is reasonably well satisfied with the organization. Personal talks, guidance and counselling efforts are made to remove the difficulties experienced by the new entrant.

A crucially important aspect of the induction process is that of informing recruits where to go for help if they experience problems. Entrants should know whom to approach, and the correct procedures to follow. Appropriate contacts might be supervisors, personnel officers, higher managers or trade union representatives. In any event, the recruit should know what to do if he or she:

- has a problem with money or understanding the wage system.
- has a medical problem.
- feels that working conditions are unsafe.
- does not get on with other people in the department.
- has difficulty with the work.
- is bullied or harassed.
- has a complaint.
- does not receive adequate training.

Placement or actual posting of an employee to a specific job has an experimental element in it; for most employees it is a decisive step.

Self-assessment Questions Set-II

1. Define the terms 'Recruitment' and 'Selection'. How do they differ from each other? Discuss in detail.
2. What do you understand by 'Recruitment Policy' of an organization? Also, discuss the pre-requisites of a good recruitment policy.
3. Examine critically the objectives of a recruitment policy.
4. Discuss different stages of recruitment and selection. Illustrate through schematic diagrams the flow of work and main decisions required in a recruitment and selection programme.
5. Evolve a staff requisition form as per the recruitment policy and selection process followed in your organization.
6. Discuss different methods of recruitment. Critically examine the relevance of indirect methods of recruitment in India.
7. What is selection process? Define and explain the four different categories of selection tests.
8. Point out the sequential steps in an induction and placement process. Critically examine one of them.
9. 'Management implies control'. Discuss this statement with an illustrative diagram.
10. What is the purpose of a job interview? Mention the rules to follow when conducting interviews.

4.4 Training and Development Programmes

4.4.1 Definition

Training and development programmes are necessary in any organization to improve the quality of work of the employees at all levels, particularly in a world of fast changing technology, changing values, and deteriorating environment. The purpose of both programmes is similar. The main difference between the two concerns the levels of employees for whom these programmes are meant, and the contents and techniques employed.

Training is a short-term process utilizing a systematic and organized procedure by which non-managerial personnel acquire technical knowledge and skills for a definite purpose. It refers to instructions in technical and mechanical operations such as operation of a machine.

Development is a long-term educational process utilizing a systematic and organized procedure by which managerial personnel get conceptual and theoretical knowledge. It involves broader education and its purpose is long-term development.

Though training and development programmes are both necessary for any organization, not all organizations show awareness of the need for development. This is possibly due to the fact that the benefits of training programmes are more apparent and can be obtained rather quickly than those from the long-term development process.

4.4.2 Training

Training can be defined variously as the modification of behaviour through experience; the transfer of skills and knowledge from those who have them to those who do not; or to bring about significant improvements in performance as a result of instructions, practice and experience. These definitions indicate what training is but not as to how it can be made effective. The only way of achieving good results from training is to tackle it systematically. The benefits that result from this approach are:

- Reduction in waste and spoilage.
- Improvement in methods of work.
- Reduction in learning time.
- Reduction in supervisory burden.
- Reduction in machine breakdowns and maintenance costs.
- Reduction in accident rate.
- Improvement in quality of products.
- Improvement in production rate.
- Improvement in morale and reduction in grievances.
- Improvement in efficiency and productivity.
- Reduction in manpower obsolescence.
- Enabling the organization to provide increased financial incentives, opportunity for internal promotion and raising of pay scales.
- Wider awareness among participants, enhanced skills.
- Personal growth.

Identifying Training Needs

The aim of analysis of training needs is to define the gap between what is happening and what should happen. This gap is what has to be filled by training (Fig. 4.7).

The gap may consists of the difference between:

- How the company or a function within the company is performing and how it should perform.
- What people know and can do and what they should know and do.
- What people actually achieve and what they should achieve.

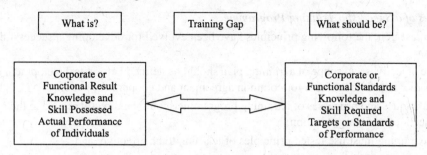

Fig. 4.7   The training gap

The analysis of training needs covers corporate, group and individual needs as shown in Fig. 4.8.

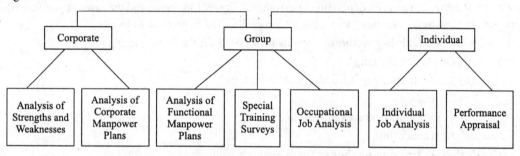

Fig. 4.8   Training needs—areas and methods

Corporate training needs should come from the analysis of a company's strengths and weaknesses as part of the corporate planning process. The company manpower plan will also indicate the numbers and types of people required in the future.

Group needs are identified by analysing functional or departmental manpower plans or by conducting special surveys using questionnaires and interviews. Job analysis can be used to determine the knowledge and skills required in specific jobs and this information can be supplemented by analysing the results obtained from the assessment of individual needs.

Individual training needs are identified by using the techniques of job analysis, skill analysis and performance appraisal.

Most commonly used methods for identifying training needs are: Analysis of an activity; analysis of problems; analysis of behaviour; analysis of an organization; performance appraisal; brainstorming; buzzing; card sort; checklist; committee; comparison; conference; consultants; counselling; in-basket; incident pattern; informal talks; interviews; observation; problem clinic; research; role playing; self-analysis; stimulation; skill inventory; slip writing; studies; surveys; tests; task force; questionnaire; and workshops.

Training Objectives

Following are the *three* basic objectives of training:

(*a*) Preparing employees for the job meant for them while on first appointment or transfer, or on promotion, and imparting them the required skill and knowledge;

(*b*) Assisting employees to function more effectively by exposing them to the latest concepts, information, techniques, and developing the skills required to perform in their respective areas; and

(*c*) Building a second line of competent officers and preparing them to occupy more responsible positions.

Principles of a Successful Training Programme

Based on research, the following principles have been evolved for developing a successful training programme:

(a) The objectives and scope of a training plan should be defined before its development is begun, in order to provide a basis for common agreement and cooperative action;

(b) Techniques and processes of a training programme should be directly related to the needs and objectives of an organization;

(c) The training must use tested principles of learning to be effective; and

(d) Training should be conducted in the actual job environment to the maximum possible extent.

Training Methods

A number of training methods have been evolved and any one method, or a combination of any two or more of these, can be used depending upon the training requirements and the level of people to be trained. Following are the *two* main methods generally used to provide training:

(i) **On-the-job training methods:** Various methods of on-the-job training are:

    (a) On-the-job training,

    (b) Vestibule training or training-centre training,

    (c) Simulation,

    (d) Demonstration and examples, and

    (e) Apprenticeship.

(ii) **Off-the-job training methods:** These methods include:

    (a) Lectures,

    (b) The conference method,

    (c) Seminar or team discussion,

    (d) Case discussion,

    (e) Role-playing, and

    (f) Programmed instruction.

Responsibility for Training

The total responsibility for training has to be shared among:

(a) The top management, who should frame and authorize the basic training policies, review and approve the broad outlines of training plans and programmes, and approve training budgets;

(b) The personnel department, which should plan, establish and evaluate instructional programmes;

(c) The supervisor, who should implement and supply the various developmental plans; and

(d) Employees, who should provide feedback, revisions and suggestions for improvements in the programme.

Training Scene in India

In an endeavour to build up the career of young persons, the Directorate General of Employment and Training (DGET) has evolved various training programmes. These are formulated within the national framework, as far as possible, and also in collaboration with other countries. The training programmes are:

1. **Craftsmen's training:** 1447 Industrial Training Institutes (ITIs) were set up all over the country in 38 engineering and 26 non-engineering trades for men and women in the age-group 15-25 years. Besides these 64 trades, the state governments and union territories have introduced training in additional trades to meet the requirements of the new industries established in their states.

2. **Craft instructors' training:** Six central training institutes were established at Mumbai, Kolkata, Hyderabad, Kanpur, Ludhiana and Chennai to train craft instructors required by the industrial training establishments.

3. **Advanced vocational training system:** The system was introduced in six advanced training institutes for instructors located at Mumbai, Kolkata, Hyderabad, Kanpur, Ludhiana, Chennai and 16 selected ITIs under 15 state governments.

4. **Foremen training/supervisory training:** An institute to train foremen was established in Bangalore in 1971. It trains existing and potential shop foremen and supervisors in technical and managerial skills and also trains workers from industry in advanced technical skills. The Government established the second Foremen Training Institute at Jamshedpur in 1982 to cope with the increasing demand for trained foremen.

5. **Apprenticeship training scheme:** The Apprentices Act, 1961 makes it obligatory for employers in specified industries to engage apprentices. The apprenticeship training consists of basic training followed by on-the-job or shop-floor training in accordance with the standards prescribed by the government in consultation with the Central Apprenticeship Council.

6. **Part-time training to industrial workers:** Courses are conducted in Central Training Institute, Chennai, in five advanced training institutes and 48 ITIs.

7. **Vocational training research:** A Central Staff Training and Research Institute was set up in Kolkata, in 1968 for developing indigenous training techniques, conducting training programmes for officers and staff of the central and state governments as well as from industry.

8. **Vocational training for women:** The Central Training Institute for Women in New Delhi is a national level vocational training institute for women. Also, three regional vocational training institutes for women are functioning at Mumbai, Bangalore, and Thiruananthapuram.

Apart from this, several training programmes, short-term courses and workshops are organized by some professional institutions, associations, etc. for officers and staff to update their knowledge in areas of their professions. Large public/private sector undertakings have their own training institutes to impart training to employees.

4.4.3 Management Development

Management development is a systematic process of training and growth by which managerial personnel gain and supply skills, knowledge, attitudes and the insight into managing the work in their organizations effectively and efficiently.

Need for Management Development

Management development is necessary for the following reasons:

1. Society is facing a rapid technological and social change. Management personnel need to be developed as they have to tackle problems arising out of introduction of automation, intense market competition, growth of new markets, enlarged labour participation in management and more interest taken by the public and the government in various activities of business.

2. Business and industrial leaders are increasingly recognizing their social and public responsibilities which call for a much broader outlook on the part of management.

3. Management-labour relations are becoming increasingly complex.

4. For handling problems arising out of increasing size and complexity of the organization.

5. For understanding and adjusting to changes in socio-economic forces, including changes in public policy and concepts of social justice, industrial democracy, problems of ecology (smog or pollution), ekistics (problems of human settlements), ergonomics (problems of working environment) and cultural anthropology (problems of fitting machines to men).

Management Development Concepts

A management development programme has to be based on the development of certain important concepts evolved in the past such as:

1. Management development is not a 'one shot' affair but continues throughout an executive's professional career.
2. There always exists some gap between actual performance and capacity, which provides considerable opportunity for improvement.
3. Increased understanding of others, their behaviour and attitude, and of oneself definitely aids in managing and contributing to personal development.
4. There are certain forces which may retard further growth, for example, age, habits, and reduced motivation.
5. Development requires clear-cut objectives and goals as well as methods of achieving the same.
6. Participation is essential for growth. Spoon feeding seldom brings any significant or lasting improvement.
7. Feedback from a superior to a subordinate and from a group to an individual is necessary for the recognition of shortcomings and for keeping oneself in touch with the progress that has been achieved.
8. An important responsibility of the personnel department is that of development.

Management Development Objectives

A management development programme must aim at achieving the following objectives:

1. To assure the organization of availability of required number of managers with the required skills to meet the present and anticipated needs of the business.
2. To encourage managers to grow as persons and in their capacity to handle greater responsibility.
3. To improve the performance of managers at all levels in the jobs that they hold.
4. To sustain good performance of managers throughout their careers.

Management development must relate to all managers in the organization. It must lead to growth and self-development of the organization. Its focus should be on requirements of the future rather than those of today. Management development must be dynamic and qualitative, rather than static replacement based on mechanical rotation.

Some objectives of development of managerial personnel at various levels of management are given below:

Top Management

1. To improve thought processes and analytical ability in order to uncover and examine problems and take decisions in the best interests of the organization and the country.
2. To broaden the outlook of the executive towards his role, position, and responsibilities within the organization and outside.
3. To think through problems which may confront the organization now or in the future.
4. To understand economic, technical and institutional forces in order to solve business problems.
5. To acquire knowledge about the complexity of human relations.

Middle Line Management

1. To establish a clear picture of executive functions and responsibilities.
2. To bring about an awareness of the broad aspects of management problems, and an appreciation of interdepartmental relations.

3. To develop an ability to analyse problems and take appropriate action.
4. To develop familiarity with the managerial uses of financial accounting, psychology, business law and business statistics.
5. To inculcate knowledge of human motivation and human relationships.
6. To develop responsible leadership.

Middle Functional Executive and Specialists

1. To increase knowledge of business functions and operations in specific fields in marketing, production, finance, personnel.
2. To increase proficiency in management techniques such as work study, inventory control, operations research, quality control.
3. To stimulate creative thinking in order to improve methods and procedures.
4. To understand the functions performed in a company.
5. To understand human relations.
6. To develop the ability to analyse problems in one's area or functions.

Organizational Climate for Management Development

Organizational climate refers to the circumstances or conditions in which the management guides the development and growth of people at all levels by training, counselling, delegation and communication. This refers to the manner in which things are managed, the way people are treated, the extent of delegation of authority, system of encouraging ideas, initiative and enterprise, opportunity for experimenting and testing new concepts, tools and techniques for projection of a company's goals, policies and philosophy.

Management development is not possible unless a favourable climate is created for it in the organization.

There must be a definite, comprehensive and coordinated plan for the development of managers. It should be drawn after consultation with the people concerned and communicated to all those who have to administer and function under the plan. Implementation must begin from the top so that management at the senior level may set an example.

Techniques of Management Development

Various methods of management development are described laying emphasis on handling situations, people and managerial problems. These methods are:

1. Planned progression.
2. Job rotation:
    (*a*) rotation in non-supervisory work situations,
    (*b*) rotation in observation assignments,
    (*c*) rotation among managerial training positions,
    (*d*) middle-level rotation in 'assistant' position, and
    (*e*) unspecified rotation among managerial positions.
3. Creation of 'assistant-to' position.
4. Under-study.
5. Coaching-counselling.
6. Temporary promotions.
7. Committees and junior boards of management.
8. Syndicate.
9. In-basket exercise.

10. Sensitivity training.

11. Management of business games.

12. Transaction analysis.

4.4.4 Evaluation of Training Programmes

As part of training, each training programme should make provision for evaluation. Some of the criteria for evaluation could be:

(*a*) Reaction of trainees,

(*b*) Learning,

(*c*) Behavioural changes, and

(*d*) Impact on organization effectiveness—increased output, improved quality and lower costs.

These criteria can be viewed as either subjective or objective. Subjective criteria call for the opinion of participants about the effectiveness of the training programme during the period of training, at its close or after completion of training. Similar evaluation may be made by trainers and management. Objective criteria relate to effects of training by measuring specific outcomes.

After the evaluation, it is necessary to find the probable causes for a difference between the expected outcome and the actual outcome. The causes may lie in the designing aspects of a programme and/or its implementation. In fact, the investment of the organization in terms of energy, time and money must be justified by the related outcome, in terms of the increased effectiveness and efficiency of the participants.

Self-assessment Questions Set-III

1. Define the term 'Training' and differentiate it from 'Development'.

2. Examine critically the need and importance of training. How does training help different sections of the industry? Discuss in detail.

3. Point out the training objectives and discuss the various principles of training.

4. List the important methods of training used in industries and academic institutions. What method of training would you recommend for a student from a polytechnic?

5. Both 'On-the-job' and 'Off-the-job' training methods are important at their own places. Justify.

6. What types of training programmes has the Director General of Employment and Training initiated in India? Discuss one of them briefly.

7. Define 'Management Development'. Elaborate the need for management development.

8. List the important concepts of management development.

9. What are the objectives of management development? Explain the objectives of development of managerial personnel at various levels of management.

10. Describe the various methods of management development.

11. Why is it essential to evaluate the training and development programmes? Examine critically.

4.5 Motivation

Motivation must work as a major factor in the study and practice of management. Organized effort—that is, getting work done through and in association with others—requires motivating interdependent effort, as opposed to effort that is self-cancelling. Thus, Henri Fayol, one of the early observers of organized effort, shares the contemporary opinion that motivation constitutes the core of management.

Dramatic changes have occurred in our understanding of motivation. The periods following the two world wars saw cumulative breakthroughs in describing and influencing motivational states, and advances made in the last few years promise far more striking results.

4.5.1 Definition

'Motivation' often receives no precise conceptual definition; and implicit and explicit meanings of the term commonly differ. The concept, however, covers at least one area of meaning: 'Motivation refers to the degree of readiness of an organism to pursue some designated goal, and implies the determination of the nature and locus of the forces inducing the degree of readiness.' The necessity of considering all of these factors together must be underscored, particularly since the common emphasis has been upon motivating behaviour with a specific direction, such as high satisfaction or high output. The danger is that all low producers be considered as unmotivated, when in fact, they may be highly motivated towards goals other than, for example, high output. The point has a crucial practical significance, for changing the direction of intense motivation poses quite a different set of problems than motivating the phlegmatic. Relatedly, the locus of motivating forces has often been assumed to be in the formal organization or the individual. The assumption is too restrictive, as will become clear.

Thus, observers tend to agree that motivation will occur only under specific conditions referred to by three key notions; *expectancy, instrumentality, and valence*, building upon the seminal work of Victor Vroon. Thus, individuals will be motivated to the degrees that:

1. They *expect* that their effort will lead to enhanced performance.
2. They believe that enhanced performance will be *instrumental* in leading to their reward, both extrinsic and intrinsic.
3. They value the expected reward which, in terminology of the expectancy theory, has a high valence for individuals.

4.5.2 Some Common Assumptions about Motivation

1. It is commonly stated that it is the subordinates or rank and file among the workers or non-supervisory staff in an organization who need to be motivated and not the supervisory and managerial staff. The fact is that the latter need to be motivated first and it is they who will then be able to motivate their subordinates and other workers at the shop-floor level.
2. Motivation and higher productivity go together. This may be true, by and large, but individual motivation at the workplace or group motivation as in the case of trade unions may not have such a correlation with productivity.
3. All motivational techniques are designed and applied by the personnel department, managers and other line executives, who directly control and take work from those under them. In fact, the latter are more concerned as it is their primary function to see that the persons under them work efficiently. As they are in closer touch with their workers, they can understand their problems better and also know their needs. If necessary, they can take the advice of the personnel executive or industrial psychologist or any consultant.
4. Standard theories of motivation developed by psychologists will also apply to an industrial situation. Most of these concepts and theories have been developed by the study of human material other than industrial personnel, and so their application to the latter may not be fruitful or provide dependable results.

4.5.3 Types of Motivation

In an industrial set-up, motivation may be intrinsic as well as extrinsic. Intrinsic motivation is related to the job one is doing. When a skilled operative performs a job well, he derives a sense of satisfaction. This is intrinsic motivation which satisfies the creative instinct in man.

Extrinsic motivation is external to the job or task. For example, financial incentives or giving a higher production bonus for doing a job well may motivate the workers. Other external motivations are praise from the superior for good work, recognition of good performance by the company in the form of public citations and awards, admiration of fellow workers, and provision of improved working conditions and other facilities.

4.5.4 Determinants of Motivation

The traditional approach that man could be made to work by giving monetary rewards has been gradually giving place to a more complete pluralistic explanation which recognizes that man works to fulfil a variety of needs. It is recognized that motivation is the result of the following three groups of factors:

1. **Individuals:** To know what can motivate employees, and to know their aims, objectives and values. Human needs are both numerous and complex, and often are difficult to identify. Motivation is not an easily observable phenomenon. First, it is required to observe individual action and behaviour at work and interpret the same in terms of underlying motivation. This interpretation may not necessarily reveal the individual's true motivation, as some of the human needs may be difficult to describe and identify.

2. **Organizational components:** Motivation is influenced by the organization structure, technological system, and the physical facilities which constitute the internal environment of an organization. Some machines are more interesting to work with than others; or many persons may find certain kinds of work boring. As shown by the Hawthorne experiments, the job-connected experience of a worker is a factor that determines his motivation.

3. **External or exogenous variables:** A worker's life outside the factory is also an important factor affecting his motivation or willingness to work inside the factory. Life at work and life outside the work are bound together. Troubles and joys of the off-job life cannot be put aside when reporting for work, nor can the factory matters be dropped when returning home after work. A strong motivational role is also played by culture, customs and norms, images and attributes conferred by society on particular jobs. An individual, for example, may find that his work commands a substantial degree of respect and social acceptance quite apart from holding a position in a particular organization, and so he may be more willing or feel more motivated to perform such a work.

4.5.5 Characteristics of Motivation

Some important characteristics of motivation are:

1. **Individuals differ in their motivation:** There is no single economic drive which determines behaviour. As the desires and goals of individuals differ, so do their motivations. One may be doing a particular job because it is remunerative, another may be doing it because it gives a sense of achievement, and third individual may be doing it because it enables him to serve a cause which is dear to him.

2. **Motivation is highly situational:** A person may work very well in one organization and poorly in another in the same position or type of the job. The performance may vary with working conditions and type of supervision.

3. **Motivation change:** Motivation of each individual changes from time to time even if he may continue to behave in the same way. For example, a temporary worker may produce more in the beginning to become permanent. After he has been made permanent, he may continue to produce more to gain promotion and so on.

4. **Motivation is expressed differently:** Needs and the way in which they are translated into action may vary considerably between one individual and another. Different persons may also react differently to successful or unsuccessful fulfilment of their needs. One person may feel frustrated if his need has not been met, but the other may feel motivated by his failure and redouble his effort to get his need met (say by writing and publishing additional scholarly articles or books). Again, one individual with strong security need may avoid accepting responsibility for fear of failure and dismissal and the other with a similar need may seek out responsibility for fear of being fired for low performance.

5. **Sometimes the individual himself is not aware of his motivation:** This can be better explained by an example drawn from the famous Hawthorne experiment. One girl worker complained to her counsellor about her foreman. Later on, it was found that the reason why she disliked the

foreman was that she had a step-father whom she feared and whose physical appearance resembled with the foreman. The result was that she had unconsciously transferred to her foreman the unfavourable characteristics of her step-father.

6. **Motivation is complex:** It is difficult to explain and predict the behaviour of workers. Use of one motivational device may not produce the desired result if it brings an opposing motive into play. In a factory when a blue-green device was introduced to reduce eye strain, the output of male workers increased while that of female workers decreased. It was found that the latter disliked this change as the new type of light falling on them made them look ghastly.

4.5.6 Signs of Motivation and Demotivation

Some common indications of motivation are:

(*a*) One who is eager to work and works willingly.

(*b*) When at work, he gives his best.

(*c*) He has a definite sense of belonging to the organization and works with pride towards improvement of management effectiveness.

Some common indications of demotivation are:

(*a*) Increasing absenteeism among employees and excessive labour turnover.

(*b*) Low output and productivity.

(*c*) An increase in the rate of accidents and excessive wastage of raw materials.

(*d*) Rank indiscipline.

(*e*) Frustration and unrest in the workforce.

(*f*) Defiant and violent behaviour of workers at or outside the workforce, and frequent confrontation or argument with supervisors and managers.

(*g*) Non-cooperation, strikes, *gheraos,* abusive and violent demonstrations.

4.5.7 Theories of Motivation

Some of the important theories of motivation, based on research conducted by clinical psychologists, behavioural scientists and management writers, provide explanations of the behaviour outcome.

McClelland's Need for Achievement Theory

This theory has particular reference to industrial enterprises, as the achievement motive has naturally much to do with the success and failure of an enterprise. In the USA, maximum research has been conducted on the achievement motive: According to McClelland, 'The three human needs are need for affiliation, need for power and need for achievement.' His theory postulates that some people are more achievement oriented than others and they attain job satisfaction, and derive a special kind of joy in attaining an objective successfully or accomplishing a challenging job rather than receiving a monetary or some other reward. According to him, 'Need for achievement or self-actualization is the strongest and lasting motivating factor particularly in case of persons whose power needs are satisfied.' Unfortunately this type of motivation is not found in most of the Indian organizations. This type of motivation may be seen more among people with high technical skills and professional knowledge than in labour-intensive traditional organizations.

BF Skinner's Theory of Operant Conditioning

According to this theory, people behave the way they do because in past circumstances they learned that certain behaviour was associated with pleasant outcomes, while certain other behaviour was associated with unpleasant outcomes. In the simplest language, this is a theory of learning, i.e., how to make an animal or a human being learn positive or desirable behaviour. Skinner did not conduct any research in the area of industries, but he conducted his research to study the learning process among rats, and also experimented with school children and found that stimulus for desirable behaviour could be strengthened by rewarding it at the earliest. In the industrial situation, the relevance of this theory may be found in the installation of financial and non-financial incentives. The more immediate the reward the more stimulation or the motivation it creates. Withdrawal of reward in case of substandard work may also produce the desired result. However, research shows that it generally is more effective to reward desired behaviour than to punish undesired behaviour.

Herzberg's Two-Factor/Hygiene/Maintenance Theory of Motivation

Herzberg's theory postulates two different categories of needs which are essentially independent of each other and affect behaviour in different ways:

1. **Hygiene factors:** These factors describe man's job environment and, if absent, serve the primary purpose of expressing job dissatisfaction. Hygiene factors include company policies, administration, supervision, working conditions, interpersonal relations, wages and allowances, status and security.

2. **Motivators/job content factors:** These factors include achievement, recognition, increased responsibility, challenging work, growth and development.

According to Herzberg, "Both sets of factors work in one direction only." Therefore, this theory is relevant to better paid executives in developed economies. Under Indian conditions, the research evidence points to a different direction. Hardly any organization can offer unbounded opportunities to its executives for personal growth. Hence, a middle way has to be found.

JS Adam's Equity Theory

In this theory, employees make comparison of their efforts and rewards with those of others in similar work situations. Inequity exists when these ratios are not equivalent. The existence of perceived inequity creates tension and such a tension may motivate the worker to increase or decrease his output/input to attain equity. The importance of this theory to management lies in the area of determining appropriate levels of rewards.

McGregor's 'Theory X' and 'Theory Y'

Douglas McGregor in *The Human Side of Enterprise* presents what he terms a new 'Theory Y' with respect to the management of people. He sets forth six assumptions about industrial behaviour, contrasting them with the traditional view, which he terms 'Theory X'.

1. The expenditure of physical and mental effort is as natural as play or rest. This is contrasted with *Theory X* which states that the average human being has an inherent dislike for work, and will avoid it if he can.

2. Man will exercise self-direction and self-control in the service of objectives to which he is committed. This is contrasted with *Theory X* which states that most people must be coerced, controlled, directed, and threatened with punishment in order to get them to put forth adequate effort towards the achievement of organizational objectives.

3. Commitment to objectives is a function of the rewards associated with their achievement.

4. The average human being, learns under proper conditions, not only to accept but also to seek responsibility. This is contrasted with *Theory X* which states that the average human being prefers to be directed, wishes to avoid responsibility, has little ambition, and wants security above all.

5. The capacity to exercise a relatively high degree of imagination; ingenuity, and creativity in the solution of organizational problems is widely distributed in the population.

6. Under the conditions of modern industrial life, the intellectual potentialities of the average human being are only partially realized.

AH Maslow's Need Hierarchy Theory of Motivation

Significant among the theories of motivation are some ideas advanced by AH Maslow. Dr Maslow postulates five basic needs—physiological needs, safety needs, love needs, esteem needs, and self-actualization needs—which are organized into successive levels as shown in Fig. 4.9. For example, hunger is a basic physiological need, but when there is plenty of food, higher needs emerge. When the higher needs are satisfied, newer and still higher needs come to the fore, and so on. It follows that gratification becomes as important a concept in motivation as deprivation. The levels of basic needs, starting with the lowest, are explained below. However, it should not be assumed that one need must be entirely satisfied before another emerges. Most people are partially satisfied in all of their basic needs at the same time.

Fig. 4.9 Hierarchy of human needs

1. **Physiological needs:** These are basic needs for sustaining human life such as food, water, shelter, sleep. These needs are at the lowest level of hierarchy and are the starting point of human motivation.
2. **Safety needs:** If the physiological needs are relatively satisfied, a set of needs emerges for protection against danger and threats. Expressions of safety needs are thus seen in preferences for job security, security against disease, misfortune, old age, etc. as also against industrial injury.
3. **Social/love needs:** Going up the scale of needs, the needs for love and affection, and 'belongingness' will emerge, and the cycle will repeat itself with this new centre. The person now seeks affectionate relations with people in general, a place in his (her) group. If deprived of these goals he would want to attain them more than anything else in the world, and as Dr Maslow puts it, 'he may even forget that once when he was hungry, he sneered at love'. The love needs involve both giving and receiving love.
4. **Esteem needs:** Practically everyone has a need for self-respect and for the esteem of others. This results in the desire for strength, adequacy, confidence, independence, reputation or prestige, recognition, attention, and appreciation. These 'egoistic' needs are rarely satisfied completely. It is the recognition of these needs that has forced so much attention upon ways to provide employees with a sense of participation. Extreme advocates call for a broad participation, covering even allocation of work and setting of the workplace, and criticize scientific management as deliberate means of thwarting these esteem needs.
5. **Need for 'self-actualization' for self-fulfilment:** Even if all the needs mentioned above are satisfied, one can still expect that a new discontent and restlessness will develop unless the individual is doing what he is suited for. Dr. Maslow writes, 'A musician must make music, and artist must paint, a poet must write, if he is to be ultimately happy. What a man can be he must be. This need is called *self-actualization*.' People who can realize their full potential are basically satisfied people, and it is from such people that one can expect the fullest and healthiest creativeness.

Alderfer's ERG Theory of Motivation

According to Clayton Alderfer, 'Maslow's five levels of needs can be merged into three, i.e., 'existence, relatedness and growth' resulting in his approach being termed 'ERG' theory.' His 'existence needs' include all forms of physiological and safety needs; 'related needs' include social needs and esteem needs: and 'growth needs' are concerned, like self-actualization, with the desire to be creative and to achieve full potential in the existing environment.

4.5.8 Motivation of Employees in Actual Practice

According to FW Taylor, "It is for the employer to find the right way that could make workers more productive." He writes that an employee is a bundle of untapped energy, ready to work if he is properly trained and fairly treated. In managing an organization, some of the important factors which could improve motivation and morale of employees are:

1. A well-defined humanistic personnel policy.
2. A long-term employment policy.
3. Fair wages and salary administration.
4. Reward for good performance.
5. Performance appraisal and merit rating.
6. Handling of workers' grievances in a cordial environment.
7. Handling disciplinary cases conforming to the principles of natural justice.
8. Participative management, supervision and increased autonomy in work.
9. Job enrichment and growth.
10. Self-motivation by top management, senior and middle level managers, and supervisors.

   Apart from other characteristics, motivation is a situational and complex problem as it relates to human behaviour and attitude towards work, which is subject to change and hence difficult to predict.

4.5.9 Incentive Schemes and Promotion Policies

Incentive Schemes

Incentive is another method of payment to workers. While wage incentives increase the earnings of workers, they can at the same time improve the efficiency of an organization. The Study Group of the National Commission on Labour recommended that wages incentives should be used for effective utilization of manpower, which is the cheapest, quickest and surest means of increasing productivity. It further stated that the only practicable and self-sustaining means of improving manpower utilization is to introduce incentive schemes and stimulate human effort in order to provide a positive motivation to greater output.

   Wage incentives constitute extra financial motivation. A wage incentive scheme is the payment for work of an acceptable quality produced over and above a specified quantity or standard. One can apply an incentive scheme to an individual, a group, or to all employees of the organization.

Principles of Incentive System of Wage Payment

For any scheme of incentive wage plan, a set of principles should be followed. These include:

1. The incentive plan must be thoroughly worked out and explained to all those affected by it.
2. Expected earnings must be higher than those provided by hourly rates. Increases ranging from 15 per cent to 25 per cent are widely regarded as reasonable.
3. A small section of all employees, who are especially apt in various operations, earn as much as 50 per cent more than this average.
4. Declining rate at higher levels of output is generally not acceptable except at high levels where a negative rate may protect the health of the employee.

5. Fix the standards of output by taking performance of previous years and adding to it the required percentage in order to bring it to an acceptable level. Time study represents the satisfactory means of setting a reasonable standard.

6. Rate on various jobs must be interrelated. Job evaluation is the ideal means for establishing such relationships.

7. Means must be provided to ensure prompt adjustment in rates for changes in job content.

8. Time study may be conducted and rates established unilaterally by the employer or jointly with unions of employees.

Keys for a Successful Incentive Wage Plan

WH Spencer has provided a list of 10 basic considerations in planning incentive wages. These are:

1. Establish the plan and its operation.

2. The plan must have the understanding and interest of the top management.

3. The plan must receive the constant attention of competent supervisors.

4. There should be an effective work measurement system, and efficient production planning and control, and inventory control procedures.

5. Fix standards to stimulate workers to greater productivity.

6. There should be an accepted norm for the workers.

7. Unit labour cost should not be increased appreciably.

8. For productivity below standard, there should not be any premium.

9. Do not indulge in a subterfuge to increase pay without a corresponding increase in productivity.

10. Do not have the scheme to avoid a justifiable base for hourly increase.

A scientifically designed and systematically administered incentive scheme can be an effective method to stimulate workers to greater productivity.

Advantages of Incentive Wage Plans: Following are the advantages of incentive wage plans to workers as well as to producers:

1. **Advantages to workers:** Increase in the wages of workers; improvement in productivity; and improvement in living standard.

2. **Advantages to producers:** Increase in productivity coupled with decreasing production costs; minimum supervision; good labour relations; improvement in organization; and standardization.

4.6 Performance Management and Appraisal

Performance management is the integration of employee development with results-based assessment. It encompasses performance appraisal, objective-setting for individuals and departments, appropriate training programmes, and performance-related pay. Appraisal of managers by their subordinates, peers and people in other departments (perhaps even customers) might also be included in the scheme.

4.6.1 Target Setting

An employee's targets could be stated in terms of achieving a certain standard (i.e., an ongoing performance criterion, such as a specified departmental staff attendance rate or the attainment of minimum quality levels) that is to be maintained indefinitely; or as an *ad hoc* goal (Fletcher and Williams, 1992). The advantages of bosses and employees jointly setting personal objectives are as follows:

• It forces everyone in the department to think carefully about his or her role and duties, about why tasks are necessary, and how best to get things done.

• Targets are clarified and mechanisms created for monitoring performance.

• Crucial elements are identified in each job. This information is useful for determining training and recruitment needs.

- Personal achievements of employees are recognized and rewarded.
- Bosses and their colleagues are obliged to communicate—in consequence, bosses can quickly identify which employees are ready for promotion and the help they will need in preparing themselves for this.
- Performance is appraised against quantified targets, not subjective criteria.
- There is forced co-ordination of activities—between departments, between junior and senior management, and between short-term and long-term goals.

  The targets set should adhere to the following guidelines:

- Targets should be precise, unambiguous and, if possible, expressed numerically. Generic objectives such as 'increase profits' or 'cut costs' are not acceptable.
- Targets should relate to the crucial and primary elements of employees' jobs and not to trivial matters.
- Targets should be consistent.
- Each target should be accompanied by a statement of how it is to be achieved, by when, the resources necessary and how and where these will be acquired.

  A good way to assess the usefulness of objectives is to ask whether they pass the SMART test, i.e., targets need to be:

  > S pecific
  > M easurable
  > A greed between boss and worker
  > R ealistic
  > T ime related

Both parties should share a common perspective on the situation intended to exist after the achievement of objectives and on how soon results may reasonably be expected.

4.6.2 Appraisal

Managers frequently make *ad hòc* judgements about employees, but are loath to discuss the grounds on which the opinions are based. Performance appraisal replaces casual assessment with formal, systematic procedures. Employees know they are being evaluated and are told the criteria that will be used in the course of the appraisal. (Indeed, knowledge that an appraisal is soon to occur could motivate an employee into increased effort aimed at enhancing the outcomes of the assessment). Specifically, appraisal is the analysis of employees' past successes and failures, and the assessment of their suitability for promotion or further training. Its advantages include the following:

- Boss and employee are compelled to meet and discuss common work-related problems. Appraisees become aware of what exactly is expected of them and of their status in the eyes of their line managers.
- Appraisal monitors the feasibility of targets set by higher management, who receive valuable feedback on problems encountered when implementing policies. Thus, it creates a cheap and effective early warning system within the organization's management information structure.
- It enables bosses to learn about employees and the true nature of their duties. Conducting appraisals helps a manager to remain in touch with the staff in his or her department. Unknown skills and competencies might be uncovered. This data can be incorporated into the firm's human resource plan and hence assist in avoiding compulsory redundancies, in career and management succession planning, and in identifying needs for employee training (Kinnie and Lowe, 1990).

  A successful appraisal is one that results in:

- Reasonable targets which are mutually agreed, not arbitrarily determined.
- Recognition of the employees's achievements.

- Clear identification of obstacles to improved performance (organizational problems as well as individual difficulties).
- Enthusiastic pursuit of measurable objectives.
- Two-way communication between boss and worker.

It is important for appraisal to be seen as a staff development exercise, intended to be helpful to everyone concerned, and not as a form of restrictive control or disciplinary measure. The purpose therefore must be to assist both individuals and the organization in improving their performances. Appraisal reviews are usually categorised into three types:

1. **Performance reviews**, which analyse employees' past successes and failures with a view to improving future performance.
2. **Potential reviews**, which assess subordinates' suitability for promotion and/or further training.
3. **Reward reviews**, for determining pay rises. It is a well-established principle that salary assessments should occur well after performance and potential reviews have been completed, for two reasons:
   - Performance reviews examine personal strengths and weaknesses in order to improve efficiency. If salary matters are discussed during these meetings, they might dominate the conversation.
   - Ultimately, salary levels are determined by market forces of supply and demand for labour. Staff shortages could cause the firm to pay high wages quite independent of the objective worth of particular workers.

4.6.3 Self-Appraisal and Peer Group Appraisal

Appraisal might be more useful to the appraisee, and lead in the longer term to greater efficiency, if it is conducted either by the employee or by a colleague of equal occupational status. Such appraisals may analyse issues more critically than when people fear the career consequences of admitting mistakes. Appraisees state—using any of the methods previously discussed—how they regard their performance, the adequacy of the training they have received, effects of alterations in job content, perceptions of key objectives, and future aspirations. They identify their own strengths and account for their failures and weaknesses, suggesting ways in which the firm might better use their talents, skills and recently acquired experiences.

There are, of course, problems with self-appraisal, including the following:

1. Many people are quite incapable of analysing themselves. It is unusual for individuals to assess their own competence in other walks of life. At school, college, and during the early stages of a career the individual becomes accustomed to being directed and evaluated by others. The transition of appraisee to self-assessor might require skilled and detailed guidance by someone already competent in appraisal techniques. Most appraisees in lower-level positions will have received no training in self-analysis or appraisal.
2. To the extent that appraisals form a basis for future career development, appraisees might overstate their successes while ignoring their failings.

On the other hand, employees are compelled to think carefully about the adequacy of their contribution, about barriers preventing improved performance, about their future, and the quality of their relationships with others.

4.6.4 Problems with Performance Appraisal

There are a number of problems with performance appraisal, including the following:

- Dangers of favouritism, bias and stereotyping by managers who conduct appraisals.
- Possibilities that inconsistent criteria will be applied by different managers when assessing the calibre of subordinates (Schneier *et al.*, 1991).

- All the information relevant to a particular case might not be available.
- Information might not be interpreted objectively.
- Assessors might seek to evaluate every subordinate as 'fair' for all performance categories.
- Assessors might focus on specific cases of outstandingly good and bad performance while ignoring the employee's average overall ability.
- Appraisal systems require appraising managers to undertake extra work, which they might be reluctant to accept. Hence, the process becomes a ritualistic chore to be completed as quickly as possible in a manner that causes the least comment from those affected by the scheme.

Douglas McGregor (1957) noted the great reluctance with which many managers undertake assessment responsibilities; preferring to treat subordinates as professional colleagues rather than as inferiors upon whom they are entitled to pass judgement. Senior managers, McGregor asserted, dislike 'playing God'. Usually they are fully cognisant of their own biases and thus rightly seek to avoid situations where prejudice could arise. Also, subordinates may bitterly resent their personal qualities being commented upon, seeing the appraisal as a patronising exercise designed to humiliate or to punish past inadequacies in their work.

Appraisal requires concentration, diligence and competence in the manager conducting the appraisal. Training in appraisal techniques is required, followed by substantial guided experience in their practical application. McGregor pointed out the fact that:

- few managers receive any instruction in appraisal methods; and
- even managers who are properly trained might not possess all the information needed to undertake fair appraisals. They may be out of touch with current working practices or unfamiliar with environmental problems affecting subordinate's work.

4.7 Promotion, Transfer, Demotion and Dismissal

The need for defining a clear promotion policy is a prerequisite to assure employees that they have a foreseeable future with the organization.

4.7.1 Promotion

1. Promotion is recognition of a job well done by an employee.
2. It is a device to retain and reward an employee for his years of service to the company.
3. Promotion helps increase individual and organizational effectiveness.
4. Promotion promotes a sense of job satisfaction in the employee.
5. It builds loyalty, morale and a sense of belongingness in the employee.
6. Promotion conveys a clear message to others that opportunities are also open to them in the organization, if they perform well.

4.7.2 Promotion Policy

An organizational policy on promotion helps state formally the broad objectives, and helps formulate both manpower and individual career plans. Such policy documents are being increasingly issued by Indian organizations in keeping with the changed environment of employee awareness and the accent on career planning.

One of the first requirements of a promotion policy is a statement of the ratio of internal promotions to external recruitment at each level, the method and procedure of selection (trade-test, interview), and the qualifications desired. Such a statement would help planners project a number of internally available candidates for promotions. In some organizations, such a ratio is fixed by a collective bargaining agreement, while in government and the public sector it is laid down in rules.

The second exercise is to identify the network of related jobs and the promotional channels of each job, taking into account job relatedness, opportunities to interact with higher-placed executives to foster job learning, and the qualifications—both academic and work experience. Such an exercise will assist in succession planning and also help aspirants acquire the necessary formal qualifications or on-the-job training, and encourage them to attend suitable external development programmes. The network of related jobs can be established by job analysis. This process would also help in identifying promotion channels and stepping-stone jobs, which once finalized should be made known to the concerned employees.

Such channels and training leading to promotion are well defined, for instance in the Armed Forces. While exercising the right of promotion, the criteria of seniority (length of service) has to be given the highest weightage along with eligibility and suitability, due to influence of the government's administrative culture, which has permeated into public sector companies and most other establishments, as also in privately owned industries.

Seniority is given heavy weightage in the government, and also in industry and this has led to the rules providing for its consideration.

The fifth schedule of the Industrial Disputes Act prohibits the following "Unfair Labour Practices", concerning promotion:

(a) Changing the seniority rating of a workman, because of involvement in Trade Union activities;

(b) Refusing to promote workmen to higher posts on account of their Trade Union activities; and

(c) Giving unmerited promotions to certain workmen, with a view to creating discontent amongst other workmen, or to undermine the strength of their Trade Union.

To show favouritism or partiality to one set of workers regardless of merit will be considered to be an Unfair Labour Practice and under the law, trade unions or officers' associations can take such matters to courts as "Industrial Disputes". Favouritism is quite common in the government and also frequently resorted to even by officers' associations in the public sector and private sector.

It can be appreciated that once a matter of management policy becomes a dispute in court, it is extremely difficult to justify each step or action. Therefore, in India, promotion does not remain only a matter of rational personnel policy, it is also subject to legal disputes and unfavourable court awards.

Yet there are other more important elements of a sound promotion policy which should be spelled out by managements:

(a) A clear statement of policy that all higher jobs, as far as possible, shall be filled in by promotions from within the organization. This would motivate existing employees to work better and aspire for a promotion;

(b) Establishment of *'lines of progression* or *ladders of promotion'* within the organization. It may be called career planning and should be chalked out by the personnel department or by the top management;

(c) Job analysis and other techniques can be resorted to as aids, and the competence and experience of existing employees together with their educational background and training may be considered, as far as possible, while plotting a career graph for each employee;

(d) The line managers should also be made responsible for planning careers of people working under them and managers should be encouraged to transfer their subordinates to better openings in other departments, in the overall interest of organizational efficiency; and

(e) Adequate provision should be made by managements for training as a means of preparation for promotion to higher posts; special on-the-job training, special institutional training or other avenues should be made available to deserving employees.

4.7.3 Demotion

Demotion is a move to a job within the company which is lower in importance. It is usually, though not always, accompanied by a reduction in pay. An employee may be demoted for the following reasons:

- His or her job may disappear or become less important through a departmental or company reorganization.
- The worker may no longer be thought capable of carrying out his or her present responsibilities efficiently.

Unless the employee has requested it, demotion will probably have adverse effects:

- There will be less satisfaction of esteem and self actualisation needs. The employee may show negative reactions to frustration.
- The employee may become a centre of discontent in the organization.
- Other employees may lose confidence in the organization.

An employee who resigns in consequence of a demotion may complain of unfair dismissal under a special category known as 'constructive dismissal.'

4.7.4 Transfers

A transfer is a move to a job within the company which has approximately equal importance, status and pay. To manage human resources in a constructive way, it is sometimes necessary to transfer employees to other jobs, sometimes because of changed work requirements and sometimes because an employee is unhappy or dissatisfied in his or her present job.

In some organizations it is the custom for the least satisfactory employees to be transferred from one department to another, with the result that a transfer is regarded as discreditable, particularly if it occurs at short notice and without explanation. An unhappy employee may therefore prefer to leave rather than seek a transfer.

In other organizations transfers are used as a means of developing promising employees by giving them experience in several departments. A few organizations advertise all vacancies internally and consider applicants for whom the new job would be a transfer rather than a promotion.

Transfers can increase job satisfaction and improve utilisation under the following circumstances:

- A transfer is regarded as a re-selection.
- The need for a transfer is explained.
- Unsatisfactory employees are not dealt with by transferring them to other departments.
- Requests by employees for transfers are fully investigated.
- No employee is transferred to another district against his or her will.
- An employee transferred to another district is given financial assistance from the organization to cover removal costs, legal fees, refurnishing, etc.

4.7.5 Dismissal

Dismissal means the termination of employment by:

- the employer, with or without notice or
- the failure of the employer to renew a fixed-term contract or
- the employee's resignation, with or without notice, when the employer behaves in a manner that demonstrates refusal to be bound by the contract of employment.

The latter is termed *constructive dismissal*. It means the employer is behaving so unreasonably that the worker has no alternative but to quit.

Normally, an employer must give the employee notice of dismissal as stated in the worker's contract of employment. Occasionally, however, dismissal without notice is permissible. This is known as *summary dismissal* and could occur when an employee's behaviour makes impossible the fulfilment of a contract of employment. Examples are theft, persistent drunkenness, violence, abusiveness to colleagues or customers, wilful disobedience, or incompetence that immediately causes damage to the employer's business.

Many countries have statutes that govern how employees may be fairly dismissed. Under the Employment Protection (Consolidation) Act 1978, employees covered by the Act (i.e., those with at least two years' continuous service) may only be fairly dismissed for genuine redundancy or for:

(*a*) gross misconduct, *e.g.*, refusal to obey reasonable instructions, dishonesty, persistent absenteeism, neglect of duties, etc;

(*b*) incapacity to do the job, caused by such things as incompetence, illness (once the workers' contractual sick pay entitlement has expired), or the person not having the skills or aptitude for the work; and

(*c*) some other substantial reason, *e.g.*, going on strike, disruption of staff relations, or a temporary job coming to an end, provided the impermanent nature of the work was fully explained to the worker when the employment started.

'Redundancy' means that the organization's need fer employees to do work of a particular kind has ceased or diminished, so that someone has to lose their job. The criteria used to select individuals for redundancy must by law be fair and reasonable. Workers declared redundant are entitled to redundancy payments.

'Wrongful', as opposed to 'unfair', dismissal occurs when insufficient notice is given. It gives rise to a civil action for damages equivalent to the actual loss incurred. Wrongful dismissal may be claimed by any dismissed worker, regardless of length of service—a worker who has been with the organization for only a few days may be 'wrongfully' sacked.

Allegations of wrongful dismissal are heard by normal county courts; cases concerning unfair dismissal are heard in industrial tribunals. Note that whereas costs in the latter are intended to be minimal (and in normal circumstances are never awarded to the other side), costs in the county court can be huge.

Self-assessment Questions Set-IV

1. Define motivation and describe its characteristics.
2. Distinguish between what can motivate and what can demotivate workmen.
3. Explain Maslow's and Herzberg's theories of motivation, and their relevance to labour conditions in India.
4. Compare McGregor's theory X and theory Y for motivation.
5. Discuss Maslow's need hierarchy theory of motivation.
6. Outline the types of motivation and explain its determinants.
7. What are the salient issues which can improve motivation and morale of the employees in an organization?
8. What do you mean by an incentive scheme? Outline the principles of incentive system of wages payment.
9. List the salient features of a successful incentive wage plan.
10. What do you understand by promotion policy of an organization? Discuss in brief the essentials of a promotion policy.
11. Enumerate the factors considered for promotion of an employee in an organization.
12. What is performance management? What are the advantages of setting personal objectives jointly by bosses and employees?
13. Define self-appraisal and peer group appraisal. Discuss the problems generally faced by manager with performance appraisal.
14. What are the reasons under which an employee may be demoted?
15. Explain the term 'Transfer'. Under what circumstances transfers can increase job satisfaction.
16. Explain the meaning of 'Constructive Dismissal' and 'Summary Dismissal'.

4.8 Participative Management (Collective Decision-making)

Decision-making has been identified as one of the primary responsibilities in any management process. Decision may involve allocating resources, recruiting people, investing capital or introducing new products. Decision-making is at the core of all planned activities. Most decisions of critical importance in any large organization are usually taken collectively by a group of people (Board of Directors, Committees, Task Force, etc.). The impact of the groups in decision-making processes has been summarized by Harrison as follows:

- Groups are typically superior to individuals in establishing objectives. They possess greater cumulative knowledge that can be brought to bear on problems.

- Individual efforts are still important in identifying alternatives to ensure that different and perhaps unique solutions are identified from various functional areas which can be considered by the group later.

- Group judgement is often superior in comparison to individual judgement because it brings into play a wider range of viewpoints.

- Involving group members often leads to a greater acceptance of the final outcome in choosing an alternative.

- Individual responsibility is generally superior to group responsibility in implementing the choice.

Groups do have some edge over individuals in certain stages of the decision-making process. Therefore, it is important to 'decide' to what extent one should involve others (especially subordinates in the work group) to participate in decisions affecting their jobs.

In general, two phenomena—'Risky shift phenomenon' and 'Groupthink' have been observed in group decision-making situations.

4.8.1 Risky Shift Phenomenon

There is a general belief that groups make riskier decisions than do individuals. There are four possible reasons: (*a*) Risk takers are persuasive in getting more cautious companions to shift their position; (*b*) Since members of a group familiarize themselves with the issues and arguments, they seem to feel more confident about taking risks; and (*c*) The responsibility for decision-making can be diffused across members of the group.

4.8.2 Groupthink

Groupthink phenomenon, first discussed by Janis (1977), refers to a mode of thinking in a group in which seeking concurrence from members becomes so dominant that it overrides any realistic appraisal of an alternative course of action. Janis found that development of group norms improved the morale at the expense of critical thinking. One of the most common norms was the tendency to remain loyal to the group by continuing to adhere to policies and decisions to which the group has already committed, even when the decisions proved to be in error.

Groupthink can have several deleterious consequences on the quality of decision-making. These consequences are: (*a*) Groups often limit their search for possible solutions to problems to one or two alternatives instead of a comprehensive analysis of all possible alternatives; (*b*) Groups often fail to re-examine their chosen course of action after new events suggest a change; (*c*) Group members spend little time to see whether alternative courses of action are more feasible compared to the chosen course of action; (*d*) Groups often make no attempt to seek the advice of inside/outside experts of their own organization; (*e*) Group members show positive interest in facts that support their preferred decision and ignore or show negative interest in facts that fail to support it; and (*f*) Groups often ignore any consideration of possible roadblocks to their chosen decision and, as a result, fail to develop contingency plans for potential set-backs.

Taking a cue from Janis, it is possible to formulate some strategies to overcome the barriers. The strategies include:

(a) Group leaders can encourage each member to be a critical evaluator of various proposals;

(b) When groups are given a problem to solve, leaders can refrain from stating their own position and instead encourage open enquiry and impartial probing of a wide range of alternatives;

(c) The organization can give the same problem to two different groups and compare the resulting solutions;

(d) Before the group reaches a final decision, members of the group may seek advice from other wings of the organization;

(e) Outside experts can be invited to group meetings and encouraged to challenge the views of group members;

(f) At every group meeting, one member could be appointed to challenge the testimony of those advocating the majority position;

(g) When considering the feasibility and effectiveness of various alternatives, divide the group into two sections for independent discussions and comparing results; and

(h) After deciding on a preliminary consensus on the first choice for a course of action, schedule a second meeting during which members of the group may express their residual doubts and rethink the entire issue prior to finalizing the decision and initiating action.

If groups are aware of the problems of groupthink, several specific and relatively simple steps can be taken to minimize the likelihood of such problems. In fact, recognizing the problem itself solves half the problem in the effort to make more effective decisions in organizational settings.

4.8.3 Advantages and Disadvantages of Group Decision-making

According to Maier (1967), there are certain obvious advantages and disadvantages of group decision-making. The advantages include:

(a) Groups can accumulate more knowledge and facts;

(b) Groups have a broader perspective and consider more alternative solutions;

(c) Individuals, who participate in decisions, are more satisfied with the group decision and are more likely to support it; and

(d) Group decision processes serve an important communication function as well as a useful political function.

The disadvantages of group decision-making are:

(a) Groups often work more slowly than individuals;

(b) Group decisions involve considerable compromises which may lead to less than optimal decisions;

(c) Groups are often dominated by one individual or a small clique, thereby negating many of the virtues of group procedures; and

(d) Over-reliance on group decision-making can inhibit the management's ability to act quickly and decisively, when necessary.

It is observed that there are some inherent advantages of group decision situations. At the same time, some phenomena like risky-shift or groupthink might emerge in the group process and affect the quality of decisions made by an individual.

Self-assessment Questions Set-V

1. Define decision-making process and discuss the impact of groups in the decision-making process.
2. Discuss in detail the phenomena 'Risky shift' and 'Groupthink', which *are* commonly observed in group decision-making situations.
3. What are the deleterious consequences on the quality of decision-making in 'groupthink' phenomenon? Discuss some strategies to overcome these barriers.
4. Enumerate the advantages and disadvantages of group decision-making process.
5. What specific steps could be taken by individuals to improve the process of group decision-making?

4.9 Trade Unions

Trade unions are unique organizations whose role is variously interpreted and understood by different interest groups in society. According to Webbs, 'A trade union is an association of wage earners for improving conditions of employment'. This narrow conception of the role of unions has often been criticized. The predominant view is that the scope of trade unions extends beyond 'bread and butter' issues. According to Allen Flanders, the major function of trade unions is 'regulation, a governmental role, whose essence lies in rule-making, The effects of union action extend beyond the securing of material gains, to the establishment of workers' rights in an industry. The constant inroads that unions have made into managerial role and prerogatives bring about a dual power structure in the enterprise. Flanders opined that unions restrain the exercise of managerial authority in deploying, organizing and disciplining the labour force after it has been hired.

4.9.1 Definition

The term 'Trade Union' is defined under the Trade Unions Act, 1926 as 'any combination, whether temporary or permanent, formed primarily for the purpose of regulating the relations between workmen and employers, or between workmen and workmen or between employers and employers, or for imposing restrictions on the conduct of any trade or business and includes any federation of two or more unions', provided that this shall not affect: (a) any agreement between partners as to their own business, (b) any agreement between an employer and those employed by him as to such employment, or (c) any agreement in consideration of the sale of the goodwill of a business or of instruction in any profession, trade or handicraft.

According to this definition, not only workmen but also employers can combine and get their unions or associations registered under this Act, and function as such.

4.9.2 Registration of Trade Unions

Any seven or more members (workers in a factory) of a union may, by subscribing their names to the rules of the trade union, apply for registration to the Registrar of Trade Unions. Each application for the registration of a trade union should be accompanied by: (a) rules of the trade union, (b) names, occupation and addresses of the members making such an application, (c) name of the trade union and the address of its headquarters, and (d) title, name, age, address and occupation of all office bearers of the union. The minimum age prescribed is 15 years for a member and 18 years for an executive. In case, a trade union is in existence for more than one year before submitting an application for registration, a general statement of assets and liabilities of the trade union must be submitted to the Registrar along with the application.

The rules of the trade union must incorporate the following:

(a) Name of the trade union;
(b) Objects for which it is established;
(c) Purpose for which its general funds shall be applicable;
(d) Maintain the list of members and provide adequate facilities for the inspection thereof by office bearers and members of the trade union;

(*e*) The admission of ordinary members connected with the trade, and also the admission of a number of honorary/temporary members, as office bearers, required to form the Executive Committee of the Trade Union;

(*f*) Payment of subscription by members of the trade union, which shall not be less than 25 paise per member in a month;

(*g*) Conditions under which a member shall be entitled to get any benefit or be imposed fine or undergo forfeiture as per the rules;

(*h*) Provision under which the rules shall be amended, varied or rescinded;

(*i*) Rules for the appointment/removal of executive committee members and other office bearers of the trade union;

(*j*) Safe custody of funds of the union, annual audit of accounts and facilities for inspection of account books by the office bearers and members of the trade union; and

(*k*) Provision by which the trade union may be dissolved.

The Registrar of Trade Unions, on being satisfied that the union has complied with all the technical requirements for registration, shall register the union. Thereafter, he shall issue a certificate of registration in the prescribed form stating that the trade union has been duly registered.

4.9.3 Rights and Liabilities of Trade Unions

A registered trade union has the following rights:

(*a*) To collect the membership fee in the premises of the factory without any interference by the management;

(*b*) To display notices of meetings and other activities of the union in the premises of the factory;

(*c*) To use the general funds for specific purposes;

(*d*) To raise funds for political purposes at the option of the members;

(*e*) To conduct a strike by peaceful methods;

(*f*) Exemption from the provisions of Section 120 B, sub-section (2) of the Indian Penal Code if the members conduct a peaceful strike;

(*g*) To appoint outsiders as members to the executive committee of the union who should not be more than one-half of the total number of office bearers; and

(*h*) To prepare an audit statement of receipts and expenditures to be sent to the Registrar every year.

4.9.4 Recognition of Trade Unions

It makes it obligatory on the part of the Registrar to recognize a trade union which is truly representative of the workers engaged in a factory or the concerned industry. The executive of such a union shall be entitled to negotiate with the employers. In case the employer refuses to recognize the trade union, the matter is referred to the labour court, appointed by the government.

The recognition granted to the union is liable for withdrawal under the following conditions:

(*a*) If the executive committee of the union has adopted any unfair practices specified in the Act;

(*b*) If the union fails to submit the prescribed returns; and

(*c*) If it has ceased to be representative of its workers.

4.9.5 Membership of Trade Unions

Any person who has attained the age of 15 years may be a member of a registered trade union subject to other rules of the trade union and may enjoy all the rights of a member. Verification of membership of the central trade union organization for giving representation on tripartite consultative bodies, development councils, boards, etc. at national and international levels, including International Labour Organization (ILO) is done by the office of the Chief Labour Commissioner (Central). With the emergence of new trade union organizations claiming an all-India character and membership strength, the final verification results of the 10 central trade union organizations listed in Table 4.1 as on December 31, 1980 were announced on August 30, 1984.

Table 4.1 Membership of Central Trade Union Organizations

Central Organization	Claimed		Verified	
	No. of Unions	Membership, in lakhs	No. of Unions	Membership, in lakhs
INTUC	3,457	35.09	1,604	22.36
BMS	1,725	18.80	1,333	12.11
HMS	1,122	18.48	426	7.63
UTUC (LS)	154	12.39	134	6.21
NLO	249	4.05	172	2.47
UTUC	618	6.08	175	1.66
TUCC	182	2.72	65	1.23
NFITU	166	5.27	80	0.84
AITUC	1,366	10.64	1,080	3.45
CITU	1,737	10.33	1,474	3.31
Total	**10,776**	**123.85**	**6543**	**61.27**

Note: INTUC—Indian National Trade Union Congress; BMS—Bharatiya Mazdoor Sabha; HMS—Hind Mazdoor Sabha; UTUC—United Trade Union Congress; NLO—National Labour Organization; TUCC—Trade Union Coordination Centre; NFITU—National Front of Indian Trade Unions; AITUC—All India Trade Union Congress; and CITU—Centre of Indian Trade Unions.
(*Source: India*, 1986).

4.9.6 Amalgamation of Trade Unions

Any two or more registered trade unions may be amalgamated as one trade union with or without dissolution or division of funds, provided the votes of at least 50 per cent members of each/every such trade union entitled to vote are recorded, and at least 60 per cent of the votes recorded are in favour of the proposal.

4.9.7 Penalties

(*i*) If default is made on the part of any registered trade union in giving any notice or sending any statement or other documents as required, every member of its executive committee shall be punishable with fine which may extend to Rs 5 and, in case of a continuing default, an additional amount extendable to Rs 5 for each week after the first during which the default continues, provided the aggregate fine shall not exceed Rs 50.

(*ii*) Any person who willfully makes, or causes to be made, any false entry in, or any omission from the general statement, or alteration of rules sent to the Registrar, shall be punishable with fine which may extend to Rs 500.

(*iii*) Any person who, with the intent to deceive, gives to any member of a registered trade union or to a person who intends to become a member of such union, any document purporting to be a copy of the rules of union or any alterations of the same, shall be punishable with fine which may extend to Rs 200.

(*iv*) If an employer commits any one of the following unfair practices, he shall be liable to a fine up to Rs 1000:

(*a*) Obstructing workers from joining a registered trade union;

(b) Discrimination against, or discharge from duty, of any officer/worker of the union on the grounds of being a member of the union; and

(c) Failure to negotiate with the executive of a recognized union.

4.9.8 Dissolution

When a registered trade union is dissolved, notice for the same signed by seven members and the Secretary of the union, within 14 days of the dissolution, is sent to the Registrar and such dissolution shall be registered by him if he is satisfied, and be effective from the date of such registration. Where the rules of the trade union do not provide for the distribution of funds on dissolution, the Registrar shall divide the funds amongst the members in such a manner as may be prescribed.

4.9.9 Objectives and Functions

The main objectives and functions of trade unions may be broadly divided into *three* parts:

Industrial Activities: Industrial activities are concerned directly with the betterment of employment conditions of workers such as: (i) securing good wages, (ii) ensuring job security, (iii) securing better working and living conditions. (iv) shorter period of work, and (v) getting a share in business profits.

Social Activities: Trade unions are also seen as moral institutions which will uplift the weak and downtrodden and render them the place, the dignity, and justice they deserve. Social activities are also directed towards helping workers in time of need and improving their efficiency by ensuring: (i) a spirit of cooperation and friendliness among members, (ii) increased consciousness and unity, (iii) enhanced welfare and educational facilities; (iv) provision of indoor and outdoor games, and (v) help in case of sickness, accidental benefits, and during unemployment, strikes and lockouts.

Political Activities: Trade unions are considered not merely as economic and social organizations, but also as political institutions directed towards wresting control over managerial authority. The political character of the unions has been exemplified by Marx and his followers who visualized trade unions as harbingers of social revolution to change the whole structure of class domination. Thus, the political roles of the union range from job regulation at workplace to bringing about a social revolution. In India, the nature of the working class is such that it cannot provide its own leader, thereby it is relatively easier for politicians to take positions of leadership in working class organizations. Therefore, trade unions are inevitably drawn into politics soon after their formation. Historically, the Indian trade union movement has been dependent on outsiders.

In addition to these objectives, trade unions also promote the firm's prosperity. A strong trade union movement runs on democratic principles, provides adequate protection to workers against exploitation and abuse of labour wherever the labour is organized. However, there is a widespread pessimism about the revolutionary potential of trade unions to overthrow the capitalist system.

4.9.10 Growth of Trade Unions in India

Until the middle of the nineteenth century, except coal mining, there was no industrial activity in the country in the modern sense. The setting up of textiles and jute mills and laying of the railways from 1850 paved the way for the emergence of a labour movement in India.

The origin of the movement can be traced to sporadic labour unrest dating back to 1877 when the workers of the Empress Mills at Nagpur struck work following a wage cut. In 1884, Bombay textile workers demanded improvement in wages and working conditions. It was estimated that there were 25 strikes between 1882 and 1890.

The earliest organizations to be formed on the lines of modern trade unions were: (a) the Textile Labour Association at Ahmedabad (movement started in 1917 with a strike for wage rise, but the Association was formed in 1920) led by Anasuyaben Sarabhai, and (b) the Madras Labour Union (1918) led by BP Wadia.

The Nationalist Home Rule movement and the difficult conditions after World War I led to the growth of union movement in early 1920s. The political leaders of that time, philanthropists and social workers took the initiative in organizing industrial workers at major centres either for political reasons or because they were moved by the wretched conditions of the workers.

In 1920, the All India Trade Union Congress (AITUC) was formed because of the need to have a national centre of labour to depute delegates to the International Labour Organization (I LO) formed in 1919. By 1924 there were 167 trade unions with a quarter million members.

The conditions after the war, the growing interest in unionism and the spate of strikes led the Government to consider legal initiatives in 1920s. The Indian Factories Act, 1922 enforced a 10-hour work/day. The Indian Trade Union Act of 1926 made it legal for workers to organize and protest and exempted actions flowing out of legitimate trade union activity from the purview of civil and criminal proceedings. This Act still continues to be the basic law governing trade unions in the county.

Ideological differences within the AITUC led to a three-way split between communists led by MN Roy and Dange, nationalists led by Mahatma Gandhi and Nehru and moderates led by NM Joshi and VV Giri. While party ideology was supreme for the communists, the main preoccupation of the nationalists was independence. The moderates however wanted to pursue trade unionism in its own right and not subjugate it completely to broader political aims or interests. The moderates and the communists broke away from the AITUC in the 1920s and 1930s but rejoined AITUC in 1940. In May 1947, however, the Indian National Trade Union Congress (INTUC) was formed by nationalists and moderates, since by then the communists had acquired control over the AITUC. The Congress socialists who stayed in the AITUC at the time of the formation of INTUC subsequently formed the Hind Mazdoor Sabha (HMS). Years later the HMS was split up with a faction of socialists forming the Bhartiya Mazdoor Sabha (BMS). And again when there was a split among the communists, the United Trade Union Congress (UTUC) and Centre of Indian Trade Unions (CITU) were formed. Later a splinter group of the UTUC formed another federation, i.e., UTUC Lenin Sarani. With the birth of regional parties ever since the 1960s, almost each regional party now has a trade union wing. Thus, the origin and growth of the trade union movement in India is riddled with fragmented politicization.

The growth of trade unions in India during 1977-88 is shown in Table 4.2.

Table 4.2   Growth of Trade Unions in India during 1977-88

Year	No. of Regd. Unions	No. of Unions Submitting Returns	Membership of Unions 000's	Average Membership per Union
1977	30,810	9,003	6,034	670
1978	32,361	8,727	6,203	711
1979	34,430	10,021	7,474	746
1980	36,507	4,432	3,727	841
1981	37,539	6,682	5,397	808
1982	38,313	5,044	2,999	595
1983*	38,935	6,844	5,417	792
1984*	42,609	6,451	5,150	798
1985	45,067	7,815	6,433	823
1986	45,904	7,667	6,379	831
1987	47,014	7,528	6,329	841
1988	47,648	6,456	5,079	787

* Data relate to those trade unions and memberships of unions submitting returns for the year 1977-1988.
(*Source: Indian Labour Year Book.* 1991).

National Level Federations

Of the 10 central trade union organizations listed in Table 4.1, four major federations have been in existence for a long time and have established a national network of federated unions. They are All India Trade Union Congress (AITUC), Indian National Trade Union Congress (INTUC), Hind Mazdoor Sabha (HMS), and Centre of Indian Trade Unions (CITU).

AITUC

The AITUC was established in 1921. It is led by members of the Communist Party of India (CPI). While the union does engage in plant and industry-level bargaining over economic issues, its major goal is political. The guiding principle of the union has been the policy of the CPI: the CPI leaders have always occupied top positions in the union. The policies of the CPI and the AITUC have been influenced in considerable measure by international communism. The AITUC has alternated between violent opposition and total cooperation depending upon the disposition of Soviets towards the Government at the Centre.

The organizational set-up is as follows: (*i*) the affiliated union (unit/local level); (*ii*) provincial bodies (state level); (*iii*) the general council including office-bearers (which incorporates the working committee of the general council); and (*iv*) the delegates to the general or special session. The general council consists of the president, seven vice-presidents, a general secretary, a treasurer and not more than five secretaries and one member representing every 500 members.

The working committee consists of all office-bearers of the AITUC as *ex officio* members and 35 members elected by the general council by a system of cumulative voting. The general session of AITUC is held once in two years, the general council meets once a year, and the working committee at least twice a year. The day-to-day operations are carried out by the secretariat at the national and state levels. In 1984 the AITUC claimed a membership of 10.64 lakh in 1,366 unions. The corresponding figures as per official verification were 3.45 lakh workers and 1,080 unions.

INTUC

The INTUC was organized in 1947, with active support and encouragement from the Congress party leaders. The ideology of the INTUC is to pursue industrial relations in Gandhian tradition with its emphasis on truth and non-violence. Within the INTUC, there have been two distinct traditions. One is exemplified by the Ahmedabad Textile Labour Association which has a distinct trade union tradition emphasizing the resolution of disputes through voluntary arbitration. The other group is composed of unionists who were active in AITUC and NTUF and is made up of Congressmen and Congress Socialists. They stress the need to promote the workers interests and to use the strike weapon where necessary. It is commonly argued that INTUC has been a major beneficiary of the long stint of Congress rule. But the relations in actual practice between the party and the union have been complicated and the ties have not been an unmixed blessing. The basic pattern of organization in the INTUC is the industry level federation with regional branches and a state level council. At the apex level, it has a General Council, a Working Committee and an Assembly of Delegates. The apex body takes an overall view on broader issues and gives directions to the regional branches. In 1984 it claimed a membership of 35.09 lakh (3,457 unions). As per verificiation by the Government, the membership was 22.36 lakh (1,604 unions).

HMS

This federation came into being in 1948. It espouses the socialist philosophy and has linkages with socialist parties. The major elements that constitute the HMS are the Congress Socialists who operated as a pressure group within the Congress, the Royists (who pursue MN Roy's line of thinking) and a section of the Forward Bloc. Though socialism has been the ideology of the federation, the exact brand of socialism to be advanced has been the subject of a major controversy among the constituent elements. Consequently there was a division within the socialist ranks which resulted in the emergence of the Hind Mazdoor Panchayat. In terms of trade union strategy, the HMS lies somewhere between the soft line of INTUC and the radical stance of the communists.

The general council of HMS comprises the president, not more than five vice-presidents, a general secretary, not more than two secretaries, a treasurer and other members representing various industries. In 1984 the HMS claimed a membership of 18.48 lakh (1,122 unions) and the verified membership was 7.63 lakh (426 unions).

CITU

The CITU was established in 1971 as a result of the split in the AITUC which in turn was a sequel to the split in the CPI. The CITU owes its allegiance to the CPI(M). It is animated by the goal of organizing workers to further their interests in economic, social and political matters.

The CITU has a general council which meets once in two years. The day-to-day operations and administration are carried out by the Secretariat at national and state levels. In 1984, CITU claimed a membership of 10.33 lakh (1737 unions) and the verified membership was 1.27 lakh (1,474 unions).

4.9.11 Trade Unions Act, 1926

The Trade Unions Act, 1926 provides for registration of trade unions of employers and workers and in certain respect, it defines the law relating to registered trade unions. It confers legal and corporate status on registered trade unions. The Trade Unions Act, 1926 is administered by the concerned State Governments.

The Trade Unions Act, 1926 has been amended and following amendments have been enforced from 9 January, 2002. No trade union of workmen shall be registered unless at least 10 per cent or 100, whichever is less, of workmen engaged or employed in the establishment or industry with which it is connected are the members of such trade union on the date of making the application for registration. In no case a union shall be registered without a minimum strength of *seven* members; a registered trade union of workmen shall at all times continue to have not less than 10 per cent or 100 of the workmen, whichever is less, subject to a minimum of seven persons engaged or employed in the establishment/industry with which it is connected, as its members. A provision for filing an appeal before the Industrial Tribunal/Labour Court in case of non-registration/restoration of registration has been provided. All office bearers of a registered trade union, except not more than one-third of the total number of office bearers or five, whichever is less, shall be persons actually engaged/employed in the establishment/ industry with which the trade union is connected. Minimum rate of subscription by members of the trade union is proposed to be revised as one rupee per annum for rural workers, three rupees per annum for workers in other unorganized sectors and 12 rupees per annum in all other cases.

4.9.12 Trade Union Organization and Management

With the advent of large-scale modern industries, trade unions too have become large, complex and impersonal. Although union and management are two different entities, they possess some similar characteristics in their structure and functioning.

Trade unions also require members to identify their objectives with those of the union. The individual's interests are to be integrated with the larger interests of the group to which he belongs. Depending upon the constituency, background and backing, the unions may take a partisan stand. Alienation of the employee today refers not merely to alienation from management, but also from the union. Mergers, acquisitions, takeovers, concentration and monopoly are peculiar not merely to big business houses and industrial managements but also to trade unions and trade union leadership. Capturing trade unions has become the 'in-thing' for the new breed of entrepreneurs in the trade union field. They need not go through the rigours of starting from scratch but can capture a union at the ripe time. Such capturing has become easy and simple, speaks volumes about the vulnerability of the unions. Some union leaders 'own' and control the affairs of a couple of hundred unions each and have virtual monopoly over labour markets in some industrial centres. They resort to or encourage restrictive practices and wield vast muscle power to paralyse civic life and throttle economic activity.

The unions harp on freedom and participation. However, there is little internal democracy in the functioning of most unions. Delegation and decentralization, sharing of information and proper communication are much less practised in most trade unions than in most industrial enterprises, even among the principal office-bearers of the same union there is often inadequate communication. Workers' participation in the management of their unions and participation of office-bearers of the unions in their union matters is often woefully lacking.

4.9.13 Trade Unions, Politics and Government

In all parts of the world, overt and covert involvement of trade unions in politics is discernible. The nature, form and extent of involvement may, however, vary depending upon the stage of development of the economic system, socio-cultural and other aspects. The Indian situation is rather peculiar. In India, the link between unions and the government and politics is very glaring and palpable.

Many of the demands of the union are also direct against the government for several reasons: first, the government, being a welfare state with a commitment to a socialist pattern of society, assumed a major role for the protection and welfare of workers and enacted a plethora of legislation. The many loopholes in legislation and persistent weaknesses and inadequacies of administration were responsible for the growing dissatisfaction with the government. In the context of ever-increasing expectations within a dependent socio-cultural framework, the unions often expect and demand the government to bridge the gap. At the same time, both the unions and management oppose any initiative from the government if it seems to impinge upon their autonomy or affect their sectional interests. With the result, today much of what unions do and want is determined by the government. Second, Indian trade unions were largely organized by nationalist leaders, many of whom directed the workers against the British regime. Today in the federal set-up, one finds the INTUC union more vocal in states where Congress-I is not in power. The AITUC and CITU and unions owing affiliations to other political parties turn their dissatisfaction against the governments everywhere.

Third, though the government professes its commitment to collective bargaining, in practice the main thrust was decisively towards compulsory arbitration. Morris argues that by increasingly taking away the wage-welfare functions from the trade unions in an effort to enforce a disciplined response to the requirements of the state, the trade union movement has moved closer to the Soviet model since 1934.

Fourth, there has always been considerable discretion shown by ministers in matters concerning industrial relations which rendered them susceptible to trade union pressure. According to a survey 28 ministers in various states were actively associated with organizing trade unions in 1983. Unionized employees have been generally showing preference for people with political clout in choosing their leadership. Morris observed in 1960 that, torn by conflicts between the requirements of economic development and social harmony, the State in India has perhaps conceded more to the labour force than is desirable in the interests of economic development.

Fifth, almost all national trade union federations have been affiliated to one political party or the other. The number of such national federations has been increasing since the mid-1970s, in tune with the increase in the so-called *national political parties*. It is not an exaggeration to say that almost each political party has its own trade union wing.

It is nevertheless futile to consider only trade unions as being politicized. Managements too are not apolitical. In quite a few cases, managerial responses provide the stimuli for unions to become politicized. Union shopping and divide and rule policy may have at times provided short-term gains for the managements, but in the long-run such managements do suffer. With or without politicization, in the power struggle between union and management, the union derives its strength partly, if not entirely, from the weaknesses of the management.

4.9.14 Managerial Unionism

Managerial unions (euphemistically called *associations*), a recent phenomenon, are on the rise. The purpose of managerial unions is not very different from that of trade unions for employees at lower levels in the hierarchy. The means and the strategies may differ in the sense that the managerial unions are relatively soft in their dealings than most of the blue collar trade unions. The managerial unionism is spreading rapidly and the urge to unionize is becoming intense especially when the attitude and approach of the government/management is hostile and pre-empts collectivization by managers. The National Federation of Officers' Association is now striving for statutory recognition of managers' association. The managerial unions are relatively more assertive and aggressive in nationalized industries like banking, coal and refineries. Some of the factors responsible for the growth of managerial unionism in India are:

(*a*) Job security;

(*b*) Aspects of Government policy and legal regulations which favour unionized workforce;

(*c*) Anomalies in pay;

(*d*) Nationalization and consequent rationalization of pay and perquisites;

(*e*) Protection against growing violence and intimidatory tactics of certain sections of workforce; and

(*f*) The growing influence of blue and white collar unions on joint regulation and employee control at workplace and consequent sense of erosion of power and influence among the middle and junior managers.

4.9.15 Employers' Associations as Trade Unions

According to the definition of a trade union, not only workmen but also employers can combine and get their unions or associations registered under the Act, and function as such.

In the nineteenth century, in the UK and other industrialized countries, unionization of workers was followed by combinations of employers to resist collective bargaining or pressure from workers for effecting improvements in their working and employment conditions. This resistance on the part of employers resulted in industrial conflicts causing severe hardship to both the parties. It took them time to realize the value of resolving their differences by sitting across the table to bargain collectively and arrive at collective agreements to be honoured by both the parties. In an industrial conflict, the workers asserted their right to be treated as human beings and given a fair deal while the employers' organizations asserted their unfettered right to so manage their undertakings as to attain their organizational goals. The same phenomenon happened in India, though with less intensity. The employers' associations were formed not only to protect and promote the commercial and industrial interests of their members but also to help the latter manage their relations with their employees by arranging necessary legal and other advice. Another aim was to assist the employers, in getting their labour disputes settled by conciliation, arbitration and adjudication. For this, many associations have set up separate cells in their offices staffed with qualified persons to deal with labour matters. Several employers' associations particularly at local, city or regional levels are registered under the Trade Unions Act, 1926 and are functioning as such. An important federation like the Employers' Federation of India (EFI) is registered under this Act.

As far back as 1969, the National Commission on Labour reported that there were as many as 163 employers' associations which were registered under the Trade Unions Act, 1926. Though employer's associations can be registered under the Trade Union Act, because of the nature of their role and functions, their office-bearers cannot claim, and perhaps do not require, the kind of immunities that the office-bearers of workers' unions registered under the Act become entitled to. As compared to employees' unions, associations and organizations of employers are stable and have fewer problems arising out of low membership and paucity of funds, multiplicity and inter- or intra-association rivalry. The employers' associations, unlike employees' unions, are not so much plagued by ideological differences, Whatever the other differences, their general objective has been to make more out of their investments.

At the central or national level, multiplicity has not been a problem with employers' associations. United representation of employers' interests at the tripartite forums has been effectively secured by the main employers' associations coming together under the Council of Indian Employers (CIE), but the All India Manufacturers' Organization (AlMO) has been kept outside the CIE in view of definitional problems as to what constitutes an employers' association within the framework of the ILO for representation on tripartite forums. The CIE has, however, considered the Standing Conference of Public Enterprises (SCOPE) as representing employers in public sector.

Observations of National Commission on Labour

National Labour Commission examined the working of employers' associations and made certain observations and recommendations which deserve consideration:

(*a*) Public Sector Undertakings and Cooperatives should be encouraged to join their respective industrial associations.

(*b*) Registration of employers' associations should be made compulsory. Arrangements should be made through the Industrial Relations Commissions for certification of employers' organizations at industry/area level for collective bargaining.

(*c*) A Joint Committee to deal with problems of the industry as a whole or to negotiate on behalf of the industry at that level.

(*d*) Employers' associations should encourage collective bargaining and voluntary arbitration and avoid third party intervention as far as possible.

(*e*) Employers' associations should organize regular need based training programmes for supervisors and middle rung management personnel, in skills of handling labour.

(*f*) Employers' associations should build up their internal consultation system in such a manner that all matters which have a far-reaching impact on members are scrutinized by the constituents prior to any decision that might be taken at the national level.

(*g*) From the viewpoint of labour-management relations, employers' associations should:

• Undertake promotion of collective bargaining at various levels.

• Encourage observance and implementation by their members of bipartite and tripartite agreements in real spirit and form.

• Expedite implementation of wage awards by members.

• Work towards elimination of unfair labour practices by employers.

• Encourage members towards adoption of personnel policies conducive to productivity and industrial peace.

• Promote rationalization of management to improve productivity.

• Arrange employers' education: (*a*) in the concept of labour partnership in industry, (*b*) in the need to ensure identity of interests of labour and management, (*c*) in the need to promote harmony in the goals of industry and community.

• Work towards collective welfare of its members through training, research and communication in the field of labour-management relations.

Self-assessment Questions Set-VI

1. What is a trade union? How is it registered?
2. What rights does a trade union have and how is it recognized?
3. List the ten major central trade union organizations and discuss their claimed figures of membership as on 1984.

4. What are the penalties imposed on a trade union in case of not adhering to the rules? How is a registered trade union dissolved?

5. Describe the aims and objectives of trade unions. Discuss the growth pattern of trade unions in India.

6. Explain the working of four major national level federations in India.

7. Establish the relationship between trade unions, politics and the government.

8. Outline the recommendations of the National Commission on Labour on the working of employers' associations.

4.10 Collective Bargaining

Collective bargaining is a process in industrial relations whereby an agreement is reached on factors like wages, working conditions, etc. by negotiations between employers and trade unions acting collectively on behalf of their members. Such bargaining takes place at a number of levels, from the individual plant, through the regional and up to the national level.

The system of collective bargaining may vary a great deal between countries, industries, and even individual plants. This variation may relate to the level at which the bargaining takes place, issues under negotiation, the nature and extent of third-party intervention and the legality of the contract.

The underlying idea of collective bargaining is that the employer and employee relations should not be determined unilaterally by either party, or with the intervention of any third party. In other words, both the parties should have equal say in determining their working relations, so that neither side exploits the other. In fact, workers found their collective bargaining strength as the only means of combating their exploitation by employers and obtaining fair means of working and employment conditions. The pattern of growth of the trade union movement influences the development of collective bargaining. The employers also started forming their own associations to match the collective strength of workers.

Despite the decades of experience in its practice, collective bargaining, however, continues to be an unfinished business of an emotional kind. It may be quoted that 'the type of industrial warfare with which the nation is concerned occurs mainly during the negotiation of the collective agreement.'

4.10.1 Characteristics of Collective Bargaining

The following are the *four* characteristics of collective bargaining:

1. It is a 'give and take' relation. When either party is weak, it may turn out to be 'giving in' or 'giving away'.

2. Generally, workers want to get the maximum but employers want to give minimum. If the parties wish to reach an agreement, they will have to first retreat from the position taken by them.

3. It is a process of persuasion and reasoning which may enable parties to arrive at some amicable settlement.

4. It is a power relationship in which the management tries to retain its right to manage and unions to safeguard their interests so as to strengthen their hold over the workers.

4.10.2 Collective Bargaining Process

The collective baragining process consists of *three* stages: (*a*) Negotiation, (*b*) Implementation, and (*c*) Renewal and revision of an agreement. An important feature of collective bargaining in the past has been the negotiated agreement entered into between the employer and the trade union. This negotiated agreement reflects a sense of compromise in a give-and-take-spirit and also manipulation of a power equilibrium between the parties. The signed agreement becomes a contract between the parties.

The negotiated (collective) agreement may specify the *modus operandi* to resolve disputes or problems arising out of, or in the course of, the agreement.

The collective agreement is for a specific period of operation after which the agreement can be terminated, renewed or revised. Sometimes, there is a provision in the agreement for revision during its period of operation to meet the contingencies arising from changes in economic and other conditions.

4.10.3 Prerequisites for Collective Bargaining
- Freedom of association between employees and employers.
- Mutual trust and confidence.
- A semblance of parity in the strength.
- Right of employees and employers to strike and lock out subject to national interest.
- Authorized representatives for negotiating the agreement.
- Encouragement by the Government for collective bargaining.

4.10.4 Indian Scene
In India, modern trade unionism made its first appearance at the end of the First World War, but it was not until 1920 that any serious effort was made to bargain collectively. In that year, a group of employers and their workmen in the cotton textile industry at Ahmedabad concluded collective bargaining arrangements to regulate labour-management relations. Collective bargaining as a mode of settlement of wage disputes did not, however, make further progress for the next ten years or so. The slow growth of collective bargaining during this period could be attributed to weak organization of labour and inadequate appreciation of the importance of collective agreement by trade unions.

After the Second World War, collective bargaining received fresh impetus from the legal and other steps taken by the Government as well as from the strength acquired by the trade union movement. The legal measures were provided for the establishment of machinery for negotiations, conciliation and arbitration. Voluntary measures were aimed at promoting collective agreements on basic issues like need-based wages, profit sharing, rationalization, retrenchment and lay-off compensation. These agreements were promoted through tripartite conferences and the Joint Consultative Board (constituted in 1951) at the national level, and industrial committees and working parties at the industry level. The changing attitude of employers and the emergence of a new managerial class, which dealt with labour problems with sympathy and understanding, also contributed in a large measure, to the development of collective bargaining.

With the growth of trade unionism since independence, collective bargaining and agreements have become more common. An assessment made by the Employers' Federation of India estimated that 32 to 49 per cent of the disputes were settled by collective agreements. These were arrived at either as a result of collective bargaining with or without the help of any third party, or with the help of the conciliation officer, or in the course of adjudication of disputes. The last two types of agreements had some elements of compulsion, but the first two types of agreements were purely voluntary. Most of the agreements were at the plant level. However, in important textile centres, like Mumbai and Ahmedabad, industry level agreements were also arrived at. These agreements had legal sanction under the State Acts. Such collective agreements are also found in tea and coal industries. In new industries like chemicals, petroleum, oil refining and distribution, and aluminium, arrangements for settlement of disputes through voluntary agreements have become common in recent years. In ports and docks, collective agreements have been the rule at the individual centres, and on certain matters affecting all ports, all India agreements have also been reached. In banking and insurance too, the employers and unions are coming closer to reach collective agreements.

Factors Inhibiting Collective Bargaining

In India, collective bargaining has not made that much of a headway as in developed and some developing countries and its influence on industrial relations in general and on determination of wages and other conditions of employment is only marginal. This limited development of collective bargaining in India can be attributed to the following factors:

(a) Many employers and managements refuse to accept the fact that trade unions have come to stay. They do not like their employees forming or joining any unions. With such an attitude the question of recognizing or negotiating with the union voluntarily does not arise,

(b) Trade union movement still covers only a small portion of the total industrial employment. Besides, the unions are too weak to bargain collectively on account of their small membership, poor financial resources, their multiplicity, inter-union and intra-union rivalry, politicization and poor leadership,

(c) Excessive regulation of industrial relations by legislation and readily available government intervention for settlement of industrial disputes by conciliation or compulsory adjudication,

(d) Restriction on the rights of employers and employees to lock out and strike, respectively,

(e) Unfavourable political and economic climate as the government, though favourable to collective bargaining, is not prepared to allow endless trial of strength for fear of planned economy being disrupted,

(f) Absence of suitable legislative provisions for recognition of unions as bargaining agents, and for requiring employers and employees to bargain in good faith,

(g) Lack of mutual trust and goodwill, and spirit of give-and-take among the employees and employers, and

(h) Reduced areas of collective bargaining due to encouragement of other institutions like wage boards, statutory fixation of minimum wages and payment of bonus, regulation of fines and deductions, hours of working, overtime payment, holidays, leave and other working and employment conditions, including social security measures.

4.10.5 Recommendations of National Commission on Labour

The National Commission on Labour in 1969 recommended the following six steps for promoting collective bargaining:

(a) Government intervention in industrial relations, particularly in the settlement of industrial disputes, should be gradually reduced to the minimum. Compulsory adjudication of disputes should be used only as a last resort.

(b) Trade unions should be strengthened both organizationally and financially by amending the Trade Unions Act of 1926 to make registration of unions compulsory, enhancing the union membership fee, reducing the percentage of outsiders in the union executive and among the office-bearers, and by increasing the requirement of minimum number of members of union before applying for registration.

(c) Legal provision may be made either by a separate legislation or by amending an existing enactment for:

  • Compulsory recognition of trade unions and certification of unions as bargaining agents.
  • Prohibition and penalization of unfair labour practices.
  • Bargaining in good faith by both employers and unions.
  • Conferring legal validity and legitimacy on collective agreements.

  There are such provisions in the Maharashtra Recognition of Trade Unions and Prevention of Unfair Labour Practice Act of 1972, but as this Act is applicable only to Maharashtra, there is a need for making such legislation applicable to the whole country.

(d) Stepping up of workers' education to build up internal union leadership and make workers more knowledgeable and conscious of their rights and obligations. This may help depoliticize unions and also reduce union rivalry.

(e) The idea of one union for plant or one for industry should be popularized and made a reality.

(*f*) The government should declare its policy to allow and encourage the parties to settle their conflicts and disputes by bipartite consultation and negotiation, consistent with public safety and interest of the society in general.

In fact, the recommendation regarding prohibition and penalization of unfair labour practices has already been implemented by amending the Industrial Disputes Act (of 1947) in 1982. The Government has already passed a bill to amend the Trade Unions Act, 1926 in the Parliament. It will give effect to some more recommendations of the Commission for improving the working of trade unions and this may further help promotion of collective bargaining in India.

4.10.6 Changing the Framework of Collective Bargaining

Changing frameworks of economic conditions, technological developments, increased competition, and statutory and decisional law have given rise to newer bargaining demands and counter demands. Cost-of-living improvement clauses, deferred wage increases, more paid time and new forms of job security and supplementary benefits along with pressures for increased productivity have emerged. Voluntary retirement schemes with more liberal payments, increase in payments to retirees, and enhanced insurance coverage are some examples. According to the sources, the new Industrial Relations Bill proposes to go in for the exit policy in a limited way, both in the private and public sector. The recommendations of the new bill include: (*a*) Making strike notice by workers mandatory; and (*b*) Cutting down the powers of the trade unions by allowing only one registered workers union' in any company.

| Self-assessment Question Set-VII |

1. What is collective bargaining? Why is it regarded as the most appropriate method of determining employer-employee relations?
2. Outline the characteristics of collective bargaining. Discuss in detail any one characteristic.
3. Discuss the prerequisites for the success of collective bargaining.
4. What are the stages of the collective bargaining process? Discuss them in detail.
5. Why has collective bargaining not made much headway in India? What steps do you suggest for its promotion in the light of the recommendation of the National Commission on Labour?
6. In the changed framework of collective bargaining, describe the role of collective bargaining in the Indian context.
7. Define and differentiate between industrial disputes, lockout and picketing.

4.11 Four 'C's Model of Human Resources Management

The four 'C's model was developed by researchers at the Harvard Business School as a means of investigating HRM issues in a wider environmental context than the mundane and instrumental tasks of recruitment and selection, training, appraisal, maintenance of employee records, and so on. According to the Harvard model, HRM policies need to derive from a critical analysis of:

- the demands of various stakeholders in a business; and
- a number of 'situational factors'.

4.11.1 Stakeholder Theory

This asserts that since organizations are owned and operated by different interest groups (stakeholders), management's main task is to balance the returns to various group interests. Stakeholders are generally shareholders, different categories of employees, customers/users of the product, creditors (including banks), unions, and (possibly) local or national government. Managers, therefore, need to be politicians and diplomats. They must establish good relations with each group, develop persuasive skills, create alliances, represent one faction to others, etc.

Stakeholders theory implies the recognition that each interest group possesses certain basic rights. Thus, for example, management should consider workers' interest as well as those of shareholders when taking important decisions.

Stakeholders may or may not hold formal authority, although each will have invested something in the organization. Therefore, every stakeholder will expect a reward from the enterprise and normally will wish to influence how this is determined. Management must:

- Identify the stakeholder in the organization.
- Determine the minimum return each stakeholder is willing to accept.
- Seek to influence stakeholders' perceptions of the organization (e.g. by persuading shareholders that a high dividend is not in a company's best long-term interest or convincing workers that a high wage settlement is not possible during the current year).
- Identify key individuals in specific stakeholder groups and establish good relations with these people.

4.11.2 Situational Factors

Situational factors include the state of the labour market, the calibers and motivation of employees, management style, the technologies used in production and the nature of working methods. Further situational factors that might be relevant are:

- Form of ownership of the organization (and hence to whom management is accountable).
- Influence of trade unions and employers' associations.
- Laws and business practices of the society in which the organization operates.
- The competitive environment.
- Senior management's ability to coordinate and control.

Stakeholders expectations and situational factors need to be taken into account when formulating human resources strategies, and will affect HRM policies concerning such matters as remuneration systems, degree of supervision of workers, use of labour-intensive rather than capital-intensive methods, etc.

4.11.3 Outcomes to Human Resources Management

According to Harvard researchers, the effectiveness of the outcomes to human resources management should be evaluated under four headings: commitment, competence, congruence and cost-effectiveness.'

1. **Commitment** concerns employees' loyalty to the organization, personal motivation and liking for their work. The degree of employee commitment might be assessed via attitude surveys, labour turnover and absenteeism statistics, and through interviews with workers who quit their jobs.

2. **Competence** relates to employees' skills and abilities, training requirements and potential for higher-level work. These may be estimated through employee appraisal systems and the preparation of skills inventories. HRM policies should be designed to attract, retain and motivate competent workers.

3. **Congruence** means that management and workers share the same vision of the organization's goals and work together to attain them. In a well-managed organization, employees at all levels of authority will share common perspectives about the factors that determine its prosperity and future prospects. Such perspectives concern the guiding principles that govern the organization's work; how things should be done, when, by whom, and how enthusiastically.

To some extent these perceptions may be created by management *via* its internal communications, style of leadership, organization system and working methods; but they can only be sustained and brought to bear on day-to-day operations by the organization's workers. Staff should feel they possess a common objective. They need to experience a sense of affinity with the organization and want to pursue a common cause. Congruence is evident in the absence of grievances and conflicts within the organization, and in harmonious industrial relations.

4. **Cost-effectiveness** concerns operational efficiency. Human resources should be used to the best advantage and in the most productive ways. Outputs must be maximised at the lowest input cost, and the organization must be quick to respond to market opportunities and environmental change.

4.11.4 Problems with four Cs Approach

The problems with the four Cs approach are:

- How *exactly* to measure these variables.
- Possible conflicts between cost-effectiveness and congruence.
- Huge variety of variables potentially relevant to any given HRM situation. Often it is impossible to distinguish the key factors defining the true character of a particular state of affairs.
- Sometimes a technology or set of working conditions make it virtually impossible to increase the levels of some of the Cs. Certain jobs are inevitably dirty, boring and repetitive; yet they still have to be done.

4.12 Management of Human Resources

The modern approach to the management of human resources is to emphasize cooperation rather than conflict and to integrate HRM polices into the overall corporate strategies of the organization. This requires senior management to:

- recognize the critical importance of harmonious relations with the workforce; and
- relate HRM to the attainment of increased competitiveness, improved product quality and better customer care.

Well-constructed human resources policies are essential for the well-being of the organization, and all efforts must be made to minimize the potential for conflicts between management and workers.

Self-assessment Questions Set-VIII

1. Who developed the four Cs model of human resources management and why? Explain the *two* critical factors involved in it.
2. What are the four Cs meant for? Explain each one of them.
3. Discuss the problems with four Cs approach. What are your perceptions to avoid these problems?
4. 'Management of human resources can be effectively done with cooperation rather than conflict'. Explain this statement in detail.

Facility Location and Plant Layout

5.1 Introduction

Business systems utilize facilities like plant and machineries, warehouses, etc. for their products/ services. Location of facilities is a complex problem associated with the planning. There is no set procedure to solve this problem for small entrepreneur or big industrial houses. Facility location decision is important as it has direct bearing on factors like financial, employment and distribution patterns. In the long run, relocation of plant may even benefit the organization. However, relocation of plant involves stoppage of production, cost for change over the facilities, and other inconvenience for normal functioning of the business. Therefore, best site is required to be selected after a critical analysis of several other alternate sites for commissioning the plant facilities. Facility location has direct bearing on the operational performance of the organization. Therefore, plant location is an important decision which in turn influences plant layout and facilities needed, apart from capital investment and operating costs. The aim should be to determine the location which should provide *minimum delivery-to customer cost of* produce.

Plant layout is an integration of manufacturing facilities, supporting facilities with the system's organization, data system, information system, etc. Integration and countability can yield marketable product of required value to satisfy customers. The effectiveness of the facilities influences the overall performance of the system.

5.2 Facility Location Concepts

Any place in which the factors of production, land, labour, capital, and enterprises are brought together for creation of goods/services is called *facility location*. Facility includes the physical resources and their quantity such as land; building structure to house processing facilities; supporting equipment; service area facilities; and manpower planning. Planning is to prepare a scheme to coordinate these facilities so that it may result into efficient and effective utilization of resources.

Three different aspects of facility location are:
- Selection of a region.
- Selection of a locality.
- Selection of a site.

5.2.1 Selection of a Region
- Availability of raw materials.
- Nearness to the source of motive power.
- Proximity to the market.
- Availability of transport facilities.
- Suitability of climate.

5.2.2 Selection of Locality
- Supply of labour.

- Prevailing wage rates.
- Existence of supplementary/complementary industries.
- Banking, credit and communication facilities.
- Attitude of the people in the locality.
- Local taxes and bye-laws.
- Living conditions for workers.
- Water supply and fire-fighting services.

5.2.3 Selection of a Site
- Price of land.
- Disposal of waste.

5.3 Theories of Industrial Location
There are two theories of industrial location:
- Weber's theory of industrial location.
- Sargant Florance's theory of industrial location.

5.3.1 Weber's Theory of Industrial Location
Alfred Weber, a German economist, classified factors of location into (*a*) primary or regional factors, and (*b*) secondary factors. Primary factors affecting location of the plant are transportation and labour costs. Secondary factors are agglomerative and deglomerative. Agglomeration refers to concentration while deglomeration refers to decentralization.

5.3.2 Sargant Florance's Theory of Industrial Location
Sargant Florance, the main critic of Weber's deductive theory, has maintained in his theory the relationship between the population distribution and the distribution of the industry. He developed two new concepts, i.e., *location factor* and *coefficient of location*. Location factor is an index of the degree of concentration of an industry in a particular region. Coefficient of location is the sum (divided by 100) of plus divisions of the regional percentage of works in particular industry from the corresponding regional percentage of workers in the country. It shows the propensity of each industry.

It is a statistical technique to ascertain and verify the accuracy and validity of Weber's theory and many other economic hypothesis. It is very useful in empirical investigation. This theory has been criticized for the following reasons:

- The indices indicate the present state of distribution of industries without assigning any reason for their concentration.
- The theory does not suggest any ideal allocation.
- The location factor is based upon number of workers while it should be based upon the output.
- It is not an independent theory of location. It is a statistical device to support the theory.

5.4 Factors Affecting Facility Location
Fundamental factors, which are to be considered in deciding the location of facilities, for profitable working are as follows:

- **Demography:** Attitude of population towards industrialization; expectations of local community; adequate supply of labour of different skills at competitive price.
- **Land:** Cost of land and its development; support of structure, machines, etc.; adequate availability for expansion; types of people living around.
- **Incentives:** Government provides incentives in different forms for promoting industrialization for industrial growth in the region. Some of the incentives are: Availability of loan/land on attractive terms; tax exemption; availability of resources on favourable terms; availability of

working capital from banks on competitive terms; assistance in marketing the final product(s) and processing the raw materials; availability of subsidies on purchasing the machines, equipment, building materials, raw materials, etc.; availability of adequate power, water on subsidized rates.

- **Government regulations:** Government regulations vary from place to place. Some areas are declared industrially backward and therefore additional subsidies are available to entrepreneurs for setting up facilities for different types of products. Laws related to environmental protection, building construction, waste disposal, smoke abatement, police protection, safety laws are to be enforced.

- **Climate conditions:** Local climate conditions, subsoil water, humidity, etc. are important factors for building construction, personnel, etc.

- **Information related to location:** Adequate land should be available for present and future requirements. Present requirements include building for offices, plant, machinery, parking, warehousing, etc. Future requirements include the expansion, availability of transportation facility for receipt and shipment of product(s).

5.4.1 Intangible Factors for Facility Location

Following qualitative (intangible) factors are required to be considered:

- **Personnel:** Availability of appropriate culture, climate, educational, library, banking, transport, housing, medical, shopping facilities.

- **Customers and competitors:** Availability of easy access of customers; facility for quick after sales service; availability of quality product(s) to customers; easy availability of spare parts.

- **Site:** Present and future requirements should be met.

Non-cost factors, exercising an influence on the decisions to ensure that no significant item is left out, are listed. Assign relative-point values to each factor. Range of values vary from plant to plant. Read suggested the following range:

1. Nearness to market	1–280	12. Religious place	10–12
2. Nearness to unwork goods	2–240	13. Recreational facility	13–20
3. Availability of power	3–30	14. Housing	10–14
4. Climate	4–40	15. Sensitivity to attack	10–15
5. Availability of water	5–10	16. Community attitude	16–60
6. Capital availability	6–60	17. Local laws	17–50
7. Momentum to early start	7–10	18. Labour laws	18–30
8. Fire protection	8–10	19. Growth of community	19–30
9. Police protection	9–20	20. Medical facilities	10–20
10. Schooling	10–20	21. Transportation facility	20–21
11. Union activity	11–60		

The minimum total point values assigned to various intangible factors gives the most suitable proposition. For each site/location, the degree may change and so the cost factor.

5.4.2 Tangible Factors for Facility Location

Following tangible (quantifiable) factors are required to be considered:

- **Cost for acquiring production materials:** Availability of materials (direct and indirect) in finished/semi-finished/raw form; availability of purchased parts and sub-assemblies.

- **Cost for transportation and communication:** Availability of transportation facilities (rail, road, waterways); availability of telephone, fax, post-office, courier, e-mail, etc.

- **Cost for utilities at site:** Availability of water, power, fuel, housing, waste-disposal, minimum wages for labour, safety and health facilities.

Tangible factors must be evaluated for specific location in terms of cost, rate of return, etc. At times, cost and profit become unrealistic owing to intangible factors, but it may be rejected owing to bad soil, poor land condition, etc.

5.5 A Facility Location Model

Brown and Gibson (1972) developed a model which classifies criteria on the basis of degree of effect on location. All the criteria set by management are categorized into three classes:

- **Critical:** Critical factors affect the location significantly. These factors may either be tangible or intangible.
- **Objective:** Criteria evaluated in monetary terms such as labour, materials, utilities, taxes, development cost are called *objective*. In some cases, a factor may be critical as well as objective. For example, in labour-intensive industries adequate labour availability can be considered as critical factor whereas labour cost can also be an objective factor.
- **Subjective:** Criteria, characterized by qualitatively, are said to be subjective factors. For example, nature of union relationships and activity may be evaluated but *not* in monetary terms. Again, the criteria may be subjective and critical.

Brown and Gibson proposed the model structure for site x in terms of location measure (LM_x), which reflects relative values for each criterion:

$$LM_x = CFM_x \times [z \times OFM_x + (1-z) \times SFM_x]$$

where CFM_x is the critical factor measure for site x and this can take a value 0 or 1; OFM_x, the objective factor measure for site x and its value can lie between 0 and 1 such that $0 \le OFM_x \le 1$ and $\Sigma_x OFM_x = 1$; SFM_x, the subjective factor measure for site x and its value can lie between 0 and 1 such that $0 \le SFM_x \le 1$ and $\Sigma_x SFM_x = 1$; and z, the objective factor decision weightage such that $0 \le z \le 1$.

The critical factor measure (CFM) is the product of individual critical factor indexes for site x with respect to critical factor j. The value of critical factor index for each site is either 0 or 1 depending on the site has an adequacy factor or not. In case any critical factor index is 0, then CFM_x and the overall location measure (LM_x) are also 0. Site x would therefore be eliminated from consideration.

The objective criteria are converted to dimensionless indices to establish comparability between objective and subjective criteria. The objective factor measure for site x, OFM_x, in terms of objective factor cost (OFC_x) is defined as

$$OFM_x = [OFC_x \times \Sigma x \,(1/OFC_x)]^{-1}$$

The effect of this equation is that the site, with minimum cost, will have the largest OFM_x. The relationships of total cost between sites are retained while the sum of all objective factors measure is one. Hence, the results convert the OFM_x to proportions with large value representing relatively more desirable results than small values.

The subjective factor measure for each site is influenced by the *relative weight* of each subjective factor and the weight of site x relative to all other sites for each of the subjective factors. This results

$$SFM_x = \Sigma x \,(SFW_k \times SW_{xk})$$

where SFW_k is the weight of subjective factor k relative to all subjective factors and SW_{xk}, the weight of site x relative to all potential sites for subjective factor k.

The performance theory is used to assign weights to subjective factors in the systematic manner. The procedure involves comparing subjective factors two at a time. Procedures favour higher order ranking, then the ratings are normalized so that sum of all subjective weightings for a given site adds to 1.

Factor z establishes the relative importance of the factors in the overall location problem. The decision is based on the management committee, reflecting policies and past data. An equation can be used to calculate the location measure, LM_x, for each site and the site having largest value may be selected.

5.6 Advantages and Disadvantages of Facilities Location in Urban and Rural Areas

Advantages	Disadvantages

Urban Areas

Advantages	Disadvantages
1. Well connected by rail, road and air.	1. Limited availability of land.
2. Provides a good market.	2. Cost of land and building construction are high.
3. Easy access of experts and specialists.	3. High local taxes.
4. Availability of right labour force.	4. High labour cost.
5. Factory can be set up in existing available building.	5. High living standards.
6. Good facilities of hospitals, marketing centres, schools, banks, clubs, etc.	6. Costs of consumer goods are high.
7. Easy availability of water and power.	7. Employer-employee relations are not always friendly.
8. Good educational and training facilities.	8. Union problems are more.
9. Safe to work as law and order is maintained.	9. Monotonous atmosphere and is not very pleasant.
10. Services as repair of workshop, machine shop, foundries are easily available.	10. Longer travelling distance.
11. Availability of better banking facilities.	11. Not many sites available for selection.
12. Better infrastructural and communication facilities.	

Rural Areas (Small Towns)

Advantages	Disadvantages
1. Easy availability of land for construction and expansion purposes.	1. Non-availability of skilled labour.
2. Land is cheap.	2. Inadequate transport facilities.
3. Local laws are not so strict.	3. Poor communication facilities.
4. Lower rate of taxes, insurance, etc.	4. Inadequate power availability.
5. Lower labour turnover.	5. Non-availability of experts and specialists.
6. Healthy surroundings and pleasant atmosphere.	6. Poor medical facilities.
7. Enough time for recreation.	7. Poor educational facilities.
8. Less risk of fire.	8. Specialized services may not be available.
9. Government/municipal corporation provide incentives.	9. Inadequate police protection.
10. Government employer-employee relation.	10. Non-availability of big bazars, shopping mall, etc.
11. No union problems.	11. Senior executives may not prefer to live.
12. Low rate of taxes/house rent, etc.	

5.7 Selection of Facilities Location in Suburban Areas

Facility location in suburban areas has the advantages of both the large city and small town. There may only be a few disadvantages as it is a combination of all that is good in large city and a small town.

5.8 Important Factors for Potential Facilities Locations

Some important factors for potential facilities locations are as follows:

Software Company
- Availability of vast pool of IT skill.
- Presence of world class educational institutes.
- Cost of operations should be comparatively less.
- Easy land availability.
- Lower power tariff.
- Availability of support industries and services at reasonable cost.
- Government support in tax incentives, sales-tax exemption, etc.
- Suitable climatic conditions for living.
- Easy availability of expertise, partners and customers.

Cotton/ Textile Industry
- Humid climate.
- Raw cotton availability.
- Excellent transport facility.
- Availability of cheap labour.

Jute Industry
- Availability of raw materials.
- Network of waterways.
- Availability of cheap thermal power.

Iron and Steel Industry/Steel Plant: Easy availability of raw materials such as iron ore, coal, limestone, manganese, dolomite, and refractories.

5.9 Locational Break-even Analysis

The economic comparison of location alternative is facilitated by the use of cost volume profit analysis known as *locational break-even analysis*. The analysis can be done numerically/graphically. Following steps are involved in break-even analysis:

(a) Determine fixed and variable costs associated with each location alternative;

(b) Draw the total cost lines for all locational alternatives on same graph; and

(c) Determine the location having the lowest total cost for the expected level of output.

This method assumes that (a) fixed costs are constant for the range of probable output; (b) the required level of output can be closely estimated; and (c) only one product is involved.

Example 1. Allahabad, Gurgaon, and Pune are the three potential locations for producing telecommunication set expected to sell for Rs 90. Find the most economical location for an expected volume of 1,850 units/year.

Site	Fixed cost/year, Rs	Variable cost/unit, Rs
Allahabad	20,000	50
Gurgaon	40,000	30
Pune	80,000	10

Solution. Total cost   = Fixed cost + Variable cost

Total cost at Allahabad $= 20,000 + (50 \times 1,850) = 1,12,500$

Total cost at Gurgaon $= 40,000 + (30 \times 1,850) = 95,500$

Total cost at Pune $= 80,000 + (10 \times 1,850) = 98,500$

The cost volume graph is shown in Fig. 5.1.

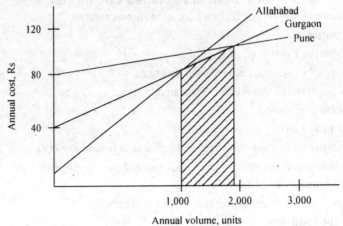

Fig. 5.1   Cost volume graph

It is evident from the graph that the most economical location for a volume of 1,850 units is Gurgaon. Expected profit is

Total revenue – total cost $= (90 \times 1,850) - 95,500 = 71,000/\text{year}$

It is to be noted that for volume less than 1,000 units, Allahabad would be preferred, and for volumes greater than 2000 units, Pune would be preferred.

Example 2. An operations manager of XYZ Breweries has narrowed down the search for a new facility location to seven cities. Annual fixed costs (land, property, taxes, insurance, equipment and buildings) and variable costs (labour, material, transportation and variable overhead) are shown below:

Site	Annual Fixed Cost, Rs.	Unit Variable Cost, Rs.
A	1,600,000	17
B	2,000,000	12
C	1,500,000	16
D	3,000,000	10
E	1,800,000	15
F	1,200,000	15
G	1,700,000	14

Find the (*a*) sites to be eliminated from further consideration (owing to high variable and fixed costs, and (*b*) plot the total cost curves and identify the range over which each site provides the lowest cost.

Hint. Sites A and C are dominated by F, as both fixed and variable costs are higher than F. E is dominated by G; (*b*) F is best for low volume, B for intermediate volumes, and D for high volumes. Although G is not dominated by any community, it is the second/third choice over the entire range. G does not become the lowest cost choice at any volume.

Break-even point between sites F and B is

$$1,200,000 + 15\ Q = 2,000,000 + 12\ Q$$

or $Q = 2,66,667 \text{ units/year}$

Break-even point between sites D and B is

$$3,000,000 + 10\ Q = 2,000,000 + 12\ Q$$

or $Q = 5,00,000 \text{ units/year}$

5.10 Plant Layout

Plant layout is an integration of facilities such as equipment, department, section, etc. inside the plant or workplace. In order to develop an efficient integration, a thorough knowledge of following factors is essential:

- Principles and objectives.
- Input data.
- Types of layout.
- Tools and aids.
- Design a layout.

  The classical definition of plant layout is:

  "Plant layout means placing the right equipment coupled with right methods in the right place to permit the processing of product(s) in the most effective manner through the shortest move in shortest time."

5.10.1 Characteristics of an Efficient Layout

The plant layout should be such that can maximise the return and output and minimise the cost of production. It is possible only when the following characteristics are found in the internal planning of an enterprise:

- Smooth flow of production.
- Utilisation of maximum space available.
- Sufficient space left in-between the machines for easy flow of materials, workers and machines.
- Minimum handling of one operation to the next operation of a product.
- Appropriate facilities of water, ventilation, retiring room, air, etc. to safeguard the health of workers.
- Capable of incorporating any change in the management policies.
- Store in a plant must be established at convenient place.
- Facilitation of supervision, coordination and control by workers.
- Safety of workers under the provisions of Factories Act.
- Adequate inter-departmental space.
- Effective coordination and integration among men, materials and machines for maximum utilization.

5.11 Objectives of Plant Layout

The main objective of plant layout is to maximise the production at the minimum cost. Therefore, objectives of plant layout are:

- Optimum utilization of resources.
- Economics of materials handling.
- Better inventory control.
- Good work flow.
- Efficient control.
- Avoidance of changes.
- Safety.
- Better services.
- High morale.
- Flexibility.

5.12 Principles of Plant Layout

Following principles should be followed for an efficient plant layout:

- Maximum flexibility.
- Maximum coordination.
- Maximum use of volume.

- Maximum visibility.
- Maximum accessibility.
- Maximum movements.
- Minimum discomfort.
- Minimum handling.
- Inherent safety, maximum security, visible routes.

5.13 Procedure in Planning the Layout
Following steps are necessary for developing a layout plan for a new enterprise:

(*a*) Fixing the objectives.
(*b*) Collection and compilation of data.
(*c*) Formulation of an overall plan.
(*d*) Service activities.
(*e*) Building specification.
(*f*) Layout for individual machine.
(*g*) Preparation of layout drawings and test run.

5.14 Plant Layout Tools and Techniques
The tools and techniques for plant layout are:

- **Process charts:** It is a classification and graphic representation of various production activities in a plant. The study of these charts can reveal the operations that can be eliminated/rearranged/ simplified to achieve economy in production. This chart can be divided into two categories, viz., *operation process chart* and *flow process chart*. **Operation process charts** divide the whole manufacturing process into operations and inspections. It indicates the points at which materials are introduced into the process and exhibits the sequence of all operations and inspection except those involved in material handling. It represents the basic activities required to manufacture a product: **Flow process chart** is graphic representation of all production activities take place on the floor of the plant. It reveals the operations which can be eliminated, rearranged or simplified to achieve economy in production, including inflexibility of the layout.

- **Process flow diagrams:** These diagrams aid to visualize the movement of material on an existing layout of the floor. Also, they show tracking and excessive movement of materials and helps in relocations of plant activities to reduce the distance for material movement.

- **Machine data cards:** These cards provide necessary information for placement/layout of the equipment, showing its capacity, space and power requirement, handling needs and corresponding dimensions.

- **Visualization of layout:** It indicates a layout by making replicas of machines, racks, benches and the equipment and arranging them on a two- or three-dimensional of the floor space. In practice, templates are used to develop the layout.

5.15 Factors Influencing Plant Layout
Important factors influencing the planning of effective layout are:

- Nature of the product.
- Volume of production.
- Basis of managerial policies and decisions.
- Nature of plant location.
- Types of industrial process: Intermittent/continuous.
- Methods of production: (*a*) Job order production; (*b*) Batch production; and (*c*) Mass production.
- Nature of machines: Heavy or light in weight.
- Climate: Temperature, illumination, and air.
- Nature of materials: Design and specifications; physical and chemical properties; quantity and quality; and combination of two or more materials.

- Type of machine and equipment in terms of their space, speed and material handling process.
- Human factor and working conditions: Human comfort, viz. rest rooms, drinking water, lavatory, etc, and safety, e.g., free movement of workers.
- Waiting and service centres.
- Plan of the building: Shape, covered and open areas, number of storeys, facility of elevators, starts, parking area, storing place, etc.

5.16 Types of Plant Layout

There are four types of plant layout: (*a*) Product/line layout; (*b*) Process/functional layout: (*c*) Fixed position/static layout: and (*d*) Cellular/group technology layout.

5.16.1 Product/line Layout

It is the arrangement of machines, assembly stations and inspection stations arranged in a line (not always straight) or a sequence in which they would be used in the process of manufacture of the product or group of related products. Thus, machines are engaged to the maximum time provided continuous supply of inventories is established. This type of layout is normally used for development of efficient assembly-line for automotive parts, steel rolling mill, textile, sugar, petroleum, paper and pulp, etc. (Fig. 5.2).

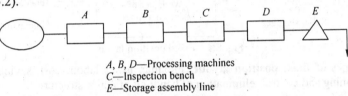

A, B, D—Processing machines
C—Inspection bench
E—Storage assembly line

Fig. 5.2   Product/line layout

   Advantages of product/line layout: Smooth flow of production, mechanization of material handling, economy in manufacturing time, saving in material handling cost, lesser work-in progress, easy inspection, introduction of production control, maximum utilization of available space, and effective utilization of available sources.

   Disadvantages of product/line layout: Expensive, inflexible, difficulty in supervision, difficulty in expansion, stoppage of work through breakdown, high labour cost.

5.16.2 Process/functional Layout

This layout is designed for non-repetitive, intermittent type of production, where low volume of production of variety of jobs/design can be obtained and is suitable for job-shop production. This type of layout is most suitable when same facilities must be used to fabricate and assemble a wide variety of parts or when part and product designs are not stable. Figure 5.3 shows the schematic process layout where each work-area carries similar type of machine.

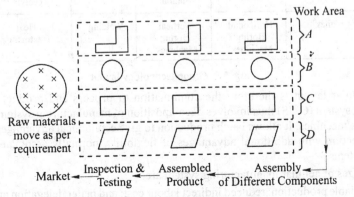

Fig. 5.3 Process/functional layout

Advantages of process layout: Flexibility, scope for expansion, maximum utilization of equipment, low financial investment, better working conditions, high output rate, better supervision.

Disadvantages of process layout: Inefficient material handling, diseconomy to floor space, high inventory investment, high cost of supervision, accumulation of work-in-progress, requirement of highly skilled labour; and involvement of complexity of production planning and control owing to lack of balancing and coordination.

5.16.3 Fixed Position/Static Layout

In this layout, materials and compositions are positioned at fixed position because they are either too heavy/big and their handling may be uneconomical. Men and machines are moved to the place of materials for necessary operations. This type of layout is suitable for heavy machines, hydroelectric turbines, turbogenerators, shipbuilding, locomotive industry, etc. Fixed position layout is shown in Fig. 5.4.

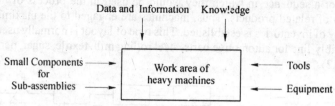

Fig. 5.4   Fixed position layout

Advantages of fixed position layout: Flexible, lower labour cost, saving in time, simple production planning and control, elimination of handling of major structure.

Disadvantages of fixed position layout: Higher capital investment, unsuitability for manufacturing of small products in large quantities, requirement of highly skilled workers to maintain the quality of work, high production cost.

5.16.4 Cellular/Group Technology Layout

This layout is based on the group technology (GT) principle. It is suitable for a manufacturing environment where large variety of products are needed in small volumes. According to GT principle, parts, which are similar in design/manufacturing operations, are grouped into one family, called part-family. For each part-family, a dedicated cluster of machines (cell) are identified. All processing requirements of a particular part-family are generally completed in its corresponding cell. In other words, intercell transfer of part should be zero. A GT layout is shown in Fig. 5.5. In this job-shop, ten varieties of processing steps are carried. The number of possible combinations in which these facilities can be arranged would be 10! (factorial ten).

Drill[1]	Planner[2] (Machines)	Inspection Station[3]	Saws[4]	Shipping and Receiving[5]
Lathes[6]	Horizontal Boring Machines[7]	Vertical Boring Machines[8]	Welding[9]	Heat Treatment[10]

Fig. 5.5 Group technology layout

The cellular layout is therefore the combination of process and product layout. Cellular manufacturing system (CMS) thus involves decomposition of manufacturing system into subsystems of similar parts/machines. It allows batch production to give economical advantages similar to those of mass production with additional advantages of flexibility, normally associated with job shop production systems.

Advantages of cellular manufacturing system are:
- More reliable production; reduced indirect labour cost; and better delegation and accountability as all parts and machines of the group are close together and under same supervision.

- Stepping stone to automation because it is the flexible manufacturing system with some manual operation.
- Short throughput times; low stock; low stock holding cost; better customer service; and lower material handling cost because groups complete parts and machines are close together under foreman in each group.
- Increased capacity due to easy sequencing and reduction in set-up times.
- Easy retrieval of parts due to standardized product design, coding, and classification.
- Efficient production planning and control due to similarity of parts in each cell.
- Flexibility to adopt to market fluctuation due to low stock and easy switch over from one part to another inside a cell.
- Reduced scrap and wastage due to specific machines for each part family.
- Easy plant maintenance due to decomposition of plant into smaller cells.
- Simplified tooling and set-ups as specific jigs and fixtures are designed for each part family.
- Simple estimation, accounting and work measurement due to one supervision for each cell, and decomposition of plant into smaller but independent cells.
- Better utilization of manufacturing resources and space due to dedicated machines cell for each part-family, and less material handling, less WIP.

Limitations of CMS: (*a*) Initial planning and implementation are difficult; (*b*) Layout cost is high; (*c*) Frequent changes or many changes are difficult; (*d*) Non-standardized or new part is difficult to produce; and (*e*) Curtails flexibility owing to much dependence on group technology.

The implementation of CMS can significantly increase productivity, an essence for survival in today's competitive environment. Many large and medium size industries have experienced quality improvements after adopting CMS. It is an important element in successful implementation of Just in Time (JIT), and the building block of flexible manufacturing system (FMS).

5.17 Comparison of Layout Designs

Table 5.1 gives the characteristics of *four* layout designs.

Table 5.1   Comparison of Different Characteristics of Layout Designs

Factor	Layout Design			
	Product/Line	*Process/Functional*	*Fixed Position*	*Cellular (GT)*
1. Operation-type	Continuous and repetitive	Job or small batch	Large-scale project, shipbuilding, construction, etc.	Small to medium batch
2. Facility arrangement	Placed along the line of product flow	Grouped by speciality	Facilities moves to a fixed product	Similar parts are grouped in part-family, and one machine cell is formed for each part-family.
3. Material handling	Less	High	Moderate	Less
4. Facility utilization	Very high	Low	Moderate	High
5. Operating facilities	Special purpose	General purpose	General purpose	Special purpose
6. Q/P ratio (Q-Production) qty.; P-no. of products)	Large (Q/P)	Small (Q/P)	Normally a single product production	Moderate (Q/P)
7. Material travel	Fixed path	Variable path	Variable path	Fixed path
8. Skill of employee	Unskilled	Skilled	Unskilled/skilled	Multi-skilled as one person may operate more than one operation
9. Cost of layout	Moderate to high	Moderate to low	Moderate to low	Moderate to high

5.18 Computerised Layout Design Procedures

Computerised layout design procedures can be classified into constructive-type algorithms and improvement-type algorithms.

Improvement type algorithms: Computerised Relative Allocation of Facilities Technique (CRAFT).

Construction type algorithms:

- Automated Layout Design Program (ALDEP).
- Computerised Relationship Layout Planning (CORELAP).

5.18.1 Systematic Layout Design Procedure

An organized approach to layout planning has been developed by Muther and has received considerable publicity due to the success derived from its application in solving a large variety of layout problems. This approach is referred to as systematic layout planning (SLP). This procedure is shown in Fig. 5.6. In comparison with the steps in the design process, SLP begins after the problem is formulated.

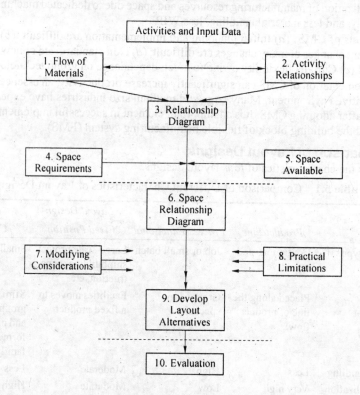

Fig. 5.6 Systematic layout planning procedure (Francis and White, 1974)

5.18.2 Computerised Relative Allocation of Facilities Technique (CRAFT)

CRAFT algorithm, originally developed by Armour and Buffa, is widely used. It starts with an initial layout and improves the layout by interchanging the departments pairwise so as to minimize the transportation cost. The algorithm continues until no further interchanges are possible to reduce the transportation cost. The result given by CRAFT is not optimum in terms of minimum cost of transportation. However, the result will be close to optimum in majority of applications. Hence, CRAFT is mainly a heuristic algorithm.

CRAFT Requirements

1. Initial layout.
2. Flow data.
3. Cost per unit distance.
4. Total number of departments.
5. Fixed departments:
    - Number of such departments.
    - Location of those departments.
6. Area of departments.

CRAFT Procedure

Stepwise procedures of CRAFT algorithm are given below:

1. Input: Number of departments.
    Number of interchangeable departments.
    Initial layout.
    Cost matrix.
    Flow matrix.
    Area of departments.
2. Compute centroids of departments in the present layout.
3. Form distance matrix using the centroids.
4. Given data on flow, distance and cost, compute the total handling cost of the present layout.
5. Find all possible pairwise interchanges of departments based on common border or equal area criterion. For each possibility, interchange the corresponding centroids and compute approximate costs.
6. Find the pair of departments corresponding to minimum handling cost from among all possible pair of interchanges.
7. Is the cost in the previous step less than the total cost of the present layout? If yes, go to step 8. If not, go to step 11.
8. Interchange the selected pair of departments. Call this as the *new layout*. Compute centroids, distance matrix and total cost.
9. Is the cost of new layout less than the cost of the present layout? If yes, go to step 10. If not, go to step 11.
10. The new layout is considered as the present layout. Its data on centroids, layout matrix and the total cost is retained. Go to step 5.
11. Print the present layout as the *Final Layout*.
12. Stop.

5.18.3 Automated Layout Design Program (ALDEP)

ALDEP uses basic data on facilities and builds a design by successively placing the departments in the layout. After placing all the departments in the layout, a score is computed. This is the sum of the closeness rating values of different neighbouring departments in the layout. This algorithm is repeated for a prespecified number of times and the best layout is selected based on the maximum layout score.

ALDEP Requirements

1. Total number of departments.

2. Area of each department.

3. Length and width of layout.

4. Closeness ratings of various pairs of departments in the form of *relationship chart*.

5. Minimum department preference (MDP) value.

6. Sweep width.

7. Number of iterations to be performed.

8. Location and size of each restricted area in the layout, if present.

Relationship Chart

It is a triangular matrix whose elements represent the closeness relationships among the departments. Following symbols are used to denote the various degrees of closeness.

Closeness	Notation	Value
Absolutely necessary	A	64
Especially important	B	16
Important	I	4
Ordinary closeness	O	1
Unimportant	U	0
Not desirable	X	$-1,024$

ALDEP Procedure

Stepwise procedure of ALDEP algorithm are given as follows:

1. Input: Number of departments in the layout.

   Area of each department.

   Length and width of the layout.

   Relationship chart.

   MDP value.

   Sweep width.

   Number of iterations to be carried (N).

   Current iteration number (I), 1.

   Location and size of fixed departments, if present.

   Score of current layout (it is assumed as a very high negative value before performing the first iteration).

2. Select a department randomly and place it in the layout.

3. Scan the relationship chart and classify the unselected departments into two lists—list A and list B. List A contains the unselected departments whose relationship values, in relation to the lastly selected department, are less than the MDP value. List B contains the unselected departments whose relationship values, in relation to the lastly selected department, are greater than or equal to the MDP value.

4. Is the list B empty? If so, go to step 5, otherwise go to step 6.

5. Select a department randomly from list A and place it in the layout. Go to step 7.

6. Select a department randomly from list B which has the maximum relationship value, in relation to the lastly selected department, and place it in the layout.

7. Whether all departments are placed in the layout? If not, go to step 3, otherwise go to step 8.

8. Compute the score of the layout.

9. Is the score of the layout more than the score of the current best layout? If yes, update the new layout as the current best layout and store the corresponding score. Otherwise, drop the new layout.

10. Is the current iteration number $I = N$? If yes, go to step 11, otherwise increment the iteration number by 1 ($I = I + 1$) and go to step 2.

11. Print the current best layout and the corresponding score.

5.18.4 Computerised Relationship Layout Planning (CORELAP)

This algorithm is based on Muther's procedure given in systematic layout planning explained earlier. A computer algorithm was developed by R.C. Lee. Interactive version was developed by James Moore.

Input Requirements

1. Number of departments and their area.
2. Closeness relationship as given by REL-chart.
3. Weighted ratings for REL-chart entries.

Optional Input Information

1. Scale of output.
2. Building length to width ratio.
3. Department pre-assignment.

General approach is to select the most critical department first, and place it at the centre of the layout. Then the department having highest closeness relationship, with the departments which are already placed, is selected and placed in the best location adjacent to the previously placed departments. CORELAP builds the layout from centre. The final layout will not have a regular rectangular shape. The user has to modify it slightly to suit the situation. Final score of the layout is developed by using the closeness values and rectilinear distances between all pairs of departments.

CORELAP Algorithm

Major steps of CORELAP algorithm are:

1. Define basic data.
2. Determination of placement order.
3. Placements of departments in the layout.
4. Finding the total score of the layout.

Self-assessment Questions

1. Why is facility location important? Discuss different aspects of facility location.
2. Discuss the major factors for selection of a region, locality and the site. Explain each of them in brief.
3. Why is the facility location problem considered as a strategic decision?
4. Mention two major theories of industrial location and classify major factors of location.
5. Give separate regions for location of steel, software and mines industry.
6. What are the fundamental factors to be considered in deciding the location of facilities for profitable working?
7. List out the intangible and tangible factors for facility location.
8. Discuss in detail the Brown and Gibson model for a facility location.
9. Compare the advantages, limitations and suitability of rural, semi-urban and urban industrial sites.
10. What is locational break-even analysis? Discuss the assumptions made for this analysis.
11. Potential locations at Bangalore, Chennai and Pune have the cost structures shown below for manufacturing a product expected to sell for Rs 2,700 per unit. Find the most economical location for an expected volume of 2000 units/year.

Site	Fixed Cost/Year, Rs	Variable Cost/Unit, Rs
Bangalore	6,000,000	1,500
Chennai	7,000,000	500
Pune	5,000,000	4,000

12. There are three proposed sites for locating a plant. The details are given below. Find the best site for locating the plant:

Description of Item	Site 1	Site 2	Site 3
Total cost due to quantitative factors, Rs	9,585,450	10,850,480	9,840,950
Qualitative Factors			
Community facilities	Normal	Good	Excellent
Housing facilities	Poor	Poor	Very good
Cost of living	High	Normal	Normal
Community attitude	Satisfactory	Not encouraging	Encouraging (Ans. Site 3)

13. What is plant layout? Explain the objective of good plant layout.

14. 'Plant layout' must maximise the return and output and minimise the cost of production? Comment on this statement with characteristics of such a layout.

15. Explain the principles of plant layout. Discuss the essential steps required to be taken for a plant layout of a new enterprise.

16. Discuss in detail various tools and techniques for plant layout.

17. Outline the important factors influencing the planning at effective layout.

18. What are the types of layout? Explain each of them with examples.

19. Discuss merits and demerits of process layout and product layout.

20. 'Cellular layout is the combination of process and product layouts'. Justify the statement with appropriate reasons.

21. Compare the most common approaches for plant layout designs.

22. What is systematic layout planning? Explain the steps after formulating the problem.

23. What is CRAFT? Discuss its requirements and algorithm.

24. Explain the requirements, relationship chart and the procedure of ALDEP.

25. Discuss the input requirements, optional input information and major steps for CORELAP.

26. Why is the facility location decision important to an organisation? What factors do affect the choice of locations in manufacturing? How do the location decisions for service facilities differ from that of manufacturing facilities?

27. What is layout planning? Based on the firm's flow strategy, how many basic types of layout are possible? How do you design for a process layout?

28. (a) Briefly describe the theories of locating any industrial plant, considering alternative locations. How the factors be considered keeping in mind the theories of Alfred Weber, Sargent and others?

(b) Suggest any quantitative equation integrating most of the important factors.

29. What factors need to be considered for deciding the location of a manufacturing plant? Suggest the type of locational analysis to be carried out for this purpose.

30. Briefly explain a cellular layout. For what type of products and operations it is employed? Compare this layout with other layouts. Give two examples.

31. Why is it important to plan factory layouts? Differentiate between fixed position and assembly line layouts.

32. Identify the layout objectives in the following lettings: (a) Airport, (b) Bank, (c) Fabrication of sheet metal components, and (d) Office of product designers.

Maintenance Planning and Management

6.1 Introduction

Maintenance planning and management is considered to be one of the most neglected areas of the management. It is a combination of many actions to be performed to retain an equipment in an acceptable condition. Maintenance management of components of an operational system suffer from deterioration and occasional failure in performing the assigned job. The frequency and pace of deterioration and breakdown which causes idleness of workers, equipment and perhaps of the entire system, depend on the effective planning and operating conditions. Poor maintenance can result in negative output, unsafe working conditions, and higher production costs due to delays, repairs and excessive downtime (idle time).

Maintenance is often associated with servicing equipment, replacing broken and worn out components, carrying out emergency repairs, upkeep of buildings, and service facilities. Nonetheless, human resource needs proper care, training programmes, etc. Thus, a combination of actions carried out to keep or restore any asset (machine, material-equipment, building, etc.) to a satisfactory operating condition can be considered as maintenance activity.

It is in this context, maintenance assumes importance as an engineering function. Adequate provision is required to be made to keep the machines in an operating condition. Therefore, management for maintenance is to be cost-effective. Hence, management techniques used to improve efficiency in the maintenance department not only to control rising costs and improve operational effectiveness but also to develop a controlled (managed) situation is essential.

6.2 Objectives of Maintenance Management

The main objectives of maintenance management are as follows:

(a) To maximize the availability and reliability of all assets, to obtain the maximum possible return on investment;

(b) To extend the life of assets by minimizing wear and tear and deterioration;

(c) To ensure operational readiness of all equipment required for emergency use at all times, such as standby units, fire-fighting and rescue units, etc.; and

(d) To ensure the safety of personnel using facilities.

From the line manager's viewpoint, the reasons for 'improving' maintenance methods include: (i) protecting the plant and buildings; (ii) increased utilization and reducing downtime of the facilities; (iii) economizing in the maintenance department; (iv) maximizing utilization of resources; (v) maintaining a safe installation; (vi) preventing waste of tools, spares and materials; and (vii) providing cost records for future budgeting.

Keeping in view the trend towards increased mechanization, computerization and automation, there will be a new level of responsibility for, and increased dependence upon, the maintainer, since:

(a) Plant output capacities are raised, making downtime very costly;

(b) Dependence on control systems can produce total disruption of output when one machine or an element in a process fails; and (*c*) The possibilities for operator's intervention to compensate for machine errors or failures have decreased.

The requisites for the maintenance department include:

 (*i*) A requirement for new skills in repair of computer-controlled systems,

 (*ii*) A need for improved multidisciplinary working, and

 (*iii*) A requirement for a systems approach to maintenance.

By adopting systematic maintenance, it is possible to achieve substantial savings in money, material and manpower. Failure or plant breakdown could create problems such as a loss in production time, rescheduling of production, material loss due to sudden breakdown of a process, failure to recover overheads, etc.

6.3 Functions of Maintenance

Important functions of the maintenance are:

- Inspection/check-ups.
- Lubrication.
- Planning and scheduling.
- Records and analysis.
- Storage of spare parts.
- Training to maintenance staff.

Inspection/check-ups: Maintenance staff kept for this purpose should be well trained. The staff carries out both internal and external inspection. Internal inspection means inspection of internal parts such as gears, bushes, bearings, tolerances in parts, etc. when machine is under pre-planned shutdown. External inspection means detecting abnormal sound, vibration, heat, smoke, etc. when machine is in operation. Frequency of inspection should be decided carefully considering the past history of the machine and scheduled programme for inspection.

Lubrication: Systematic lubrication means the application of right type of lubricant at the right time, at right place and in right quantity. For this purpose, lubrication schedule should be prepared to follow strictly.

Planning and scheduling: Every maintenance work should be pre-planned on the basis of analysis of past record. Thus, schedule programme must specify the attention to be given daily/weekly/monthly/bi-annually/annually.

Records and analysis: Effective record keeping is essential for good maintenance. For this purpose, records generally maintained are: (*a*) Operation manual; (*b*) Maintenance instruction manual; (*c*) History cards and history register; (*d*) Spares procurement register; (*e*) Inspection register; (*f*) Log books; (*g*) Defects register; etc. With the help of these records, possible cause for major repetitive failures can be examined and rectified so as to avoid repetition. These records help the plant engineers to (*i*) prevent defect rather rectification after breakdowns; (*ii*) know the reliability of machine(s) for effective production planning; (*iii*) decide life of the machine; (*iv*) forecast defects and plan to rectify them; (*v*) frequency of inspection and check-ups; (*vi*) decide for purchase of a new machine. In spite of best inspection and other preventive measures, failures are bound to occur but can be reduced to a large extent.

Storage of spare parts: It is essential to keep the spare parts in adequate quantity to avoid loss of production. The level of spare parts must be determined by considering factors as source of supply, delivery, period, and availability. Standardization will help reduce the spare parts inventory and will also help in specialisation of maintenance of particular type of machine.

Training of maintenance staff: An appropriate training is essential for the maintenance personnel, to carry out maintenance, inspection and repairs in a systematic manner.

6.4 Failure Analysis

Failure analysis plays a vital role in taking decisions pertaining to maintenance planning and control. It helps to identify the nature and occurrence of failures. It is useful in designing and ensuring reliable performance. Figure 6.1 shows the generalized relationship of failure depicted as a bath-tub curve.

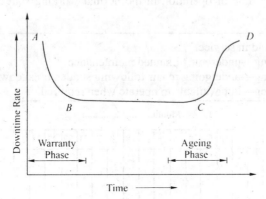

Fig. 6.1 Bath-tub curve

The bath-tub curve is typical of all operating mechanisms—including the human body with a relatively high, but falling, mortality rate at the stage of life A-B, slow but relatively stable rate over the time span B-C, followed by a rapidly rising mortality rate over the period C-D.

Every engineer knows that new or recently serviced equipment is initially at a higher risk of failure, i.e., it is less reliable until, after successive minor breakdowns, vulnerable and/or damaged components are replaced or repaired. This is the period of 'infant mortality', shown in section A-B of the failure risk curve (Fig. 6.1). Such a behaviour can be approximated to a 'hype exponential distribution. This behaviour indicates design and installation defects.

The equipment will then become progressively more reliable, i.e., the number of breakdowns in a given period of operation reduces to a minimum average failure rate, F, which can be written as:

$$F = \frac{N}{T} = \frac{1}{MTBF}$$

where N = number of failures encountered in operating time T, T = operating time, and $MTBF$ = mean time between failures.

In this phase of the operating life cycle of the equipment (section B-C in Fig. 6.1), failure risk is near constant, i.e., failures are random events. The phenomenon can be approximated to a 'negative exponential' distribution.

Subsequently, components fail due to 'ageing' and wear-out, and the failure risk will increase with operating time as in section C-D of the failure risk curve. Such a failure pattern could be represented by a symmetrical boat-shaped normal distribution.

Three distributions discussed above-hyper exponential, negative, abnormal—can be combined into one, known as the Weibull distribution. Hence, the failure rate (bath-tub) curve can be represented by Weibull distribution. As calculations for Weibull distribution are lengthy and cumbersome, Weibull graphs are available for determining $MTBF$.

The profitable decision in engineering is the one that costs the least over a defined period, which may be called *the life cycle of the equipment*. To make such a decision, the engineer must know the characteristics of the failure risks of the equipment for which he is accountable, and how these risks are affected by operational use, operating environment, and maintenance attention—all of which should be factually accurate and comprehensive.

One method of making such an assessment is to keep a simple 'reliability log.' The reliability of a plant (Fig. 6.2) can be defined as

$$A = \frac{T_{up}}{T_{up} + T_{down}}$$

where T_{up} = cumulative time of operation in the normal working state and T_{down} = cumulative downtime.

State 1 : Operating and in service.																															
State 2 : Not operating—undergoing planned maintenance.																															
State 3 : Not operating—undergoing repair following sudden breakdown																															
State 4 : Not operating—but available to operate when required.																															
Plant No.	Month..........................																														Remarks
	1	2	3	4	5	6	7	8	9	10	11	12	13	14	15	16	17	18	19	20	21	22	23	24	25	26	27	28	29	30	31	

Fig. 6.2   Reliability log

From the reliability log, it is possible to quantify plant reliability and establish its characteristics, namely 'infant mortality', random or 'old age' wearing out, by identifying the state of the plant at specified and appropriate times.

6.5 The Maintenance System

The objective of the maintenance system is to ensure performance of the operation system at minimum total maintenance cost. The reliability of an operation system is measured in terms of probability of its satisfactory operation for a certain period under specified conditions. The maintenance system is needed to protect the operation system from deviations, in accepted standards, in the quality of output or in the cost and time to produce the same. The basic components of an operations management maintenance system are shown in Fig. 6.3.

6.6 Types of Maintenance

The various types of maintenance and their relationship are shown in Fig. 6.4.

6.6.1 Planned Maintenance

Maintenance work is organized and carried out with forethought, control and records. This can be classified into two main activities—preventive and corrective.

Preventive Maintenance

This type of maintenance is used in those cases where deterioration and failure pattern of an item can be described with a probability distribution. The routine inspections and servicing are designed to detect potential failure conditions and suggest action which may range from minor or major repairs to replacing parts or even entire assemblies either immediately or at a later time. Preventive maintenance can be carried out on machines either when running or during shutdown, called *running maintenance* and *shutdown maintenance*, respectively.

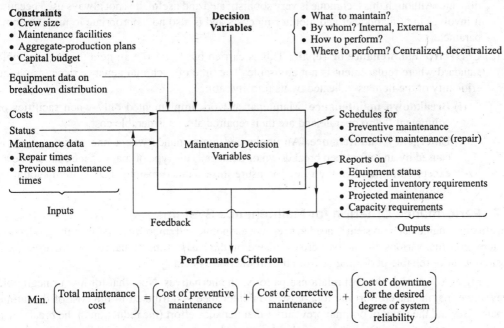

Fig. 6.3 Basic components of an operation management maintenance system

(*Source:* Kostas N. Dervitsiotis, *Operations Management*).

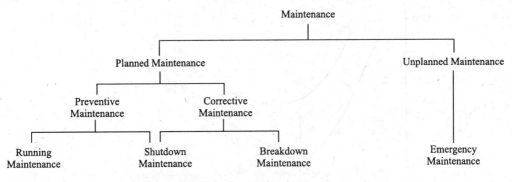

Fig. 6.4 Types of maintenance

(*i*) **Running maintenance:** Maintenance which can be done when the item is in service.

(*ii*) **Shutdown maintenance:** Maintenance which is carried out when the item is out of service.

The preventive maintenance can be time-based or condition-based.

(*a*) **Time-based preventive maintenance:** This maintenance is effective when the failure of any item of an equipment is time-dependent and the item is expected to wear out within the life of the equipment. In addition to this, the total cost of replacement of the item should be substantially less than that of failure replacement repair.

(*b*) **Condition-based maintenance:** It is corrective maintenance based on condition monitoring, where continuous checks are made to determine the 'health' of an item and to expose incipient faults. Here one can also make use of predictive maintenance by using a technique called 'Signature Analysis', which is intended to continually monitor the health of the equipment by systematically recording signals or information derived from the form of mechanical vibrations, noise signals, acoustic and thermal emissions, smell, pressure, changes in chemical composition, etc. Although this technique is very sophisticated and useful, it is not always used because it involves high manpower and monitoring costs and is also not appropriate to monitor some parameters.

(c) **Corrective maintenance or repair:** This is carried out to restore an item to the acceptable standard where replacement is not advisable. The time of such maintenance depends on the criticality of the item as indicated by its priority rating.

  (i) **Breakdown maintenance**. Maintenance work implemented only when facilities or equipment fail to operate and are then repaired at a considerable cost.

  (ii) **Emergency maintenance:** An unplanned maintenance where maintenance work is caused by an unforeseen breakdown or damage. This type of maintenance should be an exception rather than the rule. To ensure this, planned maintenance system should be followed.

6.7 Performance Criterion for Maintenance Systems

An effective maintenance system is needed to ensure economic and smooth operation of the production system. For this, various alternatives are evaluated on the basis of maintenance cost incurred for a desired level of reliable performance from the production system.

Figure 6.5 depicts the cost relationships for such alternatives. Note that for low or negligible preventive maintenance effort the total cost of maintenance is attributed to the cost of downtime repairs. Beyond the point of optimal preventive-maintenance effort (the reduction in the breakdown cost is not enough to offset), an increasingly higher level of preventive maintenance cost is incurred for inspection, service and scheduled repairs, and so the firm would be better off waiting for a breakdown to occur.

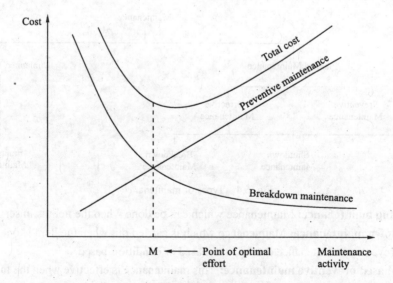

Fig. 6.5   Cost relationship of maintenance alternatives

6.8 Maintenance Planning and Control

6.8.1 Preparation

Total maintenance planning embraces all activities necessary to plan, control and record all works done in connection with running an installation at the acceptable standard. In a fully controlled situation, only the time spent on emergency work is 'unplanned' and this could well be less than 10 per cent of the available manhours in the maintenance department. This situation could be substituted by moving away from the emergency maintenance method to a policy of planned maintenance. The three basic requirements of a planned maintenance system are:

1. A programme of maintenance for the buildings, plant and equipment.
2. Ensuring that the programme is fulfilled.
3. Recording and assessing results.

The basic elements of a planned maintenance system are:

(*a*) Maintenance Request,
(*b*) Assets Register,
(*c*) Maintenance Schedules,
(*d*) Work Specifications,
(*e*) Maintenance Programmes (Planned),
(*f*) Inspection Reports,
(*g*) Maintenance Records,
(*h*) Planned Lubrication,
(*i*) Work Priority, and
(*j*) Safety.

These elements are explained below in detail.

Maintenance Request: The maintenance request, also termed as work order, job card, etc., details the defect and work expected to be carried out. It also mentions the type of labour employed, and the time labour has taken to execute the job.

Assets Register: A comprehensive register of all plants and buildings (also those parts of the plants and buildings which are the subject of planning) is an essential base for the planning operation. Each asset must be identified in terms of name and code; description; reference number related to manufacturers, suppliers (if any), users; location with provision for changes if item is interchangeable or mobile; and supplier's details. When the items are recorded, their classification can be sub-divided in terms of asset usage/availability, technical groups, and maintenance methods. Items subject to special statutory requirements are also separated. The assets register is the information centre of the planned maintenance system.

Maintenance Schedules: A maintenance schedule must be prepared for each item listed in the assets register. A typical maintenance schedule card indicates the grade of labour required, frequency of the work to be done, details of the work to be done, and estimated time for execution of the work. The preparation of the maintenance schedule is a skilled task, not only because all necessary maintenance activities need to be identified and recorded, but also because the frequencies must be evaluated. Maintenance schedules are of *two* types:

(*a*) Preventive maintenance procedures, and
(*b*) Calibration and repair schedules.

Work Specifications

Work specifications are prepared from maintenance schedules. Precise specifications for the activities on the schedule vary in depth and presentation according to the system, the local labour requirements, the complexity of the items to be maintained, etc. Work specifications must be clear and unambiguous. A numerical sequence must be followed and all part names used must be identical with those in the part list. Instructions must be concise and terse.

Much of the maintenance work can be specified in detail—preventive, overhaul or corrective. Specifications for corrective work are subject to modification in content and frequency as experience is gained.

Planned Maintenance Programmes

Planning within the maintenance department should aim at developing a situation in which operation of an annual or other periodic programme of work can be set in motion, and controlled effectively through a work plan. This can greatly simplify the approach to annual shutdown periods (for which techniques like bar chart, PERT/CPM are used). The weekly planned maintenance programme can be derived from the annual planned maintenance programme. However, tactical planning is required at the weekly level by interacting with the production planning and control section especially. It is essential to communicate the weekly planned programme to all concerned at least a week ahead of the commencement date.

Inspection Reports

These are used only for reporting the results of planned maintenance inspections, as set out in the work specifications. The inspection report, resembles closely the maintenance request discussed earlier. It is expected that inspection reports would have been consulted by the controller of maintenance and supervision section prior to filling the maintenance records.

Maintenance Records

The planned maintenance procedure entails building up a detailed historical record of the results of maintenance on every machine. Plant maintenance record should be carefully updated so that they can be referred to and made use of meaningfully.

An effective maintenance record system provides information about: (a) the percentage of planned work achieved in the period; (b) the ratio of planned to unplanned work; (c) the downtime for the period; (d) the ratio of preventive work to corrective work; (e) comparison of maintenance requirement between individual items, between types of item, or between groups of item; (f) indicators for reliability of the products of particular manufacturers; (g) trends in consumption of spare parts; (h) equipment failure patterns; (i) performance details of personnel—individual or by trade group; (j) material used for guidance on re-stocking policies; and (k) indicators on possible standardization policies.

Records are kept in many different ways ranging from card files to computer stores.

Planned Lubrication

Planned lubrication is considered to be an integral part of plant maintenance by most firms, yet this is a responsibility which is relegated to an oil greaser who may have little or no training before being provided with an oil can, a grease gun and a dubious supply of lubricants. Lubrication schedules are usually provided by planning engineers of oil companies. The schedules include information about the number of application points, frequency of each application, method used (grease gun, oil can, etc.), amount and the type of lubricant required. From this register, the planning engineer develops a rational approach to the lubrication requirements of the plant including (a) total work-load assessment depending on the number of points and the frequency of application, (b) sub-division of the work-load to indicate manpower requirements, (c) development of effective routes between the application points, (d) provision for plant shutdown when necessary for lubrication, (e) provision for access (ladders, etc.) and for extended oil pipes or grease lines to reduce access times, (f) development of identification techniques—labels on the machines or pictorial work-specification sheets, (g) rationalization of lubricants whenever possible.

In preparing this plan, the planning engineer takes due account of environmental and operating conditions and recommendations of plant vendors.

Work Priority

According to the work priority scheme, all work done by maintenance department personnel is separated into 10 classes, most important being class 10 and the least class 1. Emergency maintenance (I, II and III), modification, capital, sundry and special maintenance, and housekeeping are respectively ranked from 10 to 1.

   Facility priority factor is one in which each facility, plant, building, etc., is placed in one of the 10 classes, most important being class 1. Key services, the key production plant, flowline or process plant, multi-production machines, standby services, mobile transport, buildings and roads, machines, offices and furniture fittings are respectively ranked from 10 to 1.

   For calculating the 'priority index' of any job, 'work priority' should be multiplied by 'facility/ machine priority'. The ten classes have been chosen so that the priority index for each job can be expressed as a 'percentage priority'. For example, for an emergency repair of a leakproof building over a production machine, the priority index would be $(10 \times 4) = 40$ per cent.

Safety

The operation of maintenance planning contributes significantly to industrial safety. Some of the main safety considerations, while carrying out a maintenance management task, are the following:

   (*a*) **Guards** are supplied by plant manufacturers or subsequently fitted by the company. Care should be taken to ensure that these are not tampered with, resulting in potential hazard.

   (*b*) **Protective clothings** such as helmets, gloves, goggles, gas masks, etc., must be given full consideration especially in chemical and allied industries. The need for having protective clothing must preferably be included in the 'maintenance request' or in the 'work specification.'

   (*c*) **Power isolation** by the use of appropriate fuses might be necessary while effecting certain types of maintenance tasks.

   (*d*) **Pressure vessels, lifting appliances** should have some type of a 'permit' system to open and/ or blank off these.

   (*e*) **Permit to work** for maintenance tasks should remain valid for a specific period only. A copy of the certificate should be posted/affixed in such a place so that it is not possible for anyone to start up the plant or machine without referring to it.

6.8.2 Operation

The adoption of planned inspection and maintenance procedure calls for a discipline of application which is often lacking. No maintenance organization can operate effectively without the discipline of a planning system, this being the tenet of several aspects. Figure 6.6 shows diagrammatically one approach to systematic maintenance.

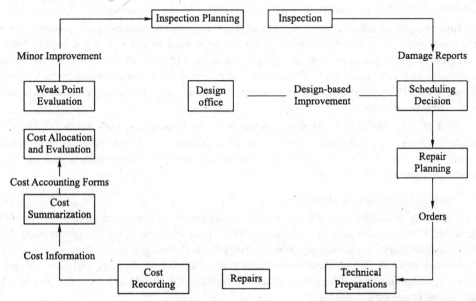

Fig. 6.6   The planning and control of work to improve performance

Inspection of plant is seen as the starting point from which one prepares damage reports or factual statements on wear and tear of the plant. This gives rise to scheduling and detailed planning of the repair/maintenance task. Once this has been executed, the feedback loop starts with the recording of cost information followed by its subsequent allocation and analysis. The reports also provide pointers/indicators for minor improvements in the plant towards decreasing the frequency/scope of the repair tasks. Also, in a more fundamental way, it should stimulate the design office to look for weak points in the production plant and progressively eliminate these through a design-out maintenance approach.

With complex modern plants, however, there is no doubt that such a scientific approach needs the support of a formal system which can take the form either of a paper planning system or of one using computers to assist the engineers in this task. Such a planning system must have the following four abilities:

(*a*) To recognize repetitive jobs and to produce action documentation in order to ensure that such jobs are carried out on schedule;

(*b*) To accept a 'breakdown' routine in the event of any sudden plant breakdown;

(*c*) To analyse breakdown and routine maintenance cost at an 'appropriate' engineering level in a plant asset register so that corrective action can be taken to minimize the cost; and

(*d*) To be run by practical engineers rather than specialist planners.

A planning system should therefore produce information to enable the maintenance force to inspect plant on a proper basis; to carry out any necessary repair/maintenance work programme for management control and priority allocation; and, finally to produce useful information in terms of cost, manpower utilization, spares consumption, etc., from which the plant engineer can 'tune' his system.

In a progressive engineering organization, plans will exist to improve performance in all these areas. In the first of these—minimizing damage—the regular review of breakdown and determination of their major causes will generate appropriate action such as the training of operatives; better protection of vulnerable plant components; more effective control of plant; better layout of control panels; improved visibility and so on. Only by an ongoing review of such situations an inroad be made to check the cost of plant damage. Damage reports can also arise, incidentally, from the safety function and the use of these to improve performance should not be overlooked.

Minimizing the downtime for repair calls largely for an adequate stores/spares inventory, proper organization on the shop-floor, flexibility in the use of the maintenance force, effective back-up from a central engineering workshop, and proper motivation of the craft force and management in the execution of the job. Again, computers can help in ensuring that the stores/spares system operates as defined; establishing maximum/minimum stores level, adjusting purchasing procedures to match delivery times and so on.

About 50 per cent of the cost of maintenance is often associated with the use of materials. Materials may vary in form from structural steelwork to microchips and any reduction in their initial cost or prolongation of life of engineering components can play a significant part in cutting maintenance costs.

6.8.3 Work Measurement Techniques

Most engineering managers would agree that work planning in maintenance areas is both possible and desirable. However, when it comes to setting certain standards/norms for the largely non-repetitive nature of maintenance work, one encounters divergent and strongly held views on the subject. Incentives may motivate the maintenance workers to carry out their tasks effectively and efficiently. Different organizations have different schemes of remuneration for direct production workers and indirect maintenance staff.

The work measurement techniques used in the maintenance department range from simple job timing to the data block system. On the one hand, actual tasks are timed, wholly or partly, as executed by an employee and on the other, maintenance work is classified in terms of standard work blocks. The detailed examination of each task determines the number and type of work blocks used in any particular task. Within these extremes, a number of other work measurement techniques, such as estimated time standards, are practised.

Repetitive work in the maintenance department can be timed. For accurate results, the timing operation should be repeated over a period of weeks/months to produce average results for various personnel involved.

Non-repetitive work may be allotted time based on analytical estimation. Analytical estimation is a task for a skilled tradesman (sometimes called an *applicator*) who breaks down the task in terms of standard units combined with non-standard estimated work. This gives a closer control over maintenance than the whole-task estimating process and again facilitates examination of the methods employed and the work sequence adopted. Where standard work data exists for a particular task, or for its near equivalent, the breakdown must isolate this task, as maximum use of standard data reduces the time taken by the applicator and increases the reliability of the measured times.

Three work measurement techniques are commonly used for maintenance activities:

(*a*) Direct standards—used for repetitive work such as lubrication routines;

(*b*) Work sheets—used for craft data calculations on painting, machining and other tasks; and

(*c*) Work content comparison—used for non-repetitive work for the majority of maintenance jobs.

6.8.4 Progression

Critical Analysis

As maintenance work progresses and practical information becomes available, it is essential to carry out a critical analysis. Here the Pareto principle comes in handy, namely the principle of 'the significant few and trivial many.' A critical breakdown analysis [Fig. 6.7 (*a*)] reveals that a small percentage (say, 10 per cent) of equipment would contribute to about 70 per cent of the breakdown time. Such types of equipment are called *critical 'A' type*. A defect analysis [Fig. 6.7 (*b*)] also reveals that a few, about 10 per cent, defects contribute to about 70 per cent of the breakdown time.

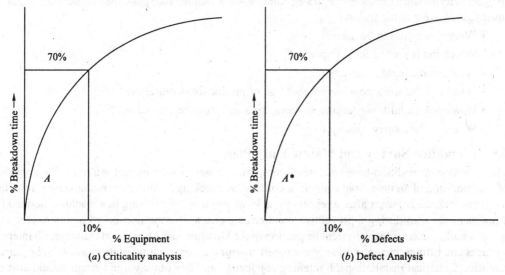

(*a*) Criticality analysis   (*b*) Defect Analysis

Fig. 6.7

Taking critical A type of equipment and the critical A* type of defects into account, it is required to devise appropriate preventive maintenance management schemes and design-out maintenance, wherever feasible. There are three steps in dealing with a maintenance problem:

(*a*) Can it be eliminated? If no, go to the next step.

(*b*) Can it be simplified? If no, go to the next step.

(*c*) Can it be improved? If no, is there no other option.

Some maintenance problems, such as a lubrication problem, can it be tackled through the above three-step procedure.

6.8.5 Simulation

This technique involves construction of a logistics model which is not analytical but is only a basis for carrying out experiments and testing hypotheses. The activity, in its turn, leads to the solution eventually.

The potential contributions of simulation in the maintenance management include:

(*a*) Examining alternative plant designs and layouts with the objective of reducing the impact on production of maintenance activity and plant failure;

(*b*) Assessing the optimal level and mix of resources (manpower and equipment) required to provide a certain services to a particular plant area;

(*c*) Examining alternative schedules for planned maintenance activities; and

(*d*) Assessing the impact on overall performance of an increase or decrease in availability of an item of plant caused by a change in maintenance practice.

Within a steel plant, for example, this technique has tried to evaluate the effect of alternate plant layout, ladle repair facilities, phasing of steel making vessel and continuous caster maintenance, and crane availability.

The latest developments in simulation mean that users can observe the course of a computer simulation run, and therefore understand the implications of what they are testing, on a dynamic mimic diagram of the plant shown on a graphics display terminal.

6.9   The Maintenance Strategy

In order to formulate a maintenance strategy and evolve a maintenance plan, the maintenance engineer must find answers to the following:

- What is required to be done?
- Which items are the most important?
- What are the legal requirements?
- When can the work be done without loss of production/facilities/service?
- How often should inspections, surveys, tests and work be carried out?
- Where is the money coming from?

6.9.1   Condition Survey and Maintenance Plan

The definition of condition-based maintenance is, 'Maintenance work initiated as a result of knowledge of the condition of an item from routine or continuous checking.' Corrective maintenance, initiated by a maintenance engineer after a report of cracks in a wall or overheating in a machine, noticed by a maintenance man during a preventive maintenance check, is condition-based maintenance. The report should include close physical inspection of the structure and its external cladding, all internal surfaces and fittings, etc., and all services together with the surrounding estate grounds and external facilities. Electrical installations, lightening conductors and any other wired system should also be tested.

The notes and comments are set out in a comprehensive report supplemented by drawings and photographs. Recommendations on items of work required and their priority are included. This document is called a 'Condition Survey' and will prove invaluable in the preparation of a maintenance programme. The work necessary, as indicated by a condition survey, can be programmed according to its priority and executed within a defined period.

Having been evaluated in terms of cost and programmed, the maintenance plan should be supported by specific recommendations and presented to the senior management. The presentation must include the order of priority of tasks so that decisions are made according to need and do not reflect solely the financial allocations in the plan period.

Once the plan has been approved in whole or in part, it forms the basic programme of work, keeping in mind that some flexibility will still be required as priorities and circumstances may change. As changes are disruptive and may delay the whole programme, they should be kept to the minimum.

6.9.2 Legal Responsibilities

Legal responsibilities affecting maintenance are very wide. They cover not only the fabric of the property and its equipment but also the owner, the occupier, and the general public. The relevant acts are designed to safeguard the people who may need to enter or use the property.

Attention will need to be given to (a) notices received from any local authority concerning defective or dangerous buildings and demolition work, (b) obtaining any necessary hoarding or scaffold permits for works affecting or abutting streets, (c) observing the requirements of the Noise and Control of Pollution Act where noise or air pollution, etc., is likely to cause a nuisance, and (d) notifying the local fire authority for any material modification or work which may possibly affect any conditions contained in a Fire Certificate issued under the Fire Prevention Act.

The maintenance engineer has a responsibility for ensuring that the legal requirements are met and that appropriate action is taken and documented. This may entail seeking expert legal, professional or scientific advice but this in itself does not remove the burden of responsibility from the maintenance engineer.

6.9.3 When can the Work be Carried Out?

Table 6. 1 provides examples of the types of property for which maintenance engineers may have the responsibility, together with an indication as to when major maintenance and related work may be executed. External maintenance work can usually be carried out in normal working hours. It is important that all maintenance work is pre-planned and the time duration agreed upon in consultation with the senior person responsible for the premises.

Table 6.1 When Internal Maintenance Work can be Carried Out

Organization	Examples of Property	Access for Maintenance
Government	Public offices, workshops	Public holidays, evenings and weekends
Public utilities	Offices, shops	Public holidays, evenings and weekends
Municipal authority	Housing estate offices	Normal working hours
		Public holidays, evenings and weekends
	Leisure facilities	Off-season, nights and special closures
Educational establishments	Lecture halls, classrooms, living accommodation	During recesses; minor works in evening and normal working hours
Hospitals—public or private	Operation theatres, wards, living accommodation	Special closures required, special closures except for small emergency work, normal working hours
Industrial firms	Factories	Holidays, evenings and weekends
Hotels	All areas	Off-season closedowns or special closures

6.9.4 Maintenance Standards

There are two main divisions of maintenance standards:

(a) Quality standards; and

(b) Service standards.

Quality standards depend on the products used, skill of the operatives, standard of supervision during the work and the approval (or rejection) upon inspection of the completed work by the maintenance engineer. Quality assurance (QA) is a growing movement in building and other industries. Companies participating in the scheme give guarantee in respect of their products, their craftsmanship or both.

Service standards are important to quantify maintenance in terms of time period or response time, in which the work is to be completed. From this, the programme of work can be prepared and performance measured against the standards. Service standards are, therefore, essential as a basis for calculating the workload, labour requirements and the required financial resources. It is also important that standards are included to cover legislation. Inspections should be fully documented and should bear the signatures of the officers carrying out the inspection.

6.9.5 Sources of Finance

Internal

(a) Current cash flow generated from sales and service;

(b) Savings and investments—money previously set aside from profits on savings and investments;

(c) Property—proceeds of the sale or lease of the property or the use of the property as a security for a loan;

(d) Reserve—money set aside to meet the cost of specific projects; and

(e) Rates—money raised from the ratepayers.

External

(a) Shareholders—issuing of further company shares or right issues;

(b) Banks and other financial institutions—short- or long-term loans or overdrafts;

(c) Credit—negotiated special credit terms with suppliers;

(d) Leasing arrangements—plant and equipment may be leased or sold to raise cash;

(e) Tax allowances/concessions/grants—tax advantages and grants are available for a wide range of property investment in both the private and public sectors; and

(f) Government funds.

6.9.6 Value for Money

Time values for elements of maintenance work can be readily obtained by work study, and allowances made for travelling, gaining entry to work place, fatigue, etc. The total standard hours produced provide the basis for calculating productivity payments as well as make available to management information on performance. Motivation of other personnel is probably best gauged through 'management by objectives' (MBO), geared to evaluate the performance of operatives and supervisors.

Maintenance work can be contracted either through competitive tendering or through inviting quotation for individual job. Alternatively, term contracts may be used for day-to-day repairs, generally covering a period of two or three years. A schedule of rates for different trades is obtained from a detailed repairs schedule or specification. This will give the lowest market price for day-to-day repairs.

6.9.7 Contractors

To obtain a realistic quotation from a specialist or general contractor, it is important to prepare a list of compact, unambiguous and detailed specifications, together with drawings where necessary, for all the works or services required. Inadequate specifications generally lead to high estimates. It is essential that all contractors quoting for work receive identical documents.

Other points to remember, when giving a job to a contractor, are:

(*a*) Orders for the work must be clear;

(*b*) Payment for satisfactory work should be prompt;

(*c*) Additional work, or variations on contract, must be thoroughly documented and prices for these must be obtained before variation orders are issued;

(*d*) The contract must not be overspent without a written authority from the client;

(*e*) Supervision of work must be adequate to ensure satisfactory quality control and progress as per approved work programme; and

(*f*) The client must ensure that the contractor has adequate access to the work place so that delays are minimized.

6.10 A Systems Approach to Maintenance Management

Management in manufacturing and service industries, and those responsible for financing the maintenance work, have appreciated the need to ensure that full value must be obtained from expenditure on a service which in itself is unprofitable in the sense that it does not add to the value of goods produced, but is in fact an additional 'on cost' capable of affecting profits.

Figure 6.8 shows the main tools capable of providing sound maintenance management. However, it should be noted that in many instances adjuncts to the system are not discussed in detail. In particular, research and development, costing information and training are not specific functional operations of a maintenance manager, but are important aspects of the system in which he should work. It is equally important that he simultaneously provides the feedback, necessary to produce information and services he needs. This does not, however, preclude his own direct personal involvement within the total management structure. He may have to consider the setting up of a training programme capable not only of meeting the immediate requirements of maintenance, but also of establishing the skills necessary for dealing with long-term planning.

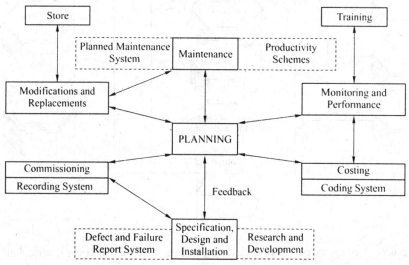

Fig. 6.8 Systematic maintenance management system

Arising out of the need to obtain maximum benefits from expenditure, many systems of control have been devised and used in efforts to minimize maintenance costs, increase output per unit of machine life and reduce capital outlay on new plant and buildings. In exercising systems of control, those responsible have tended to use well tried and document methods, and have applied these in a manner that appeared to meet best their individual needs.

A computerized information management system for maintenance scheduling is shown in Fig. 6.9.

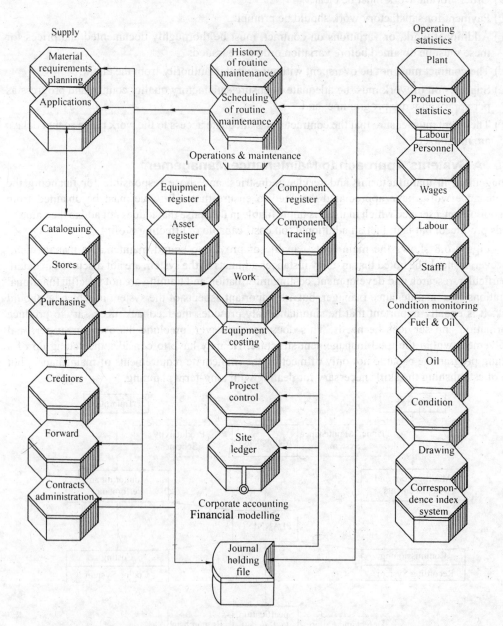

Fig. 6.9   A computerized information management system for maintenance scheduling

6.11   Maintenance Costing and Budgeting
Costing and budgeting for the maintenance department refers to the provisions of finance on labour and material expenditure, its allocation to various cost centres to cater to manpower resources and development of objectives. The basis for cost control is provided by the use of cost account codes.

Typical major code headings may include (*a*) capital projects, (*b*) planned preventive maintenance, and (*c*) workshop services. The cost attributable to the cost codes consists broadly of wages and salaries, overhead charges, materials cost, transport cost and sundry items.

The overhead-charge laid upon maintenance including charges occurring within the maintenance department as well as the overhead charges reflected from other departments like administration, personnel, general management, etc. Changes arising from within the department include services, rent and rates, transport and insurance.

A budget could be prepared on the basis of different types of costs estimated for different heads. A budget may show

Maintenance labour	25%
Maintenance material	40%
Fuel cost	25%
Overheads	10%

When producing a departmental business plan, it is necessary to include in the budget a set of objectives and strategies for implementation in the planned maintenance programmes, information about completion of certain capital works and the operation of a planned overhaul programme. One objective for the department may be the reduction of resources allocated to corrective and emergency maintenance and an increase in planned preventive work.

Cost reports can be analysed for variance of actual from planned. For this, it is relevant to introduce the concept of 'life-cycle cost' of an asset. It includes the initial cost (the total cost of procurement and setting to work), the cost of ownership during the life cycle, and the cost of downtime. Initial cost includes the cost of services, commissioning, product support and ancillary equipment. The cost of ownership includes the annual cost of operation and maintenance, multiplied and factored for the life term, together with the cost or income expected when the asset is disposed of. The cost from downtime includes loss due to use, repair cost and cost owing to damage. In addition, inflationary trends should be suitably accounted for, if they exist.

Once fully understood, formal budgeting is a useful discipline not only in predicting and controlling expenditure but also in encouraging the prediction and pre-planning of activity with the necessary resources to meet the plan.

6.12 Maintenance Performance Indices

Chandra has proposed some indices, which may help management achieve their objectives effectively and efficiently.

1. Maintenance Productivity Index $= \dfrac{\text{Output of product}}{\text{Cost of maintenance effort}}$

2. Maintenance Cost Index $= \dfrac{\text{Maintenance cost} \times 100}{\text{Capital cost}}$

3. Downtime Index $= \dfrac{\text{Downtime hours} \times 100}{\text{Production hours}}$

4. Waste Index $= \dfrac{\text{Quantity of waste produced} \times 100}{\text{Quantity of total output}}$

5. Breakdown Maintenance Index $= \dfrac{\text{Total hours spent on breakdown} \times 100}{\text{Total manhours available}}$

6. Level of Maintenance $= \dfrac{\text{Total hours spent on scheduled maintenance} \times 100}{\text{Total manhours available}}$

7. Inspection of Effectiveness $= \dfrac{\text{Standard minutes of work saved on improved inspection}}{\text{Total standard minutes of inspection carried out}}$

It is possible to reduce the volume of maintenance to the lowest possible extent through inspection.

. 8. Technical Competence Ratio = $\dfrac{\text{Annual saving in labour and material costs}}{\text{Total annual maintenance cost}}$

Here also capital saving can be effected by utilizing work study and value engineering techniques at the design stage.

9. Overtime Hours Ratio = $\dfrac{\text{Overtime worked (hours)}}{\text{Total maintenance manhours}}$

In fact, overtime hours worked indicates failure of planning. Emergency maintenance should be reduced to the extent possible.

Example 6.1. A railway reservation office faced the following number of breakdowns/month in its automated reservation processing system over a period of two years:

Number of breakdown:	0	1	2	3	4
Number of the month:	3	9	11	5	2

Each breakdown costs the agency an average of Rs 2,800. For a cost of Rs 1,500/month the agency could have engaged a data processing firm to perform preventive maintenance which guaranteed to limit the breakdowns to an average of one per month. However, if the breakdown exceeds one, the firm will process the agency's data free of charge. Which maintenance arrangement is preferable from a cost standpoint—the current breakdown policy or a preventive maintenance contract arrangement?

Solution. Based on the given data, the expected cost/month of breakdown is shown below:

No. of Breakdowns (x)	Frequency (in months) $f(x)$	Frequency (in per cent) $p(x)$	Expected Value $\mu = x \cdot p(x)$
0	3	0.10	0.10
1	9	0.30	0.30
2	11	0.36	0.72
3	5	0.17	0.51
4	2	0.06	0.24
	30		1.87

$$\text{Expected breakdown cost/month} = \left(\frac{1.87 \text{ breakdowns}}{\text{months}}\right)\left(\frac{\text{Rs } 2800}{\text{Breakdown}}\right) = \text{Rs } 5236/\text{month}$$

The expected number (1.87) of breakdowns is more than the average of one breakdown. But due to the guarantee given by the preventive maintenance firm, the travel agency will incur the cost of only one breakdown/month. Thus:

Average cost of one breakdown/month	=	Rs 2,800
Maintenance contract cost/month	=	Rs 1,500
Total		Rs 4,300

Therefore,

Preventive maintenance advantage = Rs (5,236 – 4,300) = Rs 936/month.

Example 6.2. An Engineering Consultant firm received an order from private industrial enterprise to study the total cost at the present maintenance policy for machinery in a decentralised section of its manufacturing plant. Data on machinery breakdown over a 16-hr period is as follows:

Request for Repair (arrival time)	Total Repair Time Required (worker hours)
01.00	2.00
07.30	5.00
08.00	1.00
11.50	3.00
12.20	0.50

The company has two maintenance engineers and charges their time (working or idle) at Rs 250/hr each. The downtime cost of machines, from lost production, is estimated at Rs 1,200/hr. Determine the:

(a) Simulated service maintenance cost;

(b) Simulated breakdown maintenance cost; and

(c) Simulated total maintenance cost.

Solution. (a) Simulated service maintenance cost

Service cost = 2 engineers × Rs 250/hr × 16 hrs = Rs 8,000.

(b) To calculate the simulated breakdown maintenance cost, let us assume that the two engineers are twice as effective as one, and they, therefore, reduce total repair to half.

Arrival Time	Repair Time (2 engineers)		Repair Time begins	Repair Time ends	Machine Downtime (2 engineers)
	hr	min.			
01.00	1.00	60	01.00	02.00	1.00
07.30	2.50	150	07.30	10.00	2.50
08.00	0.50	30	08.00	08.30	0.50
11.50	1.50	90	11.50	13.20	1.50
12.20	0.25	15	12.20	12.35	0.25
	5.75 hr				**5.75 hr**

Breakdown cost = Rs 1,200/hr × 5.75 = Rs 6,900

(c) Simulated total maintenance cost

Total cost = service cost + breakdown cost

= Rs 8,000 + Rs 6,900 = Rs 14,900/period.

Self-assessment Questions

1. What is Maintenance planning and management? Discuss its importance in Indian industrial scenario.

2. What are the objectives of maintenance management? How can a maintenance manager achieve these objectives?

3. There is a trend to automate different processes possibly to cut-down the production time and manpower cost. Discuss its impact on the maintenance function.

4. Explain the important functions of maintenance.

5. Discuss the 'Bath-tub Curve' phenomenon of failure rate, with an appropriate diagram. Give an example which either conform to or is at variance from the failure rate phenomenon.

6. What is the purpose of maintaining a 'Reliability Log' in a plant and quantify the plant reliability?

7. Explain different types of maintenance systems. Give an example for each system. An example of a small car, motor cycle or any other item of your choice for elaborating your answer explicitly.

8. How can work measurement technique be usefully applied in maintenance department?

9. What is 'Critical Analysis'? How does the Pareto principle find its application in devising an effective maintenance planning and control system?

10. How would you formulate your maintenance strategy for effective maintenance planning? Illustrate with an example.

11. Explain how preventive maintenance is better than breakdown maintenance.

12. Discuss the main tools capable of providing sound maintenance management, with a suitable diagram.

13. What is 'Priority Index' and how would you obtain it?

14. What precautions one should take in applying work study techniques to maintenance engineering.

15. Describe the utility of maintenance performance indices. Explain the need for devising such indices.

16. Discuss the key features of a maintenance system with regard to (a) Input, (b) Constraints, (c) Output, (d) Decision variables, and (e) Performance criterion.

17. How does the breakdown distribution influence the choice between preventive and repair-maintenance policies?

18. How are maintenance activities differ from other normal production activities.

19. Identify major components of preventive and breakdown maintenance costs. Which components are most significant?

20. XYZ textile mill has kept a record of breakdowns on its carding machines for a 300-day work year as shown below:

Number of breakdowns	Frequency (in days)
0	40
1	150
2	90
3	50
4	20

The production engineer estimates that each breakdown costs Rs 1,600 and is considering to adopt a preventive maintenance programme that would cost Rs 500/day and limit the number of breakdowns to an average of one/day. What is the expected annual saving from the preventive maintenance programme?

21. A manufacture of plastic products operates 25 moulding machines which breakdown at random according to the distribution shown below:

Failure-free time (week):	1	2	3	4
Frequency of breakdowns:	0.10	0.20	0.35	0.35

The repair of a machine breakdown requires two engineers, whose salary is Rs 400/day? With the same engineers, preventive maintenance takes only 2 hours per machine. The cost of spares is Rs 1,200 per repair and Rs 300 for preventive maintenance per machine. Downtime costs are assumed to be negligible due to multiple assignments for the maintenance engineers.

(a) Determine the cost of a maintenance policy based on repairs only of breakdowns; and

(b) Evaluate the cost of an alternative preventive-maintenance policy.

22. A manufacturing firm uses a Rs 300/hr cost for direct and indirect labour maintenance and estimates downtime cost on any of a large group of machines at Rs 1,500/hr per machine. If breakdowns are distributed according to the Poisson distribution with a mean, $\lambda = 4$/hr and the mean (μ), number of units a worker can service is 6 breakdowns/hr-worker and distributed exponentially. What is the optimal maintenance crew size?

[Hint: The number of units in breakdown is the mean number in the system, $Ls = \dfrac{\lambda}{\mu - \lambda}$].

23. A copper refinery in the country has 50 floatation cells which can be serviced on a preventive maintenance schedule at Rs 3,000 each. If the cells breakdown, it costs Rs 15,000 to get them back into service (including unscheduled cleanout time and all breakdown cost). Records show that the probability of a breakdown after maintenance is as shown in the table below:

Months after maintenance:	1	2	3	4
Probability of breakdown:	0.3	0.2	0.4	0.1

Should a preventive maintenance policy be followed? If so, how often should the cells be serviced?

Materials Management

7.1 Introduction

Materials management integrates all activities of planning, scheduling and controlling of materials from design stage through production, including delivery to the customer. Therefore, it applies the function of planning, organising, integrating and measuring to the volume and flow of materials. Hence, it establishes a single responsibility over the material flow system with accountability of quality, delivery and cost. In an organization, material management requires constant balancing of interrelated objectives, which often need the sacrifice of one objective for achievement of another. For example, industries using scarce materials for the manufacture of some components and parts to be used in complex machines, availability in time dominates the cost factor. In aircraft and precision-instrument industries, consistency in quality and reliability is the sole criterion due to high complexity of end-products. In many other industries, inventory turnover may be the turning point because they stock not only thousands of spares and parts that go to make a complicated machine, but also keep them ready for after-sale customer service. Therefore, a balance between stockouts and the built-in-inventory is the single most objective of materials management.

7.2 Definition of Materials Management

The International Federation of Purchasing and Materials Management accepted the definition as 'a total concept involving an organizational structure unifying into a single responsibility for the systematic flow and control material from identification of the need through customer delivery'.

According to National Association of Purchasing Management, USA: 'an organizational concept in which a single manager has authority and responsibility of all activities concerned with the flow of materials into an organization'.

Another definition is 'management function primarily concerned with the acquisition, control, use of materials needed, flow of goods and services connected with production processes'.

7.3 Objectives and Functions of Materials Management

7.3.1 Objectives

Materials management objectives may be broadly divided into *three* categories:
- Primary objectives.
- Secondary objectives.
- Corporate objectives.

The primary objectives include purchasing, stores and inventory management, continuity of supply, quality of materials, good supplier relations, and departmental efficiency.

Secondary objectives help to achieve the primary objectives, but different organizations put different emphasis on them. Following are a few examples: make-or-buy decisions, value analysis and value engineering, standardization, product development and new product. demand and requirements forecasting.

Corporate objectives include achievement of organization's objectives and targets, actual performance figures, data and statistics, corrective action, if any, required on the basis of feedback.

The following are the main steps involved in achieving objectives of materials management:

1. Classification of items required in terms of both quality and quantity of each item.
2. Purchasing the items from a reliable source at economic rate.
3. Ensuring timely supply from suppliers.
4. Ensuring good storage facilities.
5. Ensuring scientific record-keeping and developing an effective control mechanism.
6. Controlling pilferages.
7. Ensuring proper distribution at the point of usage.
8. Employing only trained and efficient personnel in the material management department.
9. Ensuring good performance.

It has become important for the Materials Manager to make his own performance criteria based on the following parameters:

1. Inventory position.
2. Coverage of major items.
3. Status of non-moving inventory and its disposal action plan.
4. Defective/surplus inventory.
5. Ordering status.
6. Status on value engineering and cost reduction exercises.
7. Vendor development.
8. Purchase variation report from standard/estimated cost.
9. Stores documentation status.

7.3.2 Functions

Materials management functions, therefore, include planning, organising, staffing, directing, and controlling. It involves the formulation of an intelligent scheme of action designed to accomplish its objectives effectively and economically. Therefore, materials management is a function that every materials manager performs irrespective of his level or location in the organization.

Materials management has been established as a corporate profit centre. In view of increasing competition in the market, persistent pressure to be cost-effective and added force of hi-tech infusion, material contribution to corporate strategy is bound to go upwards. Therefore, key issues associated with organizing the material's functions are listed as below:

- Material planning, programming and budgeting.
- Purchasing and procurement.
- Receiving, inspection and warehousing.
- Inventory control.
- Store keeping.
- Value analysis and standardization.
- Material handling.
- Packaging, dispatching, shipping, disposal of scrap and surplus.

In order to coordinate these functions, liaison between various functionary units becomes significant. The importance is amply clear from the statement: *Right material of right quality at right price in the right quantity at the right time and place.*

7.4 Materials Requirement Planning and Manufacturing Resources Planning

7.4.1 Materials Requirement Planning (MRP)

According to American Production and Control Society, MRP constitutes a set of techniques that use bill of material, inventory data, and the master production schedule (MPS) to calculate requirement of materials. It is a computer–based system that takes MPS to explode into required amount of raw materials, parts, sub-assemblies, and assemblies needed in each of the planning horizon. Finally, it develops a schedule of order for purchased materials and produced parts over the planning horizon. For manufacturing, planning and control system, MRP has its core relationship with bill of materials and use of MRP records to calculate the time-phased release of orders. A well-defined structure of MRP is shown in Fig. 7.1.

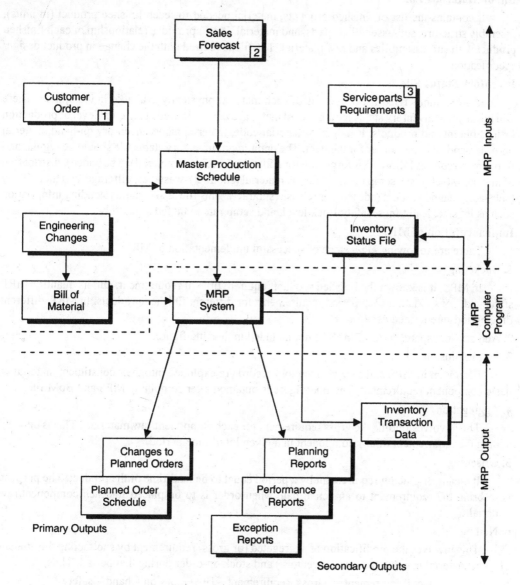

Fig. 7.1. MRP system

There are following three essential inputs to MRP:
- Master Production Schedule (MPS) and other order data
- Bill of materials (BoM) file defining the product structure
- Inventory status file.

Master Production Schedule

MPS is a list of items, indicating end products to be produced. It consists of item name and code, quantity to be produced, and time for completing the production. It is based on accurate estimation of product demand available from sales forecast for the given period. Also, realistic assessment of production capacity determines the possibility of production of the forecasted item.

Bill of Materials File

It contains the list of finished products, material needed for each finished product (in units), assembly structure, sub-assemblies, parts, and material. It also provides relationship of each finished product with sub-assemblies and raw material. The file is revised with the change in product design/specification.

Inventory Status File

It is a computerised list of records of each material physically available in the system. There will be only one inventory status for individual material even if it is used at different level of production or in different end products. It indicates material code, material name, inventory on-hand, material on-order, and customer order for the item. The updating of inventory status file should be regular and frequent. It requires following information for updating: Receipt of material (to be added), distribution of inventory (subtract), scrap reported for the material (subtract), wastages, pilferage, and theft, if any (subtract), planned orders (add), order release (subtract). This file also contains standing information such as lot size, lead times, safety stock level, and scrap rate to be fed separately.

Implementation of MRP

There are following *eight* steps of successful implementation of MRP:

1. Bucketing

In MPS, it is known the finished product required, time of requirement, and its quantity. MRP starts with consolidating each period requirements for different finished products. In MRP, different time periods are termed as *buckets*.

2. Add service (spare) parts in MPS, if not included in demand figure.

3. Part Explosion

Each item in MPS and service inventory record are exploded into their constituent material or basic component requirement. The final figure is obtained after combining MPS and BoM file.

4. Aggregation

This involves finding the gross requirement for each component/raw materials. This is done by adding the requirement of any component in a given lot of time period.

5. Offsetting

It means displacing requirement by a period equal to be lead-time of the product. The purpose is to bring the requirement to an actual date when order is to be placed for each component/raw material.

6. Netting

This involves the modification of aggregated (or gross) requirement by subtracting the amount of same material in stock (on-hand inventory) and stock on-order during that period. Thus,

$$\text{Net Requirement} = \text{Gross Requirement} - [\text{Inventory on} - \text{hand} - \text{safety}$$
$$\text{stock} - \text{Inventory allocated to other users}]$$

In case net requirement is positive, order for material must be placed in that period.

7. Procurement Schedule

This lead-time pertains to production process lead time, while lead time in step 4 was due to supplier lead time.

8. Lot sizing

This is used to consolidate the requirements in pre-specified lot sizes so that economic order quantity (EOQ) may be ordered. EOQ concept is applied to MRP output pertaining to the order-quantity for each time-period (bucket). This leads to lot-sizing.

There are following *five* outputs of MRP:

1. Planned Order Schedule

This contains the quantity of each material to be ordered in each time period. Suppliers may be given order for purchase as per this schedule. The production department uses this schedule to order parts, sub-assemblies, or assemblies from upstream production department. This schedule is used to determine the future production and supply at suppliers end along with guide for in-house production schedule.

2. Changes in Planned Orders

In this case, the order quantity may be changed, cancelled, delayed, or advanced. Changes may occur due to changes in MPS and changes in due date for open orders.

3. Exception Report

Exception reports are for orders requiring special attention of management. This may be for reporting errors, late orders, shortages, or excess scrap and wastages, etc.

4. Performance Report

This provides information related to performance of the system, e.g., inventory turnover ratio, delivery promises kept in percentage, stock-out index, etc.

5. Planning Report

This is used for future planning of inventory, e.g., purchase commitment reports, traces to demand sources (pegging), etc.

Benefits of MRP

MRP is helpful to know the effect of changes in future in production control department. After implementation, it is required to establish correct BoM and a cycle-count process to guarantee reliable inventory records. It triggers a process of self-study to improve BoM. Inventory tracking often leads to marking of non-value added activities. Other benefits of MRP are:

- Improvement of customer service
- Reduction in lead time
- Reduction in work-in-process
- Reduction in past-due orders
- Elimination of annual inventory
- Reduction in finished good inventory, raw material, components and parts, and safety stock
- Increase in productivity
- Better understanding of capacity constraints
- Increase of inventory turnover.

Drawbacks of MRP

Major drawbacks of MRP system are:
- Incorrectness in supplier's lead time
- Incorrectness in inventory data
  - Miscounting
  - Scrap not being accounted for
  - Items lost in transit.

- Inaccuracy in manufacturing lead time
  - Change in customer's demand
  - Change in workload of factory, causing changes in lead time of manufacturing: Busy factory causes more work-in-process and queue before operations, resulting in higher lead times. Less factory load may lead to quick processing on machine, i.e., shorter lead time. In case of incorrect lead time, resultant effect will be affected.
- Inaccuracy in BoM structure
  - Change in design
  - Implementation of component substitution without prior recording.

Any inaccuracy in computational intensive approach of MRP causes failure at MRP to a great extent.

7.4.2 Order Point System *vs.* MRP

In the order point inventory system, the time for replenishment order is triggered by an order-point-rule. For this purpose, inventory level is continuously monitored and as the inventory level falls below a certain level (called as reorder point), a replenishment order for a fixed quantity is issued. A comparison between MRP model and order point is given in Table 7.1

Table 7.1 Comparison between Order Point and MRP Model

Feature	MRP	Order Point
Demand	Dependent	Independent
Order philosophy	Requirement	Replenishment
Objectives	Meet manufacturing needs	Meet customer needs
Demand pattern	Lumpy and predictive	Random
Type of inventory	Work-in-process and raw material	Finished goods and spare parts
Forecast	Based on MPS	Based on past demand
Control concept	Control all items	ABC analysis
Lot sizing	Discrete	EOQ

7.4.3 Closed Loop MRP

The MRP system (open loop) so far discussed is static. Hence, problems with production machines, quality, labour, late delivery, etc. make the output of the MRP more or less irrelevant. Manual updating is not only difficult but also time-consuming. It is error-prone also.

Closed-loop MRP is designed to handle the problem of updating. It is done by interfacing the purchase and production activities control modules with MRP module. Dynamic updating of order-status is done by purchasing interface. After updating, new schedule is generated. Shop-floor interface updates MRP production status by collecting daily production and operator time-sheet data. These feedbacks to MRP constitute closed loop MRP.

7.4.4 Manufacturing Resources Planning (MRP II)

MRP and closed-loop MRP do not provide a link with other areas of business such as finance and marketing. For example, pricing decision, billing of suppliers, collection of payment from customers, change of new product design, etc., are not directly included. Inclusion of these causes overload on the system resulting to inefficient system. In recent past, an attempt has been made to have an integrated system encompassing business functions other than manufacturing. MRP II and enterprise resource planning are attempts in this direction. MRP II includes linking of financial and marketing functions to manufacturing function. MRP II system is shown in Fig. 7.2.

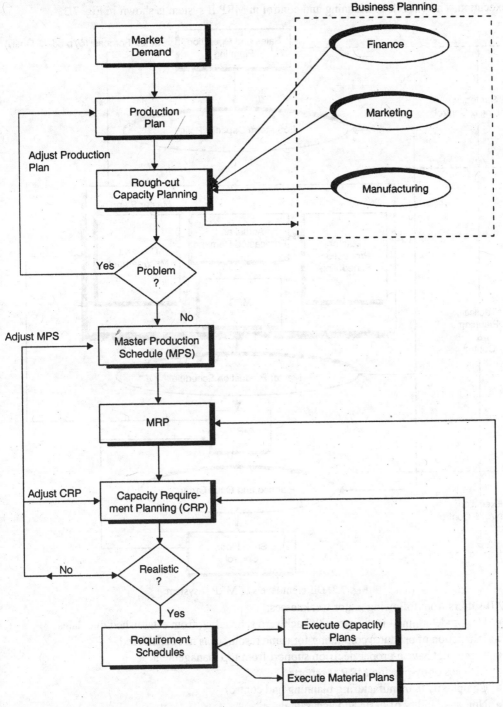

Fig. 7.2. MRP II system.

Benefits and Limitations of MRP II

Oliver Wight (1990) in his survey provided MRP II to achieve improved customer service (26%), improved productivity (20%), less purchase cost (13%), and higher inventory turnover (30%). MRP II contains 'what if' capabilities, and encompasses every facets of the business, from planning to execution. Three levels of planning and control in MRP II system is shown in Fig. 7.3.

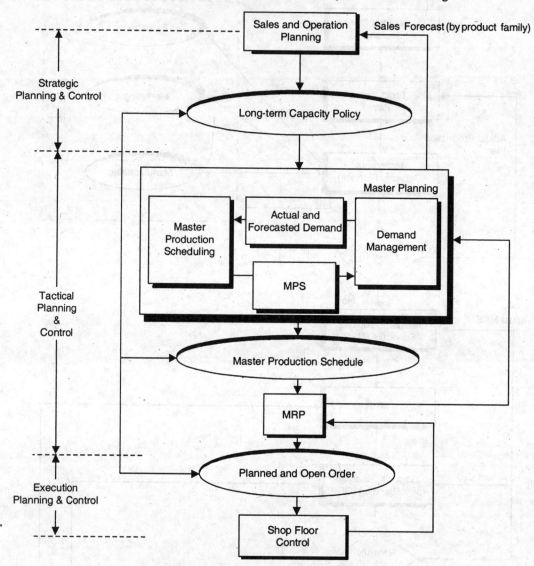

Fig. 7.3. Different levels of MRP II system

MRP II suffers from following major weaknesses:

- Use predetermined lead time with backward scheduling from established due dates.
- Interaction of products competing for same resources is not considered.
- It does not have a proper decision support from top management.
- Chances of by-passing MRP II reports.
- Complexity in manufacturing planning and control
- Non-availability of basic and accurate data.

7.5 Integrated Approach to Materials Management

A well coordinated and integrated approach is essential towards various problem areas involving decision-making with respect to materials. Important areas to improve efficiency on materials management are:

(a) Value analysis and purchase price analysis,

(b) Material handling,

(c) Inventory control,

(d) Stores management, and

(e) Waste management.

An integrated **approach** to materials management must look at all these problem areas in a coordinated manner with a view to maximize material planning effectiveness. Hence, these problem areas are discussed in the following sections in detail.

7.5.1 Value Analysis and Purchase Price Analysis

Value Analysis

Value analysis is defined as a systematic application of recognized techniques which identify the function of a product or service, establish a monetary value for that function, and provide the necessary function at the lowest overall cost. The objective of value analysis is to provide a means of total cost control anywhere within a product's life cycle. It stresses only the reduction or elimination of certain cost components.

Every product or service possesses two types of values—*aesthetic value* and *functional value*. A buyer, therefore, must determine first which value is more important to him in the product, he is purchasing. In industry, a large number of materials and components are purchased for their 'functional' value. A buyer is not generally interested in the 'aesthetic' value of the machine parts that are hidden from view. Attempts are made through value analysis, therefore, to determine how a specific 'function' can be performed effectively at the lowest total cost.

The techniques of value analysis are synonymous with the basic objective of good purchasing. Value analysis runs parallel to the activity involved in the inter-departmental development of material specifications. The major differences are in the depth of the analysis and in the timing. In most value analysis applications, management attempts to coordinate the talents of personnel in engineering, production and purchasing in conducting a meticulous investigation which usually leads to improvement of existing specifications.

The following two general approaches appear basic to the operation of a value analysis programme of a required material:

1. **Design analysis:** The analysis entails a systematic study of each phase of the design of a given product in relation to the function it performs. This approach, however, is not concerned with the appraisal of any given part of the product. Rather, it is concerned with the functional relationships of various parts to the performance of the complete unit or assemblage. The analysis of each part attempts to answer four specific questions:

   (a) Can any part be eliminated without impairing the operation of the complete unit?

   (b) Can the design of the part be simplified to reduce its basic cost?

   (c) Can the design of the part be changed to permit the use of simplified and cheaper production methods?

   (d) Can less expensive but equally satisfactory materials be used in the part?

   The approach to the problem of design analysis is highly creative and, therefore, differs from one analyst to another. The commonly used approaches which are used to stimulate and organize the analyst's efforts are:

   (i) The value analysis checklist;

   (ii) The functional cost approach;

   (iii) The use of brainstorming; and

   (iv) The use of suppliers.

2. **Cost analysis:** It involves a theoretical study of the total cost of producing a given product. Total cost involves the cost of materials, labour, manufacturing overheads and general overheads.

The selling price of the product is then normally decided by adding a reasonable profit margin to the theoretical total cost. The cost analysis plays two major roles:

(a) It is conducted for currently purchased items whose costs appear excessive. The information is useful in the process of further price negotiations with the supplier; and

(b) It becomes the means of identifying high-cost parts which should be subjected to design analysis. Few such high-cost parts are frequently isolated. Subsequent design analysis leads to specification changes and production modifications and ultimately to reduced costs.

Purchase Price Analysis

Price per unit of an item comprises the unit purchase price, transportation cost, handling cost, inspection, insurance, and the administrative variable cost. The right price simply means the lowest possible total price.

The typical approaches purchase price analysis comprise printed price lists, competitive bidding, and negotiations. Price lists printed by the suppliers give initial indication of the price. In competitive bidding, the requests for bids are sent to several suppliers. Usually the lowest bidder gets the order. Normal practice requires at least three competitive quotations wherever possible. Bids are normally secured when the size of an order exceeds a minimum amount.

Negotiation is the approach resorted to when time is too short, the number of bidders is small, the value of purchase is high, willingness to compete is lacking, or the specifications are too vague. In such circumstances, the buyer contacts the potential supplier and negotiates for a fair price and prompt delivery. Both advance planning and analysis are expected to bring about satisfactory results out of price negotiations.

While determining the price, shipping terms should also be clarified. Further, purchase contracts can be fixed price (quite common), cost plus (no definite limit to costs) or blanket order (for six months or one year) type.

An important aspect of price analysis involves discounts that can be secured. The following types of discounts are common:

(a) **Trade discount:** To protect certain distribution channels when it is economical to buy from the distributor than the manufacturer.

(b) **Quantity discount:** For purchases worth beyond a certain amount of money.

(c) **Seasonal discount:** For purchases in the off-season period.

(d) **Cash discount:** For prompt and full payment.

7.5.2 Material Handling

Whilst performing the activities of material handling, the basic aim is to minimize the production costs. This general objective can be further sub-divided into specific objectives as follows:

(a) To reduce costs by decreasing inventories, minimizing the distance to be handled and increasing productivity;

(b) To increase the production capacity by smoothening the work flow;

(c) To minimize waste during handling;

(d) To improve distribution through better location of facilities and improved routing;

(e) To Increase the equipment and space utilization;

(f) To improve working conditions; and

(g) To improve the customer service.

The different material handling systems can be classified according to the type of equipment used, material handled, method used or the function performed.

Equipment-oriented systems: Depending upon the type of equipment used, there are several systems:

(a) Overhead systems,

(b) Conveyor systems,

(c) Tractor-trailor systems,

(d) Fork-lift truck and pallet systems,

(e) Industrial truck systems, and

(d) Underground systems.

Method-oriented systems: According to the method of handling and the method of production, the material handling systems can be:

(a) Manual systems,

(b) Mechanized or automated systems,

(c) Job-shop handling systems, or

(d) Mass-production handling systems.

Function-oriented systems: The system can be defined according to the material handling function performed as follows:

(a) Transportation systems,

(b) Conveying systems,

(c) Transferring systems, and

(d) Elevating systems.

In essence, material handling is the art and science involving the movement, packaging and storing of substances in any form.

7.5.3 Inventory Control

Inventory control aims at usable but idle resources having economic value. Scientific inventory management is an extremely important problem area in the material management function. Inventory management is highly amenable to control. In Indian industries, there is substantial potential for cost reduction through inventory control.

7.5.4 Inventory Control Models

Inventory models can be classified according to the following factors:

Inventory-related Costs (Economic Parameters)

Four types of inventory costs are associated with keeping inventories of items:

1. Purchase (production) cost.

2. Ordering (set-up) cost.

3. Carrying (holding) cost.

4. Shortage (stockout) cost.

1. **Purchase cost:** The cost of purchasing (or producing) a unit of an item is known as the purchase (production) cost. If the cost per unit of the item is constant irrespective of quantities ordered, the total cost of items purchased during planning horizon is constant. It is taken into consideration when quantity discounts/price breaks can be secured for purchases above a certain quantity or when economies of scale suggest that the per unit production cost can be reduced by larger production runs.

2. **Ordering (set-up) cost:** This cost varies directly with each purchase order placed and includes administrative cost (paper work, telephone calls, postage, etc.), cost incurred on transportation of items ordered, receipt and inspection of goods, processing payments, etc.

3. **Carrying (holding) cost:** It consists of costs incurred due to money invested in inventory, storage cost, insurance, losses due to pilferage, spoilage or breakage, security, depreciation, taxes, etc. Therefore, the total carrying cost may be expressed as follows:

$$\text{Carrying cost} = I \times P$$

where I is the average amount of inventory held per unit time as a percentage of average rupee value of inventory, and P, the price (value) of holding one unit per unit time.

4. **Shortage (stockout) cost:** This cost includes the loss of potential profit that otherwise would have accrued through sales of items demanded, loss of goodwill, and permanent loss of customers and associated loss of profit through future sales.

The inventory model showing the relationship of inventory costs with order quantity and inventory level over time is shown in Fig. 7.4.

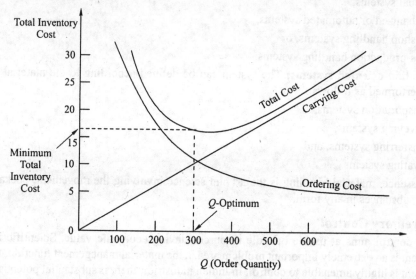

Fig. 7.4   Economic order quantity graph

Demand

Size of demand, rate of demand and pattern of demand for a given item are important for determination of an optional inventory policy. The size of demand is the number of items required for a specific period. It can be either deterministic or probabilistic. The rate of demand is the size of demand over a particular unit of time. It can be variable or constant, deterministic or probabilistic, depending on the size of the demand. Similarly, the pattern of demand is the manner in which items are drawn from inventory. The pattern of demand affects the total carrying cost of inventory.

Order Cycle

The time period between placement of two successive orders is referred to as an *order cycle*. The order may be placed on the basis of (*a*) continuous review, and (*b*) periodic review.

Time Horizon

The period over which the inventory level will be controlled is referred to as time horizon.

Lead Time

The time between ordering a replenishment of an item and actually receiving the item into inventory is referred to as lead time. The *lead time* can be either deterministic, constant or variable, or probabilistic.

Stock Replenishment

The replenishment of items (stock) may occur at a uniform rate over time or occur instantaneously. Uniform replacement generally occurs when the item is manufactured within the factory whereas instantaneous replacement occurs when the items are purchased from outside sources.

Reorder Level

The level between maximum and minimum stock levels at which purchasing/manufacturing activities must initiate actions for replenishment.

Reorder Quantity

This is the quantity of replacement order. In certain cases, it is the economic order quantity.

The total annual inventory cost equation can be expressed as:

$$TC = \text{Cost of items} + \text{Ordering cost} + \text{Carrying cost} + \text{Shortage cost}.$$

7.5.5 Basic Deterministic Inventory Models

Four different types of inventory models are considered, beginning with the basic economic order quantity model. The other three models reflect little changes in basic assumptions of the initial model.

Model 1: Economic Order Quantity with Uniform Demand

The aim of this model is to determine an optimum order quantity (EOQ) so that the total inventory cost is minimized. The inventory situation is characterized as:

(*i*) Annual demand is constant,

(*ii*) No stockouts are allowed,

(*iii*) Lead time is zero and independent of demand, and

(*iv*) Cost per unit is constant.

The inventory costs are determined as follows:

(*a*) Ordering cost = Total annual demand/quantity ordered each time

× Ordering cost per order

$$= \frac{D}{Q} \times C_0$$

Here D = annual demand and is constant; Q = order quantity (replenishment size); and C_0 = unit cost of ordering which is known and constant.

(*b*) Carrying cost = Average units in inventory × Carrying cost per unit

$$= \frac{Q}{2} \times C_h$$

Here C_h = unit cost of carrying inventory which is known and constant.

Now, the total cost is minimum at a point where ordering cost equals carrying cost (Fig. 7.1). Thus,

$$\frac{D}{Q} \times C_0 = \frac{Q}{2} C_h$$

or

$$Q^2 = \frac{2DC_0}{C_h}$$

Therefore, optimum order quantity, Q^*, is

$$Q^* = \sqrt{\frac{2DC_0}{C_h}}$$

This expression is widely known as the *Wilson lot size formula.*

Characteristics of Model 1

1. Optimum number of orders placed annually

$$N^* = \frac{\text{Annual demand}}{\text{Optimal order quantity}} = \frac{D}{Q^*}$$

$$= D \Big/ \sqrt{\frac{2DC_0}{C_h}} = \sqrt{\frac{DC_h}{2C_0}}$$

2. Optimum length of time between orders

$$T^* = \frac{\text{Total time horizon}}{\text{Optimal number of orders per year}} = \frac{T}{N^*}$$

$$= T \Big/ \sqrt{\frac{DC_h}{2C_0}} = \sqrt{\frac{2C_0 T^2}{DC_h}}.$$

3. Minimum total annual inventory cost

$$TC^* = \frac{D}{Q^*} C_0 + \frac{Q^*}{2} C_h$$

$$= DC_0 \Big/ \sqrt{\frac{2DC_0}{C_h}} + \frac{C_h}{2} \Big/ \sqrt{\frac{2DC_0}{C_h}}$$

$$= \sqrt{2DC_0 C_h}.$$

Model 2: Economic Order Quantity with Different Rates of Demand in Different Cycles

In this case, the total demand D is specified during time horizon T. Thus, the inventory costs are as follows

$$\text{Ordering costs} = \frac{D}{Q} C_0$$

$$\text{Carrying costs} = \frac{Q}{2} C_h T$$

Total inventory cost is the sum of the ordering and carrying costs, that is,

$$TC = \frac{D}{Q} C_0 + \frac{Q}{2} C_h T$$

For optimum order quantity, ordering costs and carrying costs are equal. Thus,

$$\frac{D}{Q} C_0 = \frac{Q}{2} C_h T$$

Therefore, optimum order quantity is expressed as

$$Q^* = \sqrt{\frac{2DC_0}{TC_h}}$$

The minimum total annual inventory cost

$$TC^* = DC_0 \Big/ \sqrt{\frac{2DC_0}{TC_h}} + \frac{1}{2} TC_h \Big/ \sqrt{\frac{2DC_0}{TC_h}}$$

$$= \sqrt{\frac{2DC_0 C_h}{T}}.$$

Limitations of EOQ Model

1. Demand is assumed to be uniform and known with certainty. In actual practice, the demand is neither uniform nor known with certainty. When the fluctuations are more, this model loses its validity.

2. Ordering is not linearly related to the number of orders. As the number of orders increases, the ordering cost rises in a stepped manner.

3. Ordering cost may not be independent of the order quantity.

4. Instantaneous supply of inventory is not possible when inventory level touches zero.

5. The formula is not applicable when inventory cost is meaningless.

6. It is cumbersome to calculate inventory carrying cost for B and C class of items.

Example 7.1. There is a contract to supply 1000 items in a month at a uniform rate and each time a production run once started will cost Rs 200. The cost of storing an item per month is Rs 20. The number of items to be produced per run has to be ascertained. Find the total amount of set-up cost and average inventory cost if the run size is 500, 600, 700 or 800. Also, comment on the result. Using the 'economic order quantity' formula, also find the optimum production run size.

Solution. From the given data,

$$\text{Monthly demand } (D) = 1,000 \text{ items}$$
$$\text{Cost per set-up } (C_0) = \text{Rs } 200$$
$$\text{Carrying cost } (C_h) = \text{Rs } 20/\text{item/month}$$

Now, it is possible to calculate the total of set-up cost and average inventory cost for different batch sizes (Table 7.1).

Table 7.1 Total of Set-up Cost and Average Inventory Cost for Different Batch Sizes

Batch Size	Set-up Cost	Average Inventory Cost	Total Cost
500	$\dfrac{1000}{500} \times 200 = 400$	$\dfrac{500}{2} \times 20 = 5000$	5,400
600	$\dfrac{1000}{600} \times 200 = 333.33$	$\dfrac{600}{2} \times 20 = 6000$	6,333.33
700	$\dfrac{1000}{700} \times 200 = 285.71$	$\dfrac{700}{2} \times 20 = 7000$	7,285.71
800	$\dfrac{1000}{800} \times 200 = 250$	$\dfrac{800}{2} \times 20 = 8000$	8,250

It can be observed from the Table 7.1 that as the batch size increases, the total **cost increases**. Now, using the EOQ formula, the optimum run size can be calculated as follows:

$$Q^* = \sqrt{\frac{2DC_0}{C_h}} = \sqrt{\frac{2 \times 1,000 \times 200}{20}}$$

$$= \sqrt{20000} = 141 \text{ units (approx).}$$

Example 7.2. A company buys in lots of 500 boxes which is a three-monthly supply. The cost of a box is Rs 125.00 and the ordering cost is Rs 150.00. The inventory carrying cost is estimated at 20 per cent of the unit value. Find (a) the total annual cost of existing inventory policy, and (b) how much money would be saved by employing the economic order quantity?

Solution. From the given data:

$$\text{Ordering cost per-order, } C_0 = \text{Rs } 150$$
$$\text{Number of units per order, } Q = 500$$
$$\text{Annual demand, } D = 500 \times 4 = 2,000$$
$$\text{Carrying cost, } C_h = 125 \times 0.20 = \text{Rs } 25$$

(a) Total annual cost of the existing inventory policy is given by

$$TC = \frac{D}{Q}C_0 + \frac{Q}{2}C_h$$

$$= \frac{2,000}{500} \times 150 + \frac{500}{2} \times 25$$

$$= 600 + 6,250 = \text{Rs } 6,850.$$

(b) $$EOQ\,(Q^*) = \sqrt{\frac{2DC_0}{C_h}}$$

$$= \sqrt{\frac{2 \times 2,000 \times 150}{25}}$$

$$= \sqrt{24,000} = 155 \text{ (approx)}$$

and the corresponding minimum annual cost is

$$TC^* = \sqrt{2DC_0\,C_h}$$

$$= \sqrt{2 \times 2,000 \times 150 \times 25} = \text{Rs } 3,873 \text{ (approx)}.$$

Therefore, by employing the economic order quantity, the company can save
Rs $(6,850 - 3,873) = \text{Rs } 2,977$.

Example 7.3. A consumer product company purchases raw materials from an outside supplier to meet its annual requirement. During the coming year, the company wishes to manufacture 1,00,000 units of its product at a constant rate. The cost of placing each order is Rs 160. For any item in inventory, the company uses an annual carrying cost equal to 20 per cent of the item's cost. The product costs Rs 20 each. Find (a) the optimum order size, (b) the total inventory cost, and (c) no. of orders to be placed during the next year. If the company decides to order for raw materials only twice a month, how much cost penalty would it suffer, in per cent. If an ordering cost of only Rs 80 had been used instead of the correct value of Rs 160, determine (i) the new order size, and (ii) how would the total cost have changed?

Solution. From the given data

$$C_0 = \text{Rs } 160$$

$$C_h = \frac{20}{100} \times 20 = \text{Rs } 4/\text{unit/year}$$

$$D = 1,00,000 \text{ units/year. Now,}$$

(a) $$Q^* = \sqrt{\frac{2DC_0}{C_h}} = \sqrt{\frac{2 \times 1,00,000 \times 160}{4}}$$

$$= \sqrt{8,000,000} = 2,828 \text{ units/order.}$$

(b) $$TC^* = \sqrt{2DC_0\,C_h} = \sqrt{2 \times 1,00,000 \times 160 \times 4}$$

$$= \text{Rs } 11,312 \text{ per year.}$$

(c) Number of orders, $$N = \frac{D}{Q^*} = \frac{1,00,000}{2,828}$$

$$= 35 \text{ orders per year.}$$

For two orders per month, the number of units per order will be

$$Q' = \frac{1,00,000 \text{ units/year}}{24 \text{ orders/year}}$$

$$= 4,167 \text{ units/order}$$

Using the equation of total inventory cost,

$$TC' = \frac{D}{Q'}\,C_0 + \frac{Q'}{2}\,C_h$$

$$= \frac{1,00,000}{4,167} \times 160 + \frac{4,167}{2} \times 4$$

$$= 3,839.69 + 8,334 = \text{Rs } 12,173.69$$

Penalty cost $= (12,173.69 - 11,312)/11,312 = 0.076 = 7.6\%$

For ordering cost of Rs 80, suppose the new optimum value of Q is Q^{**}. Then

$$Q^{**} = \sqrt{\frac{2DC_0}{C_h}} = \sqrt{\frac{2 \times 1,00,000 \times 80}{4}}$$

$$= \sqrt{4,000,000}$$

$$= 2,000 \text{ units/order}$$

The new total minimum inventory cost is

$$TC^{**} = \frac{D}{Q^{**}} C_0 + \frac{Q^{**}}{2} C_h$$

$$= \frac{1,00,000}{2,000} \times 160 + \frac{2,000}{2} \times 4$$

$$= \text{Rs } 12,000$$

Thus, the net change in the total minimum inventory cost is: Rs $(12,000 - 11,312) = $ Rs 688.

Model 3: Economic Order Quantity When Shortages (Back Orders) are Allowed

The assumptions of this model are same as model 1, except that shortages are allowed and may occur regularly. The cost of a shortage is assumed to be directly proportional to the mean number of units short. It is required to determine the optimum order quantity and the suitable time of replenishment of inventory.

Optimal values of economic order quantity (Q) and maximum inventory level $M = (Q - S)$ are obtained as follows:

$$Q^* = \sqrt{\left(\frac{2DC_0}{C_h}\right)\left(\frac{C_h + C_s}{C_s}\right)}$$

and

$$M^* = \sqrt{\left(\frac{2DC_0}{C_h}\right)\left(\frac{C_s}{C_h + C_s}\right)}$$

Here S is the maximum shortage per order (back order quantity).

Characteristics of Model 3

1. Time between receipt of orders (when to order)

$$t^* = \frac{Q^*}{D} = \sqrt{\left(\frac{2C_0}{DC_h}\right)\left(\frac{C_s + C_h}{C_s}\right)}.$$

2. The total optimum inventory cost

$$TC^* = \sqrt{2DC_0 C_h \left(\frac{C_s}{C_s + C_h}\right)}.$$

3. Reorder level $R = Q^* - M^*$

$$= Q^*\left(1 - \frac{C_s}{C_s + C_h}\right).$$

Example 7.4. A contractor has to supply diesel engines to a truck manufacturer at a rate of 20 engines/day. The penalty in the contract is Rs 100/engine/day for missing the scheduled delivery date. The cost of holding an engine in stock for one month is Rs 150. The production process is such that each month (30 days) he starts procuring a batch of engines through the agencies and all engines are available for supply after the end of the month. Determine the maximum inventory level at the beginning of each month.

Solution. From the given data,

Carrying cost, C_h = Rs 150/30 per engine/day
Shortage cost, C_s = Rs 100/day/engine
Demand, D = 20 engines/day

The maximum inventory level M^* at the beginning of each month will be

$$M^* = \frac{C_s}{C_h + C_s} Q^*$$

$$= \frac{C_s}{C_h + C_s} D \times t$$

$$= \frac{100}{5 + 100} \times 20 \times 30 = \frac{100}{105} \times 600$$

$$= 571 \text{ engines (approx).}$$

Example 7.5. The demand of an item is uniform at a rate of 25 units/month. The fixed cost is Rs 30 each time a production is made. The production cost is Rs 2 per item and the inventory carrying cost is 50 paise per unit per month. If the shortage cost is Rs 3 per item per month, determine how often a production run is to be made and of what size?

Solution. From the given data,

Monthly demand, D = 25 units
Carrying cost, C_h = Rs 0.50/item/month
Shortage cost, C_s = Rs 3/item/month
Production cost   = Rs 2/item
Production set-up cost   = Rs 30/set-up.

(*a*) The optimum *EOQ* (Q^*) is given by

$$EOQ\,(Q^*) = \sqrt{\left(\frac{2DC_0}{C_h}\right)\left(\frac{C_h + C_s}{C_s}\right)}$$

$$= \sqrt{\left(\frac{2 \times 25 \times 30}{0.50}\right)\left(\frac{3 + 0.50}{3}\right)}$$

$$= 10\sqrt{35} = 60 \text{ units (approx.)}$$

(*b*) Optimum time (t^*) between two consecutive runs

$$t^* = Q^*/D = 60/25 = 2.4 \text{ months.}$$

Example 7.6. A manufacturer has to supply his customer 24,000 units of his product every year. This demand is fixed and known. Since the unit is used by the customer in an assembly-operation and the customer has no storage space for units, the manufacturer when fails to supply the required units the shortage cost is Rs 2 per unit per month. The inventory carrying cost is Re 1 per unit per month and the set-up cost per run is Rs 3500. Determine (*a*) the optimum run size (Q); (*b*) the optimum level of inventory (M) at the beginning of any period; (*c*) the optimum scheduling period; and (*d*) the minimum total expected annual cost.

Solution. From the given data,

Annual demand, D = 24,000
                        = 2,000 units/month
Production set-up cost, C_0 = Rs 3,500 per run

Carrying cost, C_h = Re 1.00 per month

Shortage cost, C_s = Rs 2 per unit per month.

(a) Optimum run size, Q^*

$$= \sqrt{\left(\frac{2DC_0}{C_h}\right)\left(\frac{C_h + C_s}{C_s}\right)}$$

$$= \sqrt{\left(\frac{2 \times 2,000 \times 3,500}{1}\right)\left(\frac{1+2}{2}\right)} = 4584 \text{ units/run.}$$

(b) Optimum level of inventory at the beginning,

$$M^* = Q^*\left(\frac{C_s}{C_h + C_s}\right)$$

$$= 4584\left(\frac{2}{1+2}\right) = 4584 \times \frac{2}{3}$$

$$= 3,056 \text{ units.}$$

(c) Optimum scheduling period (reorder cycle),

$$T^* = \frac{Q^*}{D} = \frac{4,584}{2,000} = 2.24 \text{ months.}$$

(d) Minimum total expected yearly cost,

$$TC^* = \sqrt{(2DC_0\ C_h)\left(\frac{C_s}{C_h + C_s}\right)}$$

$$= \sqrt{(2 \times 2,000 \times 3,500 \times 1)\left(\frac{2}{1+2}\right)}$$

$$= \text{Rs 3,000 (approx.)}$$

Model 4: Economic Order Quantity with Uniform Replenishment

In the earlier models, cases have been dealt with where the entire order was received just as the inventory was out of stock. In a production situation, the production run may take a significant time to complete. At the end of the production run, the inventory would have built up to a pre-determined maximum level.

The aim of this model is to determine the optimal production lot size Q^*. For this model, it is assumed that (a) production begins immediately after the production set-up, and (b) production ends when lot size of production run is reached.

If Q is the number of units produced per order cycle, then the time of a production run is simply the number of units, or lot size, divided by the rate of production, i.e.,

$$t_p = \frac{Q}{r_p} \tag{1}$$

Here t_p = length of production run/production period and r_p = production rate.

Since the inventory is building up at the rate $(r_p - r_d)$, the quantity in inventory at the end of the run, which is the maximum inventory level, is given by

$$\text{Maximum inventory level} = t_p\ (r_p - r_d) \tag{2}$$

Here r_d is the demand rate in units per time period.

The minimum inventory level is zero. Therefore, the average inventory will be as follows:

$$\text{Average inventory} = \frac{t_p}{2}\ (r_p - r_d) \tag{3}$$

Using (1) – (3), average inventory $= \dfrac{Q}{2r_p}\ (r_p - r_d)$

$$= \frac{Q}{2}\left(1 - \frac{r_d}{r_p}\right)$$

In this case, set-up costs are analogous to ordering costs, given by the number of set-ups times the set-up cost per production run, i.e.,

$$\text{Set-up cost} = \frac{D}{Q}C_0 \tag{4}$$

Here D is the demand for inventory remains constant and uniform over a period of time.

Carrying cost is the cost per unit of average inventory times the average inventory level and is given by

$$\text{Carrying cost} = \frac{Q}{2}\left(1 - \frac{r_d}{r_p}\right)C_h \tag{5}$$

Combining (4) and (5), a total annual inventory cost is obtained, i.e.,

$$TC = \frac{D}{Q}C_0 + \frac{Q}{2}\left(1 - \frac{r_d}{r_p}\right)C_h \tag{6}$$

Here C_h and C_0 are known and constant.

Since set-up costs are decreasing and carrying costs are increasing as production quantity increases, a minimal total cost occurs when these two costs are equal. Therefore, equating (4) and (5),

$$\frac{D}{Q}C_0 = \frac{Q}{2}\left(1 - \frac{r_d}{r_p}\right)C_h$$

or

$$Q^2 = \frac{2DC_0}{C_h}\left(\frac{r_p}{r_p - r_d}\right)$$

or

$$Q^* = \sqrt{\frac{2DC_0}{C_h}\left(\frac{r_p}{r_p - r_d}\right)}. \tag{7}$$

Characteristics of Model 4

1. Optimum number of production runs per year

$$N^* = \frac{D}{Q^*}$$

$$= D \Big/ \sqrt{\frac{2DC_0}{C_h}\left(\frac{r_p}{r_p - r_d}\right)}$$

$$= \sqrt{\frac{DC_h(r_p - r_d)}{2C_0 r_p}}.$$

2. Length of each lot size production run

$$t_p = Q^*/r_p$$

$$= \sqrt{\frac{2DC_0}{C_h}\left(\frac{r_p}{r_p - r_d}\right)} \Big/ r_p$$

$$= \sqrt{\frac{2DC_0}{C_h r_p(r_p - r_d)}}.$$

3. The total minimum production inventory cost

$$TC^* = \frac{D}{Q^*} C_0 + \frac{Q^*}{2}\left(1 - \frac{r_d}{r_p}\right) C_h$$

$$= 2DC_0 \Bigg/ \sqrt{\frac{2DC_0}{C_h}\left(\frac{r_p}{r_p - r_d}\right)} + \frac{1}{2}\left(1 - \frac{r_d}{r_p}\right) C_h \sqrt{\frac{2DC_0}{C_h}\left(\frac{r_p}{r_p - r_d}\right)}$$

$$= \sqrt{2DC_0 \, C_h \left(1 - \frac{r_d}{r_p}\right)}.$$

Example 7.7. A tyre producer makes 1,200 tyres/day and sells them at approximately half of that rate. Accounting figures show that the production set-up cost is Rs 1000 and the carrying cost/unit is Rs 5. If annual demand is 1,20,000 tyres, determine (a) the optimal lot size, and (b) the number of production runs required to be scheduled per year?

Solution: From the given data,

Annual demand, D = 1,20,000 tyres
Carrying cost, C_h = Rs 5 per unit
Set-up cost, C_0 = Rs 1,000 per order
Production rate, r_p = 1,200 tyres/day
Demand rate, r_d = 600 tyres/day.

(a) Optimum run size,

$$Q^* = \sqrt{\frac{2DC_0}{C_h}\left(\frac{r_p}{r_p - r_d}\right)}$$

$$= \sqrt{\frac{2 \times 1,20,000 \times 1,000 \times 1,200}{5 \,(1,200 - 600)}}$$

$$= 9,798 \text{ tyres (approx.)}$$

(b) Optimum production runs (N^*) per year is

$$N^* = \frac{D}{Q^*} = \frac{1,20,000}{9,798}$$

$$= 13 \text{ runs/year (approx.)}$$

Example 7.8. A contractor has to supply 10,000 paper cones per day to a textile unit. He finds that when he starts a production run he can produce 25,000 paper cones per day. The cost of holding a paper cone in stock for one year is 2 paise and the set-up cost of a production run is Rs 18. How frequently should a production run be made?

Solution. From the given data,

Demand per day, D = 10,000 paper cones
Carrying cost, C_h = Re 0.02 per paper cone per year

$$= \text{Rs}\left(\frac{0.02}{365}\right) = \text{Rs } 0.000055 \text{ per paper cone per day}$$

Production set-up cost, C_0 = Rs 18
Production rate, r_p = 25,000 paper cones per day
Demand rate, r_d = 10,000 paper cones per day.

(a) Optimum number of units to be produced

$$Q^* = \sqrt{\frac{2DC_0}{C_h}\left(\frac{r_p}{r_p - r_d}\right)}$$

$$= \sqrt{\left(\frac{2 \times 10,000 \times 18}{0.000055}\right)\left(\frac{25,000}{25,000 - 10,000}\right)}$$

$$= 1,04,447 \text{ paper cones (approx.)}$$

(b) Length of each lot size production run

$$t_p{}^* = \frac{Q^*}{r_p} = \frac{1,04,447}{25,000} = 4 \text{ days (approx.)}$$

Example 7.9. The annual demand for a product is 1,00,000 units. The rate of production is 2,00,000 units per year. The set-up cost per production run is Rs 500 and the variable production cost of each item is Rs 10. The annual holding cost per unit is 20 per cent of its value. Find the optimum production lot size and length of the production run.

    Solution. From the given data,

Annual demand, D	$= 1,00,000$ units
Rate of production, r_p	$= 2,00,000$ units per year
Set-up cost, C_0	$=$ Rs 500 per production run
Variable cost of each item, C	$=$ Rs 10
Carrying cost, C_h	$= 20$ per cent of Rs 20 or Rs 2 per unit

    (a) Optimum production lot size is given by

$$Q^* = \sqrt{\frac{2DC_0}{C_h}\left(\frac{r_p}{r_p - r_d}\right)}$$

$$= \sqrt{\left(\frac{2 \times 1,00,000 \times 500}{2}\right)\left(\frac{2,00,000}{2,00,000 - 1,00,000}\right)}$$

$$= 10,000 \text{ units.}$$

    (b) Length of the production run

$$t_p = \frac{Q^*}{r_p} = \frac{10,000}{2,00,000}$$

$$= 0.05.$$

7.5.6 Inventory Control Systems

Any system of inventory control should be able to answer the following two basic questions:

    1. How much to reorder?

    2. When to reorder?

    A number of inventory models have been discussed where demand and lead time were known with certainty and were relatively constant. It is a common practice to wait for the order already placed. Thus, on the basis of a known rate of demand and a constant lead time, inventory should be reordered as soon as the inventory quantity equals the amount that will be used during the reorder period.

    If the rate of demand/usage of an item or the lead time of an item or both change unexpectedly, inventory levels may get depleted more rapidly than expected. This leads to the occurrence of shortage. The shortage can be avoided only by raising the reorder level, which is equivalent to maintaining a positive minimum inventory level or safety or buffer stock.

Reorder Level

Reorder level may be defined as the level of inventory at which an order for replenishment quantity is placed with the suppliers for procuring additional inventory equal to EOQ. When the demand for an item is known, the reorder level is set equal to that demand. In practice, when the demand is stochastic in nature, it will not be possible to predict the exact demand during the lead time period. Thus, the reorder level (R) in case the rate of demand is known with certainty is calculated as follows:

Reorder Level = Amount of inventory used during lead time in units

or $\qquad$ ROL $= D \times LT$

Here D = rate of demand for inventory during lead time in units and LT = lead time.

In the deterministic situation, when the inventory level drops to a predetermined level, called *reorder level*, an order for fixed quantity is placed. However, in order to avoid stockout, a minimum inventory level as safety stock is maintained. In this case, the reorder level is determined as follows:

Reorder Level = Safety stock + Rate of demand × Lead time

or $\qquad$ ROL $= B + DL$.

Safety (Buffer) Stock

In order to absorb variability, especially in demand and lead time, the inventory management depends upon safety stock. The greater the safety stock maintained, the less is the risk of stockouts. However, such an increase in safety stock raises the carrying cost. Thus, the objective of main stock is to balance the extra carrying cost resulting from safety stock and the expected co

One simple method for determining safety stock is as follows:

Safety stock = (Max. lead time − Normal lead time) × (Demand rate during lead time)

For example, if the demand rate is 200 units/month, the normal and maximum lead time being 15 days and 2 months, respectively. Then the safety stock would be:

$$\text{Safety stock} = \left(2 - \frac{15}{30}\right) \times 200$$

$$= 300 \text{ units}$$

Furthermore, the level of safety stock depends on the extent an organization is prepared to accept stockout risk (SOR). Since it is difficult to obtain an accurate estimate for the shortage (or stockout) cost, the management must specify reasonable *service level* (SL) so as to determine the safety stock necessary to keep the SOR within prescribed limits.

The service level is the probability of not running out of stock on any stock cycle, i.e., per cent of the order cycle in which all the demands can be supplied from stock:

Service level (SL) = 100% − SOR

The determination of the required safety stock to support a given service depends on the type of the inventory control system, i.e., whether orders are placed at fixed intervals or in fixed amounts.

We now derive a moderately complex, quantity/reorder level model in which lead time does not vary but demand does with normal probability distribution. Let $\overline{D}$ be the expected demand during lead time LT and σ_D, the standard deviation of expected demand, respectively. The safety stock is the protection for the service level (SL = 1 − probability of being out of stock) specified, $Z\sigma_D$ units. Safety stock is Z with standard deviation of protection for a given variability of demand during lead time. Thus, reorder level in this situation will become

$$\text{ROL} = \overline{D} \times \text{LT} + Z\sigma_D$$

The variance of demand during lead time is as follows:

$$\sigma_D^2 = \sum_{i=1}^{n} \sigma_i^2$$

For example, let us assume that daily demand for an item is normally distributed with a mean of 50 units and a standard deviation of 5. A 95 per cent service level is desired for customers who place orders during the reorder period. Then

$$\text{ROL} = \overline{D} \times \text{LT} + Z\sigma_D$$

$$= 50 \times 6 + 1.645\sigma_D \text{ [0.95 confidence level gives, } Z = 1.645; \text{ LT} = 6]$$

$$\sigma_D^2 = \sum_{i=1}^{n} \sigma_i^2 = 6\,(5)^2$$

or
$$\sigma_D = \sqrt{6\,(5)^2} = 12.2$$

Therefore,
$$\text{ROL} = 50\,(6) + 1.645\,(12.2)$$
$$= 300 + 20 = 320 \text{ units}$$

In case both demand and lead time vary with normal probability distribution, the reorder level is determined as follows:

$$\text{ROL} = \bar{D} \times \overline{\text{LT}} + Z\sigma_D \sqrt{\text{LT}}$$

where Z = number of standard deviations required to give the desired service level.

Method of Setting Safety Stock

Once *SOR* is fixed, a cumulative distribution of demand can be formulated and the maximum demand for a given *SOR* can be obtained directly from the cumulative distribution. Then

Safety stock = Maximum demand during lead time for a given
service level – (Average demand during lead time)

or
$$B = D_{max} \text{ LT} - D \text{ LT}$$
$$= (D_{max} - D)\text{ LT}$$

where D_{max} = maximum demand rate per unit time.

With the variations in demand, the lead time uncertainty can be handled by developing cumulative frequency distributions showing the relative occurrence of different lead times for a given inventory item. Then

Safety stock = (Lead time *SOR* for a given service level) – (Average lead time)

or
$$B = L_{SOR} - L$$

There are mainly two types of inventory control systems:

1. Fixed order quantity system.
2. Periodic review system.

Fixed Order Quantity System

In this system, also called *Perpetual Inventory System* or *Reorder Inventory System* or *Q-system*, the count of the number of units in inventory is continuously maintained. With lead time less than the reorder cycle ($L < t$), an order for a fixed quantity, Q, is placed when the inventory level drops to a predetermined reorder point R. The value of Q should be close to optimal lot size.

As shown in Fig. 7.5, the demand rate, D, deviates from its average rate. As a result, the actual lead time demand, D, varies from the average lead time demand, D. However, the quantity ordered, Q, remains the same at each time. The reorder cycle time also varies according to the demand rate during the previous cycle.

If the lead time becomes more than the reorder cycle time ($L > t$), then a replenishment order for a fixed quantity is placed when the 'stock on hand' falls to the reorder level. 'Stock on hand' is the current stock *plus* any replenishment orders still outstanding.

Buffer stock/safety stock may be held to guard against fluctuations in demand during the lead time period. The amount of buffer stock held is equivalent to the amount that the reorder level exceeds the expected demand during lead time.

The reorder level system can be used in a simplified form as the 'two-bin' system, as explained in a later section. This system is largely applicable to class *C* items. The stock of an item is stored in

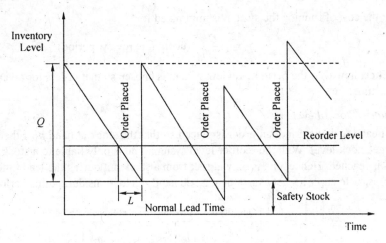

Fig. 7.5 Fixed order quantity system

two bins. One of them, usually larger, is the working bin from which demand is currently served without requisitions or paper work. The second bin is opened when the working bin becomes empty. At the time when the second bin is opened, a replenishment order for the item is released. Clearly, the amount of stock in the second bin materializes the order point. When the order comes, the second bin is refilled first and the excess amount is put into the working bin. This system works well only if there is no more than one order outstanding at any point of time. It is recommended that the order quantity should last much longer than the replenishment lead time. The order point should be set so as to offer a high service level in order to compensate for the rather loose control.

Periodic Review System

This system involves reviewing stock levels after a fixed interval called the review period, and placing replenishment orders at the end of each review. The replenishment order is variable and corresponds to the amount of stock required to bring the stock ordered *plus* the stock on hand up to the target stock level (S). This system is also known as the Fixed Period System or Replenishment Inventory System or *P*-System. A schematic diagram is shown in Fig. 7.5.

The optimal review period and the target inventory level can be determined as follows:

Review Period

It is possible to find a review period that minimizes the annual cost of acquiring and holding stock, although in practice the choice of the review period is likely to be dominated by other considerations such as type of the item held in the inventory.

Annual running cost of the system = Average inventory carrying cost + Cost of placing an order

Suppose there be r reviews per year. Then average quantity ordered will be D/r. Thus, average stock held will be $D/2r + B$, where B is the buffer stock. Hence,

$$\text{Stock carrying cost} = \left(\frac{D}{2r} + B\right)(I \times P)$$

and $$\text{Ordering cost} = r \times C_0$$

Therefore, $$TC = \left(\frac{D}{2r} + B\right)(I \times P) + r \times C_0$$

Now, if it is approximated that the level of the buffer stock is independent of the number of review periods, then optimizing the above equation, we obtain

$$\frac{d}{dr}(TC) = -\frac{DIP}{2r^2} + C_0 = 0 \text{ at minimum cost point.}$$

Hence, the cost of running the system is minimized for

$$r = \sqrt{\frac{DIP}{2C_0}} \text{ (economic review period)}$$

In practice, however, the periodic review system is chosen so that orders for all categories can be placed at a time.

Target Inventory (Stock) Level

At the end of each review period, an order is placed so that the stock at hand *plus* the order placed reaches a target stock level. With the reorder level system, one is only liable to a stock out once the reorder level is reached. Hence, one is only at risk from a stock out during the lead time period, and it is only necessary to carry a safety stock against demand fluctuations during this period (Fig. 7.6).

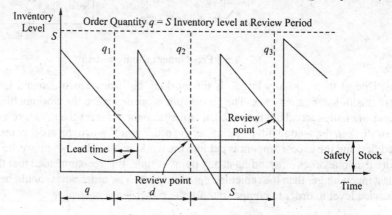

Fig. 7.6   Periodic review system

Suppose demand is normally distributed with mean demand, $\overline{D}$ and standard deviation σ_D. Then the expected demand during periodic cycle $= \overline{D}\,(\text{ROL} + \overline{\text{LT}})$. Safety stock to be held during this period $= Z\sigma_D\,\sqrt{(\text{ROL} + \text{LT})}$, where Z is the number of standard deviations to give the required service level. Therefore,

$$S = \overline{D}\,(\text{ROL} + \overline{\text{LT}}) + Z\sigma_D\,\sqrt{(\text{ROL} + \text{LT})}.$$

Comparison of Inventory Control Systems

1. The reorder level system involves ordering quantities of stock at different periods of time, whilst the periodic review system involves ordering variable quantities at fixed intervals.

2. Reorder level systems require continuous surveillance to ascertain whether the stock level has fallen below the reorder level. With periodic review systems, it is only necessary to monitor stock levels at the same time as that of the periodic review. Hence, a reorder level system may require more administrative effort than a periodic review system, though this may not be difficult if the system is computerized.

3. Periodic review systems facilitate orders for goods to be combined to achieve transport economies; to obtain discounts when the discount is based on the total value of the order; to meet given production schedules. This is not possible with the order level system, where orders are generated at an unpredictable interval. Generally, periodic review systems require a higher average stock level in order to maintain the same level of customer service.

Example 7.10. Determine (*a*) economic order quantity, (*b*) number of orders, (*c*) safety stock, and (*d*) re-order level, for the following inventory problem:

Annual demand = 36,000 units   Store charge = 5 per cent

Cost per unit = Re 1

Ordering cost = Rs 25

Cost of capital = 15 per cent

Lead time = 15 days

Safety stock = one month consumption

Solution. From the given data,

$$D = 36,000 \text{ units per year}$$
$$C_0 = \text{Rs } 25$$
$$C_h = \text{Re } 0.15 + 0.05 = \text{Re } 0.20.$$

(a)
$$Q^* (EOQ) = \sqrt{\frac{2DC_0}{C_h}} = \sqrt{\frac{2 \times 36,000 \times 25}{0.20}}$$
$$= 3,000 \text{ units.}$$

(b)
$$\text{Number of orders, } N = \frac{D}{Q^*} = \frac{36,000}{3,000} = 12.$$

(c)
$$\text{Safety stock} = \frac{30}{30} \times \frac{36,000}{12} = 3,000 \text{ units.}$$

Now, normal lead time consumption

$$= \text{Normal lead time} \times \text{Monthly consumption}$$
$$= \frac{15}{30} \times \frac{36,000}{12} = 1,500 \text{ units.}$$

(d) Hence, Re-order level $\quad = \text{Safety stock} + \text{Normal lead time consumption}$

$$= 3,000 + 1,500 = 4,500 \text{ units.}$$

Example 7.11. The following information in an inventory problem is available:

Annual demand	= 2400 units	Storage cost	= Rs 2 per year
Unit price	= Rs 2.40	Interest rate	= 10 per cent per annum
Ordering cost	= Rs 4	Lead time	= 15 days

Calculate (a) economic order quantity, (b) re-order level, and (c) total annual inventory cost. Also, how much would the total annual cost vary if the unit price is changed to Rs 5?

Solution. From the given data,

$$D = 24,000 \text{ units per annum;}$$
$$C_0 = \text{Rs } 4;$$
$$C_h = 2.40 (0.02 + 0.10) = \text{Re } 0.288.$$

(a)
$$Q^* (EOQ) = \sqrt{\frac{2DC_0}{C_h}} = \sqrt{\frac{2 \times 24,000 \times 4}{0.288}} = 258 \text{ units.}$$

(b) Re-order level
$$= D \times L$$
$$= 2,400 \times \frac{1}{2} \times \frac{1}{12} = 100 \text{ units}$$

Minimum variable inventory cost

$$= \sqrt{2DC_0 \, C_h}$$
$$= \sqrt{2 \times 2,400 \times 4 \times 0.288}$$
$$= \text{Rs } 74$$

Cost of 2,400 units
$$= 2,400 \times 2.40 = \text{Rs } 5,760$$

Therefore,

(c) Total inventory cost
$$= \text{Rs } 74 + \text{Rs } 5,670$$
$$= \text{Rs } 5,744$$

When the unit price is changed to Rs 5, then

$$Q^* (EOQ) = 258 \times \sqrt{2.40/5}$$
$$= 179 \text{ units}$$

Minimum variable cost $= 74 \times \sqrt{5/2.40}$

$$= \text{Rs } 107$$

Cost of 2,400 units $= 2,400 \times 5 = 12,000$

Therefore,

Total inventory cost $= \text{Rs } (107 + 12,000)$

$$= \text{Rs } 12,107$$

Hence, the increase in cost $= \text{Rs } (12,107 - 5,744)$

$$= \text{Rs } 6,363.$$

Example 7.12. A trailer company uses 2,400 wheels per year in the manufacture of trailers. It takes approximately 30 days to receive a shipment once an order has been placed. The company tries to keep a minimum safety stock equal to an average of 30 days requirement.

The cost associated with placing a purchase order has been estimated at Rs 100. The estimated storage cost of average annual inventory is 20 per cent. The company pays a net purchase price of Rs 50 per wheel. Determine (*a*) optimal order quantity, (*b*) maximum inventory level, (*c*) average inventory quantity, and (*d*) re-order point.

Solution. From the given data,

$$D = 2,400 \text{ wheels per year;}$$
$$C_h = \frac{20}{100} \times 50 = \text{Rs } 10$$
$$C_0 = \text{Rs } 100 \text{ per order.}$$

(*a*) Optimal (economic) order quantity

$$Q^* = \sqrt{\frac{2DC_0}{C_h}} = \sqrt{\frac{2 \times 2,400 \times 100}{10}} = 219 \text{ wheels.}$$

(*b*) Maximum inventory level $= \text{Buffer stock} + \text{Economic order quantity}$

$$= (30) \times \frac{2,400}{365} + 219 = 197.26 + 219$$
$$= 416 \text{ wheels.}$$

(*c*) Average inventory quantity $= \dfrac{\text{Buffer stock} + \text{Maximum inventory}}{2}$

$$= \frac{197.26 + 416}{2}$$
$$= 306.63 \sim 307 \text{ wheels.}$$

(*d*) Re-order point $= \text{Buffer stock} + \text{Consumption rate} \times \text{Lead time}$

$$= 197.26 + 2,400/365 (30)$$
$$= 197.26 + 197.26 = 394.52 \sim 395 \text{ wheels.}$$

7.5.7 Selective Inventory Control

In scientific inventory control, one of the major operating difficulties is a large variety of items stocked by various organizations. These may vary from 10,000 to 1,00,000 different types of stocked items and it is neither feasible nor desirable to apply rigorous scientific principles of inventory control to all these items. Therefore, inventory control has to be exercised selectively. Depending upon the value, criticality and usage frequency of an item, one has to decide on an appropriate type of inventory policy. Thus, selective inventory control plays a crucial role so that limited control efforts can be judiciously applied to more significant groups of items. In selective inventory control, items are grouped in a few discrete categories depending upon value, criticality and usage frequency. Such analyses are popularly known as ABC, VED, FSN, HML, XYZ, SDE, GOLF, S-OS analysis, respectively. These analyses are discussed here in detail.

ABC Analysis

This analysis is based on the universal Pareto's law that in any large number, there are 'significant few' and 'insignificant many.' For example, only 20 per cent of the items may be accounting for 80 per cent of the total material cost annually. The analysis is believed to have originated in the General Electric Company of America and is also known as Always Better Control (ABC) analysis.

Figure 7.7 shows a typical ABC analysis showing the relationship between the percentage of the number of inventory items and the percentage of average inventory investment (annual usage value).

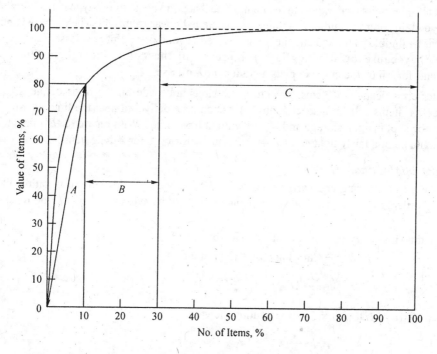

Fig. 7.7 Graphical representation of ABC analysis

Annual usage value is the demand multiplied by unit price, thereby giving the monetary worth of annual consumption. The figure shows that 10 per cent items claim 80 per cent of the annual usage value and thus constitute the 'significant few.' These items are classified as *A*-class items. Another 20 per cent items account for 17 per cent annual usage value and are called *B-class items*. The balance 70 per cent items account for only 3 per cent expenditure on material consumption and constitute 'insignificant many' and are called *C-class items*.

A simple procedure may be followed, as given below, for drawing an *ABC* type curve:

(*a*) Arrange items in the descending order of the annual usage value.

Annual usage value = Annual demand × Unit price.

(*b*) Identify cut-off points on the curve when there is a perceptible sudden change of slope.

The mechanics of ABC analysis is given in following six steps:

Step 1: Obtain a list of items along with information on their unit cost and the periodic (generally annual) consumption.

Step 2: Determine the annual usage value for each item by multiplying unit cost by the number of units and rank them in descending order on the basis of their respective usage values.

Step 3: Express the value for each item as a percentage of the aggregate usage value. Now, cumulate the per cent of annual usage value.

Step 4: Obtain the percentage value for each item. For n items, each item shall present $100/n$ per cent. Thus, if there are 20 items involved in a classification, then each item would represent $100/20 = 5$ per cent of the material. Next, cumulate these percentage values as well.

Step 5: Using the data on cumulated values of items and the cumulated percentage usage values, plot the curve by showing these respectively on X and Y axes.

Step 6: Determine appropriate divisions for A, B and C categories. The curve would rise steeply up to a point. This point is marked and the items up to that point constitute A-type items. Similarly, the curve beyond this point would only be moderately sloped towards upright. The point beyond which the slope is negligible is marked and the items covered beyond that point are classed as C-type items because they cause only a negligible increase in the cost. The other items are the B-type items for which the curve depicts a gradual upward rise.

After classification of items, inventory decisions are made on the basis of the A, B and C categories. 'A' items call for a strict control and should be delivered near the time of use. The 'C' items may be kept in open storage and issued without formalities. With regard to 'B' class items, the policy should be of a fairly tight control—though not as strict as for A-type items.

Application of ABC Analysis

In the absence of ordering and carrying cost, the *ABC* analysis is also helpful in rationalizing the number of orders to be placed, and in reducing capital from inventory. This can be illustrated as follows:

The total inventory cost per annum is given by

$$TC = \text{Carrying cost} + \text{Ordering cost}$$

$$= \frac{Q^*}{2}(I \times P) + \frac{D}{Q^*}C_0$$

Here $Q^* = \sqrt{2DC_0(I \times P)}$. Substituting the value of Q^* in TC,

$$TC = \sqrt{2DC_0(I \times P)}$$

$$= \sqrt{2C_0 P}\sqrt{DI}$$

$$= \text{Constant}\sqrt{DI}$$

The terms C_0 and P are assumed to be constant. Therefore, the total inventory cost is proportional to the square root of annual demand.

Limitations of ABC Analysis

In *ABC* analysis, ranking of items is based according to the annual consumption value. However, a minor item, though of small monetary value, may be important for running the plant and therefore requires constant attention. Hence, if the inventory of items is analysed according to the value of items in storage (*XYZ* analysis), then the results of the *ABC* analysis would be different from those of the *XYZ* analysis. Therefore, if the results of the *ABC* analysis are not periodically reviewed and updated, then the analysis loose its purpose.

Example 7.13. A company has to purchase four items *A, B, C* and *D* for the next year. The projected demands and unit prices are as follows:

Item	Demand (units)	Unit Price (Rs)
A	60,000	6
B	40,000	4
C	1200	48
D	5000	2

If the company wants to restrict the total number of orders to 50 for all the four items, how many orders should be placed for each item.

Solution. By selective inventory control, 50 orders that are to be placed next year would be distributed between all items *A, B, C* and *D* as per the square root of their annual demand. This is useful in the absence of ordering and carrying costs. The annual demand of four items is:

Item (1)	Demand (units) (2)	Unit Price (Rs) (3)	Annual Demand (Rs) (4) = (2) × (3)
A	60,000	6	3,60,000
B	40,000	4	1,60,000
C	1,200	48	57,600
D	5,000	2	10,000

The formula for determining the optimum number of orders for each item is given by

Number of orders $= \text{Constant} \sum \sqrt{\text{Annual demand}}$

Thus, the total number of orders to be placed are:

$$50 = \text{Constant} [\sqrt{\text{Annual demand of } A} + \sqrt{\text{Annual demand of } B}$$
$$+ \sqrt{\text{Annual demand of } C} + \sqrt{\text{Annual demand of } D}]$$
$$= \text{Constant} [\sqrt{3,60,000} + \sqrt{1,60,000} + \sqrt{57,600} + \sqrt{10,000}]$$
$$= \text{Constant} [600 + 400 + 240 + 100]$$
$$= \text{Constant} [1,340]$$

Therefore, constant $= 50/1,340 = 0.037$.

Hence, the number of orders to be placed for each item in the next year are as follows:

Item	$\sqrt{\text{Annual demand}}$	Number of orders in a year
A	600	22.20
B	400	14.80
C	240	8.88
D	100	3.70
		Total 49.58

Example 7.14. The following information is known about a group of items. Classify the material into *A, B, C* categories:

Model No.	Annual Consumption (pieces)	Unit Price (paise)
501	30,000	10
502	2,80,000	15
503	3000	10
504	1,10,000	5
505	4000	5

506	2,20,000	10
507	15,000	5
508	80,000	5
509	60,000	15
510	8,000	10

Solution.

Model No. (1)	Annual Consumption, (pieces) (2)	Unit Price, (paise) (3)	Usage Value, (Rs) (4) = (2) × (3)/100	Ranking as per Usage Value (5)
501	30,000	10	3,000	6
502	2,80,000	15	42,000	1
503	3,000	10	300	9
504	1,10,000	5	5,500	4
505	4,000	5	200	10
506	2,20,000	10	22,000	2
507	15,000	5	750	8
508	80,000	5	4,000	5
509	60,000	15	9,000	3
510	8,000	10	800	7

The usage value is accumulated as given in the descending order according to the ranks given below:

Model No.	Cumulative % of Items	Cumulative Annual Usage Value (Rs)	Cumulative % of Usage	Category
502	10	42,000	48	A
506	20	64,000	73	
509	30	73,000	83	
504	40	78,500	90	B
508	50	82,500	94	
501	60	85,500	98	
510	70	86,300	98.6	
507	80	87,050	99.4	C
503	90	87,350	99.8	
505	100	87,550	100	

Example 7.15. Perform ABC analysis using the following data:

Item	Unit	Unit Price, Rs.
1	700	5.00
2	2400	3.00
3	150	10.00
4	60	22.00
5	3800	1.50
6	4000	0.50
7	6000	0.20
8	300	3.50
9	30	8.00
10	2900	0.40
11	1150	7.10
12	410	6.20

Solution. ABC analysis is given as follows :

First 80% of value = A class

Next 15% of value = B class

Last 5% of value = C class

Item	Unit	Unit Price, Rs.	Consumption Value	Comulative Value	Percentage	Class
11	1150	7.1	8165	8165	23.0	A
2	2400	3.0	7200	15365	43.2	A
5	3800	1.5	5700	21065	59.2	A
1	700	5.0	3500	24565	69.0	A
12	410	6.2	2542	27107	76.2	A
6	4000	0.5	2000	29107	81.8	B
3	150	10.0	1500	30607	86.0	B
4	60	22.0	1320	31927	89.7	B
7	6000	0.2	1200	33127	93.1	B
10	2900	0.4	1160	34287	96.4	C
8	300	3.5	1050	35337	99.3	C
9	30	8.0	240	35577	100.0	C

VED Analysis

This analysis attempts to classify items into three categories—V (Vital), E (Essential) and D (Desirable)—depending upon the consequences of material stockout when demanded. 'Vital' items are the most critical having extremely high opportunity cost of shortage and must be available in stock when demanded, *e.g.* life saving drugs. 'Essential' items are quite critical with substantial cost associated with shortage and should be available in stock by and large. The 'desirable' group of items do not have serious consequences in case of non-availability but can be stocked items.

Since even a C-class item may be vital or an A-class item may be desirable, it is necessary to carry out a two-way classification of items, grouping them in nine distinct groups as A—V, A—E, A—D, B—V, B—E, B—D, C—V, C—E and C—D.

FSN Analysis

FSN analysis groups the items in three categories—Fast-moving, Slow-moving and Non-moving. Categorization of material into these three types based on value, criticality and usage enables the adoption of the right type of inventory policy to suit a particular situation. Most inventory models in literature are valid for the fast moving items exhibiting a regular consumption pattern. Many spare parts come under slow moving category which have to be managed differently. For non-moving items, optimal stock disposal rules rather than inventory provisioning rules are to be determined. The following strategies could be adopted for efficient inventory control of slow moving items.

(*a*) If spares are required only at a pre-specified time, such as the time of scheduled major maintenance for replacement, then it is desirable not to stock them but to place procurement orders sufficiently well in advance, keeping lead times in view, so that spares arrive 'just-in-time' when needed;

(*b*) If the part gives adequate warning of an impending breakdown, then the best policy is to place an order the moment a warning is received. Adequate warning means when the lead time required is less than the warning time; and

(*c*) In situations where adequate warning is not obtainable, some stock should be kept. In general, one-for-one ordering policy is useful. This means placing an order for one spare when one is consumed.

HML Analysis

This is similar to *ABC* analysis with the difference that the items are classified on the basis of unit cost rather than their usage value. The items are classified according to their cost per unit: *H*—high, *M*—medium, *L*—low. This analysis is useful for keeping control over material consumption at the departmental level.

XYZ Analysis

This analysis is based on the closing inventory value of different items. Items whose inventory values are high, are termed as *X* items, while those with low investment in them are classed as *Z* items. Other items whose inventory value is neither high nor low are *Y* items.

SDE Analysis

In this analysis, *S* stands for *scarce* items which are in short supply; *D* refers to the *difficult* items which might be available in the indigenous market but cannot be procured easily; and *E* represents *easily available* items, possibly from the local market.

GOLF Analysis

This analysis is useful for procurement strategies and is the main source of material. Here *G* refers government; *O* represents ordinary; *L*, local and *F*, foreign sources.

S-OS Analysis

This analysis is based on the nature of supplies wherein *S* represents the *seasonal* items and *OS* the *off-season* items. This classification of items is done with the aim of formulating procurement/holding strategies for seasonal items such as agricultural products.

The various types of analyses discussed are not mutually exclusive. They are often used jointly to ensure better control over materials. For example, the XYZ-FSN combined analysis will help in timely prevention of obsolescence.

7.5.8 Stores Management

Storage in any organization is an inevitable process as all the activities cannot be carried out at the same point of time. Stores management is concerned with carrying the right kind of material in right quantity, neither in excess nor in short supply, providing it quickly as and when required, keeping it safe against any kind of deterioration, pilferage or theft, and carrying out efficient performance of all these functions at lowest possible cost.

The major functions of stores management are as follows:

1. Receipt
2. Storage
3. Retrieval
4. Issue
5. Records
6. Housekeeping
7. Control
8. Surplus management
9. Verification
10. Coordination and co-operation.

In order to manage these functions, generally two kinds of organizational hierarchy are adopted for management of stores:

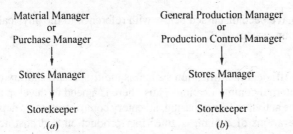

In type (*a*) organization, the stores is considered to be a material function closely related to receipt, and is clubbed with the purchasing or material management department. This is done for the following reasons:

(*i*) As the activities of stores are material-oriented, it should report to a department whose primary interests lie in the material related operations; and

(*ii*) From the viewpoint of total control, receiving and stores activities should be included with the other material activities. This facilitates the inter-relationship between stores, inventory control and purchase function, which will receive proper attention in this organizational arrangement.

In type (*b*) organization, the stores function is considered to be more significant and clubbed with the production department. The advantages of such an organizational arrangement are:

(*i*) The production management must have control over the immediate material supply from stores to run the production operation smoothly. This will ensure smooth delivery of material to the production centres as and when required; and

(*ii*) In order to avoid/discourage any kind of collusion and embezzlement of materials, the receiving and storing should be kept separate from the purchase department.

In fact, the objectives of the organizational decision regarding stores could be to store and manage the materials so that they are available in good condition when required; and procured at minimum cost. Apart from this, an important consideration in organizational design is centralization *vs* decentralization. Both types of stores functions are practised. The advantages are:

Advantages of Centralized Stores Organization

(*i*) Effective and better supervision and control,

(*ii*) Better and efficient layout of the storehouse,

(*iii*) Better inventory checks,

(*iv*) Maintenance of optimum requirement of stores,

(*v*) Fewer redundant and obsolete items,

(*vi*) Provision of better security arrangements, and

(*vii*) Reduced requirement of personnel.

Advantages of Decentralized Stores Organization

(*i*) Convenient for every department to draw material,

(*ii*) Reduced material handling requirements and associated cost,

(*iii*) Less risk of loss by fire, etc.,

(*iv*) Fewer chances of loss of production owing to easy and prompt availability of material.

7.5.9 Stores Systems and Procedures

The systems and procedures in stores can be classified under four heads:

(*a*) Identification system,

(*b*) Receipt system,

(*c*) Storage system, and

(*d*) Issue system.

These systems have been discussed below with reference to the physical system as well as the recording or information system.

Identification System

An unambiguous and efficient identification system is the first responsibility of a stores manager so as to facilitate clear internal communication. Thus, there is a need to develop a proper identification system to coordinate the activities of purchasing, inventory control and stores departments with possible integration of the operations of design, engineering, production and cost accounting. The use of codification of parts can be done in any one of the following ways:

Arbitrary approach: The inventory items are given arbitrary numbers in the sequence in which these are added in the stores account. Here each item gets a discrete number but there is no systematic relationship between the numbers assigned to related items.

Symbolic approach: This is a systematic approach to the design of a codification system. The codes assigned to different parts may be numeric or *mnemonic* (alphanumeric). A numerical system assigns a six to ten digit code number to each item, *e.g.* the code of an item may be 1 36 62 35. Here the first digit 1 indicates general class; next two digits, 36, generic class; next two digits, 62, sub-class; and the last two digits, 35, indicate the specific item number. This coding is based on the assumption that there is a maximum of 10 general classes, 100 generic classes, 100 sub-classes in each generic class, and 100 specific items in each sub-class. If the limit is exceeded in any of the categories, one more digit needs to be added in that category.

This mnemonic or alphanumeric system combines the numeric and alphabetic notation, thus making visual identifications easier because they are more descriptive and often shorter. This system may not work with large number of items.

Use of Engineering Drawing Number

This number is used as an identification number in the stores. This number has the advantage of better internal communication as it is used by other departments too. The limitation with this system is that it can be used only for manufactured items. Further, it has the non-sequencing disadvantage of an arbitrary system.

Receipt System

This system involves receiving the goods purchased, issuing it according to requisitions, and verifying the stocks. The activities are: accepting the delivery of goods purchased, verification, inspection, preparation of necessary documents, routing the purchased material to stores or to the production department as per orders, storing the material properly, adequate arrangement for its identification, assessing losses and pilferages, identification of its causes, etc.

Storage Systems

Storage systems may be classified as (*i*) physical system, and (*ii*) store records system.

(*i*) **Physical system:** The commonly followed systems for physically controlling stores materials are:

  (*a*) Closed stores system;

  (*b*) Open stores system; and

  (*c*) Random access stores system.

A firm can follow a combination of these systems depending upon the nature of production operation and the use of materials.

In a *closed stores system*, all materials are physically stored in a closed or controlled area, usually kept in physical control by locking. Only stores personnel are permitted to enter the stores area. Entry and exit of the material is permissible only with the authenticated document. Maximum physical security and strict accounting control of inventory material are ensured by such a storage system.

In an *open stores system*, no separate store-room exists. The material is stored as close to the point of use as is physically possible. This system is applicable mostly in the highly repetitive, mass production type of systems showing a continuous and predictable demand, *e.g.* a scooter assembly plant. The storage facilities are arranged at each workstation as per requirement and availability of space. The storage facilities are open and a worker has direct access to it; no authorized document is required.

This system expedites activities, cutting down retrieval time. Since material is used relatively quickly, it is not subject to high rate of deterioration or obsolescence. This system places less importance on the security of material.

Here the stores incharge/manager ensures to deliver the material to production areas and devises satisfactory physical storage arrangements with the production supervisors. Further, the responsibility of materials in production areas rests with the production supervisors.

In this system, the paperwork is reduced considerably owing to less emphasis on accounting control. No perpetual inventory records are kept. The actual usage is determined by finding the difference between the number of items in the beginning and at end of the period.

Random access control system is a form of closed stores system where no material has a fixed location in the stores, but similar types and sizes of storage equipment are grouped together. On the entry of any particular item, a punched card is prepared with the store's address. The requisitions are run on an electronic device that matches the requisition with the stored material record which contains the store's address. The main advantage of this system is that it utilizes the space more efficiently than a fixed location. Also, it provides greater flexibility by accommodating different materials and inventory mixes with little storage facilities.

Disadvantages of this system are that for large-scale operations, it requires a costly control system using electronic data processing equipment. Preservation of record card is essential, without which physical stock verification is cumbersome and time-consuming.

(*ii*) **Store records system:** It is important to develop an appropriate recording system for the store to provide correct information regarding the physical inventory and accounting of the transaction. Usually two records are kept for materials and other goods which are received, issued and transferred, namely, *Bin Card* and *Store Ledger*.

In a *bin card*, details of quantities of each type of material received, issued and kept in hand each day are shown. Normally a bin card is maintained in duplicate. One card is attached to each bin on shelf containing the material and records remain with the storekeeper for reference. Some companies use the Kardex system in which a Kardex is prepared and updated. Bin cards are also used as a check on the stock ledger accounts in the material accounting section. The format of a bin card is shown in Fig. 7.8.

BIN CARD				
Bin No .... Maximum Quantity				
Material Code No. .... Ordering Level				
Store Ledger Folio .... Minimum Quantity				
Date	Quantity Received	Quantity Issued	Balance	Remarks

Fig. 7.8 Bin card

A store ledger and a bin card are identical except that money values are shown in the former. This ledger may be maintained by the material accounting section on the basis of material ordered, received and issued and the balance in the stock.

Issue System

Issue can be of two kinds—issue to consuming sections and issue to outsiders for processing. The control of issues is regulated by production programmes. Based on the programme and bill of material, work orders are prepared, listing for each material quantity to be issued and the corresponding quantity of the component to be manufactured. Any quantity used over and above the work order quantity means excessive wastage and scrapings.

A sample of material requisition form is shown in Fig. 7.9. Usually, two copies of this work order are prepared by the concerned manager and are forwarded by the storekeeper to the material

MATERIAL REQUISITION

Material required for .... No. ....
(job or process)   Date ....
Department/Section . ...

S.No.	Description	Code No.	Quantity		Rate	Amount	Store Register Entry Page No.
			Demanded	Supply			

Requisitioned by   Approved by   Material Issued by   Received by

Fig. 7.9 Material requisition form

accounting section for pricing and entry in the store ledger. One copy of the work order is retained and the other copy is returned to the originating section where it is used as the basis for charging to the appropriate production order. Sometimes *ad hoc* material requisitions are also made. A consolidated statement of such items must be prepared periodically. When issues are made to outsiders, controls have to be more formal to take care of payments and claims.

7.5.10 Stores Accounting and Verification Systems

Stores Accounting System

The stores accounting system refers to the flow of material and estimating the cost of the product for pricing decisions. For costing the incoming materials, factors included are material price, freight charges, packing charges. insurance, taxes, duties, etc. All these factors should be suitably accounted for. There are six most frequently used systems of estimating the cost.

1. **FIFO system:** This system is known as the 'First in First out' system and is based on the assumption that material is issued from the oldest stock and cost is allocated according to the previous recorded cost. There is no 'profit' or 'loss' in the pricing arrangements. The value of the stock held in hand is the money that has been paid for that amount of stock at the latest price level. In case of too many changes in price level, the FIFO system becomes unwieldy. Another limitation of this system is that it fails to provide a satisfactory answer to costing-returns from the store. Thus, the FIFO method tends to follow the actual flow of materials and their physical movement and closely approximates the current value for the inventory of materials in hand.

2. **LIFO system:** This system, known as 'Last in First out' system, is based on the assumption that the most recent receipts are issued first. As the current price is charged to the system, it produces a lower income during periods of rising prices and thus offers savings in taxes. During the inflation period, this system tends to immunize unrealized gains or losses in inventory. This system also suffers from the same limitations as the FIFO system.

3. **Average cost system.** This system does not recognize which item goes out of inventory first or last, but considers the average cost of procurement or price paid for each item over a time period as they are held in stock. The average is calculated by dividing the total cost with the number of items and is updated with every new purchase. Three kinds of averages are employed: (*i*) Simple arithmetic average, (*ii*) Weighted average, and (*iii*) Moving average. The simple average is arrived at by dividing the sum total of the price paid for materials over a given period by the number of manufacturing runs, and then sub-dividing them by the numbers produced. Thus, it neglects the lot-size quantity and gives equal weight to all the lots purchased or produced. This distortion is corrected by giving due weight to the lot-size quantity as well as to the unit price. However, these methods cannot be operated until the average is available for the period over which the same is calculated in the past. Therefore, the moving average method is employed, which computes the average unit cost after each purchase and any addition to the existing stock is taken into account in order to arrive at the recent unit cost of materials.

4. **Market value system:** In this system, material issued is charged at the prevailing market rates. This system underestimates the stock in hand in the case of price increase, whereas it overestimates the stock in hand in the case of price decrease. This in turn leads to writing off huge amounts to make it realistic. Also, continuous monitoring of the market rates for all materials makes the system cumbersome.

5. **Standard cost system:** A detailed analysis of market price and trends is carried out to determine a standard rate for a fixed period, say six months or so. This standard rate is charged to materials issued during this period irrespective of the actual rate. After the expiry of this period, the standard rate is reviewed and updated.

6. **Costing the closing stock system:** In this system, market price or stock at cost, whichever is less, is used. The cost of closing stock is governed mainly by price units, obsolescence and deterioration.

Stock Verification System

The process of stock verification is carried out for the following purposes:

(*a*) To reconcile the store records and documents for their accuracy and usefulness;

(*b*) To identify areas deserving strict document control;

(*c*) To support the balance-sheet stock figures; and

(*d*) To minimize the pilferage and fraudulent practices.

Some of the physical verification systems are as follows:

1. **Periodic physical verification system:** Under this system, the entire stock is verified once or twice in a year, usually during the accounting period. This is usually completed within a few days so that routine work does not suffer. For stock verification of this type, it is desirable to have the following prior preparations before the team starts its work: (*i*) *Housekeeping:* Materials should be properly located and arranged to be able to prepare the inventories easily, (*ii*) *Identification:* All parts and items in inventory need to be properly identified with part numbers and nomenclatures, etc; (*iii*) *Instruction:* Everyone must know the procedures well in advance prior to undertaking the verification of inventory; (*iv*) *Training:* Training in actual counting, checking and measuring is also necessary for the personnel entrusted with the job;

and (*v*) *Team:* Establishing a physical verification team and assigning responsibilities to count, check and measure the levels of inventory for final reporting. Thereafter, top management's sanction can be sought for writing off deficiencies or valuing surplus. As all the items are checked at one time, there should not be any confusion about any item being left unchecked.

2. **Continuous stocktaking system:** Materials and inventories are verified physically throughout the year according to a plan. Each and every item is verified by a regularly assigned team of personnel specialized to do the job and in cyclic order. Different methods are adopted by different firms for continuous verification work.

The main advantages of this system are:

(*i*) The shutdown of the plant is not necessary for stock checking/taking;

(*ii*) The system is less cumbersome, less tiring, and more accurate. The method is also cheaper;

(*iii*) Discrepancies and defects in stores are readily detected and not carried over. This prevents damages and losses;

(*iv*) Slow moving stocks can be identified and proper, remedial action initiated in time; and

(*v*) Items stocked can be kept within limits.

3. **Low point inventory system:** In this system, stock level of stores is checked only when it reaches its minimum level.

7.5.11 Automated Storage/Retrieval

The concept of totally automated storage and retrieval system has been on the anvil in keeping with the rapid developments in the technology. High rise storage systems have been in use in developed countries. Automated material handling systems are used for the unit load type storage retrieval system. Some of the methods to improve the efficiency of automated storage/retrieval systems are as follows:

(*a*) Sequencing in an optimal way by choosing stops in a single picking tour;

(*b*) Allowing a single operator to perform all storage and order picking operations in an aisle;

(*c*) Generating a picking list based on a single customer's order;

(*d*) Storing items in pairs, *e.g.* nuts and bolts;

(*e*) Locating items from the rack as per the structure and importance of orders; and

(*f*) Allocating all items related to a specific facility, to a single aisle.

7.5.12 Comparison of Material Flow System

Figure 7.10 shows a comparison of material flow in a conventional manufacturing operation with one that has been automated. Elimination of in-process storage is the significant difference.

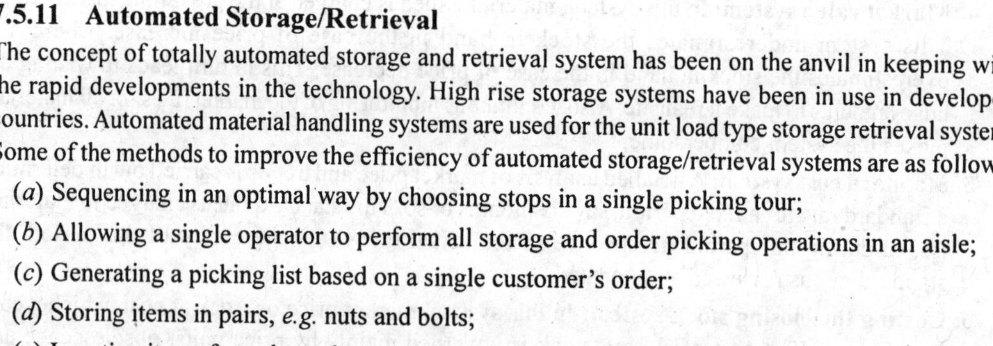

Fig. 7.10   Comparison of material flow in a conventional manufacturing operation with an automated operation

7.6 Waste Management

Waste management is a multidisciplinary activity involving engineering principles, economics, urban and regional planning, management techniques and social sciences. The main objective of waste management is to minimize the waste through aiming at the ideal system. The goal of waste management is the optimal utilization of available resources for higher efficiency and growth.

7.6.1 Functional Classification of Waste Management

Waste management can be classified into *five* basic functional elements:

1. Generation
2. Reduction
3. Collection
4. Recycling
5. Disposal.

However, waste management should be viewed in totality considering the interrelationship of basic functional elements (Fig. 7.11). Considering each element separately, it is possible to (*a*) identify the fundamental aspects and relationships involved in each element, and (*b*) develop, wherever possible, quantifiable relationships for making engineering comparisons, analysis and evaluation.

Generation of Waste

There are many factors responsible for the generation of waste in different systems. However, some general causes of waste generation are given here, out of which some may be critical. In order to find the highest aggregate cost of waste, it is required to account for the amount of waste generated against their respective causes.

1. Poor management
2. Ineffective policies

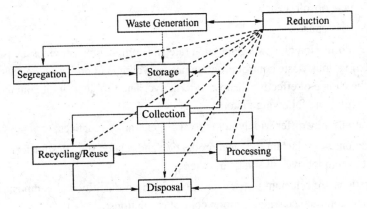

Fig. 7.11   Functional elements of waste management

3. Lack of planning
4. Faulty systems and procedures
5. Defective organizational structure
6. Political pressures
7. Emphasis on sub-system objectives instead of organizational goals

8. Personal interests

9. Carelessness and neglect

10. Lack of individual responsibility

11. Not acquainted with latest technological development

12. Resistance to adopt automation and computerization

13. Wrongly laid-down design standards

14. Lack of standardization and codification

15. Wrong choice of raw material

16. Ignorance of inventory control

17. Inappropriate storage facilities

18. Poor handling of materials

19. Poor layout of facilities

20. Information delay

21. Improper recruitment and lack of training

22. Inadequate supervision and control

23. Unhygenic work environment

24. Lack of motivation and incentives

25. Poor labour relations

26. Poor maintenance

27. Less emphasis on quality control

28. Insufficient skill and use of unsafe practices

29. Technological obsolescence

30. Miscellaneous causes.

Reliable information on waste generation rate and composition provides a basis for the design and operation of various waste control programmes, recycling and processing plants, waste disposal projects, and the choice of effective disposal alternative. The problems in obtaining information are complex and involve the following factors:

(a) Organizations may differ widely in their waste generating practices;

(b) Organizations are reluctant to reveal production and related statistics for fear of the data being used to the competitive advantage of others;

(c) Organizations are reluctant to provide information on quantity and composition of waste for fear of non-compliance with pollution control regulations;

(d) The quantum of waste generated reflects the inefficiency of the organization;

(e) The extent of salvaging, recycling or other reclamation of waste differs greatly among manufacturers; and

(f) Many organizations have little understanding of, and few records on this aspect.

The waste management system for individual organizations, sectors as well as the whole economy should be so designed as to fulfil the goal of zero waste. Zero waste should not be misinterpreted to mean that no waste is generated. Such an interpretation will be neither feasible nor justified. The idea of having zero waste is to first try to minimize the waste generated as far as it is technologically and economically feasible, and then whatsoever waste is generated it should be put to some effective use.

Waste Collection Systems

Waste collection has a significant effect on health, aesthetics, housekeeping and public attitudes concerning the operation of the system. As collection and transportation constitute the sources of major cost of waste management (up to 80 per cent), streamlining of collection techniques can considerably improve the efficiency and overall cost of waste management. The proposed strategies for waste collection are:

(*a*) Economic design to facilitate separation at source;

(*b*) Providing every organization with a set of four standard bins to separately collect the metallic, plastic, paper and other miscellaneous waste. The type and size of bins should be designed only after careful investigation of type and quantum of waste generated;

(*c*) Designing an appropriate collection system governed by public or private agencies to collect the segregated waste at regular time intervals;

(*d*) Incentives to encourage segregation of waste at source;

(*e*) Timely collection of scrapped appliances with segregated waste, and its flow through salvage industry for ultimate reuse; and

(*f*) Development of appropriate collection systems for the collection of miscellaneous organic and inorganic waste.

Recycling of Waste

Recycling refers to the use of undesirable output or waste as input to the same process or system, *e.g.* recycling of foundry scrap. The term recycling includes reuse, reclamation and recovery. Reuse may be termed as the use of waste generated from one process/system as input to some other process/system as a raw material, or for the generation of power or by-products. The conversion of damaged, rejected and undesirable output into desirable output by repair or processing is termed as reclamation, Similarly, the term recovery is utilized to denote the gain of resources from the wastes.

Waste Disposal Systems

Wastes may be categorized into (*i*) Salvable waste, and (*ii*) Non-salvable waste. Waste that has some salvage value is termed as salvable waste, *e.g.* rejected goods, obsolete items and equipment. A well designed disposal system for salvable waste may provide best returns to the organization, contribute to cost reduction, generate higher profits and aid material conservation.

Waste which does not have any salvage value, but needs further processing and treatment for disposal is termed as non-salvable waste. This type of waste is primarily responsible for environmental hazards.

Guidelines for disposal of salvable waste: The procedures for disposal of different types of salvable waste vary from situation to situation. Some suggested guidelines to aid the design of waste disposal systems and formulation of procedures thereof are as follows:

(*a*) Recycling of the scrap;

(*b*) Using the scrap for producing by-products;

(c) Transferring the surplus from one department to the other;

(d) Selling the scrap as raw material to other plants;

(e) Selling the scrap/surplus to export agencies dealing with it;

(f) Selling the scrap through advertisement and auctioning;

(g) Selling the surplus in the open market, or to the employees itself, particularly the consumer goods;

(h) Consulting vendors and returning the surplus to vendors;

(i) In case of damaged equipment, selling the parts after classifying them into serviceable, repairable or reclaimable, and scrap; and

(j) Donating the rejected material to charitable organization to gain socio-economic respect.

Processing and disposal techniques for non-salvable wastes: Processing/disposal techniques are:

(a) Mechanical processing;

(b) Thermal processing;

(c) Bio-processing;

(d) Composting;

(e) Ultimate disposal; and

(f) Sanitary land-filling.

Design of effective waste disposal systems: The design of an effective waste disposal system promotes maximum possible recycling/reuse of waste, and exposes to minimum environmental hazards. Various factors to be considered in the design of a waste disposal system are:

(a) Public attitudes, and regional and national policies,

(b) Economic considerations and land availability,

(c) Equipment requirements and maintenance,

(d) Groundwater protection and environment control,

(e) Fire prevention,

(f) Litter control, and

(g) Operational plans and records.

7.6.2 Relationship between Waste Management and Resource Management

A system basically takes some input, process it and gives the desired output. An ideal system is conceptualized to transform the total input into useful or desired output. In view of physical laws of nature, existence of an ideal system is not possible. Some waste is inevitable in the functioning of any system. The relationship of waste management and resource management is shown in Fig. 7.12.

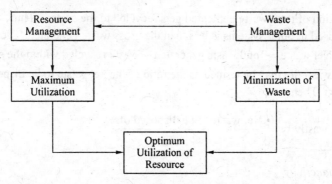

Fig. 7.12 Relationship between resource management and waste management

In fact, waste and resource management are complementary to each other. Both approaches have their advantages and limitations. Depending upon the situations, constraints, and primary and secondary objectives, resource management techniques prove to be promising in some cases, while in others, waste management offers an added advantage. Resource based classification of waste may be shown as in Fig. 7.13.

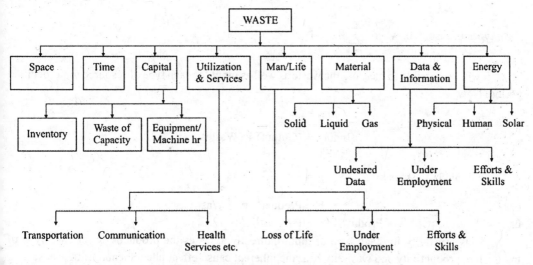

Fig. 7.13 Resource based classification of waste

7.6.3 Wastivity

Wastivity of any system is defined as the ratio of the waste to the input, i.e.,

$$\text{Wastivity} = \frac{\text{Waste } (W)}{\text{Input } (I)}$$

Depending upon the level of waste under consideration, wastivity may be termed as gross wastivity and net wastivity. Gross wastivity may be defined as the ratio of total waste generated by a specific system to the total input to that system, i.e.,

$$\text{Gross wastivity} = \frac{\text{Net waste generated}}{\text{Total input}}$$

Here a fraction of total waste generated gets recycled to the system. Thus, the net waste to be disposed of or reused in other systems is less than the gross waste generated. Therefore,

Net waste = Total waste generated − Waste recycled within the system

Hence, net wastivity may be termed as the ratio of the net waste to be disposed of to the total input to the system. Then

$$\text{Net wastivity} = \frac{\text{Net waste to be disposed of}}{\text{Total input}}.$$

Wastivity and Productivity

Wastivity can serve as an adequate measure of performance of any system and is rather easy to measure. If I_r be the wastivity index of rth resource and W_r be the relative weightage (depends upon a number of tangible and intangible factors) of rth resource, then

$$\text{Composite Wastivity Index} = \sum_{r=1}^{n} W_r I_r$$

for n types of resource, where $\sum_{r=1}^{n} W_r = 1$.

It will be possible to measure the waste as well as input for each type of resource for a specified period. Now,

$$I = O + W$$

$$(\text{Input}) = (\text{Output}) + (\text{Waste})$$

Dividing both sides by I, $\qquad 1 = \dfrac{O}{I} + \dfrac{W}{I}$

or $\qquad\qquad\qquad\qquad\qquad 1 = \text{Productivity} + \text{Wastivity}$

or $\qquad\qquad\qquad\qquad \text{Productivity} = 1 - \text{Wastivity}$

Thus, wastivity for each type of input indirectly assesses the productivity for each type of input. Here productivity and wastivity bear the inherent cause-effect phenomenon. If the cause, i.e., wastivity is checked, the effect, productivity, will obviously be improved.

7.6.4 Accounting for Waste

It is known that all material put into a process will not end up as good saleable products. Some loss, scrap or wastage is inevitable in process industries. These losses should be computed in advance before the processing operation starts. Process loss can be of two types: (*a*) normal loss, and (*b*) abnormal loss. Normal loss is unavoidable, uncontrollable and expected in normal conditions. Abnormal loss in processing is controllable and is generally caused by abnormal or unexpected conditions such as poor design, lower quality material, accident and negligence. The treatment of normal and abnormal losses differs in accounting. It is expected that normal losses are absorbed by good production.

Abnormal losses are calculated as being equivalent to the value of good units. The unit cost which is used to value good units is also applied for the valuation of abnormal loss units. The cost of abnormal loss units so computed is transferred to a separate abnormal loss account and credited to the relevant process account. Thereafter, this loss is transferred to the profit and loss account and the abnormal loss account is thus closed.

The following procedure is useful in the preparation of process cost accounts and does not present any problem:

1. Normal loss should be computed on the basis of information given.

2. The cost per unit of production should be determined assuming that abnormal loss does not exist. The cost per unit is calculated on the basis of (*i*) normal production, i.e., inputs (units) *minus* normal loss units, and (*ii*) normal cost of production, i.e., all costs incurred (debit side of a process account) *minus* proceeds, if any, realized from the sale of normal loss units. Normal cost of production divided by normal production will give the cost per unit of output.

3. The cost per unit, as calculated, is used to value abnormal loss units and that would be the cost of abnormal loss.

4. The abnormal loss account is debited and the relevant process credited with the amount and quantity of abnormal loss.

5. The cost per unit calculated will be used to determine the cost of good production units produced by the process.

6. The proceeds realized from the sale of abnormal loss representing scrap is transferred to a separate abnormal loss account and not to the relevant process account.

7. The proceeds realized from the sale of normal loss representing scrap is transferred to the relevant process account.

8. The abnormal loss account is closed by transferring the total cost of abnormal loss units to the profit and loss account if there is no scrap. In case abnormal loss represents scrap, the net amount (total cost of abnormal loss units minus scrap) will be transferred to the profit and loss account.

Self-assessment Questions

1. What do you understand by management of materials? How is this effective in an industrial organization?

2. Define materials management. Briefly outline the objectives of materials management. Also, suggest the actions required to be taken in achieving these objectives.

3. Discuss various functions of materials management.

4. Describe the salient features of integrated approach to material planning and control.

5. Explain the 'Value Analysis' technique of inventory control. What are the objectives of value analysis?

6. Explain the process of 'Value Analysis'.

7. Explain the 'Purchase Price Analysis' with examples.

8. Explain the basic objectives of value analysis.

9. What is cost analysis, and how is it used in a value analysis programme?

10. What is design analysis and how is it used in a value analysis programme?

11. 'Value analysis is more a human relations and motivation problem than anything else.' Discuss this statement.

Inventory Control

12. (*a*) What do you mean by inventory? Why is it required to manage inventory?

(*b*) What do you understand by inventory control? Explain in brief (*a*) selective approach, and (*b*) EOQ.

13. Explain the significance of EOQ, with the help of a quantity-cost curve. What are the limitations of using the formula for an EOQ?

14. 'EOQ models, however complex, are restricted by so many assumptions that they have limited practical value.' Do you agree with this statement? Illustrate your answer.

15. Derive the Wilson EOQ formula. What are the practical limitations of the EOQ formula? Discuss its sensitivity.

16. As an engineer, outline the impact of inventory policies on working capital management.

17. Discuss in brief the costs associated with inventory management. Derive the formula for EOQ so that

$$Q^* = \sqrt{\frac{2kb}{h\,(1 - b/a)}}$$

where k = ordering cost per set-up; h = holding cost per unit of time; b = usage rate per unit of time; and a = production rate per unit of time ($a > b$).

18. In a certain manufacturing situation, the production is instantaneous and the demand per day is R. Show that the optimal order quantity q per run, which minimizes the total cost, is

$$q = \sqrt{\frac{2RCs\,(C_1 + C_2)}{C_1 C_2}}$$

where C_1 = cost of holding one unit of inventory per day; C_2 = unit cost of shortage per day; and Cs = set up cost per run.

19. Compare the periodic and quantity/reorder inventory systems.

20. Explain the steps in preparing a methodology for inventory situations. Why is the understanding of this methodology important to the practising manager?

21. Why are inventories necessary? Discuss.

22. What kind of items should be selected when managers are attempting to improve an inventory system? Why?

23. Explain how the situation in the finite production (gradual replacement) rate inventory differs from the simple lot size situation. What impact does the cost of an item have on each situation? Explain.

24. Explain two common criteria to measure and establish service levels giving one example for each criterion.

25. What is meant by the ABC classification? How can an organization's inventory be analysed using the ABC classification?

26. Inventory control is a rational process in which decisions are often made irrationally. Explain.

27. Discuss the advantages and disadvantages of the periodic inventory system when compared with the quantity/re-order inventory system.

28. Discuss in brief (*i*) Re-order level, (*ii*) Safety stock. (*iii*) Lead time.

29. What is lead time? What activities occur during lead time? What bearing does this have on safety stock?

30. Differentiate between a fixed order quantity system and a fixed interval system. Mention their advantages and disadvantages.

31. Explain the basis of selective inventory control and state the different selection techniques adopted in an inventory control system. Give a brief note on each.

Store and Waste Management

32. Discuss the major functions of a store in an organization.

33. What do you understand by storekeeping? What are the duties of a storekeeper? Describe the working of a store of a big company.

34. What are the principal methods of pricing of materials taken out of a store for production? Describe each of these briefly.

35. What are the advantages and disadvantages of centralized storeroom facilities?

36. Why is store accounting important for a firm? Discuss various systems that may be followed for this purpose and their impact on product pricing.

37. What do you understand by automated storage and retrieval? In which type of companies in India and for what kind of commodities do you think this system would be appropriate?

38. Outline and explain briefly the approach you would use in planning a study of an existing storeroom, after taking responsibility for its re-organization.

39. 'Waste Management' is complimentary to 'Resource Management'. Critically comment.

40. Explain with examples the functional classification of waste management.

41. Write short notes on (a) Systematic waste reduction procedure, (b) Wastivity indices, and (c) Identification of waste.

42. Devise a method of cost accounting for waste.

Numerical Problems

1. A company requires 10,000 units of an item per annum. The cost of ordering is Rs 100 per order. The inventory carrying cost is 20 per cent. The unit price of the item is Rs 10. Calculate the economic order quantity.

2. Annual requirements of a particular raw material are 2,000 units, costing Re 1 each to the manufacturer. The ordering cost is Rs 10 per order and the carrying cost 16 per cent per annum of the average inventory value. Find EOQ and the total inventory cost per annum.

3. A company purchases 10,000 items per year for use in its production shop. The unit cost is Rs 10 per year, holding cost Re 0.80 per month, and the cost of making a purchase Rs 200. Determine the following if no shortages are allowed:

    (a) Optimal order quantity;

    (b) Optimal total annual cost;

    (c) Number of orders per year; and

    (d) Time between the orders.

4. M/s Simplex Bearings Ltd. is committed to supply 24,000 bearings annually to M/s Calcutta Fans on daily basis. It is estimated that it costs 10 paise as inventory holding cost per bearing per month and the set-up cost per run of bearing manufacture is Rs 324. Calculate:

    (a) What should be the optimal run size for bearing manufacture?

    (b) What would be the interval between two consecutive optimal runs?

    (c) Find the minimum inventory cost.

5. The details of a part to be machined are as follows:

Annual requirements	:	2,400 pieces
Machine rate	:	10 pieces/shift
Number of working days in year	:	300 days
Cost of machining a component	:	Rs 100 per piece
Inventory carrying cost per annum	:	12% of value
Set-up cost per machine	:	Rs 400 per set-up

Find the (a) optimal lot size for machining, and (b) average finished product inventory.

6. In a paint manufacturing unit, each type of paint is to be ground to a specified degree of fineness. The manufacturer uses the same ball mill for a variety of paints and after completion of each batch, the mill has to be cleaned and the ball charge properly made up. The changeover from one type of paint to another is estimated to cost Rs 80 per batch. The annual sales of a particular grade of paint is 30,000 litres and the inventory carrying cost is Re 1 per litre. Given that the rate of production is three times the sales rate, determine the economic batch size.

7. Suggest an ordering policy for the following inventory situation:

Annual demand	=	7,200 units
Cost per unit	=	Rs 4
Ordering cost	=	Rs 20
Inventory carrying charge	=	20%
Procurement lead time	=	1/2 month

Safety stock required for 1/2 month consumption.

8. A factory uses Rs 32,000 worth of raw materials per year. The ordering cost per order is Rs 50 and the carrying cost is 20 per cent per year of the average inventory. If the factory follows the EOQ purchasing policy, calculate the re-order point, maximum, minimum and average sizes of inventory. It is given that the factory works for 360 days in a year, the replacement time is 9 days and the safety stock is worth Rs 300.

9. A pharmaceutical factory annually consumes 6000 kg of a chemical costing Rs 5 per kg. Placing each order costs Rs 25 and the carrying cost is 6 per cent/year/kg of average inventory. Find EOQ and the total inventory cost (including the cost of the chemical).

   If the factory works 300 days in a year, procurement time is 15 days and safety stock is 200 kg, find the re-order point, maximum and average size of inventories.

10. Examine critically 'ABC Analysis' by giving suitable examples. For what purpose do the inventory managers use ABC analysis? Explain the use of ABC analysis in various functional areas.

11. Prepare ABC ranking and summary of ABC analysis from the following ABC analysis usage (in Rs) of a manufacturing organization.

Item	Annual Usage, Units	Unit Cost, Rs
101	1,60,000	1.00
102	2,40,000	0.80
103	80,000	0.40
104	4,000	1.20
105	4,00,000	0.80
106	64,000	0.20
107	4,80,000	1.67
108	5,600	4.00
109	72,000	2.00
110	400	8.00

12. The following information is known about a group of items. Classify the materials using ABC classification:

Model No.	Annual Consumption, Pieces	Unit Price, Paise
501	30,000	10
502	2,80,000	15
503	3,000	10
504	1,10,000	5
505	4,000	5
506	2,20,000	10
507	15,000	5
508	80,000	5
509	60,000	15
510	8,000	10

13. A company purchases three items—A, B, and C. Their annual demand and unit prices are given as follows:

Item	Annual Demand, units	Unit Price, Rs
A	1,20,000	3
B	80,000	2
C	600	96

   If the company wants to place 40 orders/year for all the three items, what is the optimal number of orders for each item?

14. An item is purchased and delivered in lots of 1000 units. Rate of use is 250 units per week, procurement time is 2 weeks and the minimum inventory is to be 100 units. Find the re-ordering point, maximum inventory and average inventory.

15. A company needs 24,000 units of raw material which costs Rs 20 per unit and the ordering cost is expected to be Rs 100 per order. The company maintains a safety stock of one month's requirement to meet any emergency. The holding cost of carrying inventory is supposed to be 10 per cent per unit of average inventory. Find the economic lot size, safety stock, and total cost.

16. A company gets 5 per cent concession on purchase price, if it places an order for 2,000 units or more, but less than 5,000 units. On an order for 5,000 units or more it gets 2 per cent concession in addition to 5 per cent concession. Given that annual demand, $D = 12,000$ units, ordering cost, $C_0 = $ Rs 15/order; and cost of item, $C = $ Rs 10. Holding cost in addition to Rs 2 per unit is estimated to be 15 per cent of average inventory per unit. Which discount offer is more profitable for the company.

17. A company uses 24,000 units of raw material per year costing Rs 1.25 per unit. Its ordering cost is Rs 22.5 and holding cost is 5.4 per cent of average inventory. Find the EOQ and the total cost (including the cost of raw material).

    Company works for 300 days in an year. The procurement time is 12 days and the safety stock in 400 units. Find the re-order point, minimum, maximum and average sizes of inventory.

    Should the company accept the offer made by the supplier at a discount of 5 per cent on the cost price on a single order of 24,000 units.

18. A firm operates on all 365 days of the year. The entire lot of a part it manufactures is delivered to the stock room at one time. The part is used by the assembly department at a uniform rate. The re-order point is 600 units and the procurement time for a replenishment order is 10 days. The lot size is such that the average inventory of the part is 1,500 units. Safety stock is 500 units. Find (*a*) the rate of use per week, and (*b*) the lot size.

19. What is the purpose of materials management? What factors do contribute significantly in MRP and how?

20. What are MRP and MRP II? Outline their merits and demerits in brief.

21. Discuss the importance of MPS in an MRP system.

22. What is the role of safety stock in an MRP system?

23. What is MRP? Draw a schematic diagram to show the interrelation between MRP and the production planning and scheduling process.

Hints and Answers

4. (*a*) 3,600 units, (*b*) $12 + (24,000/3,600) = 1.8$ months,

    (*c*) $[(24,000/3,600) \times 324] + [(3,600/2) \times 1.2] = $ Rs 4,320.

6. EOQ $= \sqrt{2 \times 30,000 \times 80/1.00\ (1 - 30,000/90,000)} = 2683.28$ units

   Number of batches per year $= (30,000/2,683.28) = 11.18$.

8. ROP $= 1,100$; 4,300 units; 300 units and 2,300 units.

14. ROP $\qquad\qquad$ = Min. Inventory (safety stock) $+ LT \times D = 600$ units

    Max. inventory $\qquad$ = Lot size + Min. Inv. $= 1,100$ units

    Average inventory $\qquad = \dfrac{Q}{2} + $ Min. Inv. $= 600$ units.

15. $\qquad\qquad\qquad C_h = 10\%$ of $20 = $ Rs 2

    Safety stock $= 24,000/12 = 2,000$ units

    $$EOQ = \sqrt{2DC_0/C_h} = 1,548 \text{ units}$$

    $$C_h^* = \left(\frac{Q}{2} + SS\right) C_h = \left(\frac{1,548}{2} + 2,000\right) 2 = \text{Rs } 5,548$$

    $TC = $ Ordering cost + Holding cost + Purchase cost

    $\qquad = $ Rs 4,87,098.40.

16. *TC* without concession $\quad = DC + \dfrac{Q}{2} C_h + \dfrac{D}{Q} C_0 = $ Rs 1,21,122.49

    If a concession of 5% on purchase price is offered, then

    New $\qquad\qquad\qquad C = 0.95 \times 10 = $ Rs 9.5

$$C_h = 2 + 15\% \text{ of } 9.5 = \text{Rs } 3.425$$

$$TC = 12,000 \times 9.5 + \frac{5,000}{2} \times 3.425 + \frac{12,000}{2,000} \times 15 = \text{Rs } 1,17,515$$

When company orders 5,000 units or more, it gets a concession of 7% on the purchase price. Thus,

$$C_h = 2 + 15\% \text{ of } 9.3 = \text{Rs } 3.395$$

$$TC = 12,000 \times 9.3 + \frac{5,000}{2} \times 3.395 + \frac{12,000}{5,000} \times 15$$

$$= \text{Rs } 1,20,123.50$$

where $Q^* = 2,000$, the TC here is less than the TC when $Q^* = 5,000$. Hence, the company should accept 5% concession on purchase price.

17. $D = 24,000$ units, $C_0 = \text{Rs } 22.5$; $C_h = 5.4\%$ of $1.25 = \text{Re } 0.0675$

Then $Q^* = 4,000$ units and $TC = \text{Rs } 30,270$

When working days are 300; $LT = 12$ days and $B = 400/$ units,

(i) $ROP = B + D \times LT$

$$= 400 + \frac{24,000}{300} \times 12 = 1,360 \text{ units.}$$

(ii)   Max. Inv. $= B + Q^* = 4,400$ units.

(iii)   Av. Inv. $= \frac{Q^*}{2} + B = 2,400$ units

When a concesion of 5 per cent on C is given,

$$C = 0.95 \times 1.25 = \text{Rs } 1.1875; \quad C_h = \frac{5.4}{100} \times 1.1875 = \text{Re } 0.06412$$

$$TC = \text{Rs } 29.282$$

Since new TC is less than the earlier one, therefore the company should accept the offer.

18.   (a) $ROP = B + D \times LT$ or $600 = 500 + D10$ or $D = 10$ units/day

$\therefore$ New $D = 70$ units

(b)   Av. Inv. $= Q/2 + B$ or $1,500 = Q/2 + 500$

or $Q = 2,000$ units.

Financial Management

8.1 Introduction

Finance is the word used to describe the money resources available to governments, firms, or individuals, and the management of these resources. The focus is on the second aspect—management. Financial management is the acquisition, management, and financing of resources by means of money, with due regard for prices in external markets. Resources are generally physical, such as cash, inventory, accounts receivable, equipment and machinery, or manufacturing and distribution facilities. Also, they include people—the employees of the firm. The money for these resources comes from a variety of sources, such as borrowing, leasing, public issues, and the internal cash flow generated by the firm's activities. The firm's goal is to provide and manage these resources as efficiently as possible, to balance needs against risks and returns. Firms keep track of resources in terms of money, and it is far simpler to use a single standard unit—money. The results of almost any activity considered by the firm can be expressed in terms of money. The primary concern is the firm and its operations. Since no firm exists in a vacuum, performance is affected by a variety of external factors such as the health of the economy, taxes, interest rates, and the prevailing political and regulatory conditions. In fact, the performance of the firm is ultimately judged by the investment community—another external factor. Hence, finance may aptly be said to be the circulatory system of the economic body of a firm. Financial management is a set of administrative actions which relate to the arrangement of cash and credit to enable the organization to carry out its objectives satisfactorily. The main feature of financial management is the formulation of the firm's strategy towards determining the efficient use of funds currently at the disposal of the firm, and selecting the most favourable sources of additional funds that the firm will need in the foreseeable future.

8.1.1 Definition

As Weston and Brigham have defined it, 'Financial management is an area of financial decision-making, harmonizing individual motives and enterprise goals.' According to Howard and Upton, "Financial management is an application of general managerial principles to the area of financial decision-making." Thus, financial management is an operational function clothed in a special garment. It involves financial planning, forecasting and provision of finance as well as formulation of financial policies. Hunt, William and Donaldson have rightly termed it as 'Resource Management.'

8.1.2 Difference between Accounting and Finance Functions

'Accounting' is a commonly used term in business circles. At times there is a confusion between accounting and finance functions. The source of this confusion is that in many countries, including India, the finance function is performed by the accountant himself. Though many organizations have financial executives besides the chief accountant, accounting and finance functions are usually clubbed. Hence, finance functions are recognized as part of the functions of the accountant. It is, therefore, necessary to know the distinction between the two.

Accounting
It is a system for collecting, summarizing, analysing and reporting, in monetary terms, financial information about an organization. This information relates to production, sales, expenditure,

investment, and losses and profits in the business. It provides information to parties inside as well as outside such as shareholders, bankers, creditors, management, etc. Accounting may be classified into three categories: (*a*) Financial accounting, (*b*) Cost accounting, and (*c*) Management accounting. Financial accounting is concerned with the recording, classification and reporting of various business transactions. Cost accounting ascertains costs of different items and presents information to the management for control of costs. Management accounting makes provision of financial costs and other monetary information for planning, coordination and control of business activities. This branch of accounting facilitates the management to take decisions with regard to determining the manufacturing or purchasing, prices, shutting down or continuing, etc.

Finance

The main function of finance is the procurement of funds and its optimum utilization. The important assignments of a financial executive are: (*a*) Assessment of capital requirements beforehand, (*b*) Obtaining funds at the lowest capital cost, and (*c*) Optimal use of the funds.

It is, therefore, apparent that the accounting and finance functions are two separate activities. In fact, finance functions include financial planning, policy formulation and control, whereas accounting is mainly concerned with the routine type of work.

The functions of a financial controller are enumerated below:

(*a*) Designing and operating the accounting system;

(*b*) Preparing financial statements and reports;

(*c*) Establishing and maintaining systems and procedures;

(*d*) Supervising internal auditing and arranging for external audit;

(*e*) Supervising computer applications;

(*f*) Overseeing cost control;

(*g*) Preparing budgets;

(*h*) Making forecasts and analytical reports;

(*i*) Reporting financial information to top management; and

(*j*) Handling tax matters.

Treasurer

He is the custodian and manager of all the cash and near-cash resources of the firm. The treasurer handles credit reviews and sets the policy for collecting receivables. He also handles the relationship with banks and other lending/financial institutions.

The Financial Executive Institute of the USA makes the following distinction between controllership and treasurership functions:

Controller	Treasurer
Planning and control	Provision of capital
Reporting and interpreting	Short-term financing
Evaluating and consulting	Banking and custody
Tax administration	Credit and collections
Government reporting	Investments
Protection of assets	Insurance
Economic appraisal	

8.1.3 Functions of Financial Management

The financial management functions encompass the entire spectrum of the firm's activities. Financial management is important not only for individuals in finance, but also for those in other areas, since these decisions, directly or indirectly, influence the fortunes of the firm. The functions of financial management can be divided into two groups:

Executive Functions

These functions involve financial, investment and dividend decision-making. These decisions require administrative skill, financial competence and technical foresight. Since the main objective of financial management is to maximize the value of the firm, it is required to make the following important decisions:

- The investment in and management of long-term assets through the capital budgeting process.
- Evaluating, securing and servicing long-term financing from within the firm or from capital market instruments such as common or preferred stock, debt, leases, warrants or convertibles.
- Management of the marginal (or divisional) cost of capital through attention to the firm's target capital structure and the various sources of funds available to the firm.
- Distribution of funds to the firm's shareholders through a cash dividend policy.
- Securing, managing, and investing in current assets such as cash, accounts receivable, and inventory.
- Obtaining short-term financing from creditors or from the money markets.
- Planning for the ongoing activities of the firm and ensuring that the firm responds to the changing financial and economic environment.
- Assessing the viability of growth through merging, and ensuring the economic viability of the firm.

Routine Functions

These functions are expected to be performed at a low level and include:

- Record keeping and reporting.
- Preparation of various financial statements.
- Cash planning and its supervision.
- Credit management.
- Custody of, and safeguarding, different financial securities, etc.
- Providing top management with information on current and prospective financial conditions of the business as a basis for policy decisions on purchases, marketing, and pricing.

8.1.4 Objectives of Financial Management

The objectives of financial management are usually considered at two levels—the macro-level and micro-level. At the macro-level, financial management is to make an intensive and economical use of scarce capital resources. This is an indirect social responsibility of financial management which can be readily defined although not easily put into practice.

Micro-level objectives of financial management are considered at the level of the firm. The goals of finance can be reasonably associated with the overall goals of business. A successful business enterprise often uses a goal-oriented financial structure. The financial manager performs certain tasks that help to achieve the goals of the finance department. These goals in turn help the firm to achieve its overall operating objectives. The functions of financial management and the objectives of a firm are shown in Fig. 8.1.

From the financial viewpoint, the following are the primary objectives of a firm:

Profit maximization. Profit maximization has been considered to be the most important business objective for the following reasons:

(*a*) It is rational to accept profit as a standard for measuring the success or efficiency of a business enterprise;

(*b*) It is difficult to survive without profit maximization;

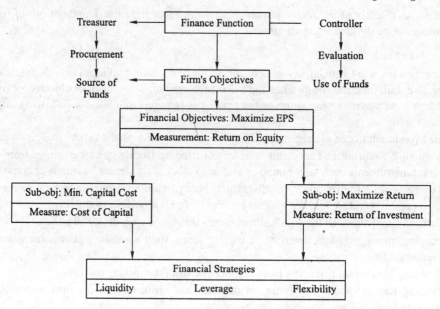

Fig. 8.1   Functions, objectives and its performance by financial management

(c) With more profits, it is possible to generate more funds, which may be utilized for expansion;

(d) In the absence of profit, business activity would remain at a static level; and

(e) Even for socio-economic welfare, maximization of profit is necessary.

The main disadvantages of profit maximization are as follows:

(a) It is an incomplete concept since it does not identify which of the returns need to be focused on;

(b) It provides no guidelines on levels of risk and uncertainty that might appropriately be accepted along with the profit forecast;

(c) This approach does not indicate the timing when profits are to be maximized; and

(d) It does not take into account the interests of others in the prosperity of the firm, such as the government, workers, community, etc.

Maximization of return. Maximization of return provides a basic guideline according to which financial decisions can be evaluated, but returns are mainly based on the profits earned by a firm.

Maximization of wealth. According to Prof. Ezra Solomon of Stanford University, "The ultimate goal of financial management should be the maximization of the owner's wealth." According to him, the maximization of profit is half and an unreal motive. The management must, therefore, work to bring about those flows that provide the highest possible market value to the ownership claim on the firm. Thus, the goal of wealth maximization and other operational goals of management are not in conflict with one another. Hence, maximization of wealth provides a basic guideline according to which financial decisions can be evaluated.

8.1.5 Role and Scope of Financial Management

Financial management is concerned with planning and control of finance functions. Some of the important areas outlining the role and scope of financial management are:

Estimating the requirement of funds. A careful estimate of short-term and long-term requirements of funds must be made. The investments in fixed assets and current assets have to be estimated through the techniques of budgetary control and long-range planning. These estimates are possible only if the physical activities of an organization have been adequately forecast.

Capital structure decisions. After an estimate of the requirements of funds, a decision has to be taken regarding various sources from which these funds could be raised. Each source of fund involves different considerations with regard to cost, risk and control. Keeping these factors in view, an optimum financing mix of various sources has to be worked out. The finance manager has to ensure that funds are procured at optimum cost with the least risk and the least dilution of control in the hands of the present owners. He examines the various methods by which a firm obtains short-term and long-term finances through various alternative sources.

Investment decisions. The investment of funds into various fixed and current assets also requires a careful scrutiny. Long-term funds should be invested in various projects only after an in-depth study through capital budgeting techniques and uncertainty analysis is made. Asset management policies should be laid down which relate to management of inventories, book debts, cash, trade creditors, etc. How the firm allocates its scarce resources and plans its growth will largely determine its value in the market place.

Dividend decision. The decision to declare a dividend involves a number of considerations such as trend of earnings, trend of share market prices, requirement of funds for future growth, cash flow situation, restrictions under the Companies Act, tax position of shareholders, etc. The controller has to strike a balance between the current needs of the firm for cash and the needs of the shareholders for adequate returns.

In addition to this, financial management involves the following subsidiary functions:

1. Supply of funds to all parts of the organization.
2. Evaluation of the financial performance.
3. Financial negotiations with bankers, financial institutions and other suppliers of credit.
4. Keeping track of the stock exchange, quotations and behaviour of stock exchange prices.
5. Financial control.
6. Keeping records of all assets.

Self-assessment Questions Set-I

1. Define and explain the following terms:
   (*a*) Finance, (*b*) Financial Management, (*c*) Treasurer, and (*d*) Controller.
2. Explain what is meant by the statement: 'Financial management is the acquisition, management and financing of resources by means of money, with due regard for prices in external markets.'
3. Define financial management and make a distinction between 'Accounting Function' and 'Finance Function.'
4. Discuss the functions of financial management in detail.
5. Briefly outline the responsibilities of financial management.
6. Explain the objectives of a firm from a financial viewpoint.
7. Outline the role and scope of financial management. Explain various aspects of capital structure decisions.
8. Explain the difference in the functioning of a treasurer and a controller.

8.2 Standard Forms of Financial Statement

Each business entity is required to prepare a set of financial statements at a definite periodic interval. Financial statements include *inter alia* the (*a*) balance sheet, and (*b*) profit and loss account. In addition to these two statements, some other statements may be prepared to suit the needs of the management. Balance-sheet and profit and loss account are obligatory to prepare by every company under the provisions of Companies Act, 1956. A set of provisions in the Act lays down the form and manner in which these statements are required to be prepared, time-limit for their submission and so on. Non-compliance/contravention of these provisions attract severe penal consequences. These statements are essentially meant for internal and external reporting.

8.2.1 Internal Reporting of Financial Statements

Internal reporting of financial statements to the management, *viz.*, board of directors/managing director/chief executive/general manager/various functional directors, etc., helps in the following areas:

• Decision on the policy matters.

- Exercise control.
- Appraise the performance at various levels of organization.
- Motivate to achieve better performance.
- Ensure better coordination.
- Planning for the future.

In fact, timely and accurate reporting of these statements at more frequent intervals is necessary. The exact pattern of internal reporting would depend upon the philosophy of the management and its expectations from the accounting information system.

8.2.2 External Reporting of Financial Statements

External reporting of balance sheet and profit and loss account includes:

- Shareholders.
- Financial institutions/banks.
- Taxation authorities.
- Government and semi-government authorities.

In addition, various other persons/parties are also interested in these financial statements such as mutual fund owners/long-term creditors or suppliers to know the solvency position of the company. Also, these statements are at times required by labour courts and/or industrial tribunal with reference to some industrial disputes between the employer and the employees.

8.2.3 Income and Expenditure Statement

Income and expenditure statement, popularly known as profit and loss account, shows the summary of income and expenses during a specified period. It includes the following segments:

(a) Sale of products/services,
(b) Income from other than sales,
(c) Manufacturing/factory cost,
(d) Office and administrative cost,
(e) Selling and distribution cost,
(f) Finance cost, and
(g) Non-operating cost.

All these segments may be shown in the main text of the profit and loss account or may be shown in the form of schedules annexed thereto, in which case only the total of each schedule will appear in the profit and loss account under the appropriate heading. The Companies Act has not prescribed any particular format for the income statement, but it has only laid down the contents and disclosures which must be embodied in the same. Hence, the company enjoys flexibility as to the presentation of the income and expenditure statement. An example is given below:

Profit and Loss Account of ABC Ltd. for the Year Ended 2006

Opening Stock	*Sales*
Raw materials	*Less:* Returns
Work-in-progress	Income from service rendered
Finished goods	Interest on investment
Purchase of raw materials	Dividend on investment
Stores and purchase	Profit on sale of fixed assets
Power and fuel	Sale of scrap
Salaries, wages, bonus, etc.	Miscellaneous income

Opening Stock	Sales
Contribution to PF, etc.	Closing stock
Staff welfare expenses	Raw materials
Rent	
Rates and taxes	
Repair and maintenance	Work-in-progress
Gratuity	

Profit and Loss Account of ABC Ltd. for the Year Ended 2006

Audit fee and legal expenses
Directors' remuneration
Printing and stationery
Postage, fax, etc.
Commission, discount, etc.
Sales promotion and advertising
Miscellaneous expenses
Freight and transport
Interest on borrowing
Depreciation
Provision for taxation
Net profit

The income and expenditure statement, irrespective of its form, lists items of income/revenue on one hand and the items of costs/expenses on the other. When both sides are summed up, one of the following three possibilities may arise: (*a*) Income is greater than expenses, (*b*) Income is equal to expenses; (*c*) Income is less than expenses. In the first case, it represents profit, while in third case, the difference represents loss. The second case indicates the situation of no loss, no profit, which is a rare occurrence in business. In case of profit, the net profit has to be placed on the side of expenses as a balancing figure. For loss, the net loss has to be placed on the income side so that both sides of the income and expenditure statement tally each other.

Profit and Loss Appropriation Account

In case of a limited company, after profit and loss account is balanced, the balancing figure of net profit/loss is transferred to yet another account, known as profit and loss appropriation account. The net profit is at the disposal of the Board of Directors for the appropriation, which is to be approved finally by the shareholders of the company. This earning has several outlets, *viz*., dividend on preference and equity shares, transfer to sinking fund, writing off intangible assets and accumulated losses, and finally transfer the residue to the balance sheet. These appropriations are proposed by the director and required to be approved by shareholders. The representative format of the profit and loss appropriation account is given below:

Transfer to sinking fund	Balance b/f. from the previous year
Transfer to contingency reserve	
Transfer to dividend equalization reserve	Net profit for the current year
Proposed dividend on preference shares	
Proposed dividend on equity shares	
Balance transferred to balance sheet as surplus	

In essence, income and expenditure statement reveals the net result of the business operations and is known as Profit and Loss Account/Statement of Income and Earned Surplus/Statement of

Income and Expenses/Statement of Earning/Operating Statement, etc. The net result of the income statement, after appropriations, finds its place in the balance sheet.

8.2.4 Balance Sheet

The balance sheet is a statement, which reveals its assets and liabilities on a particular date. It is not an account, as a convention the liabilities are recorded on the left side while the assets on the right. Total of both sides of the balance sheet must tally with each other. The liabilities are total funds of the business, which include the owner's funds (equity) and borrowed funds. These funds are invested in various assets of an enterprise to earn profit. Therefore, total of the assets must tally with the total of funds invested in them. In other words, the liabilities as resources are equal to the total assets on which the resources are deployed. This phenomenon may be expressed in the following equations:

(*a*) Total of liabilities = Total of assets

(*b*) Owner's fund + Borrowed fund = Total assets

(*c*) Equity + Debt = Total assets.

8.3 Fixed and Current Asset Items

Assets are the valuable resources owned by the business entity and are used as the main criteria to earn profit. Since the assets are acquired at cost, they have money value. For inclusion in the balance sheet, assets are divided into *four* main categories:

- **Current assets:** It consists of cash, bank balances, short-term investments, sundry debtors of accounts receivables, bills receivables, inventories or stock of all kinds, prepaid expenses, accrued income, advances recoverable in cash or in kind for value to be received, short-term loans made, deposits kept with various authorities, advance payment of income-tax, current accounts, etc.

- **Fixed assets:** It consists of land, building, plant and machinery, furniture and fittings, electric installations, equipment, vehicles, etc. (to be shown at written down value, i.e., at original cost *less* accumulated depreciation).

- **Miscellaneous assets:** It consists of deferred revenue expenditure underwriting commission, preliminary expenses, development expenditure, R&D costs, and accumulated losses (to the extent not adjusted against free reserves).

- **Intangible assets:** It consists of goodwill, technical know-how, patent, trade marks, copy rights, etc.

Therefore, total assets may be expressed as the sum of all *four* types of assets as explained above.

8.4 Fixed and Current Liability Items

Contrary to the assets, liabilities are claims on the business and against all assets by the owners and outside creditors. At the same time, they are the sources of funds. For inclusion in the balance sheet, liabilities are classified into *four* main categories:

Current liabilities: It consists of trade creditors, accounts payable, bills payable, short-term loans from banks and others, short-term fixed deposit, short-term portion of long-term loans, outstanding advances from customers, provisions for taxation, proposed dividend, unpaid dividend, etc.

Long-term liabilities: It consists of debentures, long-term loans from banks and financial institutions, deferred payment credits, long-term fixed deposits, loans from other convertible bonds, etc.

Reserves: It consists of capital reserves, committed reserves, general reserve, dividend equalization reserve, other free reserves, development rebate reserve, investment allowance reserve and residue surplus, share premium, etc.

Share capital: It consists of paid-up portion of share capital—preference and equity share.

Therefore, liability may be expressed as the sum of all four types of liabilities as explained above. Here

Current liabilities + Long-term liabilities = Outside liabilities (borrowed funds)

Reserves + Share capital = Net worth (owner's funds)

Current assets – Current liabilities = Working capital

Finally, total assets = total liabilities. Alternately, balance sheet may be analysed by the following equations:

1. Total liabilities = Total assets

If both these expressions are expanded to cover their segments, second equation is obtained.

2. Share capital + reserves + long-term liabilities + current liabilities

= Fixed assets + Current assets + Intangible assets + Miscellaneous assets

Further, following two changes are required to be made in second equation:

- Current liabilities to be shifted from left to right since, in the process, its sign will become negative (–) from positive (+).

- Miscellaneous assets are to be written off against reserves in due course in accordance with sound accounting principles. Hence, change from right to left, in the process, and sign will also change. Thus, a new equation is obtained.

3. Share capital + reserves – Miscellaneous assets + Long-term liabilities

= Fixed assets + Intangible assets + Current assets – Current liabilities

Functionally, the combination of share capital + reserves – miscellaneous assets indicates the funds contributed by belonging to owners of the business (shareholder). This is known as *net worth* or *owner's equity*. On the other hand, long-term liabilities indicate the borrowed funds known as *debt*. On the other side, the combination of fixed and intangible sunk into the business for long-term purpose, while the excess of 'current assets' over current liabilities is known as *net working capital*.

4. Owner's equity + Debt = Fixed capital + Net working capital.

Here both sides represent the total capital employed from the viewpoint of liability and asset sides of the balance sheet, respectively.

According to one school of thought, current liabilities should be included in the total capital employed. Accordingly, total capital employed (TCE) may be defined as:

TCE = Owner's equity + Long-term liabilities + Current liabilities

TCE = Fixed capital + Gross working capital

Therefore, it is necessary that total capital employed must be clearly defined and the context in which it is being used.

8.5 Mechanics of Accounting

The maintenance of books of accounts has been made compulsory under various laws. For instance, under Section 209 of the Companies Act, every company shall keep, at its registered office, proper books of accounts with respect to (*a*) all sums of money received and spent by the company and the matters in respect of which the receipt and expenditure take place, (*b*) the assets and liabilities of the company, and (*c*) all sales and purchases of goods of the company. Under Section 44A of the Income-tax Act, maintenance of books of accounts has been made obligatory for non-corporate business entities, *viz.*, proprietary firms, partnership firms, associations, etc., subject to certain exceptions.

In order to ensure the compliance with the statutory provisions, following books of accounts become necessary.

8.5.1 Cash Books

All transactions in cash and/or cheques are entered in cash book, *viz.*, receipt and payments. Transactions are recorded in appropriate columns with necessary details. This book is balanced regularly so that the balance of cash or bank account can be ascertained. Depending on the magnitude of cash transactions, more than one cash book may be maintained. Receipts and vouchers are the source documents for making entries in the cash book.

8.5.2 Sales Book

All transactions of sales are recorded in sales books. Entries in sales book are made on the basis of invoice/bills which are prepared, addressed to customers, after the goods are despatched. More than one sales book is required to be prepared for different groups of products, territories, branches, etc.

8.5.3 Purchase Book

All transactions of purchase are recorded in purchase book. Entries in purchase book are made on the basis of bills/invoices which are received from suppliers, whenever goods are purchased.

8.5.4 Debit Note/Credit Note Book

For goods purchased and sold, certain adjustments are required to be made, *viz.*, cancellations, reductions for equality rebate/discount, reduction for short quantity despatched, reduction for damaged goods, etc. To incorporate such adjustments in the accounts, either debit note or credit note is issued against or in favour of supplier/customer. These debit and credit notes are recorded in the debit/credit note registers.

8.5.5 Journal

All transactions which cannot be recorded in any other book are entered in journal. These include, *inter alia*, rectification entries, transfer entries, closing entries, adjustments, provisions, etc.

8.5.6 Ledger

Once the transaction is recorded in the appropriate book/register, it has to be posted in the ledger to the appropriate account. Since each and every transaction is recorded with respect to dual aspect, it is posted to *debit* and *credit* of the appropriate account. Each account in ledger represents a summarised record of all transactions concerning that particular account. Values appear in the final statements, *viz.*, balance sheet and income statements, are derived from the ledger, hence the importance of ledger as books of account. In the ledger, the accounts are kept for each individual item of income, expenses, assets and liabilities.

Some of these books have significance from legal viewpoint, *e.g.*, sales and purchase books are required to be maintained in compliance with tax laws. Records for salaries and wages are to be maintained in compliance with provident fund law, employee state insurance laws, etc. Each and every book is to be balanced periodically. The exact frequency of balancing will depend upon the choice of management. However, it has to be done increasingly at the close of the financial year.

8.5.7 Process of Accounting

The accounting process begins with the occurrence of business transactions, when it is recorded in the books. It may be divided into the following phases:

1. Record the transaction in the appropriate book of primary entry. For this purpose, cash book, sales book, purchase book, debit note/credit note book and journal are regarded as the books of prime entry, where the transaction is first recorded.

2. Post the transaction from the book of prime entry to the appropriate account in ledger. This is popularly known as *ledger posting*.

3. Balance each ledger account at definite periodic intervals which cannot be more than one year

4. Prepare a statement of ledger balance as on a particular day, which is known as trial balance. In this statement, the total of debits and credits must agree with each other, which is the test of arithmetical accuracy.

5. Make necessary adjustments and provisions to ensure that the accounting is done in conformity with the accepted principle, *viz., accrual* or *cash* or *mixed* as the case may be, which is to be followed consistently.

6. Prepare financial statements, *viz.,* income statement for the period ended and balance sheet as on the last day of the period.

8.6 Linkage of Two Successive Balance Sheets

The linkage between two successive balance sheets is as given below:

1. All items in the balance-sheet on both sides, i.e., assets and liabilities of one year are opened in the general ledger of the subsequent year as opening balance.

2. Items shown in the balance-sheet are as per the format fixed under Schedule VI of the Companies Act. Accordingly, it is as per the items shown as under:

Assets	*Liabilities*
Fixed assets	Share capital
Investments	Secured loan
Current assets, loans and advances	Unsecured loan
Miscellaneous expenditure	Current liabilities and provisions

(*a*) Fixed assets figures of one year is shown in the balance sheet of the next year as opening balance and if the figure differs from the last year, there must be some addition/deletion from the fixed assets. This will indicate the linkage in respect of addition/deletion.

(*b*) Investments increase or decrease will show new investments or sale of investments.

(*c*) Under current assets, items relate to core sundry debtors, total balances, closing stock, etc. Any change in these items will reflect as *addition* or *deletion*.

(*d*) Increase/decrease in liabilities will show further *addition* in liabilities or payment of liabilities.

Subsequent year balance sheet is based on the previous year balance sheet in all respects and all items of balance sheet of subsequent year are linked with the previous year for comparison and ready reference.

8.7 Funds Flow Statement

This statement indicates changes in working capital. It is a financial operational statement revealing the methods by which a business has been financed and the areas of which it applies its funds over a period of time. It tells the management about the sources from which a company has been financed, whether any excess credit has been taken and whether there are any weakness due to lack of internal capitalisation. This statement is called by different names such as *statement of sources* or *acquisition of funds, statement of derivation and disposition of the means of operations,* and *where got where gone statement.* During an accounting period, it shows how funds flow between different assets and equity items.

According to Almond Coleman, "Funds flow statement summarizes the significant financial changes occur during the accounting period of a company."

There is a general recognition in industry, business and among professional accounting bodies that financial statements should provide relevant information which meet the multiple objectives of shareholders, investors, creditors, customers, and the public, which enable them to arrive at rational economic decisions.

In general, funds flow statement offers the following advantages:

1. Provides information about how funds are obtained and how they are put to actual use.

2. Registers changes in the flow of funds during a given period of time.

3. Supplements to the conventional financial statements.

4. Indicates the way funds are generated from different financial resources of a company and how the reservoir of its assets is created. In other words, it depicts changes in the financial structure of the company.

5. It is an important tool for financial management in the process of decision-making.

6. Determines the financial consequences of business operations.

7. Enables the financial manager regarding the amount of loan requirements, purpose for which it is required, terms of repayment, source of repayment, etc.

8. Enables the financial manager to allocate resources to productive investments.

9. Evaluates the urgency of operational matters and makes it easier for a company to set a time limit within which its operating problems may come to a critical stage, i.e., when its resources are likely to be exhausted.

10. Enables the management to take decisions on planning a dividend policy with a well-set programme of financial re-organization.

11. Provides a source of information on possible managerial issues in conjunction with the balance sheet and the operating statement.

12. Closely related to the normal business decision-making process—accounting statements, balance sheets and income statements, and is related to a time span.

8.7.1 Statement of Sources and Application of Funds

It is essential to prepare a statement showing changes in working capital. In case of an increase in capital, it is an application of funds, while a decrease in it a source of funds.

Items to be Added to Net Profit
- Depreciation, depletion, amortization, etc.
- Deferred revenue expenditure.
- Loss on sale of fixed assets.

Items to be Deducted
- Gain on the sale of fixed assets.
- Income-tax payment.
- Identify the sources and application of funds.

Sources of Funds
- Funds from operations.
- Decrease in fixed assets.
- Increase in liabilities.
- Proceeds from the sale of securities and borrowings.
- Sale of investments and other fixed assets.
- Non-trading items such as dividend received.
- Decrease in working capital.

Application of Funds
- Loss from operations.
- Increase in fixed assets.
- Decrease in liabilities.
- Redemption of securities and loans.

- Purchase of fixed assets and investments.
- Cash dividends.
- Non-trading expenses such as interest on borrowings.
- Increase in working capital.

An example of fund flow statement for the year 2005-06 is given below:

Acquisition	Rs	Rs	Disposal of Assets	Rs	Rs
Proprietor's funds					
Share capital		34,750			
Debentures		10,000			
Trading profit		60,000	Bank Overdraft (opening)		1,25,000
		1,04,750			
Add: Depreciation		3,000	Increase in Assets		
		1,07,750	Fixed Assets	20,000	
			Stock	20,000	
			Debtors	10,000	50,000
Less: Taxes	25,000				
Overprovision	5,000				
	20,000				
Transfer of Tax Reserve	2,000	18,000			
		89,750			
Increase in Liabilities		15,000	Decrease in Liabilities		
Outstanding Liabilities					
for expenses		3,000	Taxes settled		25,000
Taxes		29,000	Profit distributed		20,000
	c/f	1,36,750		c/f	2,20,000
	b/f	1,36,750		b/f	2,20,000
Sales of Investments	15,000				
Add: Profit on sale of	4,500	19,500			
investments					
Bank Overdraft		63,750			
		2,20,000			2,20,000

8.8 Financial Ratios and their Applications

The relationship of one item to another expressed in a simple mathematical form is known as ratio. There are two main ways to analyse a financial ratio: (*a*) In a trend analysis, behaviour of the ratio across the time is studied; and (*b*) In a comparative analysis, the performance of a firm at a single point of time relative either to other firms in the industry or to some other accepted industry standard is studied. Standards can be measured either firm's own internal standards or firm's performance is compared with that of other firms.

8.8.1 Principles of Ratio Selection

Following points are considered for selection of financial ratio:

- The manager should be provided with a single key ratio which indicates unequivocally the extent of his success.
- Ratios should be logically inter-related.
- The manager should not be given any ratio which cannot lead to action.

- Ratios must measure a material factor of a business.
- Cost of obtaining information should be borne in mind.
- Different ratios are required for different industries.
- Different levels of management require different ratios.
- There should be consistency between the method of calculating a ratio and the standard with which it is compared.
- It is necessary to remove the inflationary effects on the assets and capital values at different times.
- While relating profits, costs or sales to assets or capital, the figures should be averaged on the basis of their values over the period to which profits, costs or sales relate.
- The calculation of ratio that relate benefit to expenditure must take into account the time lag between incurring expenditure and receiving benefit out of it.

8.8.2 Types of Financial Ratios

Financial ratios may be broadly classified as:

- Liquidity ratios
- Profitability ratios
- Debt ratios
- Operating ratios
- Turnover ratios
- Miscellaneous ratios.

1. **Liquidity Ratios:** Christy and Roden define the liquidity of an asset as moneyness. There are two kinds of liquidity: (*i*) Static, and (*ii*) Dynamic.

   Static liquidity: The financial manager can calculate static measure of liquidity from a firm's balance sheet. These ratios are static because they are measured at a single point of time.

   Dynamic liquidity: It often happens that static liquidity ratios may change with the passage of time. Since a firm undergoes different phases of business cycles, current ratios or working capital levels may also undergo similar changes. This aspect of liquidity is dynamic because it is related to time. A firm's liquidity may vary over the business cycle because: (*a*) availability of credit varies over a business cycle; (*b*) market value of assets varies over a business cycle; and (*c*) The credit worthiness of a firm's receivables varies over a business cycle.

   Liquidity ratios indicate the ability of the firm to pay its obligations and include the following:

   Current ratio: It attempts to measure the ability of a firm to meet its current obligations or, in other words, the liquidity of business. It is shown as:

   $$\frac{\text{Current Assets}}{\text{Current Liabilities}}$$

   Example: Current Assets   8,00,000

   Current Liabilities   4,00,000

   Current Ratio $= \dfrac{800,000}{400,000} = 2:1$

   The financial health of a company can, with reasonable reliability, be judged by the concept of current ratios. The device of the ratio should be taken as a useful tool in the hands of analysis who should not judge a company's strength merely on the basis of its profitability/growth. In any operating concern, the current ratio should be 2 : 1. However, it should not be accepted rigidly. Each industry has its own peculiar problems. The ratio may vary between 1.5 : 1 to 3.5 : 1.

Advantages of current ratio: (*i*) It presents a general picture of the adequacy of the working capital position of a company; (*ii*) It serves as a specific measure of liquidity and flexibility of a company, (*iii*) It is the most commonly used ratio, (*iv*) It indicates a company's current debt-paying capacity, (*v*) It represents a margin of safety, i.e., a cushion of protection against current creditors, and (*vi*) It indicates the extent to which a firm's most pressing claims can be met from assets.

Disadvantages of current ratio: (*i*) It cannot be said to be appropriate for all business, since the amount of working capital and the size of the current ratio depend upon many factors and common standards, and (*ii*) There is clearly some latitude for window-dressing, within certain limits a company may be able to manage its current assets and liabilities so as to have the desired ratios at the time the balance sheet is presented.

2. **Profitability ratios:** For the accountant and business manager, profit is synonymous with owner's earnings, and is found by subtracting costs, including interest charges from the total revenue accruing to a firm during a particular period of its operations. Being a ratio, profitability is a meaningful measure and can be used as an effective standard of performance regardless of a firm's size. Profitability ratios can be classified as follows.

Gross profit margin: This ratio is computed by subtracting cost of goods sold from sales and putting the difference over sales.

Net operating margin: This ratio goes beyond gross profit margin and indicates the firm's ability to cover administrative and selling costs. These costs require cash outlets and depreciation which a company must ultimately provide for. It is computed by dividing the net operating profit by sales.

Example 1.

		Rs	% of Sales	
Gross Profit		4,00,000	40	
Less: Selling and administrative costs	2,00,000			
Depreciation	1,00,000	3,00,000	30	(3,00,000)
				10,00,000
Net Operating Margin		1,00,000		(1,00,000)
				10,00,000

Return on investment ratio: This ratio measures a return on the owner's investment. It is shown as:

$$\frac{\text{Profit before taxes}}{\text{Sales}} \times \frac{\text{Sales}}{\text{Equity capital}}$$

Example 2. Profit before taxes: 1,16,400

Sales   10,00,000

Equity capital   6,20,000

$$\text{Return on investment ratio} = \frac{1,16,400}{10,00,000} \times \frac{10,00,000}{6,20,000}$$

Return on equity: Return on equity may be on total equity or on common equity. The total stockholders equity is the aggregate of equity and preferred stock.

$$\text{Return on Total Equity} = \frac{\text{Net Profit after Taxes}}{\text{Total Stockholders Equity}}$$

$$\text{Return on Common Equity} = \frac{\text{Net Profit for Common Stock}}{\text{Common Equity}}.$$

Return on assets: This is the return on investment. A comparison of a firm can be made with other firms.

Net profit to net worth: This ratio measures the profit return on investment. It is reward for the assumption of ownership risk.

$$\text{Net Profit to Net Worth} = \frac{\text{Net Profit Retains after Taxes}}{\text{Tangible Net Worth}}$$

$$= \frac{\text{Net Profit after Taxes}}{\text{Shareholders Funds} + \text{Profit Retains in Business}}$$

Owner's equity to total assets: This ratio is often known as *the proprietary ratio* or *shareholders equity ratio*, i.e.,

$$\frac{\text{Owners Equity}}{\text{Total Assets}}$$

Fixed assets to tangible net worth: It is shown as fixed assets/tangible net worth.

Times interest earned: It is shown as

$$\frac{\text{Earnings before Interest and Taxes}}{\text{Interest Payments}}$$

Ratio of current liabilities to tangible net worth: If current liabilities are increased on the one hand and current assets decreased on the other, it would indicate that the firm is getting very close to the stage of technical insolvency.

Total liabilities of tangible net worth: The ratio measures the freedom of action of the management towards its creditors.

3. **Debt ratios:** Debt ratios indicate the financial stability of a firm. It is shown as

$$\frac{\text{Long-term Debt}}{\text{Owner's Equity}} = \frac{5,00,000}{7,20,000} = 1:14.$$

4. **Operating ratio:** This ratio is written as: cost of goods sold + operating expenses.

It can be used as a test of financial condition after considering other revenues and expenses.

5. **Turnover ratio:** This ratio may be used to assess stock utilisation. It is written as

$$\frac{\text{Cost of Sales}}{\text{Average of Opening and Closing Stock}}.$$

6. **Miscellaneous ratio:** Working capital represents the volume of current assets advances from long-term resources. It is that part of a firm's current assets which will stay. Under this ratio, following ratios are included:
   • Inventory to working capital.
   • Long-term liabilities to working capital.
   • Fixed assets to long-term liabilities.
   • Current assets to total liabilities.

Example 3. According to the recent balance-sheet of ABC company, the following data are obtained:

Current assets :   Rs. 5,00,000
Current liability : Rs. 50,000
Sales :   Rs. 1,00,000
Inventory :   Rs. 50,000

Find the following for the company : (*a*) Current ratio, (*b*) Quick ratio; and (*c*) Inventory turnover ratio.

(*c*) Inventory turnover ratio.

Solution :   Current ratio = 5,00,000/50,000 = 10

Quick ratio = 5,00,000 – 50,000/50,000 = 9

Inventory turnover ratio = 1,00,000/50,000 = 2

8.9 Advantages of Financial Ratios

Following advantages can be derived from financial ratios:

1. The process of producing financial ratios is essentially concerned with identification of significant accounting data relationships which give the decision-maker insights into the company that is assessed.
2. Ratio analysis involves a study of the total financial picture. By thorough understanding of the importance of each ratio, the analyst can recommend and indicate positive action with confidence.
3. One of the important use of financial ratios is to predict company failures.

8.10 Limitations of Financial Ratios

Limitations of financial ratios are:

1. Financial standard data are not exact. Therefore, financial ratios should be considered with great caution.
2. The ratios refer to past events and may not represent the present/future events.
3. Financial statements are generally based on historical/original cost. The current economic conditions are ignored.
4. Financial ratios are difficult to understand by ordinary businessman.
5. Not all ratios are significant and useful.
6. A ratio is of little value in isolation. It is necessary to have some standard with which to compare it.
7. A frequent comparison of ratios between companies is questionable, particularly when there are important differences between companies, such as industry, the nature of operations, etc.
8. Ratios are based on financial statement and suffer from the limitations inherent in these statements.
9. Changes in many ratios are closely associated/connected with one another.
10. Due to change in product lines, markets, economic conditions, prices, etc., ratio during the current period with the corresponding ratio during the previous period may change.
11. Ratios are likely to be misused. In some situations they may appear to be misleading.
12. While comparing the financial ratios of a particular firm with those of similar firms, the differences between the firms should be recognised, *e.g.*, methods of accounting operations and financing.
13. Ratios derived from financial statements should be combined with an investigation of the facts before valid conclusions can be drawn.
14. A ratio analysis is a guide rather than a solution of present problems and future plans. It is not possible to suggest absolute ratios for a firm. There are factors such as competition, financial resources, company objectives, etc., which should be taken into consideration. A rigid set of rules is likely to do more harm than good.

Self-assessment Questions Set-II

1. What are the Financial Statements? Explain internal and external reporting of financial statements.
2. What is profit and loss account? What are the segments included in this account? Give an appropriate example for the profit and loss account.
3. Explain clearly the meaning of profit and loss appropriation account.
4. Profit and loss account and balance sheet are complimentary to each other and not mutually exclusive. Elucidate this statement.
5. What are the different categories of assets and liabilities? Explain with suitable illustrations.
6. Who are the different users of financial statements?
7. What are the items represented in fixed and current assets?
8. Explain the items represented in fixed and current liabilities.
9. Why is maintenance of books of account necessary?

226

Engineering Management

10. Explain how cash book, sales book, purchase book, and debit note/credit note are prepared?
11. Why is maintenance of ledger essential?
12. Explain the process of accounting in detail.
13. Outline the salient points in linking two successive balance sheets.
14. What do you understand by funds flow statement? Explain its advantages.
15. 'Preparation of a statement of sources/application of funds is essential.' Comment on this statement.
16. Define financial ratio and underlying principles of ratio selection.
17. Enumerate selected ratios under following categories and comment upon them:
    (a) Liquidity, (b) Profitability, (c) Operating, and (d) Turnover.
18. Explain and illustrate as to how turnover ratios are used in working capital management.
19. What are the applications and limitations of ratio analysis?
20. How do you calculate Return on Investment (ROI)? Explain the key factors affecting ROI.
21. (a) Distinguish among funds, working capital, networking capital, and income; and (b) Why do finance managers use a variety of measures of profits for firms.
22. (a) Differentiate between the current ratio and acid test; and (b) Why is it possible for a firm to have high profits but still beunable to pay its bill when they are due?
23. Describe the following components of a balance-sheet giving suitable examples: (a) Current assets; (b) Fixed assets; (c) Current liabilities; (d) Fixed liabilities.
24. How are inventories considered in a balance sheet—assets or liabilities?
25. Show a representative profit and loss statement of a company of your choice. Use hypothetical figures.
26. What do you understand by trial balance. Explain with a suitable example.
27. Present the account form as well as report form of a balance sheet.
28. What is investment analysis? Why is it of great importance to a firm? Discuss a method of evaluating investment proposals.
29. What is the net present value of the following cash stream, if the discount rate is 14%.

Year	0	1	2	3	4
Cash flow	5000	6000	8000	9000	8000

Hint : Year 0: $5000 \times (1.14)^0 = 5000$; Year 1 : $6000 / (1.14)^1$
$= 5263.16$; Year 2: $8000 \times (1.14)^2 = 6155.74$; Year 3:
$9000 \times (1.14)^3 = 6074.74$; and Year 4 : $8000 \times (1.14)^4 = 4736.64$
Net present value = 27230.28

30. A firm is considering two alternative investments. The first investment costs Rs. 30,000 and the second investment Rs. 50,000; The expected annual cash income streams is shown below :

Year	Cash, Inflow, Rs	
	Alternative A	Alternative B
1	10,000	15,000
2	10,000	15,000
3	10,000	15,000
4	10,000	15,000
5	10,000	15,000

Assuming 8 percent cost at capital, find which alternative has the highest net present value.
Hint : Alternative A: 3.993 (PV factor) × Rs. 10,000 = Rs. 39,930 less cost of investment, i.e., Rs. 30,000. Net present value = Rs. 9930.
Alternative B: 3.999 (PV factor) × Rs 15,000 = Rs. 59,895 less cost of investment, i.e, Rs. 50,000. Net present value = 9895. Since NPV at A exceeds that of B by Rs. 35, investment in alternative A is the best option.
31. What are different liabilities in a balance-sheet? What is owner's equity?

Managerial Economics

9.1 Introduction

Before defining the term 'managerial economics', it is necessary to know how it is different from 'economics.' There are many aspects of economics. It may concern employment, rate of exchange, the budget of the government, price level, scarcity of various products, etc. All these aspects are influenced, directly or indirectly, by the decisions of human beings concerning the allocation of resources—time and money. For example, determination of wages is influenced by the interaction of forces of demand and supply of labour. The determination of demand for labour (workers required to be employed) is based on marginal product of labour to the firm. The decision for recruiting the labour force is taken by the particular firm in question. In the same way, the currency exchange rate with other country's currency is guided by the relative demand for the currency of the two countries.

Based on the discussion, it is possible to define economics in simple words as 'Economics is one of the disciplines of social sciences which deals with that aspect of human behaviour which pertains to the allocation of resources between alternative uses.' Another definition given by PA Samuelson is as follows: 'Economics is the study of how men and society end up choosing, with or without the use of money, to employ scarce productive resources that could have alternative uses, to produce various commodities and distribute them for consumption, now or in future, among various people and groups in society. It analyses the cost and benefits of improving patterns of resource allocation.' This definition covers many aspects such as human behaviour, allocation of scarce resources and alternative use of resources. These are briefly discussed below:

Human behaviour: It may relate to the behaviour of the individual, firm or the government. Human behaviour may pertain to the allocation of his income to various activities such as education, food, transport, housing and so on. Behaviour of the firm may pertain to the allocation of resources (man, machine, material, money, etc.) to various productive activities. Behaviour of government may pertain to the allocation of resources to activities and sectors of economy such as agriculture, industry, defence, social service, law and order, etc.

Allocation of scarce resources: The allocation problem of resources (of money mainly to exercise control over goods and services) arises because of its limited supply compared to the demand. The scarcity of resources calls for an optimal allocation of resources amongst various productive activities.

Alternative uses of resources: There are resources which may be used for different purposes. For example, coal may be used in (a) generating thermal power; (b) running of steam railway engines, (c) manufacturing steel; and (d) domestic cooking, etc. If the alternative uses of a particular resource are limited, then choice of its use is relatively simple.

9.2 Managerial Economics

Managerial economics is the hybrid of two disciplines—*management* and *economics*. Management deals with a set of principles which help in decision-making under different situations, and improve the effectiveness of business organizations. Economics provides a set of propositions for optimal allocation of scarce resources to achieve the desired objectives. Some definitions given by different authors are as follows:

- *'Managerial economics deals with integration of economic theory with business practice for the purpose of facilitating decision-making and forward planning by management.'*

  — Spencer and Sigelman

- *'The purpose of managerial economics is to show how economic analysis can be used in formulating business policies.*

  — Joel Dean

- *'Managerial economics is concerned with using logic of economics, mathematics and statistics to provide effective ways of thinking about business decision problems.'*

  — Hague

- *'Managerial economics attempts to bridge the gap between the purely analytical problems that intrigue many economic theorists and the problems of policies that the management must face.'*

  — Mansfield

In other words, managerial economics provides the link between traditional economics and the decision sciences (mathematics, statistics, operations research, economics and econometrics, etc.) in managerial decision-making, as illustrated in Fig. 9.1.

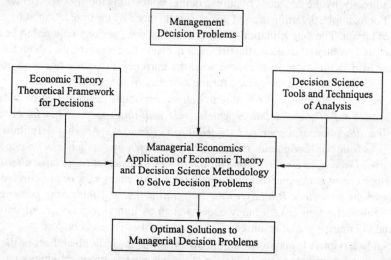

Fig. 9.1 Role of managerial economics in decision-making

The principles of managerial economics about the efficient allocation of scarce resources are equally relevant to the management of non-business, non-profit organizations such as government agencies, co-operatives, universities, hospitals, etc.

9.3 Factors Influencing Managerial Decisions

The choices and decisions made by managers are influenced by economic considerations as well as by three other variables: (*a*) human and behavioural considerations, (*b*) technological forces, and (*c*) environmental factors.

Managers, at times, do not resort to purely economic logic, but also take into account factors such as the impact of a decision on employee's morale or motivation. Many small entrepreneurs decide to remain small since they feel that any expansion will tend to strain their lifestyle or threaten their control over management.

The assessment of technological alternatives, the technological moves of competitors and emerging new technologies and processes are among the most critical factors that managers take into account while planning and allocating resources within the enterprise. No major investment decision is made without a close scrutiny of the relevant technological alternatives. Even short-run production or marketing decisions are bound to take into account the technological variables appropriate for the situation.

Environmental pressure is also growing on managerial decisions due to *two* reasons: (*a*) Growing public awareness about impact of organization's decisions on society. Therefore, political parties, trade unions, consumer groups, etc. are concerned about the nature and consequences of such decisions and always try to impose their viewpoints which may conflict with an economic viewpoint of the enterprise; and (*b*) manager's decisions are challenged on the ground that such decisions have not taken into consideration the social costs such as pollution, congestion, etc.

9.4 Micro- and Macroeconomics

9.4.1 Microeconomics

The term microeconomics is derived from the Greek word *micros* meaning 'small', and therefore microeconomics deals with a small component of the national economy of a country. Microeconomics may be defined as that branch of economic analysis which studies the economic behaviour of the individual unit, may be a person, a particular household, industry or commodity.

Microeconomic theory is concerned with *four* basic economic questions:

1. What goods shall be produced and in what quantities?
2. How shall they be produced?
3. How the goods and services produced shall be distributed?
4. How efficiently are the resources being used?

The first question arises due to limited availability of resources. The problem of allocating these resources optimally among the various uses is solved by the market system. The allocation of resources to the production of various goods and services in a free market economy depends upon the prices of various goods and factors of production. Thus, to explain how the allocation of resources is determined, microeconomics helps to analyse how the relative prices of goods and factors are determined. Since microeconomic theory is concerned with the analysis of price system, it is also called the *theory of price*.

The second question arises due to alternative methods of producing goods. Thus, there is a need to ascertain the best possible combination of resources to be used for producing any commodity. This type of problem is analysed under the *theory of production* or under the *theory of firm*.

The third question is concerned with the distribution of national product amongst various individuals and groups engaged in the production process in different capacities in the society. This problem is analysed under the *theory of distribution* or under *the theory of factor pricing*.

The fourth question is concerned with the efficient use of resources in the production of maximum quantity of various goods and services. However, such goods and services must maximize the satisfaction of the consumers. This problem is analysed and studied under *welfare economics*.

Hence, microeconomic theory can be divided into *three* groups and its sub-groups (Fig. 9.2).

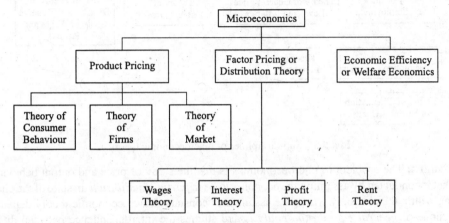

Fig. 9.2 Various aspects involved in microeconomic theory

9.4.2 Macroeconomics

The term macroeconomics is derived from the Greek word *mekros* meaning 'large', and therefore macroeconomics deals not with individual quantities but with aggregates of these quantities; not with individual income but with national income; not with individual prices but with price levels; not with individual output, but with national output. In other words, macroeconomics examines the aggregates and averages of economic variables, which include the study of money, banking and behaviour of financial institutions; general price levels (inflation, deflation) and related problems; the theory of employment and income propagation; the role of monetary and fiscal policies; and the problems of economic stabilization and growth.

According to Prof. Ackley, *"Macroeconomics is concerned with such economic variables as the aggregate volume of the output of an economy, and the extent to which its resources are employed; with the size of the national income; and with the general price level."*

The areas covered under macroeconomics are as follows:

1. **Theory of income and employment:** Income occupies the central place in the study of macroeconomics. It studies various determinants of income and employment in the short period, and explains the causes of fluctuations at the level of national income, output and employment. It explains the growth of national income over a long period of time.

   Hence, macroeconomics examines the determination of the level of fluctuations (cycles) and trends (growth) in the overall economic activity (i.e., national income, output and employment).

2. **Theory of general price level and inflation:** The occurrence of a trade cycle is a very complex phenomenon which is affected by many factors such as decrease in total savings, an increase in spending, increase in total consumption, etc.

3. **Theory of economic growth:** The resources and capabilities of an economy are evaluated to study the economics of growth in macroeconomics.

4. **Macro theory of distribution (relative shares of wages and profits):** It examines the respective shares in the total national income of various classes, particularly of workers and capitalists.

The various aspects of macroeconomic theory, as discussed, are shown in Fig. 9.3.

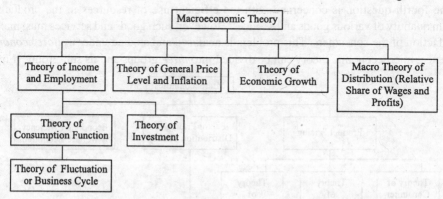

Fig. 9.3   Sub-disciplines of macroeconomic theory

Remark: The problem in microeconomics is that the study of price and output behaviour in the market is conducted by assuming the economy to be in *partial equilibrium*, in spite of the changes occurring within the economy which are assumed as constant. Macroeconomic theory depends on the technique of *general equilibrium analysis* and studies the interdependence between different market prices and output of goods and services produced in the economy.

1. Distinguish between traditional economics and managerial economics. State the important characteristics and major applications of managerial economics.

2. Discuss various aspects of economics.

3. Define managerial economics and list factors influencing managerial decisions.

4. Distinguish between microeconomics and macroeconomics. Point out their interdependence.

5. In what essential way is a macroeconomic approach different from a microeconomic approach? What is the significance of this difference in economic theory?

9.5 Production Function

The theory of production analyses the technical relationship between the type and amount of inputs (land, labour, raw material, semi-processed material, machinery, equipment, capital, etc.) and output of the finished products (quantity of commodity produced). The choice of inputs to produce a particular commodity is restricted to ones which are efficient and technologically viable. These alternatives are expressed in the form of a functional relationship between inputs and outputs. Such *technical relationship between various inputs and outputs is known as the production function*. This definition of production function represents a simple situation where only one product is produced.

The production function includes (and can provide measurements of) concepts which are useful tools in all fields of economics. The main concepts are:

(*a*) Marginal productivity of the factors of production,

(*b*) Marginal rate of substitution and elasticity of substitution,

(*c*) Factor intensity,

(*d*) Efficiency of production, and

(*e*) Returns to scale.

These concepts are discussed in a later section.

The general mathematical form of the production function is

$$Q = f\ (L, K, R, S, v, Y)$$

where Q is the specific output of various inputs as represented by L (labour), K (capital), R (raw material), S (land), v (returns to scale), and Y (efficiency parameter).

To avoid the complication that may arise in an analysis of the production function apropos a complex form, an assumption can be made that will reduce the number of variables to a conventional minimum. The assumption is that each input is well defined and there are no differences in their characteristics (inputs are homogeneous). Thus, under this assumption, the production function may be written as

$$Q = f\ (L, K, v, Y)$$

where v (returns to scale) refers to the long range analysis of the laws of production as it operates in a plant, and Y (efficiency parameter) refers to particular aspects of production. For example, two firms with similar inputs (and also returns to scale) may have different levels of output due to differences in their efficiency.

Further, for the sake of simplicity, it is assumed that maximum output, Q, can be produced using only two inputs, namely capital (K) and labour (L). Then the production function may be written as $Q = f\ (L, K)$. This implies that increase in volume of output, Q, will result from an increase in either L or K or both.

9.5.1 Short-run and Long-run Production

The short-run refers to a period during which supply of certain productive factors such as land and capital, is expected to be inelastic. Hence, supply cannot be varied. On the other hand, long-run refers to a period during which all productive factors become variable.

The firm can increase its production (assuming L to be a variable factor) in the short-run by increasing only the labour (manpower) because availability of capital is fixed. Then the production function is given by $Q = f(L, K_0)$, where $K = K_0 = $ constant. However, in the long run, the firm may have more capital and manpower and, therefore, the production function takes the form $Q = f(L, K)$.

9.5.2 Marginal and Average Product of Production Factors

The production function is usually represented as a curve on two-dimensional graph. Changes in the given factors, L or K, are shown by movements along the curve that depicts the production function. Shift may occur only if some factor other than L and K is changing. The slopes of the curve depict the marginal products of the factors L and K. The *marginal product* of a factor is, therefore, defined as the change in output resulting from a small change in this factor, keeping all other factors constant.

Mathematically, the marginal product of labour and capital is the partial derivative of the production function with respect to these factors respectively. Thus,

$$MP_L \text{ (marginal product of labour)} = \frac{\partial Q}{\partial L} = \frac{\partial}{\partial L}(L, K_0)$$

$$MP_K \text{ (marginal product of capital)} = \frac{\partial Q}{\partial K} = \frac{\partial}{\partial K}(L_0, K)$$

The average product of labour and capital is defined as the total product divided by total factor, respectively. Thus,

$$AP_L \text{ (average product of labour)} = \frac{Q}{L} = \frac{f(L, K)}{L}$$

$$AP_K \text{ (average product of capital)} = \frac{Q}{K} = \frac{f(L, K)}{K}$$

The MP_L and MP_K may assume any value, *viz.* positive, zero or negative. However, theory of production concentrates only on the range of output (Q) over which MP_L and MP_K are positive. As shown in Fig. 9.4, no firm would employ labour beyond the point OB or capital beyond OD, because an increase in the value of L or K beyond these levels would result in the reduction of total output of the firm.

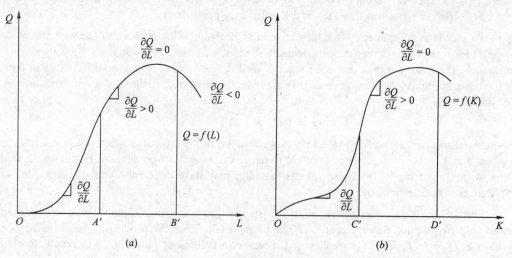

Fig. 9.4

Furthermore, theory of production concentrates on the range of output (Q) over which MP_L and MP_K, although positive, decrease, i.e., over the range of reducing marginal productivity of factors L and K as shown by $A'B'$ in Fig. 9.4 (*a*) and $C'D'$ in Fig. 9.4 (*b*).

Alternatively, as shown in Figs. 9.4 (*c*) and (*d*), theory of production concentrates on levels of use of the factors (L and K) over which their marginal products are positive but declining over these ranges, that is,

$$MP_L > 0, \text{ but } \frac{\partial}{\partial L}(MP_L) < 0$$

$$MP_K > 0, \text{ but } \frac{\partial}{\partial K}(MP_K) < 0$$

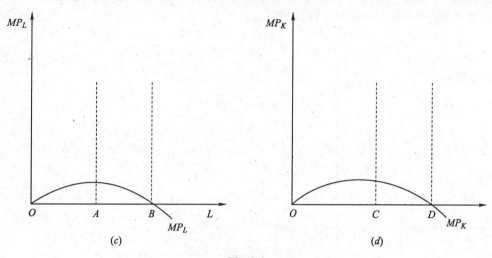

(*c*)   (*d*)

Fig. 9.4

Hence, it may be concluded that the given conditions will be satisfied:

(*i*) $\dfrac{\partial Q}{\partial L} > 0$ and $\dfrac{\partial Q}{\partial K} > 0$, i.e., marginal products of L and K are positive, respectively.

(*ii*) $\dfrac{\partial^2 Q}{\partial L^2} < 0$ and $\dfrac{\partial^2 Q}{\partial K^2} < 0$, i.e., slope of marginal product curves is negative.

9.5.3 Isoquants or Equal Product Curves

The term 'isoquant' has been derived from 'iso' which means equal and 'quant' which means quantity. Therefore, the isoquant curve is known as 'equal product curve' or 'production indifference curve.'

The production function, $Q = f(L, K)$, illustrated by considering the family of curves $f(L, K)$ = constant, is known as *isoquants*. In other words, an isoquant is a curve along which the maximum achievable rate of production is constant (various combinations of labour and capital show the same output).

An isoquant is similar to consumer's indifference curve. Thus, an isoquant curve is a locus of points representing various combinations of two inputs, capital (K) and labour (L), yielding the same output. Thus, for any given level of output (Q), the equation $Q = f(L, K)$ becomes

$$Q_0 = f(L, K)$$

where Q_0 is the parameter. The locus of all combinations of L and K, which satisfy the equation, forms an isoquant.

Since production function is continuous, the infinite combinations of both the inputs fall on each isoquant. For an increased level of output due to increase in L and K, a separate isoquant will be formed lying away from the origin. Thus, farther the isoquant from origin, the greater the level of output it will represent.

9.5.4 Principle of Marginal Rate of Technical Substitution

The slope of a curve is the slope of the tangent at any point of the curve. The slope of the tangent is defined by the total differential. In case of the isoquant, the total differential is the total change in output (Q) resulting from small changes in both the factors K and L.

The slope of the isoquant of a point can be known by the slope of the tangent drawn on the isoquant at that point (Fig. 9.5). This slope of the isoquant ($-\partial K/\partial L$) defines the rate at which factors L and K can be substituted at the margin without altering the level of output (Q). The slope of the isoquant is also called the rate of technical substitution (RTS) or the marginal rate of substitution (MRS) of factors L and K and may be written as

$$-\frac{\partial K}{\partial L} = \text{MRS}_{L, K}$$

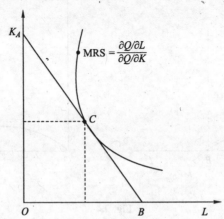

Fig. 9.5   Slope of isoquant

More precisely, MRS of factor L for factor K may be defined as the amount of factor K which can be replaced by one unit of factor L, the level of output (Q) remains unchanged. The concept of MRS can be easily understood from Table 9.1.

Table 9.1   The Concept of MRS

Factor Combinations	Labour, L	Capital, K	Output, Units	MRS of Capital for Labour
A	1	13	40	—
B	2	10	40	3 : 1
C	3	8	40	2 : 1
D	4	7	40	1 : 1

It may be noted that if K is changed by ∂K, output Q will change by the product ∂K times the marginal product of capital, i.e.,

$$(\partial K) \left(\frac{\partial Q}{\partial K} \right)$$

Similarly, if labour factor is changed by an infinitesimal amount ∂L, the resulting change in output, Q, is

$$(\partial L) \left(\frac{\partial Q}{\partial L} \right)$$

Along any isoquant, the output (Q) is constant so that the total change in Q (total differential) must be equal to zero, Thus,

$$dQ = (\partial K)\left(\frac{\partial Q}{\partial K}\right) + (\partial L)\left(\frac{\partial Q}{\partial L}\right) = 0$$

Solving for $\frac{\partial K}{\partial L}$, we get $-\frac{\partial K}{\partial L} = \frac{\partial Q/\partial L}{\partial Q/\partial K} = \frac{MP_L}{MP_K}$.

9.5.5 Equilibrium of the Firm

The concept of production can also be used by a firm to determine optimal mix of factors L and K in order to maximize the value of Q for a given level of cost and minimize cost for a given level of output.

9.5.6 Cost Minimization

Case I: *Minimization of Cost for the given Level of Output*

Suppose the production and cost functions of the firm are given by

$$Q = f(L, K)$$

and

$$C = wL + rK$$

where w and r are the wage rate and interest rate, respectively.

Now, Lagrangian function is formulated as follows:

$$F(L, K, \lambda) = (wL + rK) + \lambda \{Q - f(L, K)\} \tag{1}$$

Necessary condition: The first order condition for the minimization of a function is that its partial derivatives are equal to zero. Thus, differentiating $F(L, K, \lambda)$ with respect to L, K and λ and equating to zero,

$$\frac{\partial F}{\partial L} = w - \lambda\frac{\partial f}{\partial L} = 0 \Rightarrow w - \lambda f_L = 0; \ f_L = \frac{\partial f}{\partial L}$$

or

$$\lambda = f_L/w = \frac{\text{Marginal product of labour}}{\text{Wage rate}}$$

Similarly,

$$\frac{\partial F}{\partial K} = r - \lambda\frac{\partial f}{\partial K} = 0 \Rightarrow r - \lambda f_K = 0; \ f_K = \frac{\partial f}{\partial K}$$

or

$$\lambda = f_K/r = \frac{\text{Marginal product of capital}}{\text{Interest rate}}$$

$$\frac{\partial F}{\partial \lambda} = Q - f(L, K) = 0 \Rightarrow Q = f(L, K)$$

From first two relations, $\quad \dfrac{f_L}{w} = \dfrac{f_K}{r}$ or $\dfrac{MP_L}{w} = \dfrac{MP_K}{r}$

or

$$\frac{MP_L}{MP_K} = \frac{w}{r}$$

This relation implies that for cost minimization problem, the ratio of marginal product of inputs is equal to their price ratio. In other words, *the necessary condition of minimization of cost is that the slope of an isoquant curve must be the same as the slope of isocost line.*

Sufficient condition: The first order condition for the minimization of a function is that the rate of change in the slope of the tangent to the isoquant must be positive, i.e.,

$$\text{Slope of } MP_L = \frac{\partial}{\partial L}\left(\frac{\partial Q}{\partial L}\right) = \frac{\partial^2 Q}{\partial L^2}$$

and

$$\text{Slope of } MP_K = \frac{\partial}{\partial K}\left(\frac{\partial Q}{\partial K}\right) = \frac{\partial^2 Q}{\partial K^2}$$

Thus, the sufficient conditions for cost minimization are:

$$\frac{\partial^2 Q}{\partial L^2} < 0, \ \frac{\partial^2 Q}{\partial K^2} < 0$$

and

$$\left(\frac{\partial^2 Q}{\partial L^2}\right)\left(\frac{\partial^2 Q}{\partial K^2}\right) - \left(\frac{\partial^2 Q}{\partial L \partial K}\right)^2 > 0.$$

Cast II: *Maximization of Output (Q) subject to a Cost Limitation.*

The Lagrangian function may be written as follows:

$$F(L, K, \lambda) = f(L, K) + \lambda\{c - wL - rK\}$$

Necessary condition: As usual, differentiating $F(L, K, \lambda)$ with respect to L, K and λ and equating to zero to establish the first order necessary condition for profit maximization subject to a cost constraint, we have

$$\frac{\partial F}{\partial L} = \frac{\partial f}{\partial L} + \lambda(-w) = 0 \Rightarrow f_L - \lambda w = 0; \ \frac{\partial f}{\partial L} = f_L$$

$$\Rightarrow \lambda = \frac{f_L}{w}$$

$$\frac{\partial F}{\partial K} = \frac{\partial f}{\partial K} + \lambda(-r) = 0 \Rightarrow f_K - \lambda r = 0; \ \frac{\partial f}{\partial K} = f_K$$

$$\Rightarrow \lambda = \frac{f_K}{r}$$

$$\frac{\partial F}{\partial \lambda} = c - wL - rK = 0 \Rightarrow c = wL + rK$$

From first two relations, $\quad \dfrac{f_L}{w} = \dfrac{f_K}{r}$ or $\dfrac{f_L}{f_K} = \dfrac{w}{r}$

which is same as in Case I.

The *second order conditions* would also be the same as in Case I and can be derived in the same manner.

Case III: *Maximum Profit for a given Production Function and given Prices of Inputs and Outputs.*

In this case, the cost function is given by $c = wL + rK + b$, where b is the cost of fixed inputs. If p is the price per unit of the output (Q), then total profit is given by

Total profit = Total revenue − Total cost

or
$$P = pQ - c$$
$$= pQ - (wL + rK + b)$$

Now, the objective of the firm is to maximize the profit for a given production function. The Lagrangian function may now be written as follows:

$$F(L, K, \lambda) = \{pQ - wL - rK - b\} + \lambda\{Q - f(L, K)\}$$

Equating first order partial derivatives of F with respect to Q, L, K and λ to zero to get the first order condition for maximum profit when the firm sells in a perfectly competitive market, we have

$$\frac{\partial F}{\partial Q} = p + \lambda = 0 \tag{1}$$

$$\frac{\partial F}{\partial L} = -w - \lambda\frac{\partial f}{\partial L} = 0$$

or
$$\lambda = -\frac{w}{f_L}; \ f_L = \frac{\partial f}{\partial L} \tag{2}$$

$$\frac{\partial F}{\partial K} = -r - \lambda \frac{\partial f}{\partial K} = 0$$

or

$$\lambda = -\frac{r}{f_K}; f_K = \frac{\partial f}{\partial K} \tag{3}$$

$$\frac{\partial F}{\partial \lambda} = Q - f(L, K) = 0 \tag{4}$$

Substituting the value of λ from (2) and (3) in (1),

$$pf_L = w \text{ and } pf_K = r$$

These values indicate the rates at which the revenue would increase with increase in respective inputs. Thus, the *first order conditions* for profit maximization require that each input be increased until the value of its marginal products f_L and f_K become equal to its price.

The *second order conditions* would be the same as in Case I and can be derived in the same manner.

Remarks

1. The negative slope $(-\partial K/\partial L)$ of the isoquant implies that if one of the inputs is reduced, the other input has to be so increased that the total output remains unaffected, i.e., the reduction in production due to reduction in the quantity of an input is offset exactly by the increase in output resulting from increase in the other input.

2. The isoquant is convex to the origin. This means that the marginal rate of substitution between the two factors decreases as more of one and less of the other factor is used.

3. The marginal rate of technical substitution (MRTS) in the theory of production is matched by the marginal rate of substitution (MRS) in the indifference curve analysis of consumer's demand.

4. The slope of the isoquant at a point and hence the marginal rate of technical substitution (MRTS) can also be known by the slope of the tangent drawn on the isoquants at that point. In Fig. 9.6, the tangent AB is drawn at point C on the curve. The slope of the tangent AB is equal to OA/OB. Therefore, MRTS at point C on the curve is equal to OA/OB. EF is the tangent at point D on the curve. Therefore, MRTS at point D is equal to OE/OF.

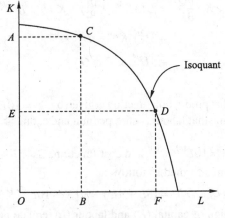

Fig. 9.6

Since slope of the isoquant is decreasing as one moves from the point C to D, it is concluded that MRS also decreases as one moves from the point C to D.

Example 9.1. Suppose there is a production of the type $z = e^{(x^2 + 2xy + 3y^2)}$, where z is the product, and x and y are different factors of production. Find the marginal product of x and y.

Solution. Marginal product of x is given by

$$MP_x = \frac{\partial z}{\partial x} = \frac{\partial}{\partial x} \{e^{(x^2 + 2xy + 3y^2)}\}$$

$$= \{e^{(x^2 + 2xy + 3y^2)}\} \frac{\partial}{\partial x} (x^2 + 2xy + 3y^2)$$

$$= z (2x + 2y)$$

Marginal product of y is given by

$$MP_y = \frac{\partial z}{\partial y} = \frac{\partial}{\partial y} \{e^{(x^2 + 2xy + 3y^2)}\}$$

$$= \{e^{(x^2 + 2xy + 3y^2)}\} \frac{\partial}{\partial y} (x^2 + 2xy + 3y^2)$$

$$= z (2x + 6y).$$

Example 9.2. The production function of a firm is given by $Q = 4L^{3/4} K^{1/4}$, $L > 0$, $K > 0$. Find the marginal product of labour (L) and capital (K). Also, show that

$$L \frac{\partial Q}{\partial L} + K \frac{\partial Q}{\partial K} = Q$$

Solution. Marginal product of labour (L) is

$$MP_L = \frac{\partial Q}{\partial L} = \frac{\partial}{\partial L} (4L^{3/4} K^{1/4})$$

$$= 4 \cdot \frac{3}{4} L^{-1/4} K^{1/4} = 3L^{-1/4} K^{1/4} \qquad (1)$$

Marginal product of capital (K) is

$$MP_K = \frac{\partial Q}{\partial K} = \frac{\partial}{\partial K} (4L^{3/4} K^{1/4})$$

$$= 4 \cdot \frac{1}{4} L^{3/4} K^{-3/4} = L^{3/4} K^{-3/4} \qquad (2)$$

From (1) and (2),

$$L \cdot \frac{\partial Q}{\partial L} + K \cdot \frac{\partial Q}{\partial K} = L (3L^{-1/4} K^{1/4}) + K (L^{3/4} K^{-3/4})$$

$$= 3L^{3/4} K^{1/4} + L^{3/4} K^{1/4}$$

$$= 4L^{3/4} K^{1/4} = Q$$

This proves the result.

Example 9.3. Assume that production function is given by $X = 10L^{4/9} K^{5/9}$, where X is output, L, labour and K, capital. Assume that labour costs 5 per unit and capital 4. Find the least-cost capital-labour ratio.

Solution. Given that $X = 10L^{4/9} K^{5/9}$ and cost function, $C = 5L + 4K$.

The Lagrangian function is formed as follows:

$$F (L, K, \lambda) = (5L + 4K) + \lambda \{X - 10L^{4/9} K^{5/9}\}$$

For least-cost combination of capital (K) and labour (L), equate partial derivatives of F with respect to L, K and λ to zero. Hence,

$$\frac{\partial F}{\partial L} = 5 - \lambda \left(10 \cdot \frac{4}{9} L^{-5/9} K^{5/9}\right) = 0$$

or

$$\lambda = \frac{9}{8} L^{5/9} K^{-5/9} \qquad (1)$$

$$\frac{\partial F}{\partial K} = 4 - \lambda \left(10 \cdot \frac{5}{9} L^{4/9} K^{-4/9}\right) = 0$$

or

$$\lambda = \frac{18}{25} L^{-4/9} K^{4/9} \qquad (2)$$

From (1) and (2), $\quad \frac{9}{8} L^{5/9} K^{-5/9} = \frac{18}{25} L^{-4/9} K^{4/9}$

or

$$\frac{25}{16} = \frac{K}{L}$$

First order condition for least-cost combination is

$$\frac{f_L}{f_K} = \frac{\partial X/\partial L}{\partial X/\partial K} = \frac{(40/9) L^{-5/9} K^{5/9}}{(50/9) L^{4/9} K^{-4/9}} = \frac{4}{5} \frac{K}{L}$$

$$= \frac{4}{5} \cdot \frac{25}{16} = \frac{5}{4} \left(= \frac{w}{r}\right)$$

Second order condition for least-cost combination is

$$\frac{d^2 K}{dL^2} > 0$$

Now,

$$\frac{dK}{dL} = -\left(\frac{f_L}{f_K}\right) = -\frac{4}{5} \cdot \frac{K}{L} = -\frac{4}{5} KL^{-1}$$

and

$$\frac{d^2 K}{dL^2} = -\frac{4}{5} [- KL^{-2} + L^{-1} (dK/dL)]$$

$$= -\frac{4}{5} \left[- KL^{-2} + L^{-1} \left(-\frac{4}{5} KL^{-1}\right)\right]$$

$$= KL^{-2} \left(\frac{4}{5} + \frac{16}{25}\right) = \frac{36}{25} KL^{-2} \; (> 0)$$

Hence, the least-cost combination ratio is 25 : 36.

Example 9.4. The production function for a competitive firm is given by

$$q = 20L + 41K - 2L^2 - 3K^2$$

The wages and rental rates are w = Rs 4 and r = Rs 5. The price of output, p = Re 1. Calculate the equilibrium output and maximum profit.

Solution. Given the cost function, $C = 4L + 5K$. Assuming that the level of output, q_0, maximizes the firm's total profit. Then

Total profit, P = Total revenue – Total cost

$$= q_0 - (4L + 5K)$$

The Lagrangian function for this profit maximization problem is formed as follows:

$$F (q_0, L, K, \lambda) = (q_0 - 4L - 5K) + \lambda (q_0 - 20L - 41K + 2L^2 + 3K^2)$$

For profit maximization, equate partial derivatives of F to zero. Hence,

$$\frac{\partial F}{\partial q_0} = 1 + \lambda = 0 \text{ or } \lambda = -1$$

$$\frac{\partial F}{\partial L} = -4 + \lambda (-20 + 4L) = 0 \text{ or } L = 4 \text{ [for } \lambda = -1]$$

$$\frac{\partial F}{\partial K} = -5 + \lambda (-41 + 6K) = 0 \text{ or } K = 6 \text{ [for } \lambda = -1]$$

$$\frac{\partial F}{\partial \lambda} = q_0 - 20L - 41K + 2L^2 + 3K^2 = 0 \text{ or } q_0 = 186$$

First order condition for maximum profit is

$$\frac{f_L}{f_K} = \frac{\partial q/\partial L}{\partial q/\partial K} = \frac{20 - 4L}{41 - 6K}$$

$$= \frac{20 - 4 \times 4}{41 - 6 \times 6} = \frac{4}{5} = \frac{w}{r}$$

Second-order condition for maximum profit requires

$$\frac{\partial^2 F}{\partial L^2} = 4\lambda = -4\ (< 0); \frac{\partial^2 F}{\partial K^2} = 6\lambda = -6\ (< 0)$$

and

$$\frac{\partial^2 F}{\partial L^2} \times \frac{\partial^2 F}{\partial K^2} - \left(\frac{\partial^2 F}{\partial L\, \partial K}\right) = (-4)\,(-6) - (0) = 24\ (> 0)$$

for $L = 4$ and $K = 6$.

Hence, the equilibrium combination of capital, labour and output is: $L = 4$, $K = 6$ and $q_0 = 186$, respectively and the corresponding maximum profit is

$$q_0 - 4L - 5K = 186 - 4\,(4) - 5\,(6) = 140.$$

Example 9.5. For the production function $q = AL^\alpha\, K^\beta$, show that the isoquants generated are always negatively sloped and convex to the origin.

Solution. The total change in production with respect to change in input is given by the total differential

$$dq = \frac{\partial q}{\partial L} \cdot dL + \frac{\partial q}{\partial K} \cdot dK; \quad q = AL^\alpha\, K^\beta$$

where

$$\frac{\partial q}{\partial L} = A\,\alpha L^{\alpha-1} K^\beta \text{ and } \frac{\partial q}{\partial K} = A\beta L^\alpha\, K^{\beta-1}$$

Since the output is constant along any isoquant, the total change in output must be equal to zero, i.e.,

$$dq = (A\alpha L^{\alpha-1}\, K^\beta)\, dL + (A\beta L^\alpha\, K^{\beta-1})\, dK = 0$$

or

$$\frac{dL}{dK} = -\frac{\alpha}{\beta} \cdot \frac{L}{K}\ (< 0); \quad \alpha, \beta, L, K > 0$$

Also,

$$\frac{d^2 L}{dK^2} = \frac{d}{dK}\left(-\frac{\alpha}{\beta}\frac{L}{K}\right) = -\frac{\alpha}{\beta}\left\{\frac{K\dfrac{dL}{dK} - L}{K^2}\right\}$$

$$= -\frac{\alpha}{\beta}\frac{1}{K}\frac{dL}{dK} + \frac{\alpha}{\beta}\frac{L}{K^2} \qquad \left[\text{using } \frac{d}{dx}\,(u, v) \text{ formula}\right]$$

$$> 0 \text{ because } \frac{dL}{dK} < 0$$

This proves the result.

9.5.7 Returns to Scale and Homogeneity of the Production Function

Laws of Returns and Production

The laws of production describe all possible ways of increasing the level of production. Laws of return to scale refer to changes in the level of production as all inputs change by the same proportion.

Suppose one starts from an initial level of input and output given by the following production function:

$$Q = f\,(L, K)$$

and all factors are increased by the same proportion λ. Then a new level of output Q^* (higher than Q) will be

$$Q^* = f(\lambda L, \lambda K)$$

Now, the output, Q^*, may increase in *three* distinct ways:

1. If Q^* increases more than proportionally with the increase in the input factors, then there is *increasing returns to scale*.

2. If Q^* increases less than proportionally with the increase in the input factors, then there is decreasing *returns to scale*.

3. If Q^* increases by the same proportion λ as the input factors, then there is *constant returns to scale*.

Remark: The distinction between *laws of returns* and *returns to scale* is that in the former case the relationship between single input and level of output is studied, whereas in the later case the relationship between all inputs and the level of output is studied.

If λ can be taken out of the brackets as a common factor from the relationship $Q^* = f(\lambda L, \lambda K)$, then a new level of output, Q^*, can be expressed as a function of λ (to any power x) and the initial level of output Q. Therefore, if

$$Q^* = f(\lambda L, \lambda K) = \lambda^x f(L, K),$$

then the production function is called *homogeneous*, otherwise it is called *non-homogeneous*.

The power x of λ is called the *degree of homogeneity* of the function and is a measure of the returns to scale. Thus, if

(a) $x = 1$, there is *constant returns to scale*. This means that the increase in output is equiproportional with λ and the production function is also called *linear homogeneous function* of degree 1.

(b) $x < 1$, there is *decreasing returns to scale*. This means that the increase in output is less proportional than λ (an increase in the level of all inputs). Such production functions are called *non-linear homogeneous functions*.

(c) $x > 1$, there is *increasing returns to scale*. This means that the increase in output is more proportional than λ. Such production functions are called *non-linear homogeneous functions*.

9.5.8 Euler's Theorem

This states that for a production function $Q = f(K, L)$ with constant returns to scale,

$$Q = L \frac{\partial Q}{\partial L} + K \frac{\partial Q}{\partial K}$$

where $\dfrac{\partial Q}{\partial L} = MP_L$ and $\dfrac{\partial Q}{\partial K} = MP_K$.

Thus, the marginal productivity theory satisfies the condition

Share of labour + Share of capital = 1

for the special case of constant returns to scale.

9.5.9 Different Forms of Production Function

Linear Function

The linear function expresses output y as a function of input x in the form

$$y = a + bx$$

The corresponding average production will be

$$y/x = (a/x) + b$$

and marginal product = $dy/dx = b$ (constant). This means that the marginal product is constant for all levels of output, which is against the theoretical economic reasoning. Thus, such production functions are not possible.

Power Function

The power function expresses output y as a function of input x in the form

$$y = ax^b, a, b \text{ constant}$$

Now, the value of y varies with change in the value of x raised to a given constant power b. This function allows for increasing, constant or decreasing marginal product of the input. For example,

(a) If $b = 1$, both MP_L and AP_L will be constant for constant value of a, and

(b) If $b > 1$, the magnitude of MP_L will increase with an increase in b.

However, this function does not prove satisfactory where data show ranges of both increasing (or positive) and decreasing (or negative) marginal productivities.

Cobb-Douglas Production Function

Cobb and Douglas discovered a production function of the form

$$Q = AL^\alpha K^\beta$$

where Q is the expected index of (manufacturing) output over the period; L, the index of employment (labour); and K, the index of fixed capital; A, the positive constant; α and β, the positive fractions; and $\beta = 1 - \alpha$. The positive fractions also represent elasticity of labour and capital, respectively, i.e., α and $1 - \alpha$ measure the percentage response of output to percentage change in labour and capital, respectively.

The production function derived by Cobb and Douglas for American manufacturing as a whole using the annual data for production was

$$Q = 1.01L^{0.75} K^{0.25}$$

This function can be used in determining the production that could be inputed to labour and capital. For example, 1 per cent change in labour input, capital remaining same, results in 0.75 per cent change in output. Similarly, 1 per cent change in capital input, labour remaining same, results in 0.25 per cent change in output.

Some important properties of this function are:

1. It is *homogeneous of degree* $(\alpha + \beta)$: Let $Q = f (L, K) = AL^\alpha K^\beta$. Then

$$f (\lambda L, \lambda K) = A (\lambda L)^\alpha (\lambda K)^\beta = A\lambda^{\alpha+\beta} L^\alpha K^\beta$$

$$= \lambda^{\alpha+\beta} f (L, K)$$

This shows that the given function is homogeneous of degree $\alpha + \beta$.

The numerical values of exponent α and β in the Cobb-Douglas (C.D.) production function characterized its nature. The sum of the exponents shows the degree of 'returns to scale' in production. Thus, if

$\alpha + \beta < 1$, decreasing returns to scale

$\alpha + \beta = 1$, constant returns to scale

$\alpha + \beta > 1$, increasing returns to scale

2. In actual practice, C.D. production function assumes that $\alpha + \beta = 1$, which implies that the constant returns to scale prevail in the economy.

3. When C.D. production function is homogeneous of degree 1 $(\alpha + \beta = 1)$ or constant returns to scale prevail in the economy, elasticity of substitution equals 1. The implication of this elasticity value is that if inputs are changed in a fixed proportion, then output also changes in the same proportion.

4. The exponents α and β represent the elasticities of output with respect to labour (L) and capital (K) share, respectively. These are given by

$$\eta_L = \frac{L}{Q} \frac{\partial Q}{\partial L} = \frac{L}{AL^\alpha K^\beta} \cdot \alpha A L^{\alpha-1} K^\beta = \alpha$$

and

$$\eta_K = \frac{K}{Q} \frac{\partial Q}{\partial K} = \frac{K}{AL^\alpha K^\beta} \cdot \beta A L^\alpha K^{\beta-1} = \beta$$

These exponents also represent percentage share of inputs in the total output. These are given by

$$MP_L = \frac{\partial Q}{\partial L} = \alpha A L^{\alpha-1} K^\beta$$

$$= \alpha (AL^\alpha K^\beta) L^{-1}$$

$$= \alpha \frac{Q}{L} = \alpha (AP_L)$$

and

$$MP_K = \frac{\partial Q}{\partial K} = \beta A L^\alpha K^{\beta-1}$$

$$= \beta (AL^\alpha K^\beta) K^{-1}$$

$$= \beta \frac{Q}{K} = \alpha AP_K$$

where AP_L and AP_K represent average product of labour and capital, respectively.

In case of profit maximization behaviour, it is known that

$$MP_L = \frac{w}{p}$$

or

$$\frac{w}{p} = \alpha \frac{Q}{L} \text{ or } \alpha = \frac{wL}{pQ} \text{ (percentage share in total output)}$$

Similarly,

$$\beta = \frac{rK}{pQ} \text{ (percentage share of capital in total output)}$$

where w is the current wages; p, the per unit price of output; and r, the price per unit of capital input.

9.5.10 Constant Elasticity of Substitution Function (CES Function)

One of the production functions which has been used in many practical situations is known as *CES function*. This function is homogeneous of degree 1 and possesses the constant elasticity of substitution but need not necessarily be equal to one. The mathematical form of this function is given by

$$Q = A [\alpha L^{-\alpha} + (1-\alpha) K^{-\beta}]^{-1/\beta}; \quad 0 \le \alpha \le 1, \ \beta > -1$$

where L and K are the two factors of production, A, α, β are parameters.

This function satisfies all the properties of a linear homogeneous function, *viz.*

(*a*) Qualifies for the application of Euler's theorem;

(*b*) Marginal and average products are homogeneous of degree zero;

(*c*) It displays constant returns to scale; and

(*d*) Generates isoquants which are negatively inclined and convex towards origin.

Example 9.6. The production function is $X = Aa^\alpha b^\beta$, where $\alpha + \beta < 1$. Show that the total product is greater than '*a*' times the marginal product of *a* plus '*b*' times the marginal product of *b*.

Solution. Marginal product of *a* is

$$MP_a = \frac{\partial X}{\partial a} = A\alpha a^{\alpha-1} b^\beta$$

or

$$aMP_a = a (A\alpha a^{\alpha-1} b^\beta) = A\alpha a^\alpha b^\beta = \alpha X \qquad (1)$$

and marginal product of b is $\qquad MP_b = \dfrac{\partial X}{\partial b} = A\beta a^{\alpha} b^{\beta-1}$

or $\qquad\qquad\qquad bMP_b = b(A\beta a^{\alpha} b^{\beta-1}) = A\beta a^{\alpha} b^{\beta} = \beta X \qquad\qquad (2)$

Adding (1) and (2),

$$aMP_a + bMP_b = \alpha X + \beta X = X(\alpha + \beta)$$
$$< X \text{ (total product [since } \alpha + \beta < 1].}$$

Example 9.7. For the linear homogeneous production function

$$x = (2Hab - Aa^2 - Bb^2)/(Ca + Db)$$

show that the average and marginal products of the factors depend only on the ratio of factors and verify that the product is always equal to 'a' times the marginal product of a plus 'b' times the marginal product of b.

Solution. Average product of factor 'a' is

$$AP_a = \frac{x}{a} = \frac{2Hab - Aa^2 - Bb^2}{a(Ca + Db)} = \frac{2H(b/a) - A - B(b/a)^2}{C + D(b/a)}$$

This implies that AP_a depends only on the ratio (b/a) of factors a and b.

Similarly, average product of factor 'b' is

$$AP_b = \frac{x}{b} = \frac{2Hab - Aa^2 - Bb^2}{b(Ca + Db)} = \frac{2H(a/b) - A(a/b)^2 - B}{C(a/b) + D}$$

This also implies that AP_b depends only on the ratio (a/b) of factors a and b.

Marginal product of factor 'a' is

$$MP_a = \frac{\partial x}{\partial a} = \frac{\partial}{\partial a}\left[\frac{2Hab - Aa^2 - Bb^2}{Ca + Db}\right]$$

$$= \frac{(Ca + Db)(2Hb - 2Aa) - (2Hab - Aa^2 - Bb^2)C}{(Ca + Db)^2}$$

$$= \frac{2Hb - 2Aa}{Ca + Db} - \frac{(2Hab - Aa^2 - Bb^2)C}{(Ca + Db)^2}$$

$$= \frac{2H(b/a) - 2A}{C + D(b/a)} - \frac{\{2H(b/a) - A - B(b/a)^2\}.C}{\{C + D(b/a)\}^2}$$

This implies that the marginal product of factor 'a' depends on the ratio (b/a) of factors.

Similarly, marginal product of factor 'b' is

$$MP_b = \frac{\partial x}{\partial b} = \frac{\partial}{\partial b}\left[\frac{2Hab - Aa^2 - Bb^2}{Ca + Db}\right]$$

$$= \frac{(Ca + Db)(2Ha - 2Bb) - (2Hab - Aa^2 - Bb^2)D}{(Ca + Db)^2}$$

$$= \frac{2Ha - 2Bb}{Ca + Db} - \frac{(2Hab - Aa^2 - Bb^2)D}{(Ca + Db)^2}$$

$$= \frac{2H(a/b) - 2B}{C(a/b) + D} - \frac{\{2H(a/b) - A(a/b)^2 - B\}D}{\{C(a/b) + D\}^2}$$

This implies that the marginal product of factor b depends on the ratio (a/b) of factors.

Now, consider the sum

$$aMP_a + bMP_b = a\left\{\frac{2Hb - 2Aa}{Ca + Db} - \frac{(2Hab - Aa^2 - Bb^2)}{(Ca + Db)^2} \cdot C\right\}$$

$$+ b\left\{\frac{2Ha - 2Bb}{Ca + Db} - \frac{(2Hab - Aa^2 - Bb^2)}{(Ca + Db)^2} \cdot D\right\}$$

$$= \frac{4Hab - 2Aa^2 - 2Bb^2 - 2Hab + Aa^2 + Bb^2}{Ca + Db}$$

$$= \frac{2Hab + Aa^2 - Bb^2}{Ca + Db}$$

$$= x \text{ (total product)}$$

Hence the result.

Example 9.8. Given the CES production function

$$q = A\left[\delta K^{-\rho} + (1 - \delta)\, L^{-\rho}\right]^{-1/\rho} \quad (0 < \delta < 1,\ -1 < \rho \neq 0)$$

where A is a positive constant, and K and L, the strictly positive quantities of two factors of production. Find the (*a*) degree of homogeneity of this production function, and (*b*) prove that the isoquants generated by this production function are always negatively sloped and convex to origin.

Solution. (*a*) Suppose

$$q = f(K, L) = A\left[\delta K^{-\rho} + (1 - \delta)\, L^{-\rho}\right]^{-1/\rho}$$

$$f(\lambda K, \lambda L) = A\left[\delta (\lambda K)^{-\rho} + (1 - \delta)(\lambda L)^{-\rho}\right]^{-1/\rho}$$

$$= A\,(\lambda^{-\rho})^{-1/\rho}\left[\delta K^{-\rho} + (1 - \delta)\, K^{-\rho}\right]^{-1/\rho}$$

$$= \lambda q$$

Since exponent of λ is 1, q is a homogeneous production function of degree 1.

(*b*) It is known that along an isoquant, $dq = 0$. Hence,

$$dq = \frac{\partial q}{\partial L}\, dL + \frac{\partial q}{\partial K}\, dK = 0$$

$$= A\left[\delta K^{-\rho} + (1 - \delta)\, L^{-\rho}\right]^{-(1/\rho)-1}(1 - \delta)(-\rho)\, L^{-\rho-1}\, dL$$

$$+ A\left[\delta K^{-\rho} + (1 - \delta)\, L^{-\rho}\right]^{-(1/\rho)-1}\delta(-\rho)\, K^{-\rho-1}\, dK = 0$$

or $(1 - \delta)\, L^{-\rho-1}\, dL + \delta K^{-\rho-1}\, dK = 0$

or $(\delta - 1)\, L^{-\rho-1}\, dL = \delta K^{-\rho-1}\, dK$

or

$$\frac{dK}{dL} = -\frac{1-\delta}{\delta}\frac{L^{-\rho-1}}{K^{-\rho-1}} = -\frac{1-\rho}{\rho}\left(\frac{L}{K}\right)^{-\rho-1}$$

$$= -\frac{1-\delta}{\delta}\left(\frac{K}{L}\right)^{1+\rho} < 0 \qquad\qquad [\text{since } 1 - \delta > 0]$$

This implies that slope of isoquant is a negative quantity. Also,

$$\frac{d^2 K}{dL^2} = -\frac{1-\delta}{\delta}(1+\rho)\left(\frac{K}{L}\right)^{\rho}\left(\frac{K}{L^2}\right)$$

$$= \frac{(1-\delta)(1+\rho)}{\delta}\frac{K^{1+\rho}}{L^{\rho+2}} > 0$$

Hence, isoquants are convex to the origin.

9.5.11 Elasticity of Substitution

The main objective of any firm is either to maximize its profit or to minimize its cost taking into consideration the prices which input factors command in the market. For this, each firm always wants to know the degree of substitutability between two factors, labour (L) and capital (K), of production.

The marginal rate of substitution (MRS) as a measure of the degree of substitutability of factors has a serious drawback: it depends on the unit of measurement of the factors. A better measure of the ease of factor substitution is provided by the *elasticity of substitution*. The elasticity of substitution is defined as the proportionate or relative change in the capital-labour ratio divided by proportionate or relative change in the rate of technical substitution. Mathematically, it is stated as follows:

$$\sigma = \frac{\text{Relative change in the ratio } (K/L)}{\text{Relative change in MRS}}$$

$$= \frac{d\,(K/L)/(K/L)}{d\,(MRS_{L,K})/MRS_{L,K}} = \frac{d\,(K/L)/(K/L)}{d\,(f_L/f_K)/(f_L/f_K)}$$

$$= \frac{K \cdot f_K}{L \cdot f_L} \cdot \frac{d\,(K/L)}{d\,(f_L/f_K)}$$

$$= \frac{f_L\,f_K\,(Lf_K + Kf_K)}{-LK\,(f_{LL}\,f_K^2 - 2f_{LK}\cdot f_L\,f_K + f_{KK}\cdot f_L^2)}$$

where

$$MRS_{LK} = \frac{\partial Q/\partial L}{\partial Q/\partial K} = \frac{f_L}{f_K}$$

or

$$f_{LK} = \frac{\partial^2 Q}{\partial L\,\partial K}$$

Remarks:

1. The above formula can also be expressed as

$$\sigma = \frac{d\,(K/L)}{K/L} \cdot \frac{MRS_{LK}}{d\,(MRS_{LK})} = \frac{d\,\{\log K/L\}}{d\,\{\log MRS_{LK}\}}\,.$$

2. Since $MRS_{LK} = \dfrac{MP_L}{MP_K} = \dfrac{w}{r}$, then formula (1) can also be re-written as

$$\sigma = \frac{d\,\{\log K/L\}}{d\,\{\log (w/r)\}}$$

where w and r are per unit prices of labour and capital, respectively.

3. If production function, $Q = f(L, K)$ is linear homogeneous, then

$$\sigma = \frac{f_L \cdot f_K}{Q \cdot f_{LK}}\,.$$

Example 9.9. For the Cobb-Douglas production function $q = AK^\alpha L^{1-\alpha}$, find the elasticity of substitution, $\sigma = \dfrac{\partial q}{\partial L} \cdot \dfrac{\partial q}{\partial K} \Big/ q \cdot \dfrac{\partial^2 q}{\partial L\,\partial K}\,.$

Solution. Suppose

$$q = f(L, K) = AK^\alpha L^{1-\alpha}$$

Hence,

$$f(\lambda L, \lambda K) = A\,(\lambda K)^\alpha\,(\lambda L)^{1-\alpha} = \lambda^{\alpha+1-\alpha}\,AK^\alpha L^{1-\alpha}$$

$$= \lambda AK^\alpha L^{1-\alpha} = \lambda f(L, K)$$

Since exponent of λ is 1, q is a homogeneous production function of degree 1. Now,

$$\frac{\partial q}{\partial L} = f_L = \frac{\partial}{\partial L}\,(AK^\alpha L^{1-\alpha})$$

$$= (1 - \alpha)\,AK^\alpha L^{-\alpha}$$

$$\frac{\partial q}{\partial K} = f_K = \frac{\partial}{\partial K}\,(AK^\alpha L^{1-\alpha})$$

$$= \alpha A K^{\alpha-1} L^{1-\alpha}$$

$$\frac{\partial^2 q}{\partial L \, \partial K} = f_{LK} = \frac{\partial}{\partial L} \left(\frac{\partial q}{\partial K} \right)$$

$$= \frac{\partial}{\partial L} (\alpha A K^{\alpha-1} L^{1-\alpha}) = \alpha (1-\alpha) A K^{\alpha-1} L^{-\alpha}$$

Substituting the values of f_L, f_K and f_{LK} in the formula of σ,

$$\sigma = \frac{\{(1-\alpha) A K^{\alpha} L^{-\alpha}\} (\alpha A K^{\alpha-1} L^{\alpha-1})}{\{A K^{\alpha} L^{1-\alpha}\} \{\alpha (1-\alpha) A K^{\alpha-1} L^{-\alpha}\}} = 1.$$

Example 9.10. Show that the production function, $Q^{-\beta} = a K^{-\beta} + b L^{-\beta}$, is homogeneous of degree one, where Q represents output; L and K denote factors of production, labour and capital, respectively. Obtain elasticity of sustitution (σ) between factors defined as $\sigma = f_L \, f_K / Q f_{LK}$, where $f_L = \partial Q / \partial L$, $f_K = \partial Q / \partial K$, $f_{LK} = \partial^2 Q / \partial L \, \partial K$.

Solution. Suppose
$$Q = f (L, K) = (a K^{-\beta} + b L^{-\beta})^{-1/\beta}$$

Hence,
$$f_L (\lambda L, \lambda K) = [a (\lambda K)^{-\beta} + b (\lambda L)^{-\beta}]^{-1/\beta}$$

$$= [\lambda^{-\beta} a K^{-\beta} + \lambda^{-\beta} b L^{-\beta}]^{-1/\beta}$$

$$= \lambda [a K^{-\beta} + b L^{-\beta}]^{-1/\beta} = \lambda f (L, K)$$

Thus, Q is a homogeneous function of degree 1.

Differentiating $Q^{-\beta} = a K^{-\beta} + b L^{-\beta}$ partially with respect to L and K,

$$-\beta Q^{-\beta-1} \frac{\partial Q}{\partial L} = -\beta b L^{-\beta-i}$$

or
$$\frac{\partial Q}{\partial L} = \frac{b L^{-(1+\beta)}}{Q^{-(1+\beta)}} = f_L$$

Also,
$$-\beta Q^{-\beta-1} \frac{\partial Q}{\partial K} = -\beta a K^{-\beta-1}$$

or
$$\frac{\partial Q}{\partial K} = \frac{a K^{-(1+\beta)}}{Q^{-(1+\beta)}} = f_K$$

and
$$\frac{\partial^2 Q}{\partial L \, \partial K} = \frac{\partial}{\partial L} \left(\frac{\partial Q}{\partial K} \right) = \frac{\partial}{\partial L} \left[\frac{a K^{-(1+\beta)}}{Q^{-(1+\beta)}} \right]$$

$$= \frac{\partial}{\partial L} [a K^{-(1+\beta)} \cdot Q^{(1+\beta)}]$$

$$= a K^{-(1+\beta)} (1 + \beta) Q^{\beta} \frac{\partial Q}{\partial L}$$

$$= a K^{-(1+\beta)} (1 + \beta) Q^{\beta} \frac{b L^{-(1+\beta)}}{Q^{-(1+\beta)}} = f_{LK}$$

Substituting the values of f_L, f_K and f_{LK} in the formula for σ,

$$\sigma = \frac{\dfrac{b L^{-(1+\beta)}}{Q^{-(1+\beta)}} \times \dfrac{a K^{-(1+\beta)}}{Q^{-(1+\beta)}}}{Q \cdot a K^{-(1+\beta)} \cdot (1 + \beta) Q^{\beta} \cdot \dfrac{b L^{-(1+\beta)}}{Q^{-(1+\beta)}}} = \frac{1}{1 + \beta}.$$

Example 9.11. If $u = \log (x + a)^{\alpha} (y + b)^{\beta}$ is one form of a utility function, find the marginal rate of substitution between the goods X and Y and deduce that the elasticity of substitution is

$$\sigma = 1 + \frac{b\alpha x + a\beta y}{(\alpha + \beta)\ xy}$$

Solution. The given unity function is

$$u = \log (x + a)^{\alpha} (y + b)^{\beta}$$

$$= \log (x + a)^{\alpha} + \log (y + b)^{\beta}$$

$$= \alpha \log (x + a) + \beta \log (y + b)$$

Now,

$$\frac{\partial u}{\partial x} = \frac{\alpha}{x + a} = f_x; \ \frac{\partial u}{\partial y} = \frac{\beta}{y + b} = f_y$$

$$\frac{\partial^2 u}{\partial x^2} = \frac{-\alpha}{(x + a)^2} = f_{xx}; \ \frac{\partial^2 u}{\partial y^2} = \frac{-\beta}{(y + b)^2} = f_{yy}$$

and

$$\frac{\partial^2 u}{\partial x\ \partial y} = 0 = f_{xy}$$

Substituting the values of f_x, f_y, f_{xx}, f_{yy} and f_{xy} in the formula for σ,

$$\sigma = \frac{f_x\ f_y\ (xf_x + yf_y)}{-xy\ (f_{xx}\ f_y^2 - 2f_x\ f_y\ f_{xy} + f_{yy}\ f_x^2)}$$

$$= \frac{\dfrac{\alpha\beta}{(x + a)\ (y + b)} \left\{ \dfrac{\alpha x}{(x + a)} + \dfrac{\beta y}{(y + b)} \right\}}{-xy \left\{ \dfrac{-\alpha\beta^2}{(x + a)^2\ (y + b)^2} - \dfrac{\alpha^2\beta}{(x + a)^2\ (y + b)^2} \right\}}$$

$$= \frac{\alpha\beta \{\alpha x\ (y + b) + \beta y\ (x + a)\}}{xy\ (\alpha\beta^2 + \beta\alpha^2)} = \frac{\alpha xy + b\alpha x + \beta yx + \beta ya}{xy\ (\alpha + \beta)}$$

$$= \frac{xy\ (\alpha + \beta) + b\alpha x + a\beta y}{xy\ (\alpha + \beta)} = 1 + \frac{b\alpha x + a\beta y}{xy\ (\alpha + \beta)}$$

This proves the result.

Self-assessment Questions Set-II

1. What is meant by a production function? What is the difference between a short-run and long-run production function?

2. Explain the concept of the production function and using illustrations show its significance in the theory of production.

3. State the main characteristics of the Cobb-Douglas production function.

4. Explain the concept of "returns to scale", and discuss the basis of increasing and decreasing returns to scale.

5. Explain the principle of diminishing rate of technical substitution, giving the important assumptions. What are its limitations?

6. How does a firm succeed in securing the least-cost combination of the factors of production?

7. The following is a linear homogeneous production function, where, X, L, K represent output, labour and capital respectively.

$$X = \sqrt{aL^2 + 2hLK + bK^2}$$

Show that L times the marginal product of labour and K times the marginal product of capital equals the total product.

8. A production function is given by: $Q = 4L^{2/3} K^{1/3}$, where L is labour and K, capital.
   (a) Find the behaviour of the marginal product of each factor.
   (b) What is the nature of returns to scale?

(c) What is the total reward of labour and capital if each factor is paid a price equal to its marginal product?

[**Hint:** (a) $MP_L = \dfrac{\partial Q}{\partial L} (8/3) L^{-1/3} K^{1/3}$ and,

$\dfrac{\partial}{\partial L} (MP_L) = (-8/9) L^{-4/3} K^{-1/3}$

This implies that as L increases, MP_L decreases. Similarly.

$MP_K = \dfrac{\partial Q}{\partial K} = (4/3) L^{2/3} K^{-2/3}$ and

$\dfrac{\partial}{\partial K} (MP_K) = (-8/9) L^{2/3} K^{-5/3}$

This implies that as K increases, MP_K decreases.

(b) Homogeneous of degree $1 \Rightarrow$ Constant returns to scale

(c) $L \dfrac{\partial Q}{\partial L} + K \dfrac{\partial Q}{\partial K} = Q$].

9. Suppose x and y be two types of items produced by a firm and $c = 18x^2 + 9y^2$ be the joint cost function. Given that $x + y = 54$, find x and y that minimize the cost.

10. Find the optimum commodity purchase for a consumer whose utility function is $U = c^{q_1 q_2}$. Prices of q_1 and q_2 are Re 1 and Rs 5 respectively, and income is Rs 10.

[**Hint:** Lagrangian function,

$$L(q_1, q_2, \lambda) = e^{q_1 q_2} + \lambda (q_1 + q_2 - 10)$$

$$\dfrac{\partial L}{\partial q_1} = e^{q_1 q_2} . q_2 - \lambda = 0 \Rightarrow \lambda = e^{q_1 q_2} . q_2 \tag{1}$$

$$\dfrac{\partial L}{\partial q_2} = e^{q_1 q_2} . q_1 - 5\lambda = 0 \Rightarrow \lambda = e^{q_1 q_2} . q_1/5 \tag{2}$$

$$\dfrac{\partial L}{\partial \lambda} = q_1 + 5q_2 - 10 = 0 \Rightarrow q_1 + 5q_2 = 10 \tag{3}$$

From (1) and (2) $e^{q_1 q_2} . q_2 = \dfrac{e^{q_1 q_2} . q_1}{5} \Rightarrow q_1 = 5q_2 \tag{4}$

Then from (3) and (4), $5q_2 + 5q_2 = 10 \Rightarrow q_2 = 1$ and $q_1 = 5$.

11. The production function of a firm is given by

$$Q = 5L^{0.7} K^{0.3}$$

where L is the amount of labour and K, the amount of capital used. The price of labour is Re 1 per unit and the price of capital is Rs 2 per unit. Find the minimum cost combination of capital and labour for an output rate of Rs 20.

[**Hint:** Minimum cost, $C = L + 2K$ under the constraint $5L^{0.7} K^{0.3} = 20$].

12. A competitive entrepreneur has the production function $q = K^\alpha L^{1-\alpha}$ $(0 < \alpha < 1)$, where q is the output, L and K are labour and capital, respectively. The competitive wage rate is w and the rate of rental for capital is r. What is the value of $d \log (K/L)/d \log (w/r)$ at profit maximizing equilibrium.

[**Hint:** The profit is given by $P = p.q - c = p.K^\alpha L^{1-\alpha} - (wL - rK)$

The first-order condition for maximum of P is

$$\dfrac{dP}{dL} = 0 \Rightarrow (1-\alpha) pK^\alpha L^{-\alpha} - w = 0 \tag{1}$$

$$\dfrac{dP}{dK} = 0 \Rightarrow \alpha pK^{\alpha-1} L^{1-\alpha} - r = 0 \tag{2}$$

From (1) and (2), $\dfrac{w}{r} = \dfrac{1-\alpha}{\alpha} \left(\dfrac{K}{L}\right)$

or $\log \left(\dfrac{w}{r}\right) = \log \left(\dfrac{1-\alpha}{\alpha}\right) + \log \left(\dfrac{K}{L}\right)$

or $d \left(\log \dfrac{w}{r}\right) = d \left\{\log \left(\dfrac{K}{L}\right)\right\}$

or $\dfrac{d \log (K/L)}{d \log (w/r)} = 1$.

13. Show that for the production function, $x = \sqrt{2HLK - AL^2 - BK^2}$, elasticity of substitution is

$$\sigma = \frac{H^2}{(H^2 - AB)\, LK} - 1.$$

[Hint:
$$x = f\,(\lambda L,\, \lambda K) = \sqrt{\{2H\,(\lambda L)\,(\lambda K) - A\,(\lambda L)^2 - B\,(\lambda K)^2\}}$$

$$= \lambda\,\sqrt{\{2HLK - AL^2 - BK^2\}}$$

$$= \lambda f\,(L,\, K)$$

This implies that the given production function is linear homogeneous. Hence, elasticity of substitution.

$$\sigma = \frac{f_L \cdot f_K}{x \cdot f_{LK}}$$

$$= -1 + \frac{Hx^2}{(H^2 - AB)\, LK}$$

where
$$f_L = \frac{2HK - 2AL}{2\,\sqrt{\{2HLK - AL^2 - BK^2\}}}$$

$$f_K = \frac{2HL - 2BK}{2\,\sqrt{\{2HLK - AL^2 - BK^2\}}}$$

$$f_{LK} = \frac{H\,\sqrt{\{2HLK - AL^2 - BK^2\}} - (HL - BK)\,\dfrac{HK - AL}{\sqrt{\{2HLK - AL^2 - BK^2\}}}}{2HLK - AL^2 - BK^2}.$$

14. The production function for a commodity is $Q = 10L - 0.1L^2 + 15K - 0.2K^2 + 2KL$, where L is labour, K, the capital and Q, the production. (a) Calculate the marginal products of the two inputs, and (b) if 10 units of capital are used, what is the upper limit for use of labour which a rational producer will never exceed?

[Hint: The upper limit for use of labour, which a rational producer will never exceed, can be obtained by applying the following condition:

$$\left(\frac{\partial Q}{\partial L}\right)_{K=10} \geq 0 \Rightarrow [2K - 0.2L + 10]_{K=10} \geq 0$$

$$\Rightarrow \frac{30}{0.2} \geq L \ \text{ or } \ L \leq 150.$$

15. If $Q = 3L^3 C^2 - 2L^2 C^3$, where L and C are input of labour and capital. Find the average product and marginal product of labour (L). If the input C is fixed, what is the value of input L for which the average product will be maximum? Does the maximum of marginal product curve reach at lower level of labour?

[Hint: Marginal product of labour,
$$MP_L = \frac{\partial Q}{\partial L} = \frac{\partial}{\partial L}\,(3L^3 C^2 - 2L^2 C^3)$$

$$= 9L^2 C^2 - 4LC^3$$

Average product of labour, $AP_L = \dfrac{Q}{L} = 3L^2 C^2 - 2LC^3$

For maximum value of AP_L, $MP_L = AP_L \Rightarrow 9L^2 C^2 - 4LC^3 = 3L^2 C^2 - 2LC^3$

$$\Rightarrow L = C/3$$

Also, MP_L is maximum when the slope of MP_L is zero, i.e., $\dfrac{\partial}{\partial L}\,(MP_L) = 0$. Hence,

$$\frac{\partial}{\partial L}\,(MP_L) = 0 \Rightarrow \frac{\partial}{\partial L}\,(9L^2 C^2 - 4LC^3) = 0$$

$$\Rightarrow 18LC^2 - 4C^3 = 0 \ \text{ or } \ L = 2C/9.$$

16. For Cobb-Douglas production function $x = f\,(L,\, K) = AL^\alpha K^\beta$, where x, L and K are the units of product, labour and capital, respectively, show that there is increasing, decreasing or constant returns to scale, that is, $(\alpha + \beta) > 1$, < 1 or 1.

17.   (a) For the production function
$$Q = 75 \left(0.3K^{-0.4} + 0.7L^{-0.4}\right)^{-2.5}$$
find the elasticity of substitution.   [Ans: $\sigma = 1/1.4$]

(b) Evaluate the elasticity of substitution of the production function
$$Z = Ax^{\alpha} y^{1-\alpha}; 0 < \alpha < 1.$$
   [Ans: $\sigma = 1$]

18.   (a) Show that average and marginal product of factors depend only on the ratio of factors and verify that the product is always L times the marginal product of labour plus K times the marginal product of capital.

(b) What are the determinant(s) of the marginal product of the two factors of production?

[Ans: (b)] $MP_L = \dfrac{1}{(CL+DK)^2} \begin{vmatrix} CL+DK & 2HLK - AL^2 - BK^2 \\ C & 2HK - 2AL \end{vmatrix}$

$MP_K = \dfrac{1}{(CL+DK)^2} \begin{vmatrix} CL+DK & 2HLK - AL^2 - BK^2 \\ D & 2HL - 2BK \end{vmatrix}.$

9.6   Theory of Cost

Total cost is classified into two categories: short-run cost and long-run cost. The cost, over a period during which factors of production (such as capital equipment) are fixed, is called *short-run cost*. Similarly, cost over a long period which permits the change in all factors of production is called *long-run cost*. Mathematically, these costs are expressed as the function of a number of factors as given below:

$$\text{Long-run cost, } C = f\left(Q, T, P_f\right)$$

and   Short-run cost, $C = f\left(Q, T, P_f, K_f\right)$

where C is the total cost: Q, the output; T, the technology; P_f, the prices of factors and K_f, the fixed factor(s).

The total cost (TC) is divided into two groups: total fixed cost (TFC), which does not vary with the change in output and total variable cost (TVC), which varies directly with output. Hence,

$$\text{TC} = \text{TFC} + \text{TVC}$$

where TFC includes salaries of staff, depreciation (wear and tear) of machinery, maintenance and repair of machinery, land, etc. The TVC includes raw material, direct labour cost, running expenses of fixed capital such as fuel, routine maintenance, and advertising expenses.

Hence, a linear total cost function may have the form of the type

$$C(Q) = aQ + b; a, b = \text{constant}$$

where b is the overhead or fixed cost.

The average fixed and variable cost of producing each unit of the output is given by

$$\text{Average fixed cost (AFC)} = \frac{\text{TFC}}{Q}$$

$$\text{Average variable cost (AVC)} = \frac{\text{TVC}}{Q}$$

$$\text{Average total cost (ATC)} = \frac{\text{TC}}{Q}$$

$$= \frac{\text{TFC} + \text{TVC}}{Q} = \text{AFC} + \text{AVC}$$

The marginal cost (MC) is defined as the change in the TC owing to the production of an extra unit of output. Mathematically, it is written as

$$\text{MC} = \frac{dC}{dQ}, \; Q > 0$$

Referring to the linear total cost function $C = aQ + b, a, b > 0$, the average and marginal cost functions are given by

$$AC = \frac{C}{Q} = a + (b/Q)$$

and
$$MC = \frac{dC}{dQ} = a.$$

9.6.1 Relationship between ATC and MC

The MC curve cuts the ATC and AVC curves at their lowest point (Fig. 9.7). Suppose n units of output are being produced at present. If the production is increased by one unit, then it is represented by MC. Let AC at production level of n units be given by

$$AC_n = \frac{TC_n}{Q_n}$$

and the AC at the level Q_{n+1} is
$$AC_{n+1} = \frac{TC_{n+1}}{Q_{n+1}}$$

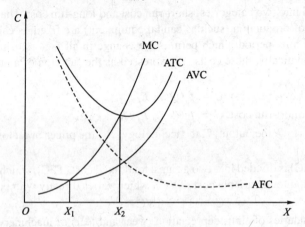

Fig. 9.7 ATC and MC curves

Obviously, $TC_{n+1} = TC_n + MC$ [change in TC resulting from production of $(n + 1)$th unit]. Thus,

(a) if MC of the $(n + 1)$th unit is less than AC_n, then AC_{n+1} will be smaller than AC_n; and

(b) if MC of the $(n + 1)$th unit is more than AC_n, then AC_{n+1} will be higher than AC_n.

9.6.2 Relationship between AC and MC

The slope of AC curve is obtained by finding its first derivative, i.e.,

$$\text{Slope of AC} = \frac{d}{dQ}\left(\frac{C}{Q}\right)$$

$$= \frac{Q\dfrac{dC}{dQ} - C}{Q^2} = \frac{1}{Q}\left(\frac{dC}{dQ} - \frac{C}{Q}\right) = \frac{1}{Q}(MC - AC)$$

Given that $AC > 0$ and $Q > 0$, the following results emerge:

(a) If slope of AC is negative, i.e., it is sloping downward, or $d\,(AC)/dQ < 0$, then $(MC - AC) < 0$ or $MC < AC$;

(b) If slope of AC is positive, i.e., it is sloping upward, or $d\,(AC)/dQ > 0$, then $(MC - AC) > 0$ or $MC > AC$; and

(c) If the slope of AC becomes zero which happens at its minimum point, i.e., $d\,(AC)/dQ = 0$, then $(MC - AC) = 0$ or $MC = AC$.

It means that the point where the intersection of MC and AC occurs, AC has reached its minimum level.

Example 9.12. The rate of change of total cost (y) of a commodity per unit change of output (x) is called the *marginal cost of the commodity*. If there exists a relation between y and x in the form

$$y = 3x \left(\frac{x+7}{x+5}\right) + 5,$$

prove that the marginal cost falls continuously as the output increases.

Solution. Given that

$$y = 3x \left(\frac{x+7}{x+5}\right) + 5 = 3\left(\frac{x^2 + 7x}{x+5}\right) + 5$$

Now,

$$MC = \frac{dy}{dx} = 3 \left[\frac{(x+5)(2x+7) - (x^2 + 7x)}{(x+5)^2}\right]$$

$$= \frac{3(x^2 + 10x + 35)}{(x+5)^2} = 3\left[\frac{(x+5)^2 + 10}{(x+5)^2}\right] = 3\left[1 + \frac{10}{(x+5)^2}\right]$$

This implies that as output x increases, the value of MC decreases.

Example 9.13. The average cost function (AC) for a commodity is given by

$$AC = x + 5 + (36/x)$$

in terms of the output x. Find the output for which AC is increasing and the output for which AC is decreasing with increasing output.

Solution. The slope of

$$AC = \frac{d}{dx}(AC)$$

$$= \frac{d}{dx}\left(x + 5 + \frac{36}{x}\right) = 1 - \frac{36}{x^2}$$

The AC will increase if $1 - \frac{36}{x^2} > 0$ or $x > 6$ and will decrease if $x < 6$.

Now,

$$AC = \frac{C}{x} \quad \text{or} \quad C = x \text{ AC. Hence,}$$

Total cost,

$$C = x\left[x + 5 + \frac{36}{x}\right] = x^2 + 5x + 36$$

and the marginal cost,

$$MC = \frac{dC}{dx} = \frac{d}{dx}(x^2 + 5x + 36) = 2x + 5.$$

9.6.3 Average and Marginal Revenue Function

The term *revenue* refers to the amount of money obtained by a firm from the sale of certain quantity of its output at different prices.

Total Revenue (TR). It is also called the *'gross revenue.'* Its value depends upon the total sale. If p denotes the price of one unit of a commodity when q units of this commodity are sold at that price, then the total revenue as a function of the total quantity sold is given by

$$TR (q) = pq = pf (q)$$

Average Revenue (AR). It is obtained by dividing the total revenue by the number of units sold. Therefore,

$$AR = \frac{TR (q)}{q} = \frac{p \cdot q}{q} = p \text{ (price)}$$

This implies that the average revenue (revenue per unit) and the price per unit of the commodity are equal. Thus, the average revenue curve indicates the *price curve* or *demand curve* of the product.

Marginal Revenue (MR). Marginal revenue is the revenue obtained from the sale of an additional unit of a commodity. In other words, it is the difference between the total revenue of n units and the total revenue of $n - 1$ units, i.e.,

$$\text{MR} = \text{TR}_n - \text{TR}_{n-1}$$

This means that MR is the rate of change of total revenue when q units are demanded, i.e.,

$$\text{MR} = \frac{d}{dq}(\text{TR}) = \frac{d}{dq}(p \cdot q) = p + q\,\frac{dp}{dq}$$

$$= \text{AR} + q\,\frac{dp}{dq}$$

or

$$\text{MR} - \text{AR} = q \cdot \frac{dp}{dq}$$

Since $dp/dq \leq 0$ and $q \geq 0$, $\text{MR} - \text{AR} \leq 0$. Therefore, the MR curve always lies below the AR curve. This means that MR declines more rapidly than AR.

AR and MR behave differently under different types of market conditions: pure competition, monopoly or imperfect competition.

Under pure competition, the price charged is the same (p is constant) for all the units sold. Thus, $dp/dq = 0$, i.e., the price of an additional (or marginal) unit or MR will be same. Hence, AR and MR curves become identical ($\text{AR} = \text{MR}$) and horizontal for all q. Under perfect competition, an individual seller supplies only a small part of total supply and therefore he cannot influence price by his own action. He has to sell his product at a price determined by the market forces of demand and supply. This means that demand curve for his product is perfectly elastic.

Under monopoly or imperfect competition, demand curve slopes downward ($dp/dq < 0$) to indicate that monopolist will be able to sell more at lower price. This is the basic difference between a competitive firm and a monopoly firm, viz. the competitive firm has a horizontal demand curve, whereas the monopoly firm has a downward sloping demand curve. Since $dp/dq < 0$, therefore $\text{MR} - \text{AR} < 0$ or $\text{MR} < \text{AR}$. This means that, under monopoly, MR curve is below the AR curve for all $q > 0$.

9.6.4 AR, MR and Elasticity of Demand (η_d)

The elasticity of demand measures the variation in the quantity demanded of a commodity due to changes in its own price. If the changes in the price are very small, the *point elasticity of demand* is used as measure of the consumer response of demand. In case changes in the price are not small, the *arc elasticity of demand* is used as the relevant measure.

The point elasticity of demand is defined as the percentage change in the quantity demanded resulting from a very small percentage change in price. Symbolically, it is expressed as

$$\eta_d = \frac{dQ/Q}{dp/p} = \frac{p}{Q} \cdot \frac{dQ}{dp}$$

where dQ/dp represents the change in quantity demanded when the change in price approaches a value equal to zero.

If the demand curve is linear, then its slope dQ/dp is negative. Substituting in the elasticity formula,

$$\eta_d = -\frac{p}{Q} \cdot \frac{dQ}{dp}$$

The price elasticity is always negative because of the inverse relationship between Q and p implied by 'law of demand.'

The range of values of the price elasticity is

$$0 \le \eta_d \le \infty$$

as shown in Fig. 9.8.

For comparing the nature of changes in demand due to changes in price of commodity under question, the following *five* values of η_d are used:

(a) If $\eta_d = 0$, the demand is perfectly inelastic;

(b) If $\eta_d = 1$, the demand has unitary (proportional to price) elasticity;

(c) If $\eta_d = \infty$, the demand is perfectly elastic;

(d) If $0 < \eta_d < 1$, the demand is inelastic; and

(e) If $1 < \eta_d < \infty$, the demand is elastic.

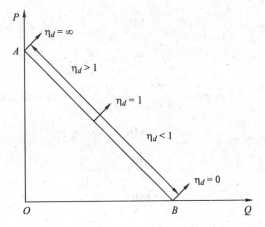

Fig. 9.8 Range of values of the price elasticity

Example 9.14. If the demand law is $x = 20/(p + 1)$, find the elasticity of demand at the point where $p = 3$. What type of curve is the demand function? What is its economic importance?

Solution. The elasticity of demand is given by

$$\eta_d = \frac{p}{x} \frac{dx}{dp} = -\frac{p}{20/(p+1)} \frac{d}{dp} [20 (p+1)^{-1}]$$

$$= \frac{p (p+1)}{20} [-20 (p+1)^{-2}]$$

Hence, at $p = 3$,

$$\eta_d = \frac{-3 (3+1)}{20} [-20 (3+1)^{-2}] = \frac{3}{3+1} = \frac{3}{4} (<1)$$

The demand is inelastic and this type of demand curve is a rectangular hyperbola and is called a '*constant returns*' curve.

Example 9.15. If the elasticities of a function $f(x)$ of x is defined to be $\eta = \frac{x}{f(x)} \cdot \frac{d}{dx} [f(x)]$, show that the elasticities of $xf(x)$ and $f(x)/x$ are respectively $(\eta + 1)$ and $(\eta - 1)$.

Solution. The elasticity of a function $xf(x)$ of x is given by

$$\frac{x}{xf(x)} \cdot \frac{d}{dx} [xf(x)] = \frac{1}{f(x)} \{xf'(x) + 1 \cdot f(x)\}$$

$$= \frac{x}{f(x)} \frac{d}{dx} [f(x)] + 1 = \eta + 1$$

and elasticity of a function $f(x)/x$ of x is given by

$$\frac{x}{f(x)/x} \frac{d}{dx} [f(x)/x] = \frac{x^2}{f(x)} \left\{ \frac{xf'(x) - 1 \cdot f(x)}{x^2} \right\} = \frac{x^2}{f(x)} \left\{ \frac{f'(x)}{x} - \frac{f(x)}{x^2} \right\}$$

$$= \frac{x}{f(x)} f'(x) - 1 = \frac{x}{f(x)} \frac{d}{dx} f(x) - 1 = \eta - 1.$$

9.6.5 Relationship between MR, AR and Price Elasticity

Suppose demand function is $p = f(Q)$, where p is the price per unit of commodity and Q, the quantity of demand. Then, total revenue is given by

$$TR = pQ$$

and
$$\text{MR} = \frac{d}{dQ}(p \cdot Q) = p + Q \cdot \frac{dp}{dQ} = p\left\{1 + \frac{Q}{p} \cdot \frac{dp}{dQ}\right\} = p\left\{1 - \frac{1}{\eta_d}\right\} \qquad (1)$$

where
$$\eta_d = -\frac{p}{Q} \cdot \frac{dQ}{dp}.$$

Since $\text{AR} = \dfrac{\text{TR}}{Q} = \dfrac{p \cdot Q}{Q} = p$, therefore from (1),

$$\text{MR} = \text{AR}\left\{1 - \frac{1}{\eta_d}\right\}$$

or
$$\frac{\text{MR}}{\text{AR}} = 1 - \frac{1}{\eta_d}$$

or
$$1 - \frac{\text{MR}}{\text{AR}} = \frac{1}{\eta_d}$$

or
$$\frac{1}{\eta_d} = \frac{\text{AR}_1 - \text{MR}}{\text{AR}}$$

or
$$\eta_d = \frac{\text{AR}}{\text{AR} - \text{MR}} \qquad (2)$$

It is known that the demand curve, which falls below the TR curve, initially increases, reaches a maximum and then starts declining. The relationship (1) can be considered to understand the TR curve.

1. If $\eta = 1$, the TR curve reaches its maximum level because at this point its slope, the marginal revenue, is equal to zero, i.e.,

$$\text{MR} = p\left(1 - \frac{1}{1}\right) = 0$$

Furthermore, a decrease in price (p) results in the proportionate increase in quantity demanded (Q) and therefore demand is said to be unitary.

2. If $\eta > 1$, TR curve has a positive slope, i.e., TR increases as price decreases and hence TR does not reach its maximum point. In other words, for $p > 0$ and $\left(1 - \dfrac{1}{\eta}\right) > 0$, $\text{MR} > 0$.

Furthermore, if the demand is elastic, an increase in price results in a decrease of total revenue and *vice-versa*.

3. If $\eta < 1$, TR curve has a negative slope, i.e., TR decreases as prices decrease. In other words, $p > 0$ and $\left(1 - \dfrac{1}{\eta}\right) < 0$, $\text{MR} < 0$.

Furthermore, if demand is inelastic, an increase in price results is an increase in TR and *vice-versa*.

Example 9.16. Verify the relationship $\text{MR} = p\left(1 - \dfrac{1}{\eta_d}\right)$ for the demand function

$$p = (12 - x)^{1/2}; \quad 0 \le x \le 12.$$

Solution. Given
$$p = (12 - x)^{1/2}$$

Differentiating this demand function with respect to p,

$$1 = \frac{1}{2}(12 - x)^{-1/2}\frac{dx}{dp}$$

or
$$\frac{dx}{dp} = -2(12 - x)^{1/2}$$

Hence, $\qquad \eta_d = -\dfrac{p}{x} \cdot \dfrac{dx}{dp} = -\dfrac{(12-x)^{1/2}}{x}\{-2(12-x)^{1/2}\} = \dfrac{2(12-x)}{x}$

Total revenue, $\qquad \text{TR} = px = x(12-x)^{1/2}$

Marginal revenue, $\qquad \text{MR} = \dfrac{d}{dx}(\text{TR})$

$\qquad\qquad\qquad\qquad = \left\{\dfrac{1}{2}(12-x)^{-1/2}(-1)\cdot x + 1\cdot(12-x)^{1/2}\right\}$

$\qquad\qquad = \dfrac{-x}{2(12-x)^{1/2}} + (12-x)^{1/2} = \dfrac{-x+2(12-x)}{2(12-x)^{1/2}} = \dfrac{24-3x}{2(12-x)^{1/2}}$ (1)

Substituting the values of p and η_d in the relationship,

$$\text{MR} = p\left(1-\dfrac{1}{\eta_d}\right) = (12-x)^{1/2}\left(1-\dfrac{x}{2(12-x)}\right)$$

$$= \dfrac{24-3x}{2(12-x)^{1/2}}, \text{ which is true from (1)}$$

Hence, it is concluded that, $\text{MR} = p\left(1-\dfrac{1}{\eta_d}\right)$.

Example 9.17. Show that for maximum revenue, elasticity of demand is unity.

Solution. Suppose $Q = f(p)$ be the demand curve. Then

$$\text{TR} = pQ = pf(p) = p$$

and $\qquad\qquad \text{MR} = \dfrac{d}{dQ}(p\cdot Q) = p + Q\cdot\dfrac{dp}{dQ}$

For maximum value of TR, $\dfrac{d}{dQ}(\text{TR}) = 0$, i.e.,

$$\dfrac{d}{dQ}(\text{TR}) = 0 \Rightarrow p + Q\cdot\dfrac{dp}{dQ} = 0$$

or $\qquad\qquad Q = -\dfrac{p}{(dp/dQ)} = -p\cdot\dfrac{dQ}{dp}$

Hence, $\qquad\qquad \eta_d = -\dfrac{p}{Q}\cdot\dfrac{dQ}{dp} = \dfrac{-p}{-p\dfrac{dQ}{dp}}\cdot\dfrac{dQ}{dp} = 1$

This proves the result.

Example 9.18. The supply of a certain goods is given by $x = a\sqrt{p-b}$, where x is the quantity demanded, p (which is greater than b) is the price, and a and b are positive constants. Find the expression for the elasticity of supply as a function of price and by using calculus, show that the elasticity decreases as price increases and becomes unity at the price equal to $2b$.

Solution. Given the supply function, $x = a\sqrt{p-b}$. Therefore, elasticity of supply is given by

$$\eta_s = \dfrac{p}{x}\cdot\dfrac{dx}{dp} = \dfrac{p}{a\sqrt{p-b}}\cdot\dfrac{d}{dp}\{a\sqrt{p-b}\}$$

$$= \dfrac{p}{a\sqrt{p-b}}\left\{\dfrac{1}{2}a(p-b)^{-1/2}\right\} = \dfrac{p}{2(p-b)}$$

To show that η_s decreases, calculate the first derivative of η_s with respect to p as

$$\dfrac{d\eta_s}{dp} = \dfrac{1}{2}\left\{\dfrac{(p-b)\cdot 1 - p}{(p-b)^2}\right\} = \dfrac{b}{2(p-b)^2}$$

Since $b > 0$ and $(p - b)^2 > 0$, therefore $d\eta_s/dp < 0$ and hence η_s is a decreasing function of p, i.e., η_s decreases as p increases.

If $p = 2b$, $\eta_s = \dfrac{2b}{2(2b - b)} = 1$.

9.6.6 Cross (Price) Elasticity of Demand

Cross (price) elasticity of demand is used to evaluate the effect of variations in the price of a product on the quantity demanded of another product. If η_{ij} denotes the relation between two goods, then, in general,

   (a) $\eta_{ij} > 0$, where i and j are substitute goods. In other words, an increase in the price of jth goods increases the quantity demanded of the ith goods.

     Hence, the sign of cross elasticity will be positive.

   (b) $\eta_{ij} = 0$ if and only if i and j are independent goods (not related).

   (c) $\eta_{ij} < 0$ implying i and j are complementary goods. An increase in the price of jth goods reduces the quantity demanded of the ith goods. Hence, the relationship between variables is negative correlation, thus cross elasticity is negative. The greater the absolute value of η_{ij} the more intense is the relationship existing between the two goods.

9.6.7 Income Elasticity of Demand

The income elasticity is defined as the proportionate (relative) change in the quantity demanded in response to the proportionate change in income. Symbolically, it is stated as

$$\eta_y = \frac{dQ/Q}{dy/y} = \frac{y}{Q} \cdot \frac{dQ}{dy}$$

where Q is the quantity demanded and y, the income per head.

   (a) If $\eta_y > 1$, a commodity is considered to be 'luxury.'

   (b) If $0 < \eta_y < 1$, a commodity is considered to be 'necessity.'

9.6.8 Cost Elasticity

The cost elasticity is defined as the proportionate (relative) change in total cost in response to the proportionate change in output. Symbolically, it is stated as

$$\eta_c = \frac{dC/C}{dQ/Q} = \frac{Q}{C} \cdot \frac{dC}{dQ}$$

where Q is the quantity demanded and $C = f(Q)$, the cost function.

9.6.9 Elasticity of Demand with respect to Advertisement

It is the ratio of percentage change in the quantity demanded of a commodity (Q) to percentage change in the advertisement outlay on the commodity (A). It is also called *promotional elasticity* of demand or advertisement elasticity. It plays an important role in the context of marketing management. It can be defined as

$$\eta_a = \frac{dQ}{dQ} \cdot \frac{A}{Q}$$

Remark: Elasticity of average cost is given by

$$\eta_{AC} = \frac{Q}{AC} \cdot \frac{d(AC)}{dQ} = \frac{Q}{(C/Q)} \cdot \frac{d}{dQ}\left(\frac{C}{Q}\right)$$

$$= \frac{Q^2}{C} \cdot \left\{ \frac{Q \cdot \dfrac{dC}{dQ} - C \cdot 1}{Q^2} \right\} = \frac{Q}{C} \cdot \frac{dC}{dQ} - 1 = \eta_c - 1$$

Further, η_{AC} can also be expressed in terms of MC and AC as follows:

$$\eta_{AC} = \frac{Q}{AC}\frac{d}{dQ}(AC) = \frac{Q}{AC}\frac{d}{dQ}(C/Q)$$

$$= \frac{Q}{AC}\left\{\frac{Q \cdot \dfrac{dC}{dQ} - C \cdot 1}{Q^2}\right\} = \frac{1}{AC}\left\{\frac{dC}{dQ} - \frac{C}{Q}\right\} = \frac{1}{AC}\{MC - AC\}.$$

Example 9.19. Find the elasticity of total cost and the average cost of the function,

$$C = 2x^2 + 4x + 3.$$

Solution. η_c = Elasticity of total cost

$$= \frac{x}{C}\cdot\frac{dC}{dx} = \frac{x}{2x^2 + 4x + 3}\{4x + 4\} = \frac{4x(x+1)}{2x^2 + 4x + 3} = \frac{4x^2 + 4x}{2x^2 + 4x + 3}$$

Also, η_{AC} = Elasticity of average cost

$$= \frac{x}{AC}\cdot\frac{d}{dx}(AC) = \frac{x}{(C/x)}\frac{d}{dx}(C/x) = \frac{x}{2x + 4 + \dfrac{3}{x}}\cdot\frac{d}{dx}\left(2x + 4 + \frac{3}{x}\right)$$

$$= \frac{x^2}{2x^2 + 4x + 3}\left\{2 - \frac{3}{x^2}\right\} = \frac{x^2(2x^2 - 3)}{x^2(2x^2 + 4x + 3)} = \frac{2x^2 - 3}{(2x^2 + 4x + 3)}$$

$$= \frac{(4x^2 + 4x) - (2x^2 + 4x + 3)}{2x^2 + 4x + 3} = \frac{4x^2 + 4x}{2x^2 + 4x + 3} - 1 = \eta_c - 1.$$

Self-assessment Questions Set-III

1. The total cost $c(x)$ of a firm is $c(x) = 0.005x^3 - 0.02x^2 - 30x + 5,000,$ where x is the output. Determine (*i*) average cost (AC), (*ii*) slope of AC, (*iii*) marginal cost (MC), (*iv*) slope of MC, and (*v*) value of x for which MVC = AVC, where VC denotes the variable cost.

   [**Hint:** (*i*) AC $= c(x)/x$; (*ii*) Slope of AC $= \dfrac{d}{dx}(AC)$; (*iii*) MC $= \dfrac{d}{dx}c(x)$; (*iv*) Slope of MC $= \dfrac{d}{dx}(MC)$;
   (*v*) VC $= 0.005x^3 - 0.02x^2 - 30x$

   $$AVC = \frac{VC}{x} \text{ and } MVC = \frac{d}{dx}(VC) = 0.015x^2 - 0.04x - 30$$

   $x = 0$ (undesirable); 2].

2. If $R(x)$ is the total revenue received from the sale of x tables, and

   $$R(x) = 600x - (x^2/25)$$

   find (*i*) the average revenue function, (*ii*) the marginal revenue when $x = 25$, and (*iii*) the actual revenue from the sale of the 26th table.

   [**Hint:** (*i*) AR $= R(x)/x$, (*ii*) MR $= \dfrac{d}{dx}R(x)$; MR $= 525$ for $x = 25$, and (*iii*) $R(26) - R(25) = $ Rs 521.96.

   Thus, MR = Rs 525 is simply an approximation of the revenue from the sale of the 26th table, whereas Rs 521.96 is the actual revenue obtained from the sale of the 26th table].

3. 'A monopolist' demand curve is: $p = 200 - 5q$. Find the marginal revenue function. What is the relationship between the slopes of the average and marginal revenue curves? At what price is marginal revenue zero?

   [**Hint:** $\qquad$ TR $= q(200 - 5q) = 200q - 5q^2$

   $$MR = \frac{d}{dq}(TR) = 200 - 10q; \quad AR = \frac{TR}{q} = 200 - 5q$$

   Slope of $\qquad$ MR $= \dfrac{d}{dq}(MR) = -10;$ slope of AR $= \dfrac{d}{dq}(AR) = -5.$ Hence,

   Slope of $\qquad$ MR $= 2\times$ Slope of AR

   For $\qquad$ MR $= 0 \Rightarrow q = 20$ and hence $p = 100$].

4. A manufacturer determines that t employees will produce a total of x units of a product per day, where $x = 10t^2 \sqrt{t^2 + 19}$. If the demand equation for the product is $p = 900/(x + 9)$, determine the marginal revenue product when $t = 9$.

[**Hint:** Marginal revenue product $= \dfrac{d}{dt}(TR) = \dfrac{dx}{dt}\left(p + x\dfrac{dp}{dx}\right)$; $TR = px$

When $t = 9$, $x = 81$ which gives $p = 10$, and

$$\left[\frac{d}{dt}(TR)\right]_{t=9} = 10.71.$$

This implies that if the 10th employee is hired, the extra revenue generated is Rs 10.71 (approx)].

5. The marginal cost of commodity is the rate of change in cost for change in the output. If $f(x) = 2x\{(x + 4)/(x + 1)\} + 6$ be the total cost of an output x, show that the marginal cost falls continuously as the output x increases.

6. If $p = k/x$ (where k is a constant) is the demand equation for a manufacturer's product, and $x = f(m)$ defines a function that gives the total number of units produced per day by m employees, show that the marginal revenue product is always zero.

7. Suppose p is the price per box of biscuits when $1000x$ boxes are demanded, and $x = 75 - p^2$.

   (a) Find the price elasticity of demand when the price of a box of biscuits is Rs 7.50.

   (b) What per cent decrease in the price would yield about a five per cent increase in the demand?

[**Hint:** (a) $\eta_d = -\dfrac{p}{x}\dfrac{dx}{dp} = \dfrac{2p^2}{(75 - p^2)}$; $\eta_d = 6$ at $p = 7.50$.

   (b) $5/6 = 0.83$ implies that 0.83 per cent decrease in price of a box of biscuits would result approximately 5 per cent increase in the demand].

8. If the demand function is $p = 4 - 5x$, for what value of x will the elasticity of demand be unitary?

$$\left[\textbf{Hint: } \eta_d = -\frac{p}{x}\frac{dx}{dp} = \frac{4.5x}{5x} = 1 \Rightarrow x = 2/5\right]$$

9. The demand function for a commodity is given by $x = 48 - 3p^2$ and at $p = 3$, $x = 21$. If the price (p) decreases by 4 per cent, determine the relative increase in demand (x) and hence an approximation to the elasticity of demand. Compare this with elasticity of demand at $p = 3$.

[**Hint:** 2.10; $\eta_d = -2.55$ at $p = 3$].

10. If the demand curve is given by $x = p^a e^{-b(p+c)}$ show that the demand increases as the price increases and the price approaches the value a/b. Find the effect of any price greater than a/b on the elasticity of demand.

[**Hint:** $\eta_d = -\dfrac{p}{x}\dfrac{dx}{dp} = bp - a$

When $p \to a/b$, then $\eta_d = \lim\limits_{p \to a/b} (bp - a) = 0$ and when $p > a/b$, then η_d will be more than zero].

11. If $AR = 20$, the elasticity of demand with respect to price is 2. Find MR and comment.

[**Hint:** $MR = AR\left(1 - \dfrac{1}{\eta_d}\right) = 20\left(1 - \dfrac{1}{2}\right) = 10$. Since $MR < AR$, AR curve is declining].

12. Let $p = mq + b$ be a linear demand equation, where $m \neq 0$ and $b > 0$. Show that (a) $\lim\limits_{p \to b} \eta_d = -\infty$, and (b) $\eta_d = 0$ when $p = 0$.

13. What is the marginal revenue for a demand curve which has infinite elasticity?

[**Ans:** MR = AR].

9.7 Theory of the Firm

A business enterprise is a combination of people, physical assets, and information (technical, sales, coordinative and so on). The people directly involved include stockholders, management, labour, suppliers and customers. In addition to these direct participants, society as a whole is indirectly involved in the operations of a business enterprise, because businesses use resources that are otherwise available for other purposes, pay taxes if operations are profitable, provide employment and generally produce most of the material output for the society. Thus, a business enterprise under one management which allocates and employs resources for production and distribution of goods and services is called a *firm*. A firm may be a large one with a number of factories and plants producing a wide range of products or may be producing only one product. Here it is immaterial whether a firm belongs to public sector, private sector or joint sector. Generally, the aim of any firm is to maximize profit and minimize the cost of production and also to produce only those goods or provide such services which are greater in demand.

9.7.1 Traditional Theory

The traditional theory of the firm is based on the following *two* assumptions:

(a) Each firm has perfect knowledge of the cost associated with each input (production factors), customer's choice, etc.; and

(b) Each firm has a single objective—profit maximization—in the long run.

The first assumption implies that no firm invests large amount of money for buying input resources because of its ignorance. Since a firm has perfect knowledge of the cost and therefore if the price charged for the product is less than the total cost incurred, then it is considered as a deliberate decision. Also, a firm has information about the preferences of customers, which enables the firm to decide on the products to be produced.

Some doubts have been raised about the validity of assumptions in the traditional theory as developed by neoclassical economists. For example, all decisions regarding the events to occur in the future involve certain amount of uncertainty. Therefore, it is argued that assuming perfect knowledge does not represent reality. Second, the theoretical concept has been developed in a static framework, whereas only a dynamic framework could be more close to the real life situation. Further, empirical studies suggest that firms do not take into account marginal cost (MC) and marginal revenue (MR) while deciding the level of production. An area which represents evidence against profit maximization as the guiding criterion is that of pricing policies. It has been empirically proved that usually the pricing policy is the policy of 'cost plus' which adds a certain profit margin to the total cost.

The second assumption implies that a firm decides on a strategy (or course of action)—whether it be output, price, expenditure on advertising—to maximize its profit.

9.7.2 Profit Maximization under Perfect Competition

The model of perfect competition is based on the following assumptions:

1. Presence of a large number of buyers and sellers (firms) so that each firm supplies only a small part of the total supply of the commodity in the market. The buyers are also in large numbers so that any one buyer cannot monopolize the purchase in the market. In other words, no firm alone can affect the price in the market by varying (or changing) the supply of its output. Hence, price (p) is independent of the commodity demanded (Q).

2. The industry, which is defined as a group of firms, produces a *homogeneous product*. This assumption along with assumption (1) implies that demand of each firm is infinitely elastic, and the firm can sell any amount of its output at the given market price as shown in Fig. 9.9.

3. There is no government intervention in the market (tariffs, subsidies, rationing of production or demand, etc.).

4. The factors of production (raw materials, labour, etc.) are neither monopolized nor unionized.

5. Both sellers and buyers have thorough knowledge about the present and future conditions of the market.

6. All resources and inputs such as material, labour, and capital are perfectly mobile so that firms can enter the market and fold up their business as and when they wish.

The firm is in short-run equilibrium when it intends to maximize its profit (P), defined as follows:

$$\text{Profit } (P) = \text{Total revenue (TR)} - \text{Total cost (TC)}$$

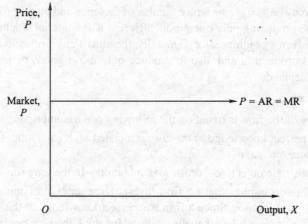

Fig. 9.9

Since TR = $p \cdot Q$, therefore, MR = $p + Q \, (dp/dQ)$. Also, as prevailing market price (p) is constant because all units are sold at the same price, therefore,

$$MR = p + Q \frac{dp}{dQ} = p + Q \cdot 0 = p \, (= AR)$$

The result MR = p = AR implies that MR and AR curves coincide under perfect competition (Fig. 9.10).

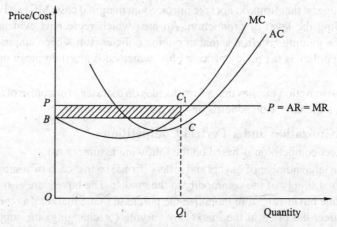

Fig. 9.10 Perfect competition—Firm short-term equilibrium

Since the firm aims at the maximization of its profit, the following *two* conditions exist:

1. The first order condition for the maximization of profit (P) is given by

$$\frac{dP}{dQ} = \frac{d}{dQ} (TR) - \frac{d}{dQ} (TC) = 0$$

$$= MR - MC = 0$$

or   MR = MC

Given that MC > 0, MR is also positive at equilibrium. Since MR = p, the first order condition may be written as MC = p. This long-run equilibrium situation is shown in Fig. 9.11.

2. The second order condition for maximization of profit requires that $d^2P/dQ^2 < 0$ (negative), that is,

$$\frac{d^2P}{dQ^2} = \frac{d^2}{dQ^2} (TR) - \frac{d^2}{dQ^2} (TC) < 0$$

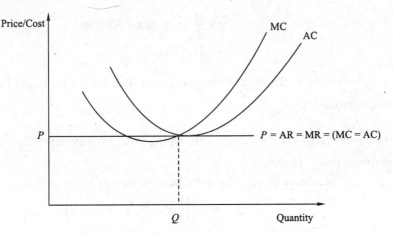

Fig. 9.11 Long-run equilibrium—Perfect competition

or
$$\frac{d^2}{dQ^2}\,(TR) \,<\, \frac{d^2}{dQ^2}\,(TC)$$

or
$$\text{Slope of MR} < \text{Slope of MC}$$

This means that MC must have a steeper slope them the MR curve or the MC curve must cut the MR curve from below.

In perfect competition, the slope of MR is zero, i.e.,

$$\frac{d^2}{dQ^2}\,(TR)\;=\;\frac{d}{dQ}\left(\frac{d}{dQ}\,(TC)\right)=\frac{d}{dQ}\,(MR)=0$$

Hence, the second order condition is simplified as follows:

$$0 < \frac{d^2}{dQ^2}\,(TC)$$

or
$$\frac{d}{dQ}\,(MC) > 0$$

This implies that the slope of MC curve is positive (or rising).

Example 9.20. If the total cost function of a firm is

$$C\,(x) \;=\; \frac{1}{3}\,x^3 - 5x^2 + 30x + 10$$

where C is the total cost and x, the output under perfect competition given as 6. At what values of x will the profit be maximized? Examine both first and second order conditions. Will the firm continue production?

Solution. Given
$$C\,(x) \;=\; \frac{1}{3}\,x^3 - 5x^2 + 30x + 10$$

Therefore,
$$MC \;=\; \frac{dC}{dx} = \frac{1}{3}\,(3x^2) - 5\,(2x) + 30 = x^2 - 10x + 30$$

The first order condition under perfect competition for profit maximization is

$$MC = \text{price } (p) \Rightarrow x^2 - 10x + 30 = 6 \text{ or } x = 4, 6$$

The second order condition under perfect competition for profit maximization requires

$$\frac{d^2C}{dx^2} \;=\; \frac{d}{dx}\left\{\frac{dC}{dx}\right\} = \frac{d}{dx}\,(MC) > 0$$

$$\Rightarrow \frac{d}{dx}(x^2 - 10x + 30) > 0$$

$$\Rightarrow 2x - 10 > 0$$

For $x = 4$, $\dfrac{d^2C}{dx^2} = 2 \times 4 - 10 = -2 \ (< 0)$. This implies that $x = 4$ is the level of output where the firm is in equilibrium.

For $x = 6$, $\dfrac{d^2C}{dx^2} = 2 \times 6 - 10 = 2 \ (> 0)$. This implies that $x = 6$ is the level of output where the firm earns maximum profit. Therefore,

$$\text{Maximum profit} = \text{Total revenue} - \text{Total cost}$$

$$= p \times x - \left\{\frac{1}{3}x^3 - 5x^2 + 30x + 10\right\}$$

$$= 6 \times 6 - \left\{\frac{1}{3}(6)^3 - 5(6)^2 + 30(6) + 10\right\} = -46$$

The negative profit (-46) indicates equivalent loss of Rs 46. Since this loss is more than the fixed cost of Rs 10, the firm will discontinue production when product price is Rs 6.

9.7.3 Profit Maximization under Monopoly

Monopoly is a market situation in which there is a single seller (or producer) of a particular commodity with no close substitutes for the commodity it produces (public utilities such as electricity, water, communication, etc.). Obviously, the monopolist tends to control free flow of quantity produced and hence the price per unit (which is the function of demand) so as to maximize his profit to the largest extent.

The following factors may be responsible for prevalence of a monopoly situation:

1. Single ownership of strategic raw material, such as uranium, and exclusive knowledge of particular techniques of production.

2. Patent rights for a product or for a production process (as in the case of drugs).

3. Government licensing or discouraging foreign competitors.

4. Economies of scale may not bear the burden of more than one plant of optimal size. For example, in public utilities such as transport, electricity, communications, etc. where substantial economies are involved, and which can be realized only at large scales of output. In such cases, the government undertakes the production of commodity (or service) to avoid consumer exploitation.

5. A pricing policy along with heavy advertising and continuous product differentiation by a firm that aims at discouraging other firms from entering the business.

The firm is in the short-run equilibrium when it intends to maximize its profit (P) by producing and selling Q units of a commodity. The profit is defined as follows:

$$\text{Profit }(P) = \text{Total revenue (TR)} - \text{Total cost (TC)}$$

or

$$P = \text{TR} - \text{TC}$$

The first order condition for maximum profit P is

$$\frac{dP}{dQ} = 0 \Rightarrow \frac{d}{dQ}(\text{TR}) - \frac{d}{dQ}(\text{TC}) = 0$$

$$\Rightarrow \frac{d}{dQ}(\text{TR}) = \frac{d}{dQ}(\text{TC})$$

or

$$\text{MR} = \text{MC}$$

The second order condition for maximum profit is

$$\frac{d^2 P}{dQ^2} < 0 \Rightarrow \frac{d^2}{dQ^2}(TR) - \frac{d^2}{dQ^2}(TC) < 0$$

$$\Rightarrow \frac{d}{dQ}(MR) - \frac{d}{dQ}(MC) < 0$$

$$\Rightarrow \frac{d}{dQ}(MR) < \frac{d}{dQ}(MC)$$

$$\Rightarrow \text{Slope of MR} < \text{Slope of MC}$$

In Fig. 9.12, the equilibrium of the monopolist occurred at the point E, where the MC curve intersects the MR curve from below. Thus, both the first order and second order conditions for equilibrium are satisfied. The monopolist realizes excess profits equal to the shaded area as shown in Fig. 9.12. It may be noted here that price (p) is higher than the MR.

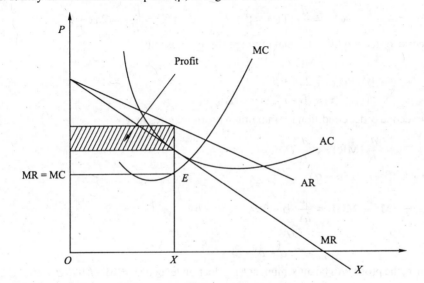

Fig. 9.12 Equilibrium under monopoly

Example 9.21. A sitar manufacturer can sell x sitars per week at p rupees each, where $5x = 375 - 3p$. The cost of production is $\{500 + 13x + x^2/5\}$ rupees. How many sitars should he manufacture for maximum profit and what is that profit?

Solution: Given $5x = 375 - 3p$ or $p = (375 - 5x)/3$. Then the total profit is given by

$$P = \text{Revenue} - \text{cost} = p \cdot x - C$$

$$= x(375 - 5x)/3 - \{500 + 13x + x^2/5\}$$

$$= -\frac{28}{15}x^2 + 112x - 500$$

The first order condition for maximum profit requires that

$$\frac{dP}{dx} = 0 \Rightarrow \frac{d}{dx}\left(-\frac{28}{15}x^2 + 112x - 500\right) = 0$$

$$\Rightarrow -\frac{56}{15}x + 112 = 0 \quad \text{or} \quad x = 30$$

The second order condition for maximum profit requires that $\dfrac{d^2 P}{dx^2} < 0$.

For $x = 30$, $\dfrac{d}{dx}\left(\dfrac{-56}{15}x + 112\right) = -\dfrac{56}{15} \, (< 0)$

Hence, the maximum profit at a production level of $x = 30$ units of sitars will be

$$P = -\frac{28}{15}(30)^2 + 112\,(30) - 500 = \text{Rs } 1180.$$

Example 9.22. A monopolist firm has the following total cost and demand functions:

$$C(x) = ax^2 + bx + c, \quad p(x) = \beta - ax \ (\alpha, \beta, a, b, c > 0)$$

(a) What is the output for the profit maximization when the firm is assumed to fix the output?

(b) Show that the firm's optimum output level is equal when it fixes (a) output, (b) price.

Solution. (a) *When the firm fixes the output level*

$$\text{TR} = px = x\,(\beta - \alpha x) = \beta x - \alpha x^2 \ \text{ and } C(x) = ax^2 + bx + c$$

and $\text{MR} = \dfrac{d}{dx}(\text{TR}) = \beta - 2\alpha x \ \text{ and } \text{MC} = \dfrac{dC}{dx} = 2ax + b$

The first order condition for maximum profit requires that

$$\text{MR} = \text{MC}$$

or $\beta - 2\alpha x = 2ax + b$

or $x = (\beta - b)/2\,(a + \alpha)$

The second order condition for maximum profit requires that

$$\frac{d}{dx}(\text{MR}) < \frac{d}{dx}(\text{MC})$$

For $x = (\beta - b)/2\,(a + \alpha)$,

$$\frac{d}{dx}(\text{MR} - \text{MC}) = \frac{d}{dx}(\beta - 2\alpha x - 2ax - b)$$

$$= -2\alpha - 2a$$

$$= -2\,(\alpha + a) < 0$$

Hence, the profit will be maximum at a production level of $x = (\beta - b)/2\,(\alpha + a)$.

(b) *When the firm fixes the price.* In this case, convert the total revenue and cost functions in terms of price.

Given $p = \beta - \alpha x$,   or $x = (\beta - p)/\alpha$

Then $\text{TR} = px = p\,(\beta - p)/\alpha = (\beta p - p^2)/\alpha$

$$\text{MR} = \frac{d}{dp}(\text{TR}) = (\beta - 2p)/\alpha$$

and $C = ax^2 + bx + c$

$$= a\,\{(\beta - p)/\alpha\}^2 + b\,\{(\beta - p)/\alpha\} + c$$

Hence, $\text{MC} = \dfrac{dC}{dp} = (-2a\beta + 2ap)/\alpha^2 - (b/\alpha)$

The first order condition for maximum profit requires that $\text{MR} = \text{MC}$. Therefore,

$$(\beta - 2p)/\alpha = \{-2a\beta + 2ap\}/\alpha^2 - (b/\alpha)$$

$$\frac{\beta}{\alpha} - \frac{2p}{\alpha} = \frac{-2a\beta}{\alpha^2} + \frac{2ap}{\alpha^2} - \frac{b}{\alpha}$$

or $\dfrac{\beta}{\alpha} + \dfrac{2a\beta}{\alpha^2} + \dfrac{b}{\alpha} = \dfrac{2ap}{\alpha^2} + \dfrac{2p}{\alpha}$

or $$\frac{\alpha\beta + 2a\beta + b\alpha}{\alpha^2} = \frac{(2a + 2\alpha)\,p}{\alpha^2}$$

or $$p = \frac{\alpha\beta + 2a\beta + b\alpha}{2\,(a + \alpha)}$$

The second order condition for maximum profit requires that

$$\frac{d}{dp}\,(MR) < \frac{d}{dp}\,(MC) \text{ or } \frac{d}{dp}\,(MR - MC) < 0$$

Then $$\frac{d}{dp}\,(MR - MC) = -\frac{2}{\alpha} - \frac{2a}{\alpha^2} = -2\,(\alpha + a)/\alpha^2 < 0$$

Since demand function is given by $p = \beta - \alpha x$, therefore,

$$\frac{\alpha\beta + 2a\beta + b\alpha}{2\,(a + \alpha)} = \beta - \alpha x$$

or $$x = \frac{1}{\alpha}\left[\beta - \frac{\alpha\beta + 2a\beta + b\alpha}{2\,(a + \alpha)}\right] = \frac{\beta - b}{2\,(a + \alpha)}$$

which is same when the firm fixes the output.

9.7.4 Effect of Taxation and Subsidy on Monopoly

Imposition of Excise Tax

The imposition of excise tax of Rs t per unit on the product will raise the total cost by Rs tQ, where Q is the number of units of the product produced. Then monopolist's total profit becomes

$$P = TR\,\{C + tQ\}$$

The first order condition for profit maximization requires that

$$\frac{dP}{dQ} = 0$$

or $$\frac{d}{dQ}\,(TR) - \frac{dC}{dQ} - t = 0$$

or $$MR - MC - t = 0 \text{ or } MR = MC + t$$

This implies that excise tax decreases MR and increases MC.

The second order condition for profit maximization requires that

$$\frac{d^2 P}{dQ^2} < 0$$

or $$\frac{d^2}{dQ^2}\,(TR) - \frac{d^2 C}{dQ^2} < 0$$

or Slope of MR < Slope of MC.

Granting of Subsidy

The grant of subsidy (negative tax) of Rs s per unit on the product will reduce the total cost by Rs sQ. Then monopolist's total profit becomes

$$P = TR - \{C - sQ\}$$
$$= TR - C + sQ$$

One must proceed in the same manner as above to establish the first and second order conditions for profit maximization.

Total Tax Revenue

Suppose Q_t be the level of output after imposition of tax of Rs t per unit. Then the total tax revenue for this given level of output shall be, $T = tQ_t$.

Now, the problem is to find the value of tax 't', which would maximize the total tax revenue (T). For this, the first and second order conditions are $dT/dt = 0$ and $d^2T/dt^2 < 0$.

Remark: A sales tax of $r\%$ imposed on sales will reduce the total revenue (TR) by

$$TR = pQ\left(100 - \frac{r}{100}\right).$$

Example 9.23. The total cost function of a manufacturer is given as $C(x) = 1/3x^3 - 5x^2 + 28x + 10$ and the market demand for his product is given by $p = 2530 - 5x$, where p and x denote the price and quantity of the product, respectively. A tax at the rate of Rs 2 per unit of product is imposed which the manufacturer adds to this cost. Determine the level of output after the tax is imposed and show that post-tax output is less than the pre-tax output.

Solution. (a) *After imposition of tax*

$$\text{Total profit } (P) = \text{Total revenue (TR)} - \text{Total cost}$$

$$= px - \{C(x) + 2x\}; \text{ tax rate Rs 2/unit}$$

$$= (2530 - 5x)\,x - \{(1/3)\,x^3 - 5x^2 + 28x + 10 + 2x\}$$

$$= (-1/3)\,x^3 + 2500x - 10$$

The first order condition for profit maximization requires that $dP/dx = 0$. Then

$$\frac{d}{dx}\{(-1/3)\,x^3 + 2500x - 10\} = 0$$

or
$$-x^2 + 2500 = 0 \text{ or } x = \pm 50$$

Neglecting $x = -50$ value of output, $x = 50$ units.

The second order condition for profit maximization requires that $d^2P/dx^2 < 0$. Then, for $x = 50$,

$$\frac{d^2P}{dx^2} = [-2x]_{x=50} = -100\,(< 0)$$

Thus, the profit is maximum when output level is $x = 50$.

Substituting $x = 50$ in the demand equation to obtain the corresponding price,

$$p = 2530 - 5 \times 50 = \text{Rs } 2,280$$

(b) *Before imposition of tax*

$$P = \text{TR} - \text{TC} = 2530 - 5x)\,x - (1/3x^3 - 5x^2 + 28x + 10)$$

$$= -1/3x^3 + 2502x - 10$$

The first order condition for profit maximization requires that $dP/dx = 0$. Then

$$\frac{d}{dx}(-1/3x^3 + 2502x - 10) = 10$$

or
$$-x^2 + 2502 = 0 \text{ or } x = \pm 50.02$$

Neglecting $x = -50.02$, value of output $x = 50.02$ units.

The second order condition for profit maximization requires that $d^2P/dx^2 < 0$. For $x = 50.02$,

$$\frac{d^2P}{dx^2} = [-2x]_{x=50.02} = -100.04 < 0$$

Thus, the profit is maximum when output level is $x = 50.02$. This amount is more than the post-tax output.

Example 9.24. The demand and total cost functions for a product facing a monopolist are given as: $p = 5(2 - x)$ and $C = 10 + 3x^2 - 2x^3$, respectively (the symbols have their usual meaning). Determine the optimum level of price and output for profit maximization. Also, determine the effect on price and output after imposition of sales tax, of 20 per cent.

Determine the price if government grants subsidy (instead of imposing tax) of 2 per cent per unit of output.

Solution. (*a*) *Before imposition of tax*

$$\text{Profit, } P = \text{Total revenue} - \text{Total cost}$$

$$= p \cdot x - C(x)$$

$$= 5(2-x)x - (10 + 3x^2 - 2x^3) = 10x - 8x^2 + 2x^3 - 10$$

The first order condition for maximizing profit requires that

$$\frac{dP}{dx} = \frac{d}{dx}(10x - 8x^2 + 2x^3 - 10) = 0$$

$$= 10 - 16x + 6x^2 = 0 \text{ or } x = 1, \ 5/3$$

The second order condition for maximizing profit requires that

$$\frac{d^2P}{dx^2} = \frac{d}{dx}(10 - 16x + 6x^2) < 0 = -16 + 12x < 0$$

For $\qquad x = 5/3, \dfrac{d^2P}{dx^2} = -16 + 12 \times 5/3 = 4 \ (> 0)$

Thus, the value of output $x = 4$ will be discarded.

For $\qquad x = 1, \dfrac{d^2P}{dx^2} = -16 + 12 \times 1 = -4 \ (< 0)$

Hence, profit is maximum at the level of output $x = 1$.

Substituting $x = 1$ in the demand equation to obtain the corresponding price,

$$p = 10 - 5 \times 1 = \text{Rs } 5.$$

(*b*) *After imposition of tax*

$$\text{Profit, } P = \text{TR} - \{C + 20\% \times \text{TR}\}$$

$$= px - \{C + 0.20 \times \text{TR}\}$$

$$= 5(2-x)x - \{10 + 3x^2 - 2x^3 + 0.20(10x - 5x^2)\}$$

$$= 2x^3 - 7x^2 + 8x - 10$$

The first order condition for maximizing profit requires that

$$\frac{dP}{dx} = \frac{d}{dx}(2x^3 - 7x^2 + 8x - 10) = 0$$

$$= 6x^2 - 14x + 8 = 0 \text{ or } x = 1, \ 4/3$$

The second order condition for maximizing profit requires that

$$\frac{d^2P}{dx^2} = 12x - 14 < 0$$

For $\qquad x = 1, \dfrac{d^2P}{dx^2} = 12 \times 1 - 14 = -2 \ (< 0)$

For $\qquad x = 4/3, \dfrac{d^2P}{dx^2} = 12 \times 4/3 - 14 = 2 \ (> 0)$

Thus, discarding $x = 4/3$ and accepting $x = 1$ at which $d^2P/dx^2 < 0$ implies that profit is maximum at output level of $x = 1$.

Substituting $x = 1$ in the demand equation to obtain the corresponding price, $p = 10 - 5 \times 1$ = Rs 5, which is same as before imposition of a sales tax of 20 per cent. Hence, there is no increase in price due to imposition of sales tax.

(c) *After a subsidy of 2 per cent per unit is granted*

Total profit, P = Total revenue – Total new cost

$$= TR - \{C - 2\% \text{ of } x\}$$
$$= p \cdot x - \{C - 2\% \text{ of } x\}$$
$$= 5(2 - x)x - \{10 + 3x^2 - 2x^3 - 0.02x\}$$
$$= 2x^3 - 8x^2 + 10.02x - 10$$

The first order condition for maximizing profit requires that

$$\frac{dP}{dx} = \frac{d}{dx}(2x^3 - 8x^2 + 10.02x - 10) = 0$$
$$= 6x^2 - 16x + 10.02 = 0 \text{ or } x = 1.66, \ 1.005$$

The second order condition for maximizing profit requires $d^2P/dx^2 < 0$.

For $\qquad\qquad\qquad\qquad x = 1.66, \ \dfrac{d^2P}{dx^2} = [12x - 16]_{x=1.66} = 3.92 > 0$

For $\qquad\qquad\qquad\qquad x = 1.005, \ \dfrac{d^2P}{dx^2} = [12x - 16]_{x=1.005} = -3.94 < 0$

Thus, discarding $x = 1.66$ and accepting $x = 1.005$ at which $d^2P/dx^2 < 0$ implies that profit is maximum at output level of $x = 1.005$.

Substituting $x = 1.005$ in the demand equation to obtain the corresponding price,

$$p = 10 - 5 \times 1.005 = \text{Rs } 4.975.$$

Example 9.25. The demand and total cost functions of a monopolist are $p = 12 - 4x$ and $C = 8x + x^2$, respectively.

(a) If the tax of 't' per unit output is imposed, find the output level and the price that correspond to maximum profit of monopolist and what will be the maximum profit?

(b) Determine the tax that maximizes the tax revenue and determine the maximum tax revenue.

(c) Find the total tax revenue if an additional 10 per cent sales tax is imposed.

Solution. (a) *After imposition of tax*

Profit, P = Revenue – $\{C + tx\}$

$$= (12 - 4x)x - \{8x + x^2 + tx\}$$
$$= -5x^2 + (4 - t)x$$

The first order condition for maximizing profit requires

$$\frac{dP}{dx} = \frac{d}{dx}\{-5x^2 + (4 - t)x\} = 0$$
$$= -10x + (4 - t) = 0 \text{ or } x = \frac{4-t}{10}$$

The second order condition for maximizing profit requires $d^2P/dx^2 < 0$.

For $\qquad\qquad\qquad\qquad x = \dfrac{4-t}{10}, \ \dfrac{d^2P}{dx^2} = -10 < 0$

Thus, profit is maximum at output level of $x = \dfrac{4-t}{10}$.

(b) *Tax Revenue*

Total tax revenue, $\qquad\qquad T = tx = t\left(\dfrac{4-t}{10}\right) = \dfrac{4t-t^2}{10}$

The first order condition for maximizing tax revenue requires

$$\frac{dT}{dt} = \frac{4 - 2t}{10} = 0 \text{ or } t = 2$$

The second order condition for maximizing tax revenue requires $d^2T/dt^2 < 0$. At $t = 2$,

$$\frac{d^2T}{dt^2} = -\frac{2}{10} < 0$$

Thus, tax revenue is maximum when tax, t = Rs 2 per unit is imposed.

Substituting, $t = 2$ in $T = 2\left(\frac{4-t}{10}\right)$, T = Rs 0.40.

(c) If additional 10 per cent sales tax is imposed, then tax revenue function is

$$TR = x (12 - 4x) \times (1 - 0.10)$$

$$= \frac{9}{10}(12x - 4x^2)$$

The first order condition for maximizing tax revenue requires

$$\frac{d(TR)}{dx} = \frac{9}{10}(12 - 8x) = 0 \text{ or } x = \frac{12}{8}$$

The second order condition for maximizing tax revenue requires

$$\frac{d^2(TR)}{dx^2} < 0$$

At $x = \frac{12}{8}$, $\frac{d^2(TR)}{dx^2} = \frac{9}{10} \times -8 = -\frac{72}{10} < 0$

Thus, maximum total tax revenue $= \frac{9}{10}\left\{12 \times \frac{12}{8} - 4\left(\frac{12}{8}\right)^2\right\}$

$$= \frac{9}{10}\left\{\frac{144}{8} - \frac{576}{64}\right\} = \frac{9}{10} \times \frac{576}{64} = \text{Rs 8.1.}$$

Self-assessment Questions Set-IV

1. Under perfect competition the price as Rs 6 per unit has been determined. An individual firm has a total cost function given by $C = 10 + 15x - 5x^2 + (1/3) x^3$. Find the quantity produced at which profit will be maximum and the amount of maximum profit.

2. For a firm under perfect competition it is given that

$$C(x) = (1/3) x^3 + 2x^2 - 4x + 6, \quad p = 8$$

where p stands for price per unit, x for units of output and C for total cost. Find (*i*) the quantity produced at which profit will be maximum and the amount of maximum profit, (*ii*) what happens to equilibrium output and profit if $p = 2$?

3. The market demand for x goods is given by the relation $p = \beta - \alpha x$. A monopolist produces x at average cost $(ax + b)$ for output x and sells to a merchant at a price π which maximizes his profits. The merchant is a monopolist with constant distributive costs and maximizes his profits by selling on the market at price x. Show that the amount of x produced and sold is $x = (\beta - b)/2 (a + 2\alpha)$ and that $\pi = \beta - 2\alpha x$ and $p = \beta - \alpha x$.

4. The demand function is $p = 500 - (x/3)$ and the cost function is $C = 20x + 15,000$, where p = price and x = output. Find the output at which the profits are maximum given that the condition for profit maximization is at the level where the marginal revenue equals marginal cost. Also, find the price charged at this level of output.

5. If the demand function of the monopolist is $4x = 98 - 4p$, and average cost is $3x + 2$, where x is the output and p, the price, find the maximum profit of the monopolist.

6. Suppose a monopolist requires a profit of at least Rs 1,500. His demand and cost function are $p = 304 - 2q$ and $C = 500 + 4p + 8q^2$. Determine his output level and price. Compare these values with those that would be achieved under profit maximization.

7. A firm under non-perfect competition has the following total cost and demand functions:

$$C = 20 + 2x + 3x^2, \quad p = 50 - x$$

(*i*) Find the values of p and x that maximize profit; and

(*ii*) An excise tax is imposed at Rs 5 per unit. Compare the profit maximizing levels of p and x with those in pre-tax situation.

8. A monopolist has a total cost of output x given by

$$C = ax^2 + bx + c \ (a, b, c > 0)$$

and the demand price for the output x is given by $p = \alpha - \beta x \ (\alpha, \beta > 0)$. Find his monopoly output, price and net revenue in equilibrium. How will these change if a tax at Rs k per unit of output is levied?

9. A manufacturer has a total cost function $\alpha x^2 + \beta x + \gamma$ and demand function as $p = a - bx$ for x items produced. He fixes price p in such a way that his profit is maximum. Government imposes a tax of Rs t per item which the manufacturer adds to his total cost. What should be the rate of tax so that tax revenue is maximum?

10. Suppose that the demand equation for a monopolist's product is $p = 400 - 2x$ and the average cost function is $AC = 0.2x + 4 + (400/x)$, where x is the number of units and both p and AC are expressed in rupees per unit.

(*i*) Determine the level of output at which the profit is maximized;

(*ii*) Determine the price at which maximum profit occurs;

(*iii*) Determine the maximum profit; and

(*iv*) If, as a regulatory device, the government imposes a tax of Rs 22 per unit on the monopolist, what is the new price for profit maximization?

11. A firm has the following function:

$$p = 100 - 0.01p \quad \text{and} \quad C(q) = 50q + 30,000$$

and a tax of Rs 10 per unit is levied. What will be the profit maximizing price and quantity before the tax and after the tax? Why does the monopolist find it feasible to increase the price by less than increase in tax?

12. Given the demand function $y = 21 - 4x$ and the average cost function $y = 2$. Determine the profit maximizing output of a monopolist firm. What would be the impact of a tax of Rs t per unit of output on profit?

13. Suppose the total cost for a firm is

$$C = 120q - q^2 + 0.02q^3 \quad \text{and} \quad p = 11 - 0.25q$$

The government imposes a tax of Rs 10 per unit of product sold. What are the optimal production levels before and after the tax, assuming that the firm is to maximize profits. What is the tax rate which maximizes the tax yield?

14. A process costs Rs 200 to setup. The run time is 5 min/piece and the run cost is Rs. 30.00 per hour. Determine the (*i*) fixed cost and variable cost; and (*ii*) total cost and unit cost for a lot of 500.

Hint: Fixed cost = Rs 200. Variable cost = Rs 5 × 30/60 = Rs. 2.50 per piece. Total cost for a lot of 500 = Rs 200 + (Rs. 2.50 × 500) = Rs 1450. Unit cost = Rs. 2.90 per piece.

15. The total cost C (x) of a firm is

$$C(x) = 0.005 x^3 - 0.02 x^2 - 30 x + 5000$$

where x is the output. Determine (*a*) average cost (AC), (*b*) slope of AC, (*c*) marginal cost (MC), (*d*) slope of MC, and (*e*) value of x for which MVC = AVC. VC represents the variable cost.

Hint : (*a*) $AC = C(x)/x$; (*b*) slope of $AC = d/dx \ (AC)$; (*c*) $MC = d/dx \ C(x)$; (*d*) slope of $MC = d/dx \ (MC)$; (*e*) $AVC = VC/x$ and $MVC = d/dx \ (VC) = 0.15 x^2 - 0.04 x - 30$, where $VC = 0.005 x^3 - 0.02 x^2 - 30x$; $x = 0$ (undesirable); 2.

Total Quality Management

10.1 Introduction

The concept of quality is gradually changing. Most of the countries are opening their economies for global competition. Companies have started giving due recognition to quality as defined by the consumer for their survival in the face of stiff competition. As quality is defined by the customer, rather than the designer or the inspector, a number of parameters associated with quality has been redefined. Now, the concept of acceptable quality level has become obsolete. Therefore, the costs associated with quality have also been redefined. As many organizations are embarking upon to adopt total quality management (TQM), there is need to understand about the basic philosophy, core issues, implementation aspects and pitfalls. There are many myths about TQM which are considerably different from quality. It is not necessary that a company received an ISO 9000 certification will achieve TQM goal. Therefore, it is essential to understand the term 'total' and 'quality' in TQM.

10.2 Meaning of 'Total' in TQM

Total in TQM means development of all aspects of an organization in satisfying the customer. This can be accomplished if a partnership environment at each stage of the business process is recognised within and outside the organization. This involves (*a*) customer-supplier relationship based on mutual trust and respect. There should be a win-win strategy for both; (*b*) organizations in-house requirements by the customers; (*c*) customer's needs are well understood by the supplier; (*d*) suppliers are partners in achieving zero-defect situation; and (*e*) regular monitoring of supplier's processes and products by the customer.

10.3 Definition of Quality

Quality is defined by customer needs and expectations. Therefore, *quality is what customer wants*. According to American Society of Quality Control, quality is the totality of features and characteristics of a product/service that bear on its ability to satisfy a given need. As defined by Badiru and Ayeni (1993), quality refers to an equilibrium level of functionality possessed by a product/service based on the producer's capability and customer's need.

10.3.1 Dimensions of Quality

Some dimensions of quality are given in Table 10.1.

Table 10.1 Dimensions of Quality

Dimension	Explanation
Performance	Being a primary operating characteristic, it determines the intended function of product/service, *e.g.*, durability of pencil battery, fuel economy of a motor bike/scooter, etc.
Features	Special features appealing to customers, *e.g.*, non-stick cooker, colour of refrigerator, memory of a computer, etc.
Durability	Time for which a product can be used before being repaired/replaced.

Dimension	Explanation
Reliability	Expected time of fault-free operation, repair/breakdown.
Serviceability	Cost and convenience of repair/maintenance as well as resolving customers complaints.
Appearance	Sound, look, taste or any other effect felt by human senses.
Safety	Harmless from health and environment viewpoint.
Time	Waiting time/completion time for a service.
Compatibility	Products/service are compatible with existing or standard interfaces, peripherals or other attachments.
Standard	Conformance with standard, matching with documentation, etc.

Thus, quality is the key attribute that customer uses to evaluate product/services. Quality is often driven by market-place, by the competition, and especially by the customer.

10.4 Deming's Fourteen Points for Management

Dr. Edward Deming provides a framework of 14 points for inducing a change in the mindset of top management which, in turn, is expected to lead to a beneficial change in the culture of the whole company. These points are:

1. Create constancy of purpose for continual improvement of the product/service.
2. Adopt the new philosophy for economic stability.
3. Cease dependence on inspection to achieve quality.
4. End the practice of awarding business on price tag alone.
5. Improve constantly the system of production and service.
6. Institute training on the job.
7. Set up and institute modern methods of supervision and training.
8. Drive out fear.
9. Break down barriers between departments and individuals.
10. Eliminate the use of slogans, posters and exhortations.
11. Eliminate work standards and numerical quotas.
12. Remove barriers that rub the hourly worker of the right to take pride in workmanship.
13. Institute a vigorous programme of education and retraining.
14. Define top management's permanent commitment to ever-improving quality and productivity.

Deming suggested a cycle of activities for creating a TQM culture conducive to continuous improvement. The cycle, known as Deming cycle or PDCA (plan, do, check and act) cycle, is shown in Fig. 10.1.

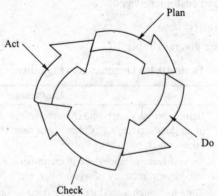

Fig. 10.1 PDCA Cycle

10.5 Juran's Quality Trilogy

While Deming gave the philosophy of TQM, Juran provided the basic foundation of its practical applications. He suggested following *three* phases of activities for continuous quality improvement:

- Quality planning.
- Quality control.
- Quality improvement.

10.5.1 Quality Planning

According to Juran, "Quality is required to be planned for which special training is required." He suggested following *four* steps for planning of quality:

- Identify the customers and their needs. Customer means not only the end users of the finished product, but also internal users using output of one section as the input for their processes. Their needs must also be given importance.
- Translate the customer's needs into technical specifications.
- Optimise the product design and process parameters capable of producing the required product.
- Place the process into operation.

10.5.2 Quality Control

Quality control is the process of detecting adverse changes in the process and taking corrective action when the process shows signs of drifting from its optimal setting. Statistical techniques and SPC should be used to control the quality. The activities include (*a*) evaluate the actual performance of the product; (*b*) compare the actual performance with product goals; and (*c*) act on the performance.

10.5.3 Quality Improvement

Quality problems may be classified into two broad categories: sporadic and chronic. A chronic problem is one which persists for a long time, whereas sporadic problem is a sudden change for the worse. Sporadic problems are best handled by statistical techniques. Chronic problems are solved by behavioural models which involve teamwork and employee participation. It is estimated that 80 per cent of the losses are due to chronic problems. A quality breakthrough is needed to reduce the chronic waste considerably and achieve a new level of quality excellence.

10.6 Total Quality Management

TQM integrates management techniques, improvement efforts and technical tools under a single discipline with the objective of giving quality products to the customer. The main features of TQM are:

- Top management's direct involvement
- Strong customer orientation
- Company-wide participation
- Systematic and documented methods for solving quality problems.

Thus, TQM is a continuous and endless process of wanting to improve. It aims to bring a change in culture in a company, where each employee can directly participate in areas and decisions concerning his work. It builds positive attitudes of employees towards quality, organization and enhances respect for each other leading to a meaningful workplace proud to be in.

10.7 Quality Gurus

The Gurus, who contributed significantly to their chosen field, have contributed the thinking and practice to the quality improvement movement in two ways. Some of them concentrated on the philosophical aspects of quality improvement and others on the tools of quality. They understood the need for improvements in productivity and efficiency in order to reduce unit costs; waste of time and materials, demeaning rules and management ineptitude. Also, they recognised that most valuable resource of an organization was its people, and the people are motivated and work best when they are valued, encouraged to contribute, and allowed to make their decisions.

Gurus	Contribution
The Early Americans	
Edward Deming	Management philosophy
J M Juran	Planning and quality costs
A V Feigenbaum	Total quality control
The Japanese	
Kaoru Ishikawa	Tools, quality circles, company-wide quality
Genichi Taguchi	Minimum prototyping
Shigeo Shingo	Poke-Yoke (zero defects)
The Westerners	
Philip B Crosby	Awareness, zero defects, do it right first time
Tom Peters	Customer-orientation
Claus Moller	Personal quality

They disagree on many peripheral issues, but all agree that TQM is a management-led, never ending process in which *top management commitment* is essential.

Summary of the Guru Teachings

1. Management commitment and involvement are essential. Management has an obligation to lead the quality process without which little will happen.

2. Make relevant measurements which state the current situation and set goals.

3. Encourage and train people in team-work and problem-solving which should include tools of quality improvement which people can use. The effect is commitment to quality improvement and the promotion of open decision-making. Team construction methods should emphasize the need to breakdown inter-departmental barriers.

4. In addition to simple tools of quality, there are many systems-based tools that can improve productivity, *e.g.*, just-in-time techniques.

5. Prevention is better than inspection. It is better to design the product of system in such a way that the possibility of error is reduced/eliminated.

6. Quality improvement should be customer-focused. There are both internal customers and external customers and all of them are equally important.

10.8 ISO 9000 Systems

In 1987, the Geneva-based ISO, the International Organization for Standardisation, published the first five international standards on quality assurance, known as the ISO 9000 standards. These standards were described as 'the refinement of all the most practical and generally applicable principles of quality systems' and 'the culmination of agreement between the world's most advanced authorities of these standards as the basis of a new era of quality management. The actual standards are:

- *ISO 9000*

  A road map for use of other standards in the series. It defines *five* key quality terms in the ISO terminology.

- *ISO 9001*

  It specifies a model when two parties require the demonstration of a supplier's capability to design, produce, instal, and service a product.

- *ISO 9002*

  It specifies a model for quality assurance in production and installation.
- *ISO 9003*

  It is a model for quality assurance in final inspection testing.
- *ISO 9004*

  It provides quality management guidelines for developing and implementing a quality system and in determining the extent to which every element is applicable.

10.8.1 ISO 9000 vs. TQM

ISO 9000 is a set of standards and focuses on documents. On the contrary, TQM focuses on developing human elements. It is not necessary that an ISO certified company follows the essentials of TQM. ISO only certifies that whatever followed is being documented. It is important to note that ISO 9000 and TQM are not in opposition. ISO 9000 standard establishes the principles for a management system which will improve a company's performance. It provides basic building block for moving towards TQM. The difference between ISO 9000 and TQM is given below:

ISO	TQM
1. Certification	1. Customer delight and satisfaction
2. Product conforms to specification	2. Total organization including 'invisible' and 'visible' resources
3. Audits and checks	3. Internal and external trust
4. Key processes	4. Leadership
5. Quality system	5. Internal customer
6. External trust	6. Human factor
7. Visibility of capability prior to delivery	7. Flexibility and change management
8. Maintenance of what is documented	8. Top management commitment
9. An assurance to external customers that a quality system is being pursued	9. Continuous improvement

10.8.2 ISO 14000 Standard

It is related to the quality system with environmental concerns. ISO 14001 is the standard entitled 'Environmental Management Systems—specification.' There is no formal relationship with ISO 9000 family of documents. Main element of ISO 14001 standard is the *Environment Policy*, which is defined by the top management. The environmental policy is carried out by the organization to ensure the "environment protection and related policy."

10.8.3 Quality in Services

The standard has succeeded in identifying service and delivery characteristics, which can be measured either quantitatively or qualitatively by subject evaluation. These are categorised under the headings *service requirements* and *service delivery requirements*.

10.8.4 Barriers to Implementation of ISO 9000 in Indian Companies

ISO 9000 implementation inside a company bring no less than a revolution. There will be substantial changes in methods, practices, record keeping, etc., apart from tremendous efforts and large investment involved. Present market trend and customer pressure will force the company to obtain ISO certification for its survival and growth, because all enterprises want to conform to ISO 9000 principles and practices without the need for external pressure. For this, total commitment by the top management to support the effort with new priorities and adequate resources, *e.g.*, quality over quantity, is an important prerequisite.

Generally, the following *four* preparatory steps are essential for ISO 9000 structure:

1. Exposure for training.
2. Developing draft quality manual for the company.
3. Internal audit of existing systems/work procedures.
4. Audit by external certifying agency.

The following *six* points are, therefore, required to be given more emphasis when embarking on registration:

1. Decide on an achievable level of quality.
2. Get everyone involved and do not forget to include off-site activities.
3. For large organizations, appoint a full time Quality Assurance Coordinator and don't use a consultant.
4. Tell yourself the truth, don't make things up; keep it simple and don't send copies of everything to everyone.
5. Only calibrate quality critical instruments.
6. Delegate control of preparatory step 3 and use it for methods and recipes.

For certification, after completion of the internal audit and implementation rectifications, the company should deliver a complete quality manual to its chosen assessing agency. When the manual is reviewed and the agency is satisfied with it, it will respond with a questionnaire. After completing the questionnaire and submitting with the appropriate fee, the inspectors will schedule a visit to audit the company's premises and systems. This will ensure, apart from having international certification for its products and procedures, a quality management system that changes the work culture. It reduces waste and downtime, improves customer relations, and boosts profits. It brings better management and control.

10.8.5 List of Certification Bodies

Following is the list of *eleven* certification bodies:

1. Bureau Veritas Quality International
   C/o Bureau Veritas International Service (India) (P) Ltd.
   44, Arcadia NCPA Marg, Nariman Point
   Mumbai 400 021

2. TUV India Pvt. Ltd.
   Fiji House, Damodardas Sukhawala Marg
   Mumbai 400 001

3. Bureau of Indian Standards
   Manak Bhawan
   8, Bahadur Shah Zafar Marg
   New Delhi 110 002

4. Indian Register Quality Systems
   72, Maker Tower 'F' (7th Floor), Cuffe Parade
   Mumbai 400 005

5. Department of Electronics
   Standardisation, Testing and Quality Control Directorate
   Electronics Niketan
   6, CGO Complex, Lodi Road
   New Delhi 110 003

6. British Standards Institution (BSI), UK

7. Australian Standards Association (ASA), Australia

8. SGS India Ltd.
   Naoroji Furdoomji Road, Colaba
   Mumbai 400 039

9. Det Norske Veritas
   96/98, 9th Floor, Maker Tower 'F'
   Cuffe Parade
   Mumbai 400 005

10. NQA
    Quality Systems Register
    720, International Trade Tower
    Nehru Place
    New Delhi 110 019

11. Quality Council of India
    The Institution of Engineers (India) Building
    Bahadur Shah Zafar Marg
    New Delhi 110 002

10.9 Management in TQM

An integrated model for managing quality and services in TQM environment is shown in Fig. 10.2. Important elements of TQM are integrated in this model.

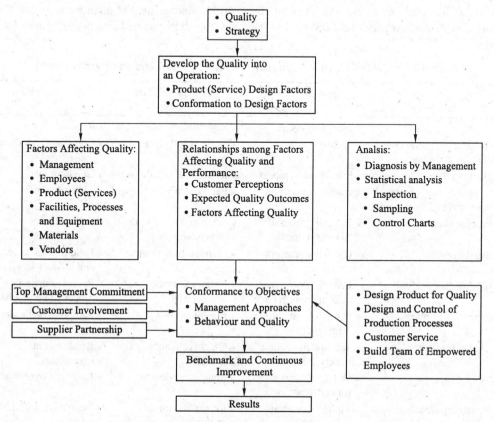

Fig 10.2 Managing for quality products and services

10.10 Implications for Management

TQM impinges on every function in an organization and will include marketing, product design, human resource development, financial resourcing, sites and buildings, estate management, and so on. The cultural change required in most organizations in order to introduce and maintain TQM has to be led by senior managers. There is need to ensure monitoring, measurement and evaluation of progress in all functions, against identified and, if possible, quantified needs and specifications. The process can be applied inside an organization as well as outside it, in the sense that everyone has a 'customer' and is a 'customer' inside the organization, relying on others work and service and passing on work and service to others.

TQM is implemented at the top of an organization first because it is at this level that change can be initiated. Top managers require skills to enable them to change the way they work. This will enable them to practise and promote quality management and then help others to acquire necessary techniques and understanding.

The introduction of TQM through the whole organization is a long-term strategy requiring a variety of approaches. For most organizations it is about the management of change and involves all aspects of human resource management, including leadership, problem-solving, coaching, counselling, communication and team-building. This style of management is participative, designed to enable people to every level to share in management decisions and in responsibility for them.

10.11 Quality Cost

It is the cost in ensuring and assuring quality as well as loss incurred when quality is not achieved. Cost of quality assurance may be classified into four categories of prevention cost, appraisal cost, internal failure cost and external failure cost (Table 10.2). Management of quality cost is useful in improving the performance of a TQM system. This is achieved by planned efforts to eliminate these costs.

Table 10.2   Cost of Quality Assurance [Gavett (1968), Adam and Evertt (1998)]

Prevention Costs	*Appraisal Costs*	*Internal Failure Cost*	*External Failure Costs*
• Quality planning	• Incoming inspection	• Rejections	• Recall
• QC administration and systems planning	• Testing	• Scrap at full shop cost	• Complaints handling
• Quality related training	• Inspection in process	• Rework, at full shop cost	• Goodwill loss
• Inspection of incoming, inprocess and final product	• Quality audits	• Failure analysis	• Warranty costs
• Process planning	• Incoming test and laboratory tests	• Scrap and rework, fault of vendor	• Bad publicity
• Design review	• Checking labour	• Material procurement	• Field maintenance and product service
• Quality data analysis	• Laboratory or other measurement service	• Factory contact engineering	• Returned material processing and repair
• Procurement planning	• Setup for test and inspection	• Machine down	• Fall in market share
• Market research	• Test and inspection material	• QC investigations of failures	• Replacement inventories
• Vendor surveys	• Outside endorsements for certification	• Material review activity	• Low employee morale
• Reliability studies	• Maintenance and calibration work	• Repair and trouble-shooting	• Strained distributor relations
• System development			

Prevention Costs	Appraisal Costs	Internal Failure Cost	External Failure Costs
• Quality measurement and control equipment	• Product engineering review and shipping release	• Excess inventory	
• Product Qualification	• Field testing		
• Qualification of material	• Final testing		

10.12 Quality Control Tools for Improvement

There are *seven* tools used in the quality improvement process. These tools are useful in identification of the problem and establishment of measures for the improvements. These tools are:

- • Scatter diagram
- • Check sheets
- • Graph and charts
- • Histograms
- • Pareto diagram
- • Cause-effect diagram
- • Control chart.

Scatter Diagram

It is prepared by plotting paired set of data such as temperate and elongation, porosity and insulation, etc. against each other on *X* and *Y* axes [Fig. 10.3 (*a*)].

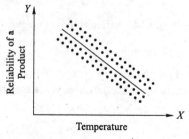

Fig. 10.3 (*a*)   Scatter diagram indicating negative correlation between two variables

It must be used for sufficiently large data set.

Check Sheets

These are forms specially prepared to enable data to be collected simply by making checkmarks. It is used for tallying the occurrences of defects/causes being addressed and graphing/charting directly. Check-sheets are to be designed only after a full clarity about the objective is known. It is helpful in identification of problem areas by frequency, location, and type of cause [Fig. 10.3 (*b*)].

A	⊬Ⅱ ⊬Ⅱ |||
B	⊬Ⅱ ||
C	⊬Ⅱ ⊬Ⅱ ⊬Ⅱ ⊬Ⅱ ||
D	⊬Ⅱ ⊬Ⅱ	
E	⊬Ⅱ ⊬Ⅱ ⊬Ⅱ ⊬Ⅱ |||

Fig 10.3 (*b*)   An example of check sheet

Graphs and Charts

Data are plotted on these diagrams and show statistical breakdowns with relationship between different quantities. These are used for organised set of observations. Line graph may be used to know trend, bar and pie charts for comparing quantities and relative proportions (Fig. 10.4).

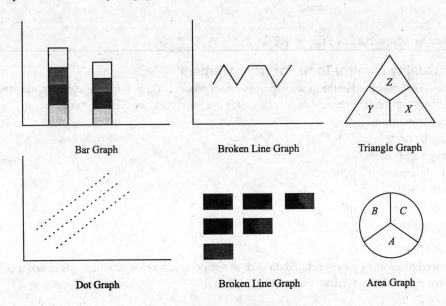

Fig. 10.4   Various types of graphs

Histogram

It is prepared by dividing the data range into sub-groups and counting the number of points in each sub-group. The number of points (also called as *frequency*) are then plotted as a height on the diagram (Fig. 10.5).

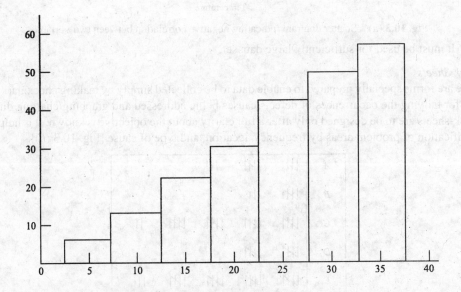

Fig. 10.5   Histogram for breakdown times

Pareto Diagram

In this diagram, undesirable events/costs are stratified according to their causes/manifestations. It is then plotted in order of importance (Fig. 10.6).

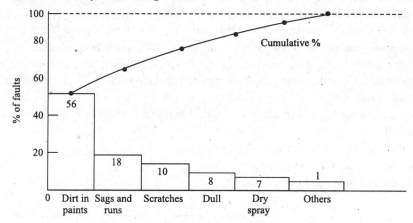

Fig. 10.6 Pareto analysis

Ishikawa Diagram (Cause-effect Diagram)

It is also called as *fishbane diagram*, being shaped like the bones of a fish. It systematically summarizes the relationship between quality characteristics, defects, etc. and their causes (Fig. 10.7).

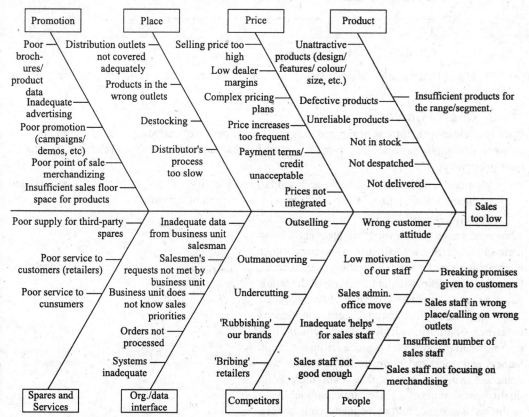

Fig. 10.7 Example of completed fishbone diagram: problem cause analysis

Control Charts

These charts are drawn for a characteristic value against time. These characteristics may be variables like length, diameter, etc. or attributes such as number of defects on sheets, porosity, etc. To construct a control chart, take the following steps:

1. Decide on a unit of measurement to use in monitoring performance; put this on the vertical axis.
2. Choose a time interval for taking measurements; put this on the horizontal axis.
3. Calculate control limits by determining the mean (average of X) and standard deviation; generally the UCL is the mean plus three standard deviations; the LCL is the mean minus three standard deviations.
4. Mark the mean and control limits on the vertical axis and draw a horizontal line for each along the length of the chart.
5. Enter data points chronologically on the chart.
6. Draw a line connecting the data points.

A specimen control chart is shown in Fig. 10.8.

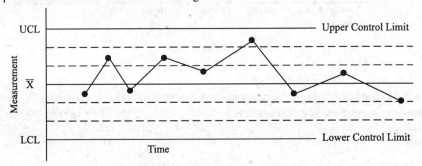

Fig 10.8   A specimen control chart

A detailed information about various control charts and acceptance sampling are given in Appendix.

10.13 Quality Circles

Quality circle movement was originated in Japan. It provides an effective channel of communication between the employees and the top management for discussion on problems related to quality. A quality circles is:

'A group who meet voluntarily and regularly to identify and solve their own work-related problems and implement their solutions with management approval'.   *(Industrial Society)*

The circle usually consists of between 6 and 12 members to generate a variety of ideas and having their say. If there are too many volunteers, either membership can be rotated or sub-groups can be formed to consider particular tasks. One of the senior and experienced members of the circle is appointed as group leader. The management encourages meetings of quality circles, opens channel of communication for reccieving ideas from the group leaders and offers incentives to the members who come out with acceptable ideas. An enterprising quality circle will, of course, anticipate as many problems as possible and solve them. Unions need also to be involved in the process so that their

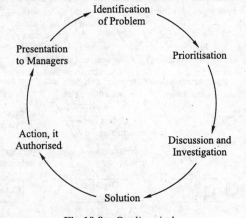

Fig 10.9   Quality circles

representatives understand what is happening. Unions are usually supporting of the process because it involves the workforce more closely in the organization and has the objective of improving job satisfaction. After all, quality circles have been described as 'a structured way of making management listen.' An illustration about quality circle is shown in Fig. 10.9.

10.14 Measuring Quality

For measurement of quality, an analysis of the organization is required at various levels. A manager needs to be both a problem solver and a planner and should be able to communicate the importance of medium- and long-term objectives to employees at all levels so as to support the attainment of objectives and targets, and measure performance against these.

Problem-solvers	Planners
Short-duration activities	Advance planning
Non-routine tasks	Agreed systems
Emphasis on decisive action	Systems and schedules
Informal interaction	Formal, regular sessions
Effectiveness through authority	Roles of coach and counsellor
Low priority given to personal task	Human resource management

In *Thriving on Chaos* (1988), Tom Peters identified 12 attributes of a quality system, which in themselves represent a checklist against which an organization's management can assess the stage it has reached in the development of such a system: (*i*) Management is obsessed with quality; (*ii*) The company has a guiding system or ideology; (*iii*) Quality is measured; (*iv*) Quality is rewarded; (*v*) Everyone is trained in techniques for assessing quality; (*vi*) There is shift of managerial philosophy from adversarial to co-operative; (*vii*) It is recognised that there is no such thing as an insignificant improvement; (*viii*) There is constant stimulation to improve quality; (*ix*) There is a structure within the company dedicated to quality improvement; (*x*) Everybody is involved in quality management, including suppliers, distributors, customers; (*xi*) It is understood that costs decline as quality increases; and (*xii*) It is recognised that quality is relative and improvement is never ending.

10.15 Quality and Reliability

A good quality without reliability is of little use and reliable product should be of overall good quality. In fact reliability is not concerned with quality aspects. It is essentially relates to functioning or performance of the product. Therefore, it gives something extra throughout its intended life, i.e., Quality now + Quality later = Reliability. Statistical techniques have extremely useful in setting standards for maintaining quality control for products and services.

10.16 Quality Control and Quality Assurance

Quality control can be defined as being *concerned with checking for errors during and after the process of manufacture.* Modern control techniques are based on the idea of an *error-free* or *zero-defect* approach, or *doing it right first time.* This concept arises because of the costs involved in correcting errors and the fact that the costs are usually greater the later they are identified. Under the TQM approach, the team is made responsible for quality control, for reducing wastage and for ensuring that adjustments are made as soon as they are identified.

At the strategic management level, decisions are made about total quality management and systems of quality control. The strategic approach includes:
- Analysis of current position.
- Choice of an appropriate starting point.
- Implementation of policy, deciding what will be done, how, by whom and by when.

Quality assurance (QA) provides a framework for quality control and quality improvement. QA supports teams of employees with systems, resources and discretion appropriate to their unique contribution to the organization, to keep them in tune with progress of quality management and improvement. This aspect of management can help teams:

- Understand quality characteristics.
- Be realistic about the standards to be attained.
- Undertake quality control through a measurement process, interpret the results and make/propose changes.

This process may be supported by a number of techniques such as QUEST (quality in every single task). The idea of service within the organization enables each individual or group to undertake a QUEST analysis.

- Who are my customers?
- What do they demand from me?
- In what way do I meet these demands?
- How can I improve my service?

and

- Who are my suppliers?
- What service do I demand of them?
- In what way do they meet these demands?
- How can they improve their service?

KRA (key result areas) is a technique aimed at focusing on realistic outcomes for each team/individual. This may be by:

- Identifying a range of quality characteristics for the team which are consistent with the company's strategy.
- Agreeing realistic standards for each of these quality characteristics.
- Devising a system which can be measured and monitored.

The Taguchi method is based on the approach to improve quality engineering at a low cost. It helps to quantify the loss due to lack of quality of a performance characteristic, with the objective of identifying the real cause of a problem. It concentrates on the design of products, reducing variation of performance against the target specification.

10.17 Investors in People

The investors in people (IIP) programme aims to help organizations improve performance through a planned approach to: (a) setting and communicating business goals; and (b) developing people to meet these goals so that (i) what people can do and motivated to do, and (ii) matches what the organization needs them to do. This is shown diagrammatically in Fig. 10.10.

The actions, required to improve quality through the IIP process, are based on *four* basic requirements:

- An investor in people makes a public commitment from the top to develop all employees to achieve its business objectives.
- An investor in people regularly reviews the training and development needs of all employees.
- An investor in people takes action to train and develop individuals on recruitment and throughout their employment.
- An investor in people evaluates the investment in training and development to assess achievement and improve future effectiveness.

In essence, TQM is a business management philosophy which recognises that customer needs and business goals are inseparable. It pervades an organization's culture, inspires commitment and encourages communication in all directions, based on work teams and quality systems which utilise resources effectively. At its best TQM can release a dynamic factor within an organization which encourages success and profitability.

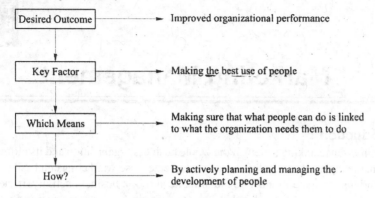

Fig. 10.10   Investors in people

Self-assessment Questions

1. Explain the concept of TQM. What do you mean by 'total' in TQM?
2. Define quality. Why has the emphasis on quality changed from the producer to the customer?
3. State and briefly describe the dimensions of quality?
4. List the Deming's 14 points for management. Illustrate the PDCA cycle suggested by Deming.
5. Explain Juran's quality trilogy giving a detailed brief for each term.
6. Briefly explain the concept of quality improvement.
7. Discuss the teachings of quality gurus.
8. What are ISO 9000 standards? Explain their significance. How does TQM and ISO certification related and different? Name *three* standards for different purposes.
9. 'An ISO certified company is a TQM company.' Comment on the statement.
10. What is ISO 14000 standard?
11. Why does reduced quality often result in decreasing market share and productivity?
12. Explain the important elements of TQM. Why is customer focuses so important in TQM?
13. How are the quality products and services managed in an organization.
14. What are the costs of quality? Explain each component of cost of quality.
15. Explain the *seven* quality control tools and their importance in TQM.
16. Define, describe and explain the use of fishbone diagram and pareto chart.
17. Develop a cause-and-effect diagram for your office/institute/club not working satisfactorily.
18. Why are Control Charts drawn? Explain the step-wise procedure to construct a control chart with an example.
19. What is Quality Circle? Explain its advantages and disadvantages.
20. What are the 12 attributes of a quality system advocated by Tom Peters.
21. Differentiate between quality control and quality assurance. How these aspects help in achieving TQM?
22. Explain how investors in people programme aims to help organizations improve performance?
23. How is TQM effective in an organization? Supplement your answer with a real-life example and a sketch.
24. 'TQM begins with education and ends with education.' Comment on this statement.
25. TQM culture will not develop in an industry if fear is not driven out from the minds of the employees. Why?
26. A company plans to monitor the number of defectives produced by workers and give an incentive to those whose performance is significantly better than the average. What will be the impact of the above on the psychology of the workers?
27. Outline the trends and challenges relating to quality in the present context of global competitiveness.
28. Give at least two definitions of quality in the context of a product. Which definition would you prefer and why?
29. Identify the trends and challenges relating to quality in the present context of global competitiveness.

Marketing Management

11.1 Introduction

Marketing is, in essence, taking a view of the whole business organization and its ultimate objectives. Concern for marketing must penetrate in all areas of an enterprise. Marketing emphasizes that 'customer is the king' and his satisfaction must be the ultimate aim of a business activity, if the business unit desires long-time success—a belief handed down to posterity by sound marketing people. Marketing has been defined in several ways by different writers. However, in general, marketing may be defined as follows:

'Marketing is a social and managerial process by which individuals and groups obtain what they need and want through creating and exchanging products and value with others.'

Philip Kotler, a well-known author in the area of marketing, defines marketing as 'A human activity directed at satisfying needs and wants through exchange processes.'

The *American Marketing Association* defines marketing as 'The performance of business activities that directs the flow of goods and services from producer to consumer or user.'

The following key concepts of marketing emerge from the above mentioned definitions: needs, wants, and demands; products; utility, value, and satisfaction; exchange, transactions, and relationships; markets; and marketing and marketers. These are illustrated in Fig. 11.1. A useful distinction can be drawn between needs, wants and demands. *'A human need is a state in which a person feels deprived of something. A need has to be converted into a want for product/service through adequate marketing strategy, such as promotion. Demands are wants for specific products that are backed up by an ability and willingness to buy them. Wants become demands when backed up by purchasing power.'*

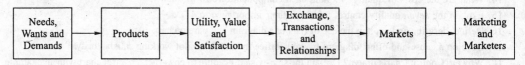

Fig. 11.1 Key concepts of marketing

Marketing is performed within a certain environment which itself is always changing. It is appropriate to divide the marketing activities into *four* basic elements. These basic elements are:

1. Product
2. Price
3. Promotion
4. Place (or physical distribution).

These are referred to as the 4 Ps in marketing. Here the product stands for the goods or services offered by the organization. Price refers to the money value that the customer has to pay. Promotion is the aspect of selling and advertising, or communicating the benefits of product or service to the target customers. Physical distribution refers to the aspect of the channels of distribution through which the product has to move before it reaches the consumer.

Coping with exchange processes calls for a considerable amount of work and skill. *Persons* become fairly adept at buying to meet their household needs. Occasionally they also undertake selling—selling personal services. *Organizations* are more professional in handling exchange processes. They must attract resources from one set of markets, convert them into useful products, and trade them in another set of markets. *Nations* also plan and manage exchange relations with others.

The *American Marketing Association* defines *marketing management* as follows:

'Marketing management is the process of planning and executing the conception, pricing, promotion, and distribution of ideas, goods, and services to create exchanges that satisfy individual and organizational objectives.'

Historically, marketing management is identified with tasks and personnel dealing with the customer market. Marketing work in the customer market is formally carried out by sales people, customer-service managers, product managers, market managers, advertising and promotion managers, market researchers, etc. They have the task of influencing the level, timing, and composition of demand is such a way that would help the organization achieve its objectives. Hence, marketing management is essentially *demand management*. These tasks are accomplished by carrying out *marketing research, planning, implementation, and control*. Today, marketing management is a subject of growing interest, in all sizes and types of organizations, within and outside the business sector.

11.1.1 Role of Marketing in a Developing Economy

A developing economy is one which is trying to achieve growth in the gross national product through the generation of additional income in various sectors of an economy such as agriculture, industry, mining, internal and external trade. Planning is a *sine qua non* in achieving the economic growth. Like economic change, social change has also to be brought about in a planned manner. Marketing functions performed at different levels of development are shown in Table 11.1.

Table 11.1 Marketing Functions Performed at Different Levels of Development

Level	Orientation	Function	Country
Subsistence	Traditional	Barter trade; exchange of goods; central markets prevalent; no specialization; no marketing activity; less trading in some form in most societies.	Undeveloped country
Transition	Self-sufficiency	Degree of specialization; small-scale cottage industry; limited entrepreneurial activity; firms are labour-intensive; producer is marketer	Less developed country
Mass Production	Local markets	Specialization; industry is transitional but with some market-orientation; separation of production and marketing; sellers' market conditions prevalent; limited marketing activities.	Developing country
Commercialization	Regional, national and international markets	Total specialization in production and marketing activities; complete market orientation; national, regional, and export markets tapped; mass distribution practices.	Developed country

(*Source:* K Erdener, *Marketing in the Third World*, Praeger, New York, 1982, p. 29).

Marketing efforts both on the part of the firm as well as the state, i.e., both at the macro- and micro-levels are relevant to growth. When the involvement of the Government in the marketing and distribution of ideas, essential goods and services is significant, it is called *macro-marketing*. On the other hand, when a firm enjoys sufficient freedom to design its marketing effort, it is considered to be a case of micro-marketing.

Considering the typical characteristics of a developing economy and its growth needs, it appears that certain sectors of the economy need relatively a greater level of marketing effort than the others, as exemplified below:

1. **Marketing in agriculture, basic industries, mining and plantation:** (*a*) Agriculture—food-grains and agricultural raw materials; (*b*) Basic industries—steel and power generation; and (*c*) Mining and plantation. All these sectors call for a minimal level of marketing effort for distributing the output.

2. **Intermediate industrial goods:** These include engineering goods, machine tools, components, accessories, etc. The marketing effort required is at a medium level and calls for careful product planning, informative advertising and personal selling in addition to essential packaging, storing and physical distribution. The pricing is either competitive or government regulated.

3. **Semi-industrial products:** These include pharmaceuticals and fertilizers, appliances for business and household use, consumer non-durables and certain types of engineering goods and machine tools. The level of marketing effort required is high.

4. **Export trade and services:** These include tourism and banking. In this sector, for certain product categories, the effort required for marketing will have to be enhanced in order to bring in steady returns.

It is essential to discuss how social change is brought about in a planned manner through social marketing technology. Kotler and Zaltman have defined social marketing as the design, implementation and control of programmes calculated to influence the acceptability of social ideas and involving consideration of product planning, pricing, communication, distribution and marketing research. To understand social marketing fully, it would be appropriate to examine the applicability of the 4 Ps of the marketing mix in terms of some well-known social issues.

A number of present-day social problems like drug abuse, pollution control, safer driving, immunization, non-smoking, birth control, etc. are in need of innovative solutions and approaches for gaining public attention and support. Marketing men by their training are finely attuned to market needs, product development, pricing and channel issues, and mass communication and promotional techniques, all of which are critical in the social context.

11.1.2 Marketing of Services

The term 'service' includes a wide variety of services. From the marketing viewpoint, Kotler defined the concept of service as 'A service is any activity or benefit that one party can offer to another that is essentially intangible and does not result in the ownership of any goods. Its production may or may not be tied to a physical product.

Some selected services are listed in Table 11.2.

Services can be distinguished from products on the basis of the following *five* most commonly accepted characteristics:

1. **Intangibility:** A service which cannot be seen, touched, smelt or tasted but can only be perceived.

2. **Inseparability:** A service that cannot be separated from the person/firm responsible for providing it.

3. **Heterogeneity :** Difficult to standardise quality as human element is involved in providing and rendering services.

Table 11.2 List of Selected Services

Utilities	*Insurance, Banking, Finance*
Electricity	Banks
Water supply	Share and stock brokers
Law Enforcing, Civil, Administrative and Defence Services	*Business, Professional and Scientific Activities*
Police	Advertising, marketing research
Army	Consultancy
Air Force	Accountancy
Navy	Legal
Judiciary	Medical
Civil administration	Educational, Research
Municipal services	Maintenance & Repairs
	Leasing
	Employment agencies
Transport and Communication	*Leisure, Recreation*
Railways	Cinema, Theatre
Air transport	Clubs, Gymnasiums
Post and Telegraph	Restaurants, Hotels
Telephone and Telecommunication	Video game parlours
All India Radio	Self-improvement courses
Doordarshan	
Distributive Trades	*Miscellaneous*
Wholesale distribution	Beauty parlours
Retail distribution	Health clubs
Dealers, Agents	Domestic help
	Drycleaning
	Matrimonial service

(*Source:* Donald Cowell, *The Marketing of Services,* Heinemann, London).

4. **Perishability:** If not used or consumed, it will be lost for ever. Services cannot be stored and are perishable.

5. **Ownership:** Customer has access to, but not ownership of, facility or activity.

These characteristics pose a challenge to the marketing manager who has to find a solution to constraints imposed by these features.

The marketing of services requires an extended marketing mix comprising production, pricing, promotion and distribution as well as people, physical evidence and process. The marketer has to lay great stress on the last three elements of the marketing strategy and combine them with the first four to achieve a harmonious blend which fulfils the customer want—satisfaction.

11.2 Marketing Planning and Organization

Two important management dimensions of marketing—planning and organising—are focussed. First, the process of planning the marketing mix and strategy are explained. Then it goes on to discuss the concept of optimum marketing mix. Thereafter, it is necessary to develop a rational and a convenient method of viewing millions of persons as potential customers. This is achieved by segmentation. Then follows the process of creating the necessary administrative and manpower hierarchy for implementing marketing decisions. Lastly, the importance of research in the context of marketing decisions and statistical techniques for data analysis are outlined.

11.2.1 Planning Marketing Mix

Four basic elements—product, price, promotion and place—constitute the marketing mix. These four elements, called 4 Ps, are used for grouping different marketing activities. McCarthy proposed this four-factor classification as follows:

1. **Product:** Activities relating to the product, service or idea to be offered.
2. **Price:** Activities relating to the price to be charged for the product, service or idea.
3. **Promotion:** Activities relating to promotion (advertising, personal selling, sales promotion and publicity, called *promotional mix*) of the product, service or idea.
4. **Place:** Activities relating to distribution of the product, service or idea (physical distribution and channels of distribution).

In addition, there are two other classifications proposed by Frey (1961) and Lazer and Kelly (1962). According to Frey (1961), all marketing decision variables could be categorized under *two* factors:

(*i*) *Offering* consisting of product, packaging, brand, price and service;

(*ii*) *Methods and tools* comprising distribution channels, personal selling, advertising, sales promotion and publicity. Lazer and Kelly proposed a three-factor classification—goods and service mix, distribution mix, and communication mix. However, McCarthy's 4 Ps of the marketing mix are discussed here in detail.

11.2.2 Elements of Marketing Mix

The *four* basic elements of marketing mix are described below in detail:

1. **Product:** Activities related to a product are quality, style, brand name, features, sizes, packaging, services, warranties, and returns. Examples—Life Insurance Corporation introduces the *new policy; nationalised and other banks introduced core banking facilities;* Dunlop introduces the concept of *Tyre Service Centres;* Titan launches Titan *Quartz Watches* for the Indian market.
2. **Price:** The following factors are generally considered by the marketers in setting prices—target customers, cost competition, the law, and social responsibility apart from other factors as well.
3. **Promotion:** Important promotional methods are—advertising, personal selling, sales promotion, and publicity and public relations.
4. **Place:** Place is made up of two components—physical distribution and channels of distribution. Some examples of physical distribution are transportation, storage, order processing, inventory control, and location. However, a physical distribution network should be oriented towards the needs and desires of target consumers. The channels of distribution are those routes on which the ownership of goods, services and ideas flow on the way from producer to consumer. The overall objective of such decisions is to maximize service to the consumer at a profit to the marketer.

11.2.3 Relationship between Marketing Planning Process and Marketing Mix

The following components constitute a typical marketing plan:

(*a*) **Current marketing situation:** The data relate to the market, product, competition, distribution and macro-environment.

(*b*) **Identification of problems and opportunities:** Identification of SWOT analysis—strength, weaknesses, opportunities and threat—of a company's product.

(*c*) **Defining aims:** Financial (long rate of return on investment; profits and cash flow during the current year) and marketing (sales revenue, sales volume, market share, average realized price, consumer awareness, distribution coverage, etc.) aims to achieve the financial objectives.

(*d*) **Marketing strategy:** It consists of broad decisions on target markets, market positioning and mix and marketing expenditure levels. Marketing strategy also involves an awareness, the expected environment, and competitive conditions.

(e) **Marketing programme development:** In developing each element of the marketing strategy, it is required to know (i) What will be done? (ii) When will it be done? (iii) Who will do it? (iv) How much will it cost?

11.2.4 Relationship between Marketing Mix and Marketing Strategy

Marketing mix is the mixture of controllable marketing elements that the firm uses to achieve the target market. Marketing strategy is a set of sub-strategies concerned with competition, segmentation, pricing, promotion and distribution. Structural criteria cover the following: (a) Coherence, (b) Consistency, (c) Contribution, and (d) Relative significance.

The following factors determine the key element. These are: (a) product, (b) type of market (industrial/consumer), (c) stage in evolution (emerging, transition and decline), and competitive conditions. Therefore, the key factor in the marketing mix is crucial in drawing up a marketing strategy, In devising an optimum marketing mix, it is important to know how various marketing-mix variables interact in their impact on sales/profits.

Development of Market Strategies vs. Elements of Marketing Mix

The development of strategies in relation to some of the elements of marketing mix is discussed. These relate to marketing mix decisions with respect to new product development, stages in the life-cycle of a product, and the role of advertising and pricing in the marketing mix.

The product life-cycle (PLC) concept helps to understand how the components of the marketing mix change during different phases of the life-cycle curve. The product life-cycle curve (S-shaped) of introduction, growth, maturity and decline is shown in Fig. 11.2.

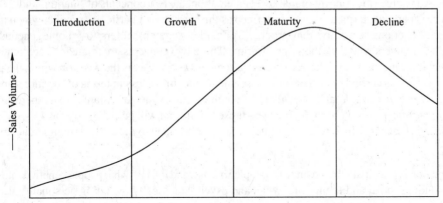

Fig. 11.2 Product life cycle

Different products will take different time periods to pass through the cycle of introduction, growth, maturity and decline. Many products such as light bulbs, machine tools, computer stationery seem to remain indefinitely at the maturity stage, while some products quickly come and go. Further, a product can be at different stages in different countries.

Table 11.3 shows some typical strategies relating to marketing mix variables in PLC stages.

11.2.5 Role of Advertising and Price in the Marketing Mix

In this type of structure, called *oligopolistic situation*, many firms prefer to increase their share by stimulating demand through advertising rather than by reducing prices. The main reason is that building up an image through advertising can be more difficult to match than a price cut.

Generally, price decisions have to be carefully coordinated with decisions on product, promotion and distribution. In general, industrial goods manufacturers tend to spend proportionately less on advertising than do consumer goods manufacturers. The relationship between 4 Ps should not be accepted without further enquiry as marketing mix variables interact not only with each other but also with non-marketing variables in the firm.

Table 11.3   Suggested Strategies Relating to Marketing Mix Variables in PLC Stages

Stage in Life Cycle	Product	Pricing	Promotion	Distribution
Introduction	Iron out product deficiencies	Highest	Create awareness of product's potential. Stimulate primary demand	Selective distribution
Growth	Focus on product quality. Introduce variations of product	High	Selective advertising of the brand. Heavy advertising to create image	Extended coverage
Maturity	Product adjustments for further brand differentiation	Moderate	Maintain and build image. Facilitate sales promotion.	Close-relationship with dealers
Decline	Simplify the product line. Seek new product uses. Introduce changes to revitalize the product.	Low	Primary demand may again be cultivated.	Selective cultivation

11.2.6 Market Segmentation

In order to introduce the concept of market segmentation, the two concepts of 'market' and 'segment' need to be separately defined. Market is defined as the market for a particular product which in effect means the functions served by that product. A 'market segment' refers to a homogeneous group consisting of buyers who seek the same offering. These two concepts are related to each other in the sense that the concept of a market as a set and a segment as a subset is the basis on which the process of segmentation is carried out. In defining a segment, one thinks less in terms of functions and more in terms of *benefits sought* and *by whom*. The output of a segmentation analysis is therefore (*a*) *a profile of customer target group*, focusing on those details that will help develop the 4 Ps, and (*b*) *the set of benefits sought*, which will constitute a critical advantage to act as the buying inducement.

Bases for Segmentation

Segmentation is principally based on what people *say*, *are*, and *do*, i.e., what people benefit demographically including social and family life cycle, and psychographically including personality variables. Some important personality variables that may be used in psychographic segmentation are: impulsiveness, sociability, achievement orientation, masculinity, self-confidence, conservativeness, prestige consciousness, alertness to change, thriftiness, and sentimentalism.

Other bases for segmentation are *usage rate* and *brand loyalty*. It is the *heavy users* category which is important so far as the usage rate is concerned. The same is the case for those who are *loyal* to some brand.

Basis for Segmentation Selection

There is no standard method to define what basis is the best in a particular case, and companies therefore resort to one or more of the following: Intuition and experience, trial and error, research on consumption patterns, research on attitudes and perceptions. Two approaches are used for breaking up a market: (*a*) the top-down approach, and the (*b*) bottom-up approach. In the top-down approach, called *logical division,* one starts with the market and breaks it down into more and more refined markets. In order to follow the bottom-up approach, called *ordering,* one starts with the individual consumers and groups, and their likely wants into segments.

Selection of Segments

The following are some important, general and specific segmentation factors that a company should consider in evaluating segment options. The general segmentation factors are: (*a*) Company thrust, (*b*) Size and growth potential, (*c*) Investment needed, (*d*) Profitability, (*e*) Risk, and (*f*) Competition. The specific segmentation factors are: (*a*) Segment durability, (*b*) Mobility, (*c*) Visibility, and (*d*) Accessibility.

11.2.7 Marketing Organization

Marketing is an important function in every firm irrespective of marketing a product or a service. The various ways in which the marketing function can be organized are discussed below.

Principles of Designing an Organization

An organization is defined as any system, body or group of people, comprising various sub-systems or parts which are interrelated or interdependent on each other. An organization may be informal or formal. An informal organization has no specific objective to achieve, whereas a formal organization has a specific objective to achieve and is the main reason for the organization's existence.

The principles involved in designing an organization are: (*a*) Specialization; (*b*) Departmentalization; (*c*) Standardization; (*d*) Formalization; (*e*) Centralization; (*f*) Evaluation; and (*g*) Structure. In making a choice out of the many kinds of organization structures formulated on these basic principles, one must evaluate the alternative structures on the basis of (*a*) facilitating achievement of objectives and accomplishment of tasks, (*b*) managerial control, and (*c*) cost.

A company that has marketing orientation comes into existence only after passing through many distinct phases. These are: (*a*) Simple sales department; (*b*) Sales department with some marketing function; (*c*) Separate marketing department; (*d*) Integrated marketing department; and (*e*) Marketing-oriented organization. The objective is to highlight the importance of marketing to every firm. As evident, with increased economic development, the importance of marketing has also been growing. No firm can afford to be without a marketing orientation. To succeed in the market place, it is essential to have a market organization, which facilitates the process of marketing and supports the achievement of objectives.

Factors Involved in Designing a Marketing Organization

In designing a marketing organization, the following *three* factors are taken into consideration:

1. **Marketing objectives and goals:** These include the desired market share, desired sales and profit levels, desired position in the industry and market, desired customer image and competitive posture.
2. **Nature of the product:** Depending on the kind of product which the firm is marketing, there is need to induct suitably educated and trained salesmen.
3. **Marketing of speciality products:** These include ethical drugs and medicines, medical and scientific equipment. For this purpose, formal educational background is foremost before the product is marketed.

Hence, the type of marketing organization that one chooses would also be influenced by the number of products. In general, firms with highly diversified range of products need separate marketing organizations to effectively market each one of them. In order to decide on essentiality of separate marketing organizations, it is necessary to identify similarities in the nature of products, and types of customer needs, customers served and the marketing channels. Thus, depending upon the unique combination of *what* you are marketing, *where* you are marketing and to *whom* you are marketing, one would design the marketing organization to suit ones needs.

Methods of Designing Market Organization

A marketing organization can be designed in many ways. Four basic methods discussed here are:

1. Functional organization.

2. Product management organization.

3. Market centred organization.

4. Matrix organization.

All other methods are either combinations or derivatives of these four methods.

1. **Functional organization:** The most common type of marketing organization consists of various functions performed as part of the overall marketing function. Each function is assigned to a marketing specialist who reports to the Director (Marketing). The most common functions in marketing are: Sales, distribution, advertising and promotion, dealer relations, customer service, new product development, marketing planning, marketing research, and marketing information system. It is quite possible that in small firms all these functions may not be individually identified and may be handled by just one or two individuals. However, as the firm grows in size, it becomes imperative to differentiate between these functions and delegate them to separate individuals. Figure 11.3 shows a typical functional marketing organization.

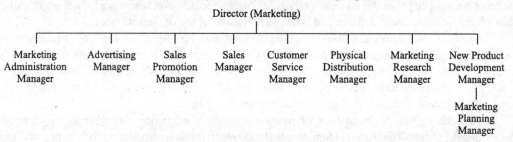

Fig. 11.3   A functional marketing organization

Thus, the functional marketing organization is based on various sub-functions performed as part of the overall marketing function. The organization of each sub-function varies from one company to another, depending on the unique combination of company's attributes and external environmental factors. This type of organization is administratively simple, but loses its effectiveness as the company's products and markets grow.

2. **Product management organization:** The product management organization is headed by a products manager, who supervises several product managers in charge of specific products. Thus, in a multi-product firm, one would have as many product managers as the number of products. The role of a product manager towards his specific product is to:

   • Develop long-term and competitive strategy.

   • Prepare annual plan and sales forecast.

   • Monitor progress.

   • Provide information relating to the product.

   • Interact with other departments of the organization, customers, distributors and advertising agencies.

Responsibilities of a product manager in eight areas of company's tasks are shown in Table 11.4. These basic functions are common to both consumer and industrial product manager. Yet there are some differences in their job functioning.

This type of organization offers several advantages: (*a*) Development of cost-effective marketing mix for the product; (*b*) Product manager can react more quickly to problems in the market place; (*c*) Smaller brands are less neglected; (*d*) Excellent training arrangement for young executives. The main disadvantages are: (*a*) Product management creates some conflict and frustration; (*b*) Product managers become experts in their product but rarely in any function; (*c*) Product management system often turns out to be costlier than anticipated; and (*d*) Product managers tend to manage their brand for only a short time.

Table 11.4 Typical Responsibilities of a Product Manager

Responsibility/Area	Task/Role
Advertising	Major responsibility for advertising strategy, arrangement for advertising campaigns, media selection.
Sales promotion	Major responsibility for budget determination, setting strategy, measuring/evaluating results.
Sales	Act as coordinator and as information centre.
Market research	Major responsibility.
New Product R&D	Major responsibility for product modifications, launches and test marketing.
Distribution	Little responsibility.
Production	Role of coordinating and communicating.
Accounting and Finance	Limited involvement.

(*Source:* N Piercy, *Marketing Organization,* George Allen & Unwin, London, 1985).

3. **Market-centred organization:** When tasks and jobs are differentiated on the basis of markets served, the organization is known as market centred. A market-centred organization is similar to the product management organization, A *chief marketing manager* supervises a number of *market managers.* Market managers are essentially staff, not line, people, with duties similar to those of product managers. This type of organization seeks its growth by serving new needs in markets where it is already well established. However, a market-centred organization has the flexibility to grow extensively by searching out closely-related needs and entering new business.

4. **Matrix organization:** A matrix organization is a blend of grouping by functions and markets, and/or products, with the objective of retaining the advantages of specialization and gaining of advantage of a sharper focus on a task or project. Advantages of a matrix organization are: (*a*) permits task/project focus without losing benefits of specialization; (*b*) provides increased information processing capability, catering to information needs of each group; (*c*) permits greater decentralization of decision-making; (*d*) provides a flexible structure; and (*e*) provides a means of coping with increased information processing needs and coordinating when the tasks are highly specific, complex and interdependent. Disadvantages of a matrix organization include: (*a*) tendency to conflict exists; (*b*) ambiguity in roles exists because each person reports to two bosses; (*c*) proves costly because of large volume of information processing; (*d*) prone to power struggles and politics as each group tries to dominate; and (*e*) problems of designing a suitable information system, catering to different requirements, exist.

Each type of organization is useful under specific conditions and has its own advantages and disadvantages. While choosing from amongst different types of organizations, one must evaluate each on the basis of its effectiveness in accomplishing the specified objectives, its amenability to managerial control and the cost involved.

11.2.8 Marketing Research and Its Applications

Crisp has defined marketing research as '... the systematic, objective and exhaustive search for and study of the facts relevant to any problem in the field of marketing.'

The American Marketing Association defines marketing research as 'the systematic gathering, recording and analysing of data about problems related to the marketing of goods and services.'

Marketing research can be used for consumer products, industrial products and services. The purpose of marketing research is (*a*) to facilitate the decision-making process, (*b*) to reduce the risk associated with the process of decision-making, and (*c*) to help firms in discovering opportunities which can be profitably exploited.

Marketing research (MR) is concerned with all aspects of marketing, relating to product design and development, product-mix, pricing, packaging, branding, sales, distribution, competition, target customer segments and their buying behaviour, advertising and its impact. Market research specifically includes customers, products, distribution, advertising, competitive information and macro-level phenomenon. The scope of marketing research mainly includes the following: (*a*) Marketing is concerned with identifying and fulfilling customer needs and wants. Thus, MR should precede marketing, (*b*) MR is helpful in determining the final design of the product and its physical attributes—colour, size, shape, packaging, and brand name; MR is useful in arriving at the right combination of product mix, number of variations of the basic product, accessories and attachments; MR helps decide the quantities to be produced according to projected demand estimates and also helps gauge customer reactions to different prices, (*c*) MR is helpful in discovering types of distribution channels and retail outlets profitable for the product; MR is useful in maximizing the return on every rupee that the firm spends, and (*d*) MR is being increasingly used at the macro-level.

Marketing Research Procedure

There are *five* steps in every marketing research process. These are:

    (*a*) Problem definition;

    (*b*) Research design;

    (*c*) Field work;

    (*d*) Data analysis; and

    (*e*) Report presentation and implementation.

    (*a*) **Problem definition** is the first stage, hence information generated here is likely to be unstructured, qualitative, tentative and exploratory. Once the problem is stated correctly and precisely, it is possible to cull out the precise objective for research.

    (*b*) **The research design** spells out how one is going to achieve the stated research objectives. Data collection methods—primary data and secondary data—specific research instrument and the sampling plan for collecting data and the corresponding cost are the elements that constitute the research design.

        (*i*) **Data collection methods:** The data which have already been collected by another organization are known as *secondary data*. It is to be ensured whether data collected by another group is suitable for the subject one is handling and if it can be put to use. Original data collected specifically for a current research are known as *primary data*. Primary data can be collected from customers, retailers, distributors, manufacturers or other information sources. Primary data may be collected through any of the three methods: *observation, survey,* and *experimentation*.

        (*ii*) **Research instrument:** Used for collection of primary data, *e.g.* camera, tape-recorder or tally sheet, must be appropriate to the occasion as well as reliable.

        (*iii*) **Sampling plan:** There are four aspects to the sampling plan: (*a*) who is to be surveyed (*sampling unit*); (*b*) How many are to be surveyed (*sample size*); (*c*) How are they to be selected (*sampling procedure*); and (*d*) How are they to be reached (*sampling media*).

    (*c*) **Field work** is the stage where the research design is converted from the planning stage to that of implementation. The two stages in field work are planning and supervision.

    (*d*) **Data analysis** has three phases: (*a*) Classifying the raw data in an orderly manner; (*b*) Summarizing the data; and (*c*) Applying analytical methods to manipulate the data to highlight their interrelationship and quantitative significance. The most commonly used classifications in MR are quantitative, qualitative, chronological and geographical. The following factors are involved in summarizing the data: Frequency distribution, mode, median, mean, range, variance and standard deviation, selecting analytical methods, correlation, regression analysis, multiple regression analysis, discriminant analysis, factor analysis, and statistical inference.

(*e*) **Report presentation and implementation** may comprise the following: objectives and methodology; summary of conclusions and recommendations; sample and its characteristics; detailed findings and observations; and questionnaire.

Applications of Marketing Research

The broad areas of applications of marketing research are as follows:

1. **Sales and market analysis:** This includes (*a*) determination of market potential, (*b*) determination of market share, (*c*) sales forecasting, (*d*) design of market segmentation studies, (*e*) test market, (*f*) distribution channel studies, (*g*) determination of market characteristics, and (*h*) determination of competitive information.

2. **Product research:** This involves (*a*) evaluating of new product ideas, (*b*) testing for new product acceptance, (*c*) evaluating change in product formulation, (*d*) testing package design, and (*e*) testing for product positioning.

3. **Business economics and corporate research:** This includes (*a*) studies of business trends, (*b*) pricing studies, (*c*) diversification studies, (*d*) product mix studies, and (*e*) plant and warehouse location studies.

4. **Advertising research:** Advertising research aims at (*a*) audience measurement, (*b*) cost-effective media plan, (*c*) copy testing, (*d*) determining advertising effectiveness, and (*e*) consumer behaviour research.

The marketing manager must decide on the desirability of conducting marketing research on the basis of cost involved and the resulting benefits expected to accrue from it.

In India, market research is commonly used in the following areas:

1. New product decisions.
2. Data collection for competitive information.
3. Demand estimation.
4. Product modification decisions.
5. Determining consumer satisfaction.
6. Diversification decision.
7. Advertising theme/message decision.
8. Pricing decisions.
9. Customer services decisions.
10. Product elimination decisions.
11. Evaluating advertising effectiveness.

Marketing research is used by both the public and private sectors. The difference lies in the fact that private sector firms tend to use MR more for decisions on new products, product positioning, measuring customer satisfaction, diversification and market segmentation than do public sector organizations. However, MR techniques used in India are still unsophisticated and simplistic. The main problem of MR in India is the meagre secondary data. The primary data is usually two to three years old and hence obsolete, which reduces its utility. Second, market research organizations are urban-biased and therefore market research is mainly confined to products used by city dwellers.

Self-assessment Questions Set-I

1. Define 'Marketing' and distinguish it from 'Selling'.
2. How does social marketing differ from business marketing in terms of objectives, approaches and the applicability of '4 Ps?' Discuss the importance of managing 4 Ps with reference to environmental issues.

3. Explain the unique characteristics of services that make them different from marketing of products. What implications do these characteristics have for the marketer?

4. What do you understand by the word 'Marketing'? Give your comments. Identify at least 15 products and services that are being currently marketed in India.

5. What are the levels involved in analysing a service product? How would you analyse the service provided by (*a*) an educational institution, (*b*) a consultancy organization, and (*c*) a government organization on a social cause like better environment?

6. Explain the four basic elements being used for marketing activities.

7. Design your marketing strategy by choosing any industrial product. Describe the steps in the marketing process, explain the designing of '4 Ps' in marketing and end with the ultimate objective of marketing.

8. Explain the marketing functions being performed at different levels of development.

9. Define marketing mix precisely. Why is marketing mix an important determinant of a firm's success? Outline the problems a marketer faces in determining a suitable marketing mix.

10. Based on your experience in the industry, which aspects of the marketing mix are most likely to be successful? Which ones are most likely to be least successful? Why?

11. Outline the strategies relating to marketing mix in product life-cycle stages.

12. Name some companies in India that follow the product differentiation strategy and market segmentation strategy.

13. (*a*) What are the different bases utilized to segment markets? (*b*) How would you segment the market in case of (*i*) personal computers, (*ii*) colour TV, (*iii*) 100 cc motorcycles, and (*iv*) readymade garments?

14. As the market becomes more and more competitive, does that necessitate more and more segmentation?

15. What are the areas of strengths and specific weaknesses of the marketing organization?

16. It is possible to overcome, wholly or partially, the weaknesses of the marketing organization? If yes, describe in detail the steps necessary for making up the deficiencies.

17. Outline the principles involved in designing a marketing organization. Explain the factors involved in designing.

18. Elucidate the principles of marketing management with examples.

11.3 Consumer Behaviour

Various physical, social and psychological factors that characterize and shape the behaviour of consumers are discussed. An attempt is made to consolidate and conceptualize current knowledge about consumer's behaviour with the help of some models.

Consumer behaviour is a process and various endogenous psychological and exogenous environmental factors influence this process. Some of these factors can be further influenced by specific elements of the marketing strategy, as a result of which the consumer behaviour moves towards a definite purchase decision. The marketer can understand and manipulate the influencing factors, and predict the behaviour of consumers. Thus, the importance of consumer behaviour lies in the fact that *behaviour* can be understood and influenced to ensure a positive purchase decision.

All consumers can be classified into two types—personal and organizational. Whenever one buys goods and services for his own or family use, he is a representative of a personal consumer. All business firms, government agencies, non-business organizations such as trusts, temples, hospitals are organizational consumers who purchase goods and services for running the organization. The process of decision-making and response constitute a simple model of consumer behaviour.

Input	External Factors	Other Factors
	Product	Economic
	Price	Technological
	Promotion	Political
	Channel of distribution	Social

Process	**Buyer Characteristics**	**Buyer Decision**
	Psychological	Process
	Personal	
	Cultural characteristics	
Output	**Consumer Decisions and Actions**	
	Product choice	
	Brand choice	
	Dealer choice	
	Purchase timing	
	Purchase amount	

11.3.1 Factors Influencing Consumer Behaviour

Consumer behaviour is affected by a number of variables. These are enumerated below:

Psychological Factors

These include:

(a) **Consumer needs:** The theory of hierarchy of needs was propounded by Abraham Maslow. According to Maslow, all human needs can be classified into five hierarchical categories: (*i*) *Physiological needs*—water, air, food, shelter, etc.; (*ii*) *Social needs*—affection, belonging-ness, friendship, etc.; (*iii*) *Ego needs*—status, prestige, self-respect, success, etc. (*iv*) *Safety and security needs*—protection, stability, etc.; and (*v*) *Self-actualization*—self-fulfilment.

Since no need is ever totally satisfied, there is always overlap amongst the different levels of needs.

(b) **Perception:** Perception can be described as 'how one sees the world around him through his five organs—eyes, ears, nose, mouth and skin. Each person recognizes, selects, organizes and interprets in his own manner based on his needs, values and expectations. This explains why different people respond differently under the same condition.

(c) **Learning:** Learning refers to the skill and knowledge gained from past experience and applied to future decisions and situations.

(d) **Beliefs and attitudes:** A belief is a descriptive thought that a person has about something. Attitude is a person's enduring feeling, evaluation and tendency towards a particular idea/object.

Social Factors

Purchase decision is influenced when the consumer interacts directly or indirectly with various social groups. These groups are:

(a) **Primary and secondary groups:** A primary group is one with which an individual interacts on a regular basis and whose opinion is important to him, *e.g.* family, close friends, colleagues. Secondary groups are those with which an individual interacts only occasionally and whose opinion is not so important to him.

(b) **Formal and informal groups:** Rotary club, labour unions, Lions club, social clubs are formal institutions as these have a defined structure, a specific role and authority positions. An informal group is loosely defined and may have no specific roles, *e.g.* meeting neighbours occasionally.

(c) **Membership and symbolic groups:** A membership group is one to which a person belongs to or qualifies for membership, *e.g.* all workers in a factory qualify for membership to the labour union. A symbolic group is one to which an individual aspires to belong to, but is not likely to be received as a member.

Personal Factors

Purchase decisions are also influenced by the consumer's personal characteristics such as education, occupation, age, sex, stages in family life cycle, income, lifestyle, his overall personality and self-concept.

Cultural Factors

To study consumer behaviour, culture can be defined as the sum total of learned beliefs, values and customs which serve to guide and direct the consumer behaviour of all members of the society. Culture is acquired through (*a*) formal learning, (*b*) informal learning, and (*c*) technical learning. Since society is undergoing a cultural metamorphosis, there are some major cultural shifts which have far-reaching consequences in the introduction of varied new products and services. These changes are: (*a*) convenience, (*b*) education, (*c*) physical appearance, and (*d*) materialism. Within each culture, there exist many sub-cultures comprising distinct nationality groups, religious groups, racial groups, geographic groups that, have their own unique values and lifestyle. Therefore, it is essential that a marketer must understand that people with different cultural, sub-cultural and social class—upper, lower upper, upper middle, lower middle, upper lower and lower—background have different product and brand preferences and need appropriate modified products and marketing strategies.

11.3.2 Consumer Behaviour Models

Consumer behaviour varies with the type of buying decision. There are *three* types of buying behaviour: (*a*) Routinized response behaviour, (*b*) Limited problem solving, and (*c*) Extended problem solving. Routinized response behaviour occurs when the customer has already some experience of buying and using the product. Consumers do not spend much time in selecting such products since they already have a preferred brand, *e.g.* soft drinks, washing powder, coffee, tea, etc. Marketers in this category must ensure the satisfaction of existing customers by maintaining consistent quality, service and value. In limited problem-solving behaviour, the consumer is familiar with the product and various brands available, but has no preferential brand. In this case, the marketer is expected to design a communication strategy which gives complete information on all the attributes of the brand and thus enhances the consumer's confidence to facilitate his/her purchase decision. The extended problem-solving behaviour is by far the most complex. In this case, the consumer is encountering a new product category and needs information on this product category as well as on several other brands available. The marketer in this category must be able to provide the consumer a specific and unique set of positive attributes regarding his own brand. The concept of extended problem-solving is most applicable to new products.

11.3.3 Buyer Behaviour Models

Consumer behaviour is a process and buying is only one stage in that process. The process of buyer behaviour is discussed with the help of the following three models:

Howard-Sheth Model

In this model (Fig. 11.4), *four* major sets of variables are considered: (*a*) inputs, (*b*) perceptual and learning constructs, (*c*) outputs, and (*d*) exogenous/external variables. For inputs, three distinct types of stimuli are provided: significative stimuli; symbolic stimuli; and consumer's family, reference groups and social class to which he belongs. Perceptual and learning constructs are composed of psychological variables such as motives, attitudes, perceptions, which influence the consumer's decision process. The purchase decision is the output. Exogenous/external variables are not directly a part of the decision-making process and are not indicated in the model. However, they are important to the extent that they influence the consumer. These exogenous variables vary from one consumer to another in areas such as consumer personality traits, social class, importance of the purchase, and financial status.

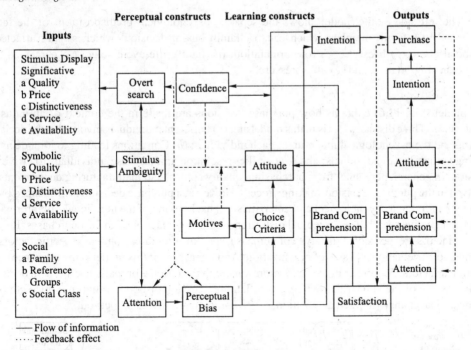

Fig. 11.4   Howard-Sheth model of buying behaviour in simpler form

Family Decision-Making Model

Family decision-making is influenced by different consumption related roles played by members in a family. These roles are: influencers, gatekeepers, deciders, buyers, preparers, and users. The roles played by different family members will vary from product to product. One such model in shown in Fig. 11.5.

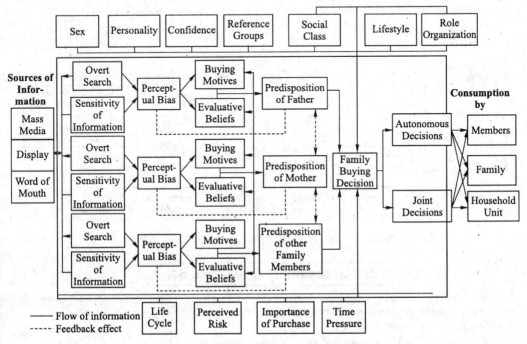

Fig. 11.5   Family decision-making model

The left side of the model shows the separate psychological predispositions of the father, mother and other family members which lead to a 'family buying decision', which is in turn affected by (*a*) social class, (*b*) lifestyle, (*c*) role orientation, (*d*) family life-cycle stage, (*e*) perceived risk, (*f*) product importance, and (*g*) time pressure.

Industrial Buyer Behaviour Model

This model (Fig. 11.6) explains how purchase decisions are made in the context of an industrial organization. Three distinct aspects in this model are: (*a*) Different individuals involved in the decision-making and the psychological make-up of each individual; (*b*) Conditions leading to joint decision-making among these individuals; and (*c*) Conflict resolution among these individuals to arrive at a decision. In general, personnel from purchasing, quality control and manufacturing departments are involved in the purchase decision-making process. However, a purchase decision is influenced by the following individual psychological characteristics: (*a*) background of the individual, (*b*) information sources, (*c*) active search, (*d*) perceptual distortion, and (*e*) satisfaction with past purchases. Product specific factors are: perceived risk, type of purchase, and time pressure. Company specific factors are organization orientation and size of organization. Another aspect of this model is the influence of the situational factors. At times, situational factors outweigh the rational or realistic criteria in decision-making. Some of the situational factors are inflation, recession or boom, rationing, price controls, organizational change (merger, acquisition, etc.), foreign trade, strikes or lock-out.

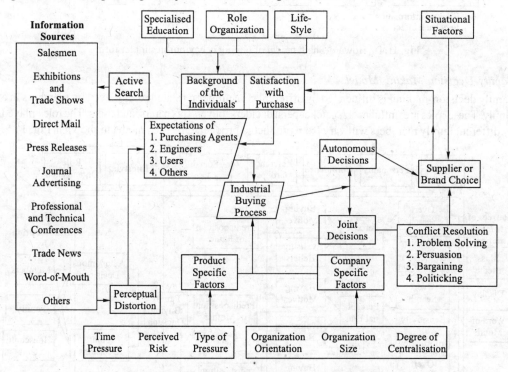

Fig. 11.6 Integrative industrial buyer behaviour model

Self-assessment Questions Set-II

1. What do you understand by consumer behaviour? Discuss the process of decision-making and response which leads to a simple consumer behaviour model.
2. Explain the factors influencing consumer behaviour.
3. Outline the types of buying behaviour. Discuss each of them in detail.

4. Name and describe the different types of groups that may have influenced your behaviour in terms of making a decision.

5. Discuss in detail Howard-Sheth model, illustrating major variables considered in the process of buyer behaviour.

6. Enumerate the different roles played by family members in influencing a decision for purchasing a product. Illustrate the decision-making factors using a diagram.

7. Outline the salient aspects of the industrial buyer behaviour model. 'Purchase decision is influenced by individual psychological characteristics.' Comment on this statement, with a sketch.

8. (*a*) What are the major reference groups that influence consumer purchase decisions?

   (*b*) As a marketer, identify the type of reference group that is likely to influence the purchase decision for (*i*) a personal computer, (*ii*) a refrigerator, (*iii*) an ultrasound equipment, and (*iv*) a stereophonic music system.

9. It is hypothesized that a consumer goes through five stages in making a purchase decision: (*i*) Problem recognition, (*ii*) Pre-purchase information research, (*iii*) Evaluation of alternatives, (*iv*) Purchase decision, and (*v*) Post-purchase behaviour. Explain these steps by taking the example of the personal luggage industry.

11.4 Product Management

A product is a composite of the characteristics and features—physical and psychological—which are offered for purchase to a customer, irrespective of his being a consumer or an industrial purchaser. In terms of marketing, a product is a bundle of benefits offered to a customer. Hence, product management means product concept, converting it into a physical product, its brand name, packing, and positioning in the market.

11.4.1 Product Decisions

Product decisions include introduction of new products, improvement of existing products, planned elimination of obsolete products, and packaging and branding. The decision is influenced by product differentiation and product positioning. Generally, products are classified into two types: (*a*) Consumer products; (*b*) Industrial products. Consumer products can be further divided into (*i*) convenience goods, (*ii*) shopping goods, (*iii*) durable goods, and (*iv*) non-durable goods. Industrial products include machinery, components, and raw materials which form the bulk of industrial goods. Consumer products require elaborate channels of distribution, but industrial products are sold through fewer outlets and often directly by the organization itself. There are basically two types of diversifications— related and unrelated. Related diversification involves going in for similar products. These products usually require the use of same production, selling and distribution facilities. However, for continued growth of an organization, it may be necessary to undertake unrelated diversification.

Product Life Cycle and New Product Development

There are four stages in the life cycle of a product: (*a*) Introductory stage; (*b*) Growth stage; (*c*) Maturity stage; and (*d*) Decline stage. The product life cycle at different stages is shown in Fig. 11.7. In the introductory stage, the product must be brought to the notice of the customer. It must be available at the distribution outlets and it takes some time before the sales pick up. Initially there is less likelihood of profits or more chances of incurring a loss. In the growth stage, the sales would climb up fast and profit will also improve considerably. This is because the cost of distribution and promotion is now spread over a larger volume of sales. As the volume of production is increased, the manufacturing cost per unit tends to decline. Thus, from viewpoint of product strategy, this is a critical stage. In the maturity stage, sales are likely to be pushed downwards by competitors while promotional efforts would have to be increased to try and sustain the sales. In the decline stage, sales are likely to decline and the product could reach the 'obsolescence' stage. The following steps should be considered to prevent obsolescence and hence avoid decline: (*a*) Improving product quality; (*b*) Adding new product features resulting in extra benefits; (*c*) Penetrating new market segments; (*d*) Giving incentives to distribution channels; (*e*) Expanding the number of distribution channels; and (*f*) Improving sales and advertising effort.

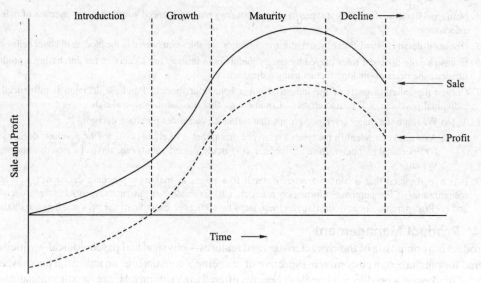

Fig. 11.7   Product life cycle

New Product Development

There are *six* stages in the development of a new product:

(a) Generation of new product ideas,

(b) Evaluation of ideas,

(c) Concept development and evaluation,

(d) Product design and evaluation,

(e) Product testing, and

(f) Launching the new product.

After the new product is launched, it must be evaluated through its life cycle.

11.4.2 Branding

Brand is a word, mark, symbol, device or a combination thereof, used to identify some product or service. Brand name is a part of a brand consisting of a word, letter, group of words/letters, comprising a name which is intended to identify the goods/services of a seller or a group of a sellers and to differentiate them from those of competitors. Hence, brand name is only one of the means used for identification. For brand selection, the following factors need to be considered: (a) Should the product be branded at all? (b) Who should sponsor the brand? (c) What quality should be built into the brand? (d) Should each product be individually or family branded? Should other products be given the same brand name? (e) Should two or more brands be developed in the same product category? (f) Should the established brand be given a revised meaning (repositioning).

There are two types of brand: (a) Family brand; and (b) individual brand. The basic advantage of using the family brand is that it reduces the costs of the product launching and ongoing promotional expenditure substantially. The firm has to promote only one brand which, if successful, would help sell the entire product line. Lining up the distribution channel also becomes comparatively easier. It is quite possible that if one product does exceptionally well, there would be positive fall-outs for other products under the same brand. It is also necessary to be cautious if the products being offered are of a highly uneven quality. For a weak individual brand, the strength of the family brand becomes the principal factor. The main advantage is that if there is a product failure, its damaging effect will be limited to that particular product and not extend to the entire product line. However, the basic disadvantage lies in the economics of developing an individual brand. It is obviously a costlier strategy than the other. Also, an individual brand does not derive any benefit from the reputation of the firm.

In brand repositioning, several market parameters might undergo a change such as introduction of a competing product, shifts in consumer preferences, identification of new needs, etc. All such changes call for a re-look as to whether the original positioning of the product is still optimal or not. Stagnating or declining sales also indicate the need for reassessment of the original product positioning.

Branding can be analysed from viewpoints of both buyers and sellers. **Buyers** can derive several advantages: (*a*) A brand generally denotes uniform quality; (*b*) It makes shopping easier; (*c*) Competition among brands can, over a period of time, lead to quality improvements; and (*d*) Purchasing a socially visible brand can give psychological satisfaction to the buyer. However, certain disadvantages are: (*a*) Brand development costs money, product prices tend to go up; and (*b*) Taking advantage of the popularity of a brand a manufacturer may reduce quality gradually. **Sellers** can derive the following advantages: (*a*) Branding helps in product identification; (*b*) In a highly competitive market, it can carve out a niche for itself through product differentiation; and (*c*) In case loyalty can be developed through successful promotion, the firm will be able to exert quasi-monopolistic power. Apart from these two viewpoints, it is also possible to have a societal view-point.

Selecting a brand name for a new product is a tricky job for two reasons: (*a*) The name should be one which satisfies several marketing criteria; and (*b*) The name should not be the one which is already being used by another firm.

11.4.3 Packaging

Packaging is the art, science and technology of preparing goods for transport and sale. Two important features of packaging are: (*a*) Facilitation in physical transportation and sale of products packaged; and (*b*) Serving a function consisting of two distinct elements: (*i*) positive aspects, *viz.* the science and technology related to package design, selection of packaging materials, etc.; and (*ii*) behavioural aspects, *viz.* the art of product design which is associated with consumer motivation research, buying research, etc. Packaging should perform the following *five* basic functions: (*a*) protect, (*b*) appeal, (*c*) perform, (*d*) offer convenience to end-users, and (*e*) cost-effective.

While managing the packaging function, constant attention needs to be given to various regulations that the Government has laid down in this respect. The most pervasive among these is the regulation relating to the information that a manufacturer is obliged to provide about the product on the package itself. This is commonly known as *labelling*. A label fulfils a legal requirement and it is also an important sales instrument. Statutory requirements generally relate to (*i*) net weight, when packed, (*ii*) date of manufacture, (*iii*) date of expiry, (*iv*) maximum retail price including local taxes, (*v*) directions for use including dosage recommendation, and (*vi*) directions for storage. Apart from the information which must be statutorily given, the label should provide (*a*) picture of the product, accurate size, colour and appearance; (*b*) description of raw products used along with methods of processing; (*c*) directions for use, including cautions against misuse; (*d*) possible adverse effects, if any; and (*e*) brand name. Being a crucial aspect of marketing, a good package must protect the contents inside it, be attractive to the consumer, convenient to handle, store and use and perform the functions required of it. New exciting types of packaging materials—paper, corrugated board, aluminium, PVC, HDPE, wood and cellulose film, aluminium foils, plastic film, polymer-polyethylene terephthalate (PET)—have revolutionized the packaging industry, and have become an important factor for marketing decisions.

Self-assessment Questions Set-III

1. What is a product? Outline product planning approach based on PLC?
2. In what situations do you feel the PLC to be an adequate tool for product management?
3. Briefly enumerate the systematic approach to new product development.
4. (*a*) Explain how the marketing mix is likely to change during PLC stages.

   (*b*) In the Indian context, identify the present stage in the respective life cycles of (*i*) 'Xerox' machines, (*ii*) Black & white TV, and (*iii*) Safety helmets. In accordance with the stage identified by you in each case, suggest a suitable promotion and pricing mix.
5. Explain the following: 'People do not buy a product. They buy benefits.'
6. Outline the advantages and disadvantages of branding.
7. Identify the basic factors that prompt a company to brand its products.
8. Select a branded consumer product of your choice. Analyse in detail the factors that have contributed to its success.
9. Do you consider branding to be of identical importance in marketing (*a*) consumer products, (*b*) industrial products, and (*c*) agricultural products. Give supportive arguments.
10. What are the brand strategy options open to a firm? Discuss their relative merits and demerits.
11. Sometimes even a well-established company tries to promote only the individual brand and keep its own name as inconspicuous as possible. Can you explain this strategy?

11.5 Pricing and Promotion Decisions

11.5.1 Pricing Strategy

Pricing is concerned with the monetary value of the product and is determined not only in terms of the cost but also in terms of major objectives of the expected market share, rate of return, and price competitiveness of the product. Pricing decision constitutes a critical dimension of the marketing strategy. Generally, pricing decisions are determined by *cost, demand* and *competition.*

Demand

The law of demand states that higher the price, the lower the demand, and *vice-versa*, other things remaining the same. There is an inverse relationship between price and demand. However, there are exceptions to the law of demand. Another important factor is *elasticity* of *demand*. Elasticity of demand refers to the response of demand to a change in price, whereas the law of demand indicates the direction of change in demand.

Competition

There are *four* types of competition: (*a*) Perfect competition, (*b*) Monopoly, (*c*) Oligopoly, and (*d*) Monopolistic. Perfect competition is said to exist when (*i*) there are a large number of buyers and sellers, (*ii*) each one is purchasing and selling such a small quantity that their withdrawal from the market will not affect the total demand and supply, and (*iii*) products sold by sellers are homogeneous in nature. Prices will be fixed at a point where supply and demand are in equilibrium. In *monopoly,* a single producer has complete control of the entire supply of a product, *e.g.* railways, electric supply. *Oligopoly* is characterized by a few sellers, each having an appreciable share in the total output of the commodity, *e.g.* dry batteries, cement, tyres, tractors, aluminium, etc. In *monopolistic competition,* there are many sellers of a particular product, but the product of each seller is in some way differentiated in the minds of consumers from the product of every other seller.

Cost

There is a popular belief that costs determine price. It is because the cost data constitute the fundamental element in the price setting process.

11.5.2 Methods of Pricing

There are various methods of pricing. The *five* most commonly used methods are:

   (*a*) Cost-plus/full-cost pricing;

(*b*) Pricing for a rate of return/target pricing;

(*c*) Marginal cost pricing;

(*d*) Going-rate pricing; and

(*e*) Customary prices.

Cost-plus/Full-cost Pricing

In this method, the price is set to cover costs (materials, labour and overhead) and a predetermined percentage of cost for profit. The percentage for profit differs strikingly among industries, firms and even products of the same firm. This method is widely used, particularly in India.

Pricing for a Rate of Return

The policies often followed in this method pertain to price revisions to maintain (*i*) a constant percentage mark-up over costs; (*ii*) profits as a constant percentage of total sales; (*iii*) a constant return on invested capital. This is a refined variant of full-cost pricing. It is based upon a concept of cost which may not be relevant to the pricing decision at hand and overplays the precision of allocated fixed costs and capital employed.

Marginal Cost Pricing

In this method, fixed costs are ignored and prices are determined on the basis of marginal cost. The firm uses only those costs that are directly attributable to the output of a specific product.

Going-rate Pricing

In this method, the firm adjusts its own price policy in response to the general pricing structure in the industry. In this case, the firm has some power to set its own price and could be a price maker if it chooses to face all the consequences.

Customer Pricing

Prices of certain goods become more or less fixed as a result of their having prevailed for a considerable period of time. For such goods, changes in costs are usually reflected in changes in quality/quantity. Only when the costs change significantly, are the customary prices of these goods changed.

From the viewpoint of the firm, price represents a kind of 'maximum' that it can charge given its own costs and nature of competition. From the customer's viewpoint, it is a representation of quality of the product. Thus, in many cases, high price is associated with good quality and *vice-versa*.

The marketer must fully understand what the connotation of price means to a customer, before designing the pricing strategy in which the choice is between penetrative and skimming pricing. In some cases, a reduction in price may lead to an increase in sales, while in others it may not. This is especially true of industrial products where the buyer is more concerned with quality, reliability, delivery schedules and after-sales services of the product rather than merely the price. Rather than a reduced price, what may be more relevant is price discounts in the form of quantity or cash discounts.

11.5.3 Advertising and Publicity

Advertising

Advertising is the most visible and glamorous method of marketing communication. It is defined as a paid form of non-personal presentation and promotion of ideas, goods or services by an identified sponsor. Some of the major marketing and communication functions performed by advertising include: to inform, entertain, persuade, influence, remind, reassure and add value to the product or service advertised. There are many types of advertising:

(*a*) *Industrial advertising*—advertisements for machinery, machine tools, etc.;

(*b*) *Consumer advertising*—edible oils, footwear, toothpastes, etc.;

(*c*) *Institutional advertising*—advertisements aimed at improving the corporate image;

(d) *Product advertising*—advertisements with a view to promoting the products;

(e) *Primary demand advertising*—advertisements promoting the consumption of tea or coffee etc.;

(f) *Brand advertising*—advertisements related to specific brand name;

(g) *Direct and indirect advertising*—advertisements aimed at effecting immediate sale of products advertised represent direct advertising, and the ones performing tasks like announcing the launch of new products, and creating interest in customers or changing their attitudes represent indirect advertising;

(h) *Manufacturer advertising*—advertisements which are sponsored and paid for by the manufacturers;

(i) *Cooperative advertising*—such advertisements whose costs are shared by the manufacturer and his wholesalers or retailers; and

(j) *Retail advertising*—when a retailer advertises for his shop entirely on his own to attract customers to his shop.

The economic and social effects of advertising have become the topics of continuing debate. This gives rise to two viewpoints—one considers advertisements as an information disseminating utility function and the other views advertising as a source of market power.

In short, the basic decision areas in advertising are: (a) setting advertising objectives; (b) determining advertising budget; (c) developing advertisement copy and message; (d) selecting and scheduling media; and (e) measuring advertising effectiveness. The approach used for (a) and (b) is the same.

Major advertising media currently available in India are:

(a) *Press*—wider circulation, limited life, good for mass communication and reminder messages;

(b) *Direct mail*—restricted circulation, flexible usage, private in nature, high impact;

(c) *Outdoor*—local circulation, durable, reminder media;

(d) *Radio*—wide reach, cuts through illiteracy barriers, quick reminder messages possible;

(e) *Television*—combines both audio and visual, fairly wide reach, high degree of viewers' involvement, suitable for product demonstration;

(f) *Cinema*—limited reach, short life, good for illiterates; and

(g) *Miscellaneous* (exhibition/fairs, etc.)—local reach, good product demonstration, impactful.

Publicity

Publicity is non-personal stimulation of demand for a product, service or business unit by placing commercial significant news about it in a published medium or obtaining favourable presentations of it upon radio, television, or stage that is not paid for by the sponsor. Publicity is one of the tools of public relations. It has acquired a sound position in assisting a firm in its marketing efforts. It has an important role in disseminating information regarding new products; new R&D achievements; product replacement policies and customer service arrangements; successful bids or contracts won; employees' welfare policies; dealer training and promotion activities; community development programmes; promotion of company trade mark and slogans, etc. Organization of newsworthy events and good relations with media also help. Besides, a large sized organization is vulnerable to rumours and damaging stories. Systematically planned publicity and public relation activities help in correcting misinformation and providing an opportunity to the public to view a firm in the right perspective.

11.5.4 Personal Selling and Sales Promotion

Personal Selling

This is the oldest method of business promotion, and makes use of direct personal communications to influence the target customers. The following tasks are performed in personal selling: (a) Sales generation; (*b*) Feedback and market information collection; (*c*) Provision of customer service covering delivery of goods, warranty administration, timely availability of repair and spares, etc; and (*d*) Performance of sales support activities, *e.g.* monitoring the distribution function, credit collection, improving manufacturer-dealer relations, implementing promotional programmes, etc. In practice, the selling task actually performed varies from company to company. To effect sales, selling situations differ due to interplay of various factors. These factors require the sales force to possess different traits and abilities suitable to the selling situation with which they are associated. Robert N. McCurry classified individual sales position, based on the creativity required, into following *seven* categories:

(*a*) Merchandise deliveries,

(*b*) Inside order-taker,

(*c*) Outside order-taker,

(*d*) Missionary salesperson,

(*e*) Sales engineer,

(*f*) Tangible product seller, and

(*g*) Intangible product seller.

It is, therefore, essential that the job of the salesperson should be defined with sufficient specificity so that he can use it as a guideline to keep himself in the right direction.

Selling Process

The following eight steps in the selling process are shown in Fig. 11. 8. These steps are: (*a*) Preparation, (*b*) Prospecting, (*c*) Preapproach, (*d*) Approach, (*e*) Sales presentation, (*f*) Handling objections, (*g*) Closing the sale, and (*h*) Post-sale follow-up. However, the degree of importance given to each step would differ under different selling situations. Although these steps are essential, they may not always be followed.

Robertson and Chase pointed out that: (*a*) The more closely matched the physical, social and personal characteristics of the customer and salesperson, the more likely is the sale; (*b*) The more believable and trustworthy the customer perceives a salesperson to be, the more likely is the sale; (*c*) The more persuadable a customer is, the more likely is the sale; and (*d*) The more a salesperson can make prospective buyers view themselves favourably, the more likely is the sale.

Post-sale Follow-up—Reassure customers on the correctness of their decision.
Closing the Sale—Make conscious efforts to close.
Handling Objections—Understand reasons for objections, with positive attitude, Avoid arguments.
Sales Presentation—Arouse desire.
Pre-approach—Study the organization and those involved in buying.
Prospecting and Qualifying—Develop sales leads from various sources. Separate the suspects from the prospects.
Preparation—Know your product, customer, competitor, and your company.

(*Source:* RM Gaedeke and DH Tootelian, '*Marketing Principles and Applications*', 1983, p. 436).

Fig. 11.8 Steps in the selling process

Sales Promotion

Stanley M. Ulanoff defines sales promotion as 'all the marketing and promotion activities, other than advertising, personal selling, and publicity, that motivate and encourage the consumer to purchase by means of such inducements as premiums, advertising specialities, samples, discount coupons, sweepstakes, contests, games, trading stamps, refunds, rebates, exhibits, displays, and demonstrations.

It is also employed to motivate retailers, the wholesaler and the manufacturer's sales force to sell through the use of such incentives as awards or prizes (merchandise, cash and travel), direct payments and allowances, co-operative advertising, and trade shows.'

The American Marketing Association referred sales promotion as to "those activities, other than personal selling, advertising and publicity, that stimulate consumer purchasing and dealer effectiveness such as display shows and exhibitions, demonstrations, and various other non-recurrent selling efforts not in ordinary routine."

Roger A. Strang offers a simpler definition: "Sales promotion are short-term incentives to encourage purchase or sale of a product or service."

Sales promotion activities thus deal with promotion of sales by the offer of incentives which are essentially non-recurring in nature. Such activities are also known as *extra-purchase value* and *below-the-line selling*.

Sales promotion methods are build around three target groups—consumers, dealers, and members of the sales force. The impact of various sales promotion schemes can be immediate and delayed/over-a-period of time (Table 11.5). The meaning and objectives of these schemes are explained in Table 11.6.

Table 11.5   Impact Categorization of Various Sales Promotion Schemes

Impact	Schemes Directed at			
	Users	Non-users	Trade/Suppliers	Sales Force
Immediate	Price-off Quantity-off Over-the-counter premium Packaged premium Banded premium Container premium	Price-off Sampling Over-the-counter premium	Discounts Shelf space allowance Gifts Push money Posting of sales force	Perquisites and allowances Gifts
Delayed/over-a-period of time	In product coupons Personality premiums	Media/door coupons Return/refund offers Trading stamps Self-liquidators Contests/lucky draws	Merchandise deals Coupons Display contests Co-op allowance Sales contest Training sales force/privileges	Sales contests Honours/Recognitions Customer service awards

(*Source:* Donald W'Cowell, 'Sales Promotion and Marketing of Local Government Recreation and Leisure Services.' *European Journal of Marketing*, Vol. 18, No. 2).

Sales promotion schemes for promoting industrial goods differ from schemes for other goods. This is evident as outlined in Table 11.6. In spite of all these sales promotion schemes offered, there is need for orderly management. For effective planning and management of the sales promotion function, the following eight steps are suggested; (*a*) Assessing and analysing the present situation of the brand in terms of market share, major competitors and brand performance; (*b*) Identifying alternative schemes and selecting the most appropriate sales promotion scheme; (*c*) Incorporating creativity in the scheme to be offered; (*d*) Examining the legal validity of the sales promotion scheme to be offered; (*e*) Taking primary decision relating to timing and duration of the scheme to be offered, location-wise selection of dealers, and conviction of the trade and sales force about the appropriateness to the scheme; (*f*) Developing evaluation criteria in relation to the goals set; (*g*) Monitoring the offer and collecting the relevant data and experience for future use as well as for mid-period corrections; and (*h*) Evaluating the effectiveness of sales promotions in the context of their goals.

Table 11.6 Meaning and Objectives of Sales Promotion Schemes

Sales Promotion Scheme	Meaning	Objectives
Price-off offers	Offering a product at lower than the normal price.	To encourage immediate sales, attract non-users, induce trial of a new product, counter competition, inventory clearance at the retail level, inventory build-up at the trade level.
Quantity-off offers	Offering more quatity of the same product at no extra cost or with a very nominal increase in the price of the larger quantity packs.	To encourage more/longer duration consumption, higher or excess quantity movement from the factory, encourage consumer for higher quantity pack size.
Premium	Offer of an article of merchandise as an incentive in order to sell product or service. Its forms are:	To encourage purchase, stimulate loyalty, off-season sales promotion, induce trial of a new product, ensure reach of premium to the consumer.
(a) Packaged Premium	When the incentive article is packed (inserted) inside the package of the product.	
(b) Banded Premium	Where the premium article is banded to the package of the product package of the product, say with cellotape, etc.	Sampling new products, adding speed to slow moving products.
(c) Over-the-counter (OTC) Premium	When the premium article is neither inserted inside nor banded to the product package but is given away to the consumer over the counter along with the product package.	To counter competition, improve inventory clearance at the trade level.
(d) Container Premium	When the product itself is placed in an attractive and reusable container which serves as a gift.	As a durable reminder at home.
(e) Self-liquidating Premiums	Where the consumer is usually asked to pay a specified amount to liquidate or offset a part of or full cost of the premium article or the scheme administration costs.	To induce consumers to appropriate premium article, reinforce brand image, encourage more consumption, enable sponsor to offer better quality premium.
(f) Personality Premium	Where the consumer is required to redeem a specified proof of purchase for the premium article. Proof-of-purchase may be labels, pack tops, bottle tops, corks, etc.	To build loyalty and reward the consumer for some counter competitive offers.
Coupons	When the consumer is entitled to redeem a specific standard certificate for a product/article free or in part payment. Coupons are used by both the manufacturer and the dealers for sales promotion. Coupons may be distributed by mail, by media, door-to-door advertisements, inside product packages, or by dealers on purchase.	To encourage product trial, build loyalty, encourage regular users, stimulate repurchase rate, solicit inquiries.

Contd....

Sales Promotion Scheme	Meaning	Objectives
Refund offers	Offer of a refund of money to the consumer for mailing a proof-of-purchase of a particular product(s)	To induce trial from primary users, motivate several product purchases, obtain displays at the retailers, help retailers tie-in with other products, switch competing brand users to sponsor's brand, loading dealers with increased stock.
Trading stamps	Organized by Trading Stamp companies or large retailers. Trading stamps are a kind of discount coupons offered to consumers linked with the quantum of their purchase. On enough accumulation, these are redeemable for various kinds of merchandise.	To encourage consumer loyalty to certain retail stores.
Consumer contests and lucky draws	Where individuals are invited to compete on the basis of creative skills. Lucky draws depend on the chance or luck factor.	To create brand awareness and stimulate interest in the brand, acquaint consumers with brand usage and benefits, build traffic at the store, precipitate brand purchase, obtain consumer feedback, promote advertising theme of the company.
Dealer stock display contests	It is a type of point-of-purchase advertising which uses the show windows of the dealers for providing exposure to the sponsor's products. Dealers participating enthusiastically and creatively are awarded.	To provide product exposure at the point-of-purchase, generate traffic at the store, infuse enthusiasm among dealers.
Dealer sales contests	Where participating dealers are invited to compete in terms of the sales performance.	To increase sales, buy dealers' loyalty, motivate dealers' staff to sell more.
Discounts	Other than normal trade and cash discounts.	To push more sales to trade, early cash recovery.
Trade allowances	These are temporary price reductions' reimbursement of expenses incurred by dealers in full or in part, its varied types are as under:	
(a) Trade or buying allowance	Offer of price reduction on purchase of a specified quantity of a product.	To load the trade.
(b) Buy-back allowance	A secondary incentive which offers a certain sum of money to trade for each additional unit bought over and above the deal.	To encourage trade co-operation and stimulate repurchase.
(c) Count and recount allowance	When a specific amount of money is offered after ascertaining the number of units sold during a specified period.	To move stocks faster, reward on sale only.

Contd....

Sales Promotion Scheme	Meaning	Objectives
(d) Merchandise (display) allowance	An allowance to trade for providing desired sales promotion and product displays.	To create enthusiasm in trade, improve traffic and exposure at the point-of-purchase, gain larger space/effort of the trade in the promotion of sponsor's product as against those of the competitors.
(e) Co-operative advertising & promotion allowance	Wherein a manufacturer shares at an agreed rate the advertising and promotional cost incurred by the dealer in the promotion of manufacturer's product.	To gain product and retail identity, motivate dealers to promote manufacturer's product, obtain local advertising and promotion.
Dealer gifts	Offer of useful articles and attractive gifts to dealers for their personal, family or office use.	To improve dealer relations, make impact on consumer scheme/contest offered.
Premium or push money	When an additional compensation is offered to trade or sales force for pushing additionally a specific product or product line.	To push a specific product or product line.
Merchandise deals	Wherein additional quantity of the same or another product of the same manufacturer is offered to trade. May be offered jointly by non-competing manufacturers.	To load dealers with inventory, expose other products of the sponsor, encourage dealers to sell more and early to realize their incentive.
Point-of-Purchase (POP)	Those special displays, racks, banners, exhibits. that are placed in the retail store to support the sale of a brand.	To attract traffic at retail store, remind customers, encourage impulse buying, ensure additional visibility to the advertising campaign.

(*Source:* D W'Cowell, 'Sales Promotion and the Marketing of Local Government Recreation and Leisure Services' *European Journal* of *Marketing,* Vol. 18, No. 2).

Attaining synergistic advantage arising out of the use of different promotional methods is the hallmark of an effective promotional strategy. It is, therefore, widely accepted that sales promotion is an important marketing function of each firm. Hardly any firm makes use of only one promotional method. The commonality in the ultimate goal of all promotional methods, apart from their limited suitability in influencing only a specific part of the consumer adoption, calls for the need to use the promotional mix in an integrated manner. Knowing the complexities in the management of the promotion function and its vulnerability to failure, it is necessary that the sales promotion function be professionally managed.

Self-assessment Questions Set-IV

1. Explain the group of individual factors which influence the price of the product.
2. Outline the different methods of pricing. Discuss each of them in detail.
3. How do the stages of product life cycle and product positioning affect pricing decisions?
4. What are the cases where marginal costing can be employed? What are its limitations?
5. What do you understand by advertising? Outline the various types of advertising and their basic decision areas.
6. Discuss some major advertising media currently available in India and their significance.
7. What do you understand by 'Publicity'? How is it useful in disseminating information?
8. What is personal selling? Outline various factors influencing individual sales position.
9. Classify the steps involved in the selling process and explain their significance in the era of modern marketing.

10. Define sales promotion elaborately. Discuss its importance in various schemes of marketing.

11. Discuss some salient sales promotion methods, their meaning and objectives.

11.6   Distribution and Legislations

11.6.1   Sales Forecasting: Tools and Techniques

A sales forecast predicts the value of sales over a stipulated period of time. There are two types of sales forecast: (*a*) *Short-term sales forecast* (approximately for one year); and (*b*) *Long-term sales forecast* (approximately for five years). In order to prepare a sales forecast, it requires: (*a*) identification of determinants of product sales, (*b*) prediction of behaviour of market forces, (*c*) availability of historical information on the product and industry sales, (*d*) use of appropriate techniques for forecasting, (*e*) judgement of executives responsible for sales forecast, and (*f*) knowledge of market share objectives of the firm.

Major determinants of product sales relating to consumer and industrial goods are: (*a*) *Consumer non-durable goods*—these are low priced, have short shelf life, and constitute the bulk of frequently purchased consumer goods; (*b*) *Consumer durable goods*—these goods have a long life and are generally bought out of savings. Purchase frequency is limited and is influenced by (*i*) discretionary income, (*ii*) availability of infrastructure support facilities, (*iii*) availability of price, credit or hire-purchase facilities, (*iv*) life-style of the household; and (*c*) *Industrial goods*—this category is influenced by (*i*) company forecast, (*ii*) industry forecast, (*iii*) national economic forecast, and (*iv*) world economic forecast. At the firm level, there are two approaches for sales forecasting: (*a*) *Breakdown approach,* (*b*) *Market build-up approach.* A combination of both these approaches is considered to be ideal and worth the effort expended.

Forecasting methods are grouped into *five* categories: (*i*) Executive judgement, (*ii*) surveys, (*iii*) time series analysis, (*iv*) correlation and regression methods, and (*v*) market tests.

With the advent of sophisticated computer hardware and software, planners can introduce subjective inputs into the forecast and test their effects quickly.

In essence, sales forecasting is useful, particularly in relation to the sales budget and profit plan of the firm. Hence, it is important to use simple, but comprehensive sales information formats in order to monitor the market and conduct sales analysis at regular intervals.

11.6.2   Distribution Channels

The institutions which perform activities and functions necessary for moving a product and its title from production to consumption are known as *distribution* channels. While designing the distribution strategy as part of marketing mix, two categories of issues and decisions are involved: (*a*) Management of marketing channels, and (*b*) Management of physical supplies. Generally, there are two types of distribution channels: (*i*) direct selling by the manufacturer; and (*ii*) indirect selling through middlemen. However, in most cases, manufacturers are required to take the help of a variety of agencies to reach their target customers. These agencies are classified as: (*a*) functional middlemen, or (*b*) merchant middlemen. Some of the salient points of direct selling and indirect selling through intermediaries, such as wholesalers and retailers, are as follows:

Direct Selling

The main characteristics of direct selling are to (*a*) enlighten the user about additional features, and (*b*) educate the user on how to use the product.

Mercantile Agents

There are *two* types of mercantile agents: (*a*) *Brokers*—They neither possess nor acquire ownership of goods but only serve to bring the buyers and sellers together. A broker is entitled to a certain percentage of commission on the business transacted by him on behalf of his principal client; (*b*) *Commission agents*—They are expected not only to negotiate the sale of goods but also to perform the functions of warehousing, grading, packing/sampling in addition to assembling and dispersion. For this purpose, they get some percentage of commission on sales. In case the commission agent is authorized to sell on credit and agrees to bear the risk of bad debts for some additional commission, he is known as a *del credere* agent.

Merchant Middlemen

In this category, merchant middlemen obtain title of the goods with a view to selling them at a profit. More important of them are wholesalers and retailers: (*a*) *Wholesalers*—A wholesaler performs the following important functions of marketing: (*i*) Assembling, (*ii*) Dispersion, (*iii*) Financing, (*iv*) Risk-assuming, (*v*) Warehousing, (*vi*) Transportation, and (*vii*) Grading and packaging; (*b*) *Retailers*— Some of the functions of retailers are: (*i*) Estimation of probable demand of consumers, (*ii*) Assembling of various types of goods from different wholesalers, (*iii*) Warehousing of goods to maintain a regular supply of goods to consumers, (*iv*) Standardization, grading and packing of goods in consumer packs, if necessary, (*v*) Assumption of risk of loss of goods by fire, theft, deterioration, etc., (*vi*) Extension of credit to some regular customers, and (*vii*) Feedback about consumer tastes and preferences to wholesalers/manufacturers. Retailers range from hawkers and peddlers to owners of big departmental stores, co-operative stores, multiple shops or chain stores.

To select an appropriate distribution channel, it is required to ensure (*a*) maximum geographical coverage of the market, (*b*) maximum promotional efforts, and (*c*) minimum cost. For this, the following factors are important: (*i*) Type of product, (*ii*) Nature and extent of the market, (*iii*) Existing channels for comparable products, (*iv*) Buying habits of consumers, and (*v*) Cost involved in distribution. The manufacturer should also consider the specific advantages of each type of intermediary before making the decision. In order to ensure a quick, smooth and optimal route for physical movement of goods, the manufacturer has also to decide the location of manufacturing facilities, warehouses, and the type of transportation to be used. Appropriate inventory management to ensure uninterrupted supply of goods is a prerequisite.

11.6.3 Managing Salespersons

The success of a distribution strategy is primarily governed by the involvement and motivation of the sales staff. For this purpose, the organization has to recruit the right persons, train them adequately and assign them to various jobs.

Apart from this, control and review of performance is also important. In essence, an organization is required to manage the following selling process (Fig. 11.9) through its sales personnel.

In Fig. 11.9, *prospecting* is the stage where the salesman collects information about prospective customers; *pre-approach,* the stage just before the salesman actually approaches the customer; *approach,* the stage when the salesman actually communicates with the prospective customers with a view to selling the product; *presentation & demonstration,* the stage where the salesman tries to effect a sale by actually displaying the product and demonstrating it in use; *meeting of objectives,* the stage for defining and stimulating sales effort and setting a quota or sales target; and the *close,* the stage where the salesman answers objections and closes the sale.

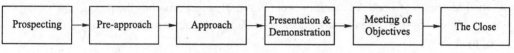

Fig. 11.9 Selling process

It is, therefore, evident that any successful marketing programme requires an effective human delivery system, which can be achieved by a selected, trained, motivated and controlled sales organization.

11.6.4 Marketing and Public Policy Framework

The numerous governmental controls on consumer as well as industrial goods affect marketing decision-making. These controls contribute to an overall public policy framework. In the form of various acts and statutes, these controls pose a major challenge to the marketing manager. The main reasons for government controls are as follows:

1. Protecting the welfare of individuals and promoting higher standards of public health, safety and general well being.
2. Restraining business from engaging in practices harmful to the interests of the public, like making false and misleading statements about a product/service, manipulating prices for personal gains, failing to support warranties, etc.
3. Protecting small firms from the dangers of unfair competition by big firms.
4. Maintaining equality of opportunity for all persons irrespective of sex, nationality, caste or religion.
5. Preventing unfair practices resulting from mergers or other forms of combinations such as price fixing.
6. Conserving national resources especially forests, water, energy, fuels, and preventing concentration of economic power and industrial wealth.
7. Preventing pollution of the environment.
8. Encouraging widely dispersed industrial growth and growth of small scale and cottage industries.
9. Protecting the economy from dominance by foreign investors and helping save the valuable foreign exchange resources.

According to Articles 39 (b) and (c) of the Constitution of India, control is a means of achieving a socialist pattern of society. These articles are meant to ensure that 'the operation of the economic system does not result in the concentration of wealth, and means of production, to the common detriment' and that the ownership and control of the material resources of the community are so distributed as to best subserve the common good. These two articles spell out the main control laws affecting marketing. It is necessary for the marketer to know these laws and to keep track of the evolving interpretations by law courts. Important laws affecting marketing are as follows:

1. The Indian Contract Act (1872). This Act regulates the economic and commercial relations of citizens.
2. The Indian Sale of Goods Act (1930). This Act governs the transactions of sale and purchase.
3. The Industries (Development and Regulation) Act (1951). By this Act, the industrial licensing system operates.
4. The Prevention of Food Adulteration Act (1954). This Act prohibits the production, storage, distribution and sale of adulterated and misbranded food articles to ensure purity in the articles of food.
5. The Drugs and Magic Remedies (Objectionable Advertisements) Act (1954). This Act prohibits the publication or issue of advertisements rendering to cause the ignorant consumer to resort to self-medication with harmful drugs and appliances.
6. The Essential Commodities Act (1955). This Act under Section 2 (a) regulates the control of production, supply and distribution of certain commodities declared as essential in the public interest. Under Section 3 (a) of this Act, the government can fix the price of such commodities.

7. The Companies Act (1956). This Act regulates the growing uses of the company system as an instrument of business and finance and eliminates possibilities of abuse inherent in that system.

8. The Trade and Merchandise Marks Act (1958). This Act deals with the registration of trade and merchandise marks. A mark includes a device, brand, heading, label, ticket, name, signature, word, letter or numeral or any combination thereof. A trademark is registered for a maximum period of *seven* years and is renewable further for the same number of years.

9. The Monopolies and Restrictive Trade Practices (MRTP) Act (1969). This Act controls the operation of the economic system such that it does not result in the concentration of economic power to the common detriment; provides measures for control of monopolies, prohibition of monopolistic, restrictive and unfair trade practices and of matters connected therewith or incidental thereto.

10. The Patents Act (1970). This Act is meant for the companies who intend to produce patented products. The patent is a grant made by the Central Government to the first inventor or his legal representative.

11. The Standards of Weights and Measures Act (1976). This Act specifies the units and quantities thereof in which certain products can be packed, e.g. tea, coffee, bread, butter, ice-cream, milk powder, spices, cleaning and sanitary fluids, etc.

12. Consumer Protection Act (1986). This Act provides better protection of the interests of consumers and makes provision for the establishment of consumer councils and other authorities for the settlement of consumer disputes and of matters connected therewith. It does not exclude or exempt, from the purview of the regulatory measures, the public enterprises, financial institutions, and co-operative societies, which previously enjoyed a privileged position under the MRTP Act of being immune from any action even against those marketing practices of theirs which were considered against consumer or public interest. With the enforcement of this Act, the consumer can get the redressal of his grievances even against the public organizations like Municipal Corporations, Indian Railways, State Transport Corporations, etc.

13. The Environment (Protection) Act (1986). This Act provides for the protection and improvement of environment and prevention of hazards to human beings, living creatures, plants and property.

14. The Bureau of Indian Standards Act (1986). This Act provides for the establishment of a Bureau for harmonious development of activities of standardization, marking and quality certification of goods and for matters connected therewith or incidental thereto. It has also been stipulated that access to the Bureau's standards and certification marks will be provided to suppliers of like products originating in General Agreement on Trade and Tariff (GATT) code countries.

In order to enforce the above mentioned laws, the Government has established a number of regulatory agencies such as Bureau of Industrial Costs and Prices (1971) to conduct enquiries about industrial products and recommend prices; the Agricultural Prices Commission (1965) to advise the Government on pricing policies for agricultural commodities. In addition to this, the Government has also framed rules such as Prevention of Food Adulteration Rules (1955) and the Standards of Weights and Measures (Packaged Commodities) Rules (1977) to enforce the provision of the related Acts.

All these Acts affect decision-making in relation to different elements of the marketing mix. The marketer must ensure that his decision in all these fields conforms to the relevant provisions of various Acts.

Self-assessment Questions Set-V

1. What is a 'Sales Forecast'? Why is it important?

2. Classify the various forecasting methods and discuss one of them in detail.

3. Under what conditions is executive judgement method useful for sales forecasting? Discuss its merits and demerits.

4. What kind of distribution channel (direct or indirect) would you recommend for the following products and why?

    (*a*) Personal Computer,

    (*b*) A lubricant for industrial use,

    (*c*) Textile machinery, and

    (*d*) Push-button telephone.

5. A company selling agricultural products in the rural markets is contemplating a change from selling through its own sales force to a system of wholesalers and retailers. What kind of distribution channel would you recommend?

6. Discuss some salient points of direct selling and indirect selling through wholesalers and retailers.

7. Outline some important factors for selecting an appropriate distribution channel. Discuss one of them in detail.

8. Explain the selling process which an organization generally follows through its sales personnel for a successful marketing programme.

9. 'It is alleged that Government control in the form of industrial licensing, MRTP Act, administered prices, etc. has affected the marketing efficiency of companies in India.' Do you agree? Discuss.

10. The Consumer Protection Act (1986) provides (*a*) an effective machinery for speedy and inexpensive redressal of consumer grievances, (*b*) a new hope to the consumer, (*c*) a new challenge to the marketing manager. Examine the above statement critically.

11. Outline the salient features of important laws affecting marketing in India.

Project Management

12.1 Introduction

Projects are the backbone of any economy. The range of activities is so wide that it almost encompasses all economic activities. These days project management is fast emerging as a new profession. Project managers are required in a construction project, R&D project, urban/rural development project, setting up a new factory for manufacture of some goods, etc. It is at times difficult to find such personnel in adequate number. Since projects need resources, there comes the need for optimum utilisation of resources. A project manager is responsible for the execution of a project or a part of it and is permitted to evolve his/her own approach for the assigned task.

The concept of project management underlines a set of principles, methods and techniques that assists in the effective planning and completion of tasks under all constraints. The necessity for project management has been felt to offset certain shortcomings of the traditional functional management which are seen in lead system development and relatively ineffective cost and schedule performances.

A first-hand understanding of the activities required to accomplish project's objective(s) is the key criterion while selecting an organizational model. There arc *three* basic organizational alternatives that can be adopted in the field of project management:

1. *Pure Project Organization*, where the project participants work directly for the project manager and the latter runs the project as if it were a one-product business enterprise.

2. *Pure Functional Organization*, where a diversely specialized manpower is grouped together to achieve projects of different nature.

3. *Matrix Organization*, composed of both project and functional human force and usually integrated to tackle large and diversified projects. This pattern of structure is distinctively project-completion oriented, and adapts itself to four different modes in accordance with varying degrees of authority and responsibility taken up by the project manager:

    (*a*) Project manager(s) reports directly to the president or general manager on a functional basis;

    (*b*) Project manager(s) reports to a manager or project management who in turn reports to the president or general manager on a functional basis;

    (*c*) The project manager is linked up to another functional department, but reports to the president or general manager on a functional basis; and

    (*d*) The project manager performs staff functions by directly advising the president or general manager.

Among the several tasks undertaken by project managers, it can certainly be stated that the functions of planning and implementing the plans are the most important.

Within the project environment, plans need to be accommodated to suit different types of projects. These projects require a diversity of resources and operate under constraints of time, cost, and possibility of small error.

12.2   Concept of a Project

There are various types of projects like steel project, power project, fertilizer project, cement project, refinery project, etc. In all these, the word 'project' is common though the plants are different. When a plant starts its operation, 'project' is said to have been completed. Thus, a 'project' may be defined as the set of 'activities' undertaken from its start to completion. The Project Management Institute (USA) defined a 'project' as, "A project is a one-shot, time-limited, goal directed, major undertaking, requiring the commitment of varied skills and resources." It also describes a project as, "a combination of human and non-human resources pooled together in a temporary organization to achieve a specific purpose." The objective (or goal or mission) and set of activities (human and non-human resources) distinguish one project from another.

After enumerating the objective(s) to be achieved through a project, it is also necessary to know how it is conceived. An industry or a business and/or service organization, whether in public or in private sector, must grow for the sake of its survival. Thus, the organization always looks forward to good business ideas in terms of:

- (*a*) Modernization of the plant equipment overcoming for obsolescence and/or by reallocation/ renovation of factory, office, etc.;
- (*b*) Enhancement of the existing capacity to produce and sell existing product;
- (*c*) Changing the existing products and adding new products to the product line; and
- (*d*) Planning obligatory and welfare projects, such as canteen, indoor games, common rooms in the factory premises, air pollution control, etc.

However, such ideas must be technically feasible, economically viable, politically suitable and socially acceptable. Once all these parameters are taken care of, an investment proposal is made. After the investment proposal is approved, the work on the project starts. A project is said to be completed once the stated objectives are achieved. The time span between start and completion of a project is known as *project life cycle*.

12.2.1   Categories of Projects

The management of any project depends on the category it belongs to. The location, technology, size, scope and speed are some of the factors which are responsible for determining the effort needed in executing a project. Industrial projects can be classified based on certain characteristics as shown in Fig. 12.1. The characteristics of two projects belonging to a particular category may be the same but they may not be treated at par. For example, a low-value R&D project may belong to a mini category but it may not get the same attention as a low-technology mini plant.

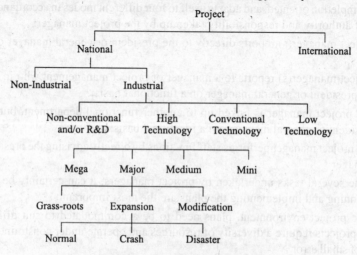

Fig. 12.1   Categories of projects

Major industrial projects are classified as shown below in terms of the speed needed for their execution:

1. **Normal projects:** All the phases in the projects of this category are permitted to take adequate time which is normally required for their execution. For such projects the capital cost required is always minimum, but there is no room for sacrifice in terms of quality.

2. **Crash projects:** In order to gain or save time in such projects, additional capital cost is incurred. Maximum overlapping of phases is encouraged and a sub-standard quality work is also not ruled out.

3. **Disaster projects:** In this category of projects, capital cost goes very high in order to drastically reduce the time. Some reasons for such a high cost are: No competitive bidding is resorted to; vendors who can supply items in shortest possible time, irrespective of the cost, are selected.

12.3 Project Management Concepts

In order to ensure the success of a project, a special approach is required. This approach may be termed as *project management*. The success of a project means that (*i*) it must get completed, (*ii*) it must be completed within *budget*, (*iii*) it must get completed within the *specified time*, and (*iv*) it must perform to satisfaction. Since the success of a project can only be achieved through the people involved with it, all principles of general management must also be applicable here. However, project management is different from areas of functional management—production, finance, marketing and personnel—in its approach to the *task* which is fully restricted by *time*, *cost* and *performance* targets and in its other internal specifications.

The project management approach consists of the following *five* steps:

1. Dividing the entire project into a group of tasks or activities to be performed. All these tasks are interdependent and interrelated with each other and contribute to the common objective. All these activities can be programmed within definite time, cost and with specified performance targets.

2. Assigning the responsibility of completing the entire project to a single person known as the *project manager*. This person coordinates, directs and controls the project.

3. Supporting and servicing the project internally within the organization by matrixing and coordinating with internal departments for preparation of drawings, specifications, maintenance and procurement of materials, and with external vendors and contractors for supply of materials and erection skills.

4. Building commitments by negotiating, coordinating and directing using schedules, budgets and contracts.

5. Ensuring adherence to objectives through regular monitoring and control using schedules, budgets and contracts as the guidelines.

12.3.1 Tools and Techniques for Project Management

Techniques used for effective project management can be grouped under the following heads:

1. Project selection techniques:
    (*a*) Cost-benefit analysis, and
    (*b*) Risk and sensitivity analysis.

2. Project execution planning techniques:
    (*a*) Work breakdown structure (WBS),
    (*b*) Project execution plan (PEP),
    (*c*) Project responsibility matrix, and
    (*d*) Project management manual.

3. Project scheduling and coordinating techniques:
   (*a*) Bar charts,
   (*b*) Life-cycle curves,
   (*c*) Line of balance (LOB), and
   (*d*) Network techniques (PERT/CPM/GERT).
4. Project monitoring and progressing techniques:
   (*a*) Progress measurement technique (PROMPT),
   (*b*) Performance monitoring technique (PERMIT), and
   (*c*) Updating, reviewing and reporting technique (URT).
5. Project cost and productivity control techniques:
   (*a*) Productivity budgeting technique,
   (*b*) Value engineering (VE), and
   (*c*) COST/WBS.
6. Project communication and clean-up techniques:
   (*a*) Control room, and
   (*b*) Computerized information systems.

12.4   Project Formulation

A project is considered to have been formulated, provided the following conditions are complied with:
1. The technical configuration of the project has been defined.
2. The performance requirement of each technical system, sub-system and vital equipment has been specified.
3. The cost estimate of the project has been completed.
4. Techno-economic viability of the project has been checked, appraised and approved.
5. The complete schedule for implementation of the project has been drawn up.
6. Financial arrangements have been made to implement the project.
7. An executive (called *project manager*) has been appointed to control and monitor the implementation of the project.
8. All prerequisite tasks (or activities) have been completed and a date (also called *zero-date*) has been fixed to implement the project.

The conditions from (1) to (5) are covered under what is known as the *feasibility analysis*. The concept of feasibility analysis is shown in Fig. 12.2.

The input to project preparation system consists of stimuli-ideas of all types. These come from within and outside the firm. These can be random or encouraged by management through suggestion schemes, brainstorming sessions, value analysis, lateral thinking and other similar techniques. The climate of the firm and its organization behaviour govern the success of such intentions.

Essentially, feasibility analysis is the first scrutiny of an incipient proposition. It endeavours to establish: (*i*) Merits of the proposition in terms of chosen criteria; (*ii*) Cost expected to be incurred; (*iii*) Company resources required; and (*iv*) Likely risks involved. The marshalling and tentative evaluation of all relevant data provides the setting for the feasibility decision. The decision often combines economic and technical appraisal.

12.4.1   Feasibility Report

The feasibility report is prepared as per the guidelines given in the Planning Commission's Memorandum *Feasibility Studies for Public Sector Projects*. The main points covered in a feasibility report include:

1. **Raw material survey:** Raw material may be available either in the form of (*i*) natural deposit, or (*ii*) semi-finished, finished or by-product from some existing operating plant(s).

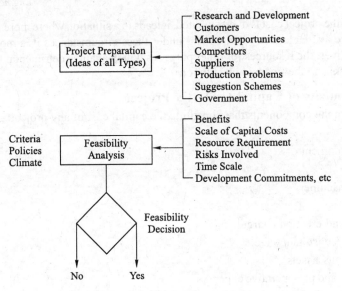

Fig. 12.2   Concept of feasibility Analysis

2. **Demand study:** A demand study establishes the following: (*i*) Pattern and location of demand of the product proposed to be manufactured; (*ii*) Level of production, capacity utilization, expert potential, etc. (*iii*) Pattern and mode of transportation, sales promotion, cost of transportation; (*iv*) Price and price elasticity of product; and (*v*) Supply and competition; Govt. policy.

3. **Technical features study:** It establishes the following: (*i*) Material and inputs; (*ii*) Production technology and process selection; (*iii*) Product mix/pattern; (*iv*) Plant capacity; (*v*) Location and site; (*vi*) Machinery and equipment; (*vii*) Structure and civil works, (*viii*) Project charts and layouts; and (*ix*) Work schedule.

4. **Location study:** Following factors are considered for location study: (*i*) Availability of land, soil characteristics and cost of the land; (*ii*) Source of raw materials; (*iii*) Transport, water supply, power facilities, etc.; (*iv*) Market of the finished product; (*v*) Social amenities in the area and acceptance of the project in that area; (*vi*) Tax incentives, if any, in a particular area; (*vii*) Adequate facilities for drainage and disposal; and (*viii*) Availability of skilled manpower.

5. **Investment study:** This includes (*a*) *Capital costs*, i.e., (*i*) assets such as land, plant, machinery, buildings and civil works, etc., (*ii*) design engineering, technical know-how fee; (*iii*) licensor's fee; (*iv*) miscellaneous fixed assets; (*v*) pre-operative expenses; and (*vi*) margin money for working capital, etc; (*b*) *Operation and production cost*, i.e., working capital and operating cost.

6. **Profitability and cash-flow analysis:** The profitability projections are essential to judge the financial desirability of a project. The profitability analysis may focus on *cost of production, working results* and *break-even level.*

12.5 Project Cost Estimation

Correct estimation of the capital cost of a project is the foundation over which the edifice of financial appraisal stands. Resources for the project are tied up after the project cost is estimated. If the project cost is under-estimated, the project will run short of funds during implementation and there is risk of the project coming to a halt if the promoter is not able to bring in additional capital to meet the increase in project cost or if the bank/financial institution that has extended financial assistance for the building up of fixed assets of the project does not come forward to extend additional loan to meet the increase in project cost. This emphasizes the need for a correct estimate of the project cost. On the other hand, if the project cost is overestimated, it leads to a situation where more funds (equity and debt together) are available than required and under these circumstances it is more likely that the promoters may divert the resources for other purposes which again is detrimental to the interests of both the promoters and the financing institutions.

12.5.1 Components of Capital Cost of a Project

The following are the components that constitute the capital cost of any project:

- Land
- Land development
- Buildings
- Plant and machinery
- Electricals
- Transport and erection charges
- Know-how/consultancy fee
- Miscellaneous assets
- Preliminary and pre-operative expenses
- Margin money for working capital

The method of arriving at the margin money for working capital is

Margin money for working capital

$$= \text{Working capital requirement} - \text{Probable working capital loan that can be obtained from bank}$$

The working capital requirement includes raw material, work-in-progress, finished goods, and debtors.

Table 12.1 lists three terms of finance, their sources and the kind of expenditure to be financed.

Table 12.1   Sources of Financing

Terms of Finance	Source	Expenditure to be Financed
Short-term finance	• Trade credit	
	• Loan from commercial banks	Working capital
	• Commercial paper (*Hundi*)	
	• Accounts receivable financing	
Intermediate-term finance	• Hire purchase	
	• Lease financing	Capital cost
	• Fixed deposits from public; Capital subsidiary by Central Govt.	
Long-term finance	• Common stock	
	• Debt	Capital cost
	• Preferred stock	

It is essential to know the approach generally followed by banks for arriving at the component of working capital finance for a given project.

Tandon Committee, appointed by Reserve Bank of India in 1974, under the Chairmanship of P.L. Tandon, accepted its recommendations for bank credit to industries. Major areas of recommendation covered are:

(*a*) Stipulation of norms for holding of inventory and for receivables;

(*b*) Style of bank credit towards working capital; and

(*c*) Maximum possible bank finance towards working capital.

Due to Govt.'s policy on economic liberalization, the RBI in 1997 had given optional freedom to decide upon the quantum of working capital finance based on their assessment of the borrowers and their credit requirements.

The project cost is arrived at by adding the estimated cost of the individual components. It is always worthwhile to have the project cost cross-checked with industry standards. This will help in identifying major deviations, if any. For example, the cost of setting up a cotton yarn-spinning mill can be arrived at in terms of cost per spindle. The cost per spindle serves as a reference since this can be compared with other similar projects.

Example 12.1. Premier Industries (P) Ltd. has proposed to set up a plant for the manufacture of plastic moulded chairs. The following are the details of the proposed project:

(a) The firm has entered into an agreement for the purchase of 2 acres of land for the project at the rate of Rs 2 lakh per acre;

(b) The company has proposed to import the plastic injection moulding machine (which is the main machine used for the manufacture of moulded chairs), and the c.i.f. value of the machine is Rs 80 lakh. Import duty on c.i.f. value is 30%. The injection moulding machine is capable of producing moulded chairs at the rate of one chair per minute. Though the machine can be used for the manufacture of chairs of different sizes, the company has proposed to concentrate only on the manufacture of chairs of normal size, which has got good market. The average weight of normal sized chair is 2.50 kg;

(c) The company proposes to acquire the following machinery indigenously:

  (i) Scrap grinder (at a price of Rs 5.00 lakh);

  (ii) Mixing machine (at a price of Rs 4.00 lakh);

  (iii) Power generator (at a price of Rs 35.00 lakh).

(d) The cost of electric motors, starters, switches, cables and other electrical items is Rs 7.00 lakh.

(e) The cost of dies required for the plant is estimated at Rs 30.00 lakh.

(f) The company has proposed to construct the following buildings:

  (i) Main factory building with Asbestos Corrugated Cement Sheet (A.C.C.) roofing over steel trusses—with a built-up area of about 375 square metres,

  (ii) Store room (for the storage of raw material and for the storage of finished products), with A.C.C. roofing over steel trusses—with a built-up area of about 95 square metres;

  (iii) Office and administrative blocks with Reinforced Cement Concrete (R.C.C.) roofing—with a built up area of about 70 square metres;

  (iv) Other amenities like toilet block, compound wall, gate, underground water tank to suit the requirements.

(g) The raw material required for the project is polypropylene granules, which is costing around Rs 60/- per kg. The wastage of raw material during the manufacturing process is estimated at about 3%.

(h) The total power requirement (connected load) is estimated at 200 H.P.

(i) The selling price of moulded chair is around Rs 350/- per chair in the retail market. The company has tied up a selling price of Rs 280/- per chair with a network of dealers across the country.

Estimate the cost of the project. Make suitable assumptions wherever necessary.

Solution. For arriving at the project cost, each component of the project cost is to be taken up separately and assessed.

(a) **Land**

Extent of land proposed	:	2.00 acre
Cost of land (at the agreed price of Rs 2.00 lakh per acre)	:	Rs 4.00 lakh
Add: Registration charges at 13% of the consideration (13% of Rs 4.00 lakh)	:	Rs 0.52 lakh
		Rs 4.52 lakh

(b) **Land development charges:** It has not been indicated that the land needs any developmental work. Hence, no provision is made.

(c) **Building**

(i) *Main factory building:*

Built up area : 375 sq. m.

Cost of construction at the rate of Rs 3,750/- per sq.m. *(estimated cost per sq.m. of construction is to be arrived at based on either detailed estimate or by making an assessment of the prevailing construction cost of similar constructions).*

= 375 × 3,750 : Rs 14,06,250/-

say   Rs 14.06 lakh   (A)

(ii) *Store room:*

Built-up area : 95 sq. m.

Cost of construction at the rate of Rs 3,750/- per sq. m.

= 95 × 3,750 : Rs 3,56,250/-

say   Rs 3.56 lakh   (B)

(iii) *Office and administrative blocks:*

Built-up area : 70 sq. m.

Cost of construction at the rate of Rs 5,300/- per sq. m.

= 70 × 5,300 : Rs 3,17,000/-

say   Rs 3.17 lakh   (C)

(iv) *Other amenities:*

Toilet block (lumpsum)	Rs 1.50 lakh
Compound wall (lumpsum)	Rs 3.00 lakh
Gate (lumpsum)	Rs 0.50 lakh
Underground water tank (lumpsum)	Rs 1.25 lakh
	Rs 6.25 lakh (D)

[**Note:** The cost of construction of amenities can be obtained by getting detailed estimates from a qualified civil engineer. Under this head, the actual requirement of amenities should be studied carefully, because this is an area where there is likelihood of underestimation due to not envisaging all the amenities required for the project. For example, if water is required for the manufacturing process and if water supply is to be made available at different points in the production line, this will necessitate construction of an overhead water tank. The capacity of overhead water tank is to be ascertained based on the storage capacity required.

Other amenities that may be required include loading/unloading platforms, canteen, restroom for workers, power distribution room, etc. The actual requirement is to be arrived at after giving a thought over the needs of the project.

Total investment required for building (A + B + C + D): Rs 27.58 lakh

(*d*) **Plant and machinery**

    (*i*) *Imported machinery*

c.i.f. value	:	Rs	80.00 lakh
Customs duty at 30%	:	Rs	24.00 lakh
*Clearing charges		Rs	0.50 lakh
		Rs	104.50 lakh

    (*Clearing charges are the charges payable to the clearing agents for their services rendered in clearing the goods from the port and this may be in the range of ½% to 1%).

    (*ii*) *Indigenous machinery*

Scrap grinder	:	Rs	5.00 lakh
Mixing machine	:	Rs	4.00 lakh
Power generator	:	Rs	35.00 lakh
Dies*	:	Rs	30.00 lakh
		Rs	74.00 lakh

    Total investment on plant and machinery

    (Rs 104.50 lakh + Rs 74.00 lakh)   :   Rs 178.50 lakh

[*The project is for the manufacture of plastic moulded chairs of normal size. Such projects require dies of different designs to suit the taste of the customers. How much is to be invested for dies is a crucial decision. If the plant has, say, 100 dies of different designs, it means that the plant can produce chairs of 100 different models, which means that the company will have an edge over its competitors in view of the product variety that it can offer. However, if the investment on dies becomes exhorbitant, it would even affect the viability of the project proposition. Dies are in general costly items and hence a proper balance should be struck in arriving at the actual requirement. Too many dies means too much investment and most of the dies will remain idle since only one die will be used in the machine at a time. On the other hand, if only a very few dies chosen, the product may lack variety and the product may find it difficult to penetrate through the market.

In the given problem, no mention has been made about the number of dies proposed, but only the total investment proposed for dies has been given as Rs 30.00 lakh. Let us presume that the optimum requirement of dies has been correctly assessed and provided for).

(*e*) **Transport and erection charges:** Expenditure under this head is to be estimated by studying to real situation. The main machine is proposed to be imported. Hence, this machine is to be carried to the factory site from the nearest port.

Indigenous machines are to be lifted from the supplier's site to the factory site. The transportation expense depends on the weight and volume of the machinery and the distance to be covered. Apart from transportation charges, loading and unloading expenses are also to be accounted for under this head. Freight carriers will be in a position to indicate the approximate amount that may be required for transporting the machinery to the factory site.

Erection charges depend upon the nature of the machine. Heavy machines and machines that generate strong vibrations need special machine foundations. The opinion of structural engineers may be used in arriving at the likely erection charges. The machinery suppliers themselves will be in a position to indicate this amount, since they are the people who know the ground realities in view of their constant exposure to such situations.

Let us assume that the transport and erection charges has been arrived at Rs 8.00 lakh after giving due consideration to the factors explained above.

(*f*) **Electrical:**

Electric motors, starters, switches, cables
and other electrical items   :   Rs 7.00 lakh

Note: In respect of projects that use high tension electric power, the State Electricity Board authorities insist that the consumers have to instal their own 'Step-down electric transformer' which is meant for reducing the high voltage of the incoming electric current to a low voltage meant for actual consumption. There may be also instances where the promoters have to meet expenses for bringing electric power line from nearby locations (like cost of cables, cost of poles, etc). These aspects are to be carefully studied.

(*g*) **Contingency:** Contingency provision is made to take care of probable increase in cost due to new additions and/or due to escalation in prices. The provision allowed ranges from 5% to 15% and it is allowed on the following heads:

- Land
- Land development expenses
- Building
- Plant and machinery
- Transport and erection
- Electricals
- Technical know-how fee
- Miscellaneous assets.

For other heads in the project cost, contingency provision is not normally made. The above elements of the project cost can be grouped under two categories *viz.*, firm items and non-firm items. Firm items are those elements whose cost are more or less fixed and are not likely to increase and hence do not require any contingency provision. Other elements whose cost are likely to fluctuate and hence require contingency provision are called non-firm items. For example, if an agreement has already been entered into for the purchase of the required extent of land at a certain price, within a certain period, the investment required to be made towards the purchase of land is tied up, provided purchase of land is not delayed beyond the agreed date. This cost of land is a firm cost and hence does not need any provision of contingency.

Among other items, it is the normal practice to provide a contingency provision of about 5% on the cost of building and about 10% on the cost of plant and machinery and electricals. However, this is not a hard and fast rule and the judgement of the appraiser plays an important role in arriving at the appropriate contingency provision. If the project involves imported machinery, there is a higher element of cost fluctuation in view of likely fluctuations in foreign exchange rate, and likely change in import duty, apart from increase in machinery price.

In the given problem, the company has already entered into an agreement for the purchase of land. Hence, it can be assumed that the land cost is tied up, i.e., it is not likely to increase.

One can provide 5% contingency on building and, say, 10% on plant and machinery (indigenous), electricals, transport and erection and, say, 15% on plant and machinery (imported). It is assumed that the cost of miscellaneous assets is firmed up and does not require any contingency pro-vision.

Thus, the required contingency is

$$5\% (27.58) + 10\% (74.00 + 7.00 + 8.00) + 15\% (104.50)$$
$$= \text{Rs } 1.374 + 8.900 + 15.675$$

$$= Rs\ 25.954$$

$$\simeq Rs\ 26.00\ lakh$$

(*h*) **Miscellaneous fixed assets:** The given data does not contain any information on the investment towards this head. The following assumptions are made:

Miscellaneous assets	Price
Office furnitures	Rs 1.25 lakh
Office equipment	Rs 1.40 lakh
Deposit to electricity board	Rs 0.75 lakh
	Rs 3.40 lakh

(*i*) **Preliminary and pre-operative expenses:** The following assumptions are made:

(*i*) Service charge on term loan : 0.75%

(*ii*) Commitment charges on term loan : 1.00%

(*iii*) Rate of interest on term loan : 15% per annum

(*iv*) Project implementation period : 11 months

(*v*) Insurance premium on fixed assets : 0.75% per annum

(*ii*) **Insurance premium on fixed assets: 0.75% per annum**

The outlay required to meet items (*i*), (*ii*), and (*iii*) depends upon the term loan amount. We have not yet arrived at the term loan component. The value of fixed assets assessed so far is given below:

	Rs (in lakh)
Land	4.52
Land development	—
Building	27.58
Plant and machinery	
(*a*) Imported	104.50
(*b*) Indigenous	74.00
Transport and erection	8.00
Electricals	7.00
Contingency	26.00
	Rs 251.60

The term loan component is not known at present.

The following is assumed:

Term loan component (at 80% of fixed assets), i.e., 0.80×251.60

$$= Rs\ 201.28\ lakh$$

$$Say = Rs\ 200.00\ lakh*$$

Interest during implementation period (for a term loan of Rs 200.00 lakh)

$$\frac{15}{100} \times \frac{11}{12} \times 200 \times \frac{1}{2}** = Rs\ 13.75\ lakh$$

Commitment charges at 1.00%, of loan amount $= Rs\ 2.00\ lakh$

Service charge at 0.75% of loan amount	= Rs	1.50 lakh
	=	Rs 17.25 lakh
Insurance premium on fixed assets @ 0.75% per annum		
$[0.75/100 \times (27.58 + 178.50 + 7.00 + 8.00 + 26.00]$	= Rs	1.85 lakh**
Other startup expenses (say)	= Rs	0.90 lakh
	=	Rs 20.00 lakh

* The loan component assumed is only a rough estimate and if the loan component arrived at after tying up the means of finance differs from this assumed figure by a larger extent, the figures of preliminary expenses are to be reworked.

** It is assumed that the loan amount of Rs 200.00 lakh is drawn during the implementation period of 11 months at a uniform phase and hence the interest is arrived at by multiplying simple interest for 11 months by 1/2.

*** Transport and erection charges for machinery are also included for arriving at the insurance charges. The entire contingency provision of Rs 26.00 lakh is also included on the assumption that the entire contingency will be used.

(*i*) **Working capital margin:** Before arriving the working capital margin, which is the last component of the project cost, the working capital requirement for the first year of operation is required to be arrived at. From the working capital requirement, if the likely working capital loan component is deducted, the balance represents the working capital margin. For arriving at the working capital requirement/margin, usually, the data relevant to the first year of operation are taken into account. Let us assume the capacity utilisation as under.

Year	I	II	III	IV	V	VI
Capacity utilisation	50%	60%	70%	80%	80%	80%

The working capital requirement/margin is to be arrived at for the first year of operation *viz.*, for 50% capacity utilisation.

The format for arriving at the working capital margin/working capital finance is as under (for working capital limit about Rs 50.00 lakh).

Total current assets	– – –
Less: 25% of the total current assets	
(to be met out of long term sources)	– – –
	– – –
Less: Current liabilities other than bank borrowings	– – –
Maximum permissible bank finance	– – –

* Capacity utilisation in the initial years is less due to the following reasons:
- Workers need time to get trained in the machine.
- Some machines normally require to be operated at a slower speed than the designed speed for some time.
- The product is at the beginning stage and capturing market share will take some time.

Thus, as per the above method, the working capital margin is nothing but 25% of the total current assets. The different current assets/current liabilities and their period of requirement (assumed) are as under.

Current Assets:

Raw material and consumables	1 month
Goods in progress	2 days

Stock of finished goods	1 month
Debtors	2 months

Current Liabilities:

Supplier's credit for raw materials and consumables	1 month

Let us calculate the total current assets using the above data.

Raw material and consumables:

The raw material used for the production is 'polypropylene' and there are virtually no 'consumables' and hence 'consumables' is ignored.

Average weight of one chair	: 2.50 kg
Quantity of raw material required for one chair, taking into account wastage of 3%	: 2.50 × 1.03
	= 2.575 kg
Output per day (for 3 shifts)	= 1,440 chairs
Output per day for the first year of operation (at 50% capacity)	= 720 chairs
Output per month (assuming 25 working days per month) [720 × 25]	= 18,000 chairs
Raw material requirement for one month (18,000 × 2.575)	= 46,350 kg
Cost of stock of one month requirement of raw material at the rate of Rs 60/- per kg (46,350 × 60)	:
	= Rs 27,81,000/-
	i.e., Rs 27.81 lakh

Expenses

(*a*) **Direct expenses**

    (*i*) *Power:*

Power charge	: Rs 3.50 per unit (assumption)
Connected power	: 200 H.P.
	: 149.20 kW

(1 HP = 0.746 kW)

Power consumption per month at the rate of 24 hours of working per day and for 25 working days per month   = 149.20 × 24 × 25 = 89.520 units

[1 kilowatt-hour = 1 unit, i.e., if one kilowatt of power is used for a period of one hour, the power consumption is one unit].

Power consumption per month for the first year of operation at 50% capacity utilisation (0.50 × 89.520)   = 44,760 units

Power charges per month for the first year of operation at the rate of Rs 3.50 per unit (44,760 x 3.50)   = Rs 1.56,660/- ≃ Rs 1.57 lakh

     = Rs 1.57 lakh

    (*ii*) *Fuel:* Certain industries may need firewood, coal, furnace oil, etc., in their production process. In the given project, the production process requires only electric power and hence no provision is made under this head. Though power generator envisaged in the project will consume diesel which can be provided for under this head, since frequent electric power cut/shortage is not envisaged, provision for fuel is not made.

(*iii*) *Wages and salaries:* The following personnel and wages/salaries are assumed for the first year of operation:

Personnel	Salary per person per month Rs	Total salary per month, Rs
General Manager—1	20,000/-	20,000/-
Production incharge—6 (at the rate of 2 persons per shift)	15,000/-	90,000/-
Skilled technicians–12 (at the rate of 2 persons per shift)	9,500/-	1,14,000/-
Semi-skilled persons—15 (at the rate of 5 persons per shift)	5,000/-	75,000/-
Unskilled workers—18 (at the rate of 6 persons per shift)	4,000/-	72,000/-
Wages for persons who are not regularly employed (lumpsum)		10,000/-
		3,81,000/-
		= Rs 3.81 lakh

(*iv*) *Repairs and maintenance:* The following assumptions are made for the first year of operation:

(*a*) Repairs and maintenance charges for building for the first year of operation $\qquad$ = 0.5% of the cost

(*b*) Repairs and maintenance charges for plant and machinery for the first year of operation = 4% of the cost

Hence, repairs and maintenance charges per month for both building and plant & machinery

$$= 1/12 \left[0.5/100 \times 27.58) + (4/100 \times 178.50) \right]$$
$$= \text{Rs } 0.61 \text{ lakh}$$

(*v*) *Rent, Insurance:* 'Rent' does not apply since the project is not set up in leasehold premises. Insurance consists of insurance on fixed assets as well as insurance on inventories. [*Note:* Insurance premium on fixed assets was already included in the pre-operative expenses. This is the insurance premium paid on the fixed assets for the period of implementation.] Once the project implementation is over, both the fixed assets and the inventories need to be insured.

As far as insurance premium on fixed assets is concerned, only the premium for industrial assets are included under this head. Thus, the insurance premium payable on office/administrative buildings are excluded. [These are considered under the head administrative overheads]

Total estimated cost of building	: Rs 22.48 lakh
Less: Cost of office and administration block, and other amenities [3.71 + 6.25]	: Rs 9.96 lakh
Estimated cost of industrial building	: Rs 17.62 lakh

Out of the total contingency provision of Rs 26.00 lakh, the proportionate contingency for office and administrative buildings and other amenities is to be excluded.

Total contingency $\qquad$: Rs 26.00 lakh/annum

Less: Contingency on office and administrative
building and other amenities at 5% [5/100 × 9.96] : Rs   0.50 lakh/annum

Contingency allowed for industrial assets   : Rs 25.50 lakh/annum

Insurance premium on industrial assets at the rate of 0.75% [assumption]

$$= \left[\frac{0.75}{100} \times (17.62 + 104.50 + 74.00 + 8.00 + 7.00 + 25.50 \right]$$

= Rs 1.77 lakhs per annum

or   Rs 0.15 per month

(*vi*) *Factory supervision*

The following are assumed for the first year of operation:

Personnel	Salary per person per month, Rs	Total salary per month, Rs
Factory supervisors—3 (at the rate of one person per shift)	12,000/-	36,000/- ≃ Rs 0.36 lakh

Total direct expenses (1.57 + 0.00 + 3.81 + 0.61 + 0.15 + 0.36) = Rs 6.50 lakh

(*b*) **Overheads**

(*i*) *Administrative overheads*

The following are assumed:

Salary to administrative staff per month   : Rs 0.46 lakh

Director's fee, audit fee per month   : Rs 0.20 lakh

Insurance premium on office and administrative
buildings and miscellaneous office assets at the
rate of 0.75% p.a. on building and 1.00% p.a. on
miscellaneous office assets

(*a*) 0.75/100 × (9.96 + 0.50*) + 1/100 × (1.25 + 1.40)

= Rs 0.105 lakhs p.a.

i.e.,   Say : Rs 0.01 lakh per month

(*b*) Insurance premium for inventory Rs 0.03 lakh per month (assumption)

Rs 0.70 lakh per month

*Rs 0.50 lakh represents proportionate contingency for office and administrative buildings.

(*ii*) *Selling overheads*

The following assumptions are made:

Packing expenses	= 0.50% of sales turnover (assumption)
Selling and advertisement expenses	= 2.00% of sales turnover (assumption)
Total	= 2.50%

Sales turnover per month for the first
year of operation at 50% capacity and
for 25 working days in a month
(25 × 720 × 280)   : Rs 50,40,000/- ≃ Rs 50.40 lakh

Selling over heads per month at
2.50% of sales turnover   Rs 1.26 lakh

Total overheads per month = (0.70 + 1.26) = Rs 1.96 lakh

Goods in progress

$$\text{Cost of goods-in-progress for 2 days} = \text{Cost of raw materials for 2 days} + \text{Expenses for 2 days}$$
$$= 2/25\,(27.81) + 2/30\,(6.50 + 0.70)*$$
$$= 2.22 + 0.48$$
$$= \text{Rs } 2.70 \text{ lakh}$$

* Raw material requirement for 2 days is arrived at by considering the monthly requirement as the requirement for 25 working days. However, monthly expenses are considered to be the expenses for 30 days.

Stock of finished goods

Cost of stock of finished goods   = Cost of raw material + Expenses

Cost of stock of finished goods   = Cost of raw materials per month + Expenses per month
per month

$$= 27.81 + (6.50 + 1.96)$$
$$= 27.81 + 8.43$$
$$= \text{Rs } 36.24 \text{ lakh}$$

Debtors

(**Note:** Profit component is excluded for the computation of sales bills)

Sales bills per month   = Cost of war material per month + Expenses per month
$$= 27.81 + (6.50 + 1.96)$$
$$= 27.81 + 8.43$$
$$= \text{Rs } 36.24 \text{ lakh}$$

Sales bills for 2 months   = Rs 72.48 lakh

Total current assets

Raw material and consumables	1 month	Rs	27.81 lakh
Goods-in-progress	2 days	Rs	2.70 lakh
Stock of finished goods	1 month	Rs	36.24 lakh
Debtors	2 months	Rs	72.48 lakh
			Rs 139.23 lakh

Working capital margin at 25% of
total current assets (0.25×139.23) = Rs 34.81 lakh
$$\simeq \text{Rs } 35.00 \text{ lakh}$$

Note: Maximum permissible bank finance for working capital is not required for the computation of capital cost of the project. However, the same is worked out below to give an exposure.

Total current assets	Rs 139.23 lakh
Less: 25% of the total current assets	Rs 34.81 lakh
Less: Current liability other than bank borrowings (suppliers credit of one month for raw material is assumed)	Rs 27.81 lakh
Maximum permissible bank finance	Rs 76.61 lakh

Since all the components of project cost have been arrived at, it can be summarised as under:

Project Cost	*Rs, in lakhs*
(*a*) Land	4.52
(*b*) Land development	—

(c)	Building	27.58
(d)	Plant and machinery	
	(i) Imported	104.50
	(ii) Indigenous	74.00
(e)	Transport and erection	8.00
(f)	Electricals	7.00
(g)	Contingency	26.00
(h)	Miscellaneous assets	3.40
(i)	Preliminary and Pre-operative expenses	20.00
(j)	Working capital margin	35.00
		310.00

The method of arriving at the working capital margin, as explained above, is a fairly accurate method.

12.6 Project Financing

Project financing may be defined as the raising of funds required to finance economically separable capital investment proposal in which the lenders mainly rely on the estimated cash flow from the project to service their loans.

Project financing differs from conventional financing in the following aspects:

- In conventional financing, cash flow from different assets and businesses are co-mingled. A creditor makes an assessment of repayment of his loan by looking at all the cash flows and resources of the borrower. In project financing, cash flows from the project-related assets alone are considered for assessing the repaying capacity. Even if one has already established many projects, for financing a new project promoted by him, the cash flows from the proposed new project are alone taken into account for carrying out the viability study.

- In conventional financing, end use of the borrowed funds is not strictly monitored by the lenders. In project financing, the creditors ensure proper utilization of funds and creation of assets as envisaged in the project proposal. Funds are also released in stages as and when assets are created.

- In conventional financing, the creditors are not interested in monitoring the performance of the enterprise and they are interested only in their money getting repaid in one way or the other. Project financiers are keen to watch the performance of the enterprise and suggest/take remedial measures as and when required to ensure that the project repays the debt out of its cash generations. Project financiers at times appoint their nominee in the board of directors of their clients (companies that are financially assisted by them) in order to monitor the operating performance of the companies.

12.6.1 Sources of Finance

After the project cost is ascertained, the sources of finances available for meeting the project cost are to be analysed and a proper combination of different sources shall be chosen that is most suitable for the project.

The various sources of finance can be broadly divided into two categories, *viz.* equity capital and debt capital (borrowed capital). The combination of equity and debt should be judiciously chosen, and it will vary according to the nature of the project.

Debt capital enforces upon the organization an obligation for repayment of principal and payment of interest. Equity capital does not impose any such obligation. Equity capital serves as a cushion at times when the business conditions are unfavourable leading to operational difficulties.

Interest paid on the debt capital (term loan, debenture, etc.) is a deductible item of expenditure from the profit earned by the organization for arriving at the tax payable by the organization on its earnings. Though equity capital does not impose any obligation for repayment, principal and payment of interest like debt capital, equity capital has got a cost.

The contributors of equity capital anticipate a return on their investment by way of dividend. In view of the provision of Income Tax Act (Section 36 (I)-III) allowing interest paid on debt capital as a deductible item of expenditure from the profit earned by an organization, the actual cost of debt capital is the cost net of tax benefits, i.e., if the interest payable on debt capital is, say, 20% and if the organization is at a tax slab of 50%, the net cost of debt capital after accounting for tax benefits is only 10% [20% − 50% of 20]. The net cost of debt capital may at times be even lesser than the cost of equity capital. However, just because debt capital costs less, a project cannot be started totally with the aid of debt capital. Institutions that finance projects by term loan do not fund the entire cost of the project; they stipulate a certain minimum percentage of equity capital to be brought in for to financing the project. In the absence of equity capital, the financing institutions will not have any cushion in asset coverage for the loan that they may provide. A debt equity ratio, generally in the range of 2 : 1 to 3 : 1, is expected by the financial institutions depending upon the nature of the project.

The following are the main sources of project finance:
1. Ordinary shares.
2. Preference shares.
3. Debentures.
4. Bonds.
5. Term loans.
6. Deferred credits.
7. Capital investment subsidy.
8. Lease financing.
9. Unsecured loans.
10. Internal accruals.
11. Bridge loans.
12. Public deposits.

12.6.2 Role of Financial Institutions in Project Financing

Normally projects are financed by a combination of equity and debt. This is more so in respect of larger projects, for the reason that arranging for equity capital to fund the entire project may not be feasible. Often, equity finance is made use of during the initial stage of project implementation. This is because financial institutions insist the project promoters to mobilize equity capital before releasing their loan component. In India, all india financial institutions (like IDBI, ICICI, IFCI, SIDBI, IRBI). State financial corporations and banks undertake project financing. Non-banking financing companies (NBFCs) also do project financing, but their share stands very low.

All India financial institutions and state financial corporations come under the category of development finance institutions (sometimes called *Development Bankers*) as against banks which come under the category of commercial financiers. Banks are the custodian of public funds and thus they occupy the position of trustee. Hence, it is their bounden duty that they lend money only after careful analysis and after getting it ensured that their money lend in safe hands. Development finance institutions were set up with the objective of promoting industrial development. They played a significant role in helping new and first generation entrepreneurs in setting up industrial ventures. Of late, the role of development finance institutions is undergoing a change and they are expected to function on commercial lines.

Whatever may be the approach to lending, the lending decision is primarily governed by *three* considerations:

1. The capacity of the project to repay the loan along with interest obligations out of its own cash generations.
2. The value of security offered for the loan.
3. The integrity and willingness of the borrower to repay the loan in time.

The first and foremost criterion is that the project should be self-sustaining, i.e., it must be able to repay its obligations out of its own cash generations. If this criterion is fulfilled, many objectives for which the project is set up, like creation of wealth, utilization of resources, creation of employment opportunities, etc. are achieved.

12.6.3 Covenants Attached to Lending

The bank/financial institution that extends term loan for the setting up of a project imposes certain conditions to be fulfilled by the borrower and these conditions (covenants) are contained in the term loan sanction orders/mortgage deeds executed by the borrower in favour of the bank/financial institution.

The covenants depend on the nature of the project and the financial soundness of the borrower. Some of the typical conditions normally stipulated are as under:

- The project sponsor (or project promoter) shall offer colateral security as required by the financial institution.
- The project promoter should furnish periodic information about the project.
- The project sponsor should use the borrowed funds only for the project implementation and for the specific purposes intended.
- The project sponsor should maintain all the assets in good condition, should insure the assets against fire, burglary and natural calamities till such time all the dues to the bank/financial institution are paid back.
- The project sponsor should not dispose of any of the assets of the project without the prior approval of the bank/financial institution.
- The project sponsor should get the consent of the bank/financial institution before declaring dividends on equity shares.
- Unsecured loans raised, if any, for funding the project should not be repaid as long as the dues to the bank/financial institution remain unpaid.
- If interest is paid on unsecured loans, the rate of interest should not be in excess of the rate payable to the bank/financial institution.

12.7 Economic Evaluation Criteria of the Project

A project can become economically unviable if a deviation occurs in its zero date. This will change eventually the earlier cost estimate and overall implementation schedule of the project. Thus, in order to see that any project is economically viable, following information are required:

1. Estimates of the net capital outlay required for a project and the future cash flows promised for the project.
2. Estimates of availability and cost of capital to the company.
3. A correct set of standards by which to select projects for execution so that the long-term economic benefits to the promoters are maximized.

Given the necessary information, a method has to be found for evaluating the profitability of new investments. In selecting a suitable criterion, the following *two* fundamental principles should be kept in view:

1. **The bigger the better principle:** Other things being equal, bigger benefits are preferable than smaller ones.

2. The bird in hand principle: Other things being equal, early benefits are preferable than later benefits.

There are *four* basic methods to assess the economic viability of a project:
1. Non-discounted cash flow method:
   (a) Payback Period (PBP).
2. Discounted cash flow method:
   (a) Net Present Value (NPV),
   (b) Benefit-cost Ratio (BCR), and
   (c) Internal Rate of Return (IRR).

12.7.1 Payback Period (PBP)

Payback period is the time period required to recover the original cash investment through annual cash savings (inflows). If the annual cash savings from the project is equal to cash investment before depreciation but after tax deduction, then PBP is given by

$$\text{PBP} = \frac{\text{Original Cash Investment}}{\text{Annual Cash Savings}}$$

$$= \frac{\text{Original Cash Investment}}{\text{Gross savings (Direct expenses + Depreciation)} - \text{Depreciation} + \text{Interest}}$$

$$= \text{Number of years}$$

For example, if the annual cash inflow (savings) is Rs 5,000 from an investment proposal of Rs 20,000, then

$$\text{PBP} = \frac{20,000}{5,000} = 4 \text{ years}$$

If the annual cash inflow from the project is not equal to cash investment, then deduct the net cash flow each year from the original investment until the remaining original investment is less than one year's cash flow required to complete the repayment of the original investment.

Advantages

The PBP is used to rank investment alternatives. Projects having the shortest payback period are given the highest ranking or preferred the most.

The method is simple to understand and easy to calculate. It basically calculates the time period in which investment in the project is likely to be recovered. The method is also widely used for projects with high risk and uncertainty. The shorter the payback period, the faster the uncertainty associated with the project is resolved. It is also helpful in those type of projects which are subject to rapid technological changes (rapid technological obsolescence) because it reduces the possibility of loss through obsolescence.

Disadvantages

Investments, however, are not made just to recover the capital. The true worth of an investment is how much income it generates after the original investment has been paid back. Since PBP ignores inflow after payback period, it discriminates against projects which generate substantial cash inflow in later years. Further, it concentrates more on the recovery of capital, without paying attention to the ultimate profitability of the investment. Though it measures a project's liquidity, it does not indicate the liquidity of the company as a whole.

Example 12.2. An investment proposal requires an investment of Rs 50,000. The cash flow expected to be generated in different years is as follows:

Year	1	2	3	4	5
Cash flow	20,000	22,000	12,000	12,000	10,000

Should the proposal be accepted if the maximum acceptable payback period is 3 years?

Solution. If the cash flow for a year is expected to be generated uniformly throughout the period, then the payback of Rs 50,000 investment (20,000 + 22,000 + 8,000 out of 12,000) can be estimated as follows:

$$2 + \frac{8,000}{12,000} = 2.66 \text{ years } (< 3 \text{ years})$$

Since investment can be recovered in 2.66 years, which is less than 3 years, the proposal should be accepted.

Example 12.3. A company is trying to decide which of the two machines, A or B, to purchase. Each of these machines costs Rs 1,50,000. Earning after taxation is expected to be as follows:

Year	Cash Flow	
	Machine A, Rs	Machine B, Rs
1	35,000	15,000
2	45,000	35,000
3	55,000	45,000
4	35,000	65,000
5	25,000	45,000

Indicate which of the machines would be chosen on the basis of payback method of ranking investment proposals.

Solution. The calculation of payback period is shown as follows:

Year	Machine A			Machine B		
	Cash Flow, Rs		Payback	Cash Flow, Rs		Payback
	Actual	Needed	Years Required	Actual	Needed	Years Required
1	35,000	35,000	1	15,000	15,000	1
2	45,000	45,000	1	35,000	35,000	1
3	55,000	55,000	1	45,000	45,000	1
4	35,000	15,000	$\frac{15,000}{35,000} \times 12$ = 5 months approx.	65,000	55,000	$\frac{55,000}{65,000} \times 12$ = 10 months approx.
5	25,000	—	—	45,000	—	—
Total		1,50,000	3 years 5 months (approx.)		1,50,000	3 years 10 months (approx.)
Ranking			I			II

Since payback period for machine A is less than that of machine B, machine A should be chosen.

12.7.2 Net Present Value (NPV)

The PBP method discussed earlier gives little attention to timing, but does not work as per 'bird in hand' principle because it gives higher weightage to all the receipts before the recovery of the investment and no weightage to all the subsequent receipts. However, those methods which could take into consideration the time value of money need to be discussed. The NPV method as well as other methods are discussed below for this purpose.

The NPV method is based on the following *three* steps:

1. Selecting an appropriate interest rate.
2. Calculating the present value of the future stream of cash inflow.
3. Calculating the present value of the cash outflow owing to investment.

Thus, the net present value of an investment is determined by discounting the cash inflow *minus* the present value of cash outflow. Cash inflows are computed by adding depreciation to profit after tax deduction arising out of each project. The working capital is taken as a cash outflow in the year in which the project starts commercial production.

The present value of future cash flow is computed as

$$PV = \frac{R_t + s}{(1+r)^t}$$

where PV is the present value; R_t, the cash inflow in the year t; s, the salvage value of the asset in the tth year; r, the interest rate (or discount rate); and $1/(1+r)^t$, the discount factor.

Thus, the net present value (NPV) can be computed as

$$NPV = \sum_{t=0}^{n} \frac{R_t}{(1+r)^t} = \sum_{t=1}^{n} \frac{R_t}{(1+r)^t} + \frac{s}{(1+r)^t} - I$$

where n is the operating life of the project; t, the operating year; and I, the original capital investment.

Obviously, in the above formula, when $t = 0$, it represents the initial capital investment represented by I. It is considered as cash outflow and is treated as negative cash inflow for computation purposes.

If NPV > 0, the investment is worthwhile and if NPV < 0, the investment is not worthwhile.

Advantages

1. It takes into consideration the time value of money as it is based on the principle that the sum of money today has a higher value than an equivalent amount after a year from now.
2. It considers the return from the project in its entirety in evaluation of the capital expenditure project.
3. The NPV of various projects measured as they are in today's rupees can be added. This property ensures that a project having NPV < 0 will not be accepted just because it is combined with a project having NPV > 0.

Drawbacks

1. It requires data on discount rate.
2. It is not an easy method to understand and computation of NPV is also difficult.

Example 12.4. A company is trying to decide which of the two machines, A or B, to purchase. Each of these machines costs Rs 1,50,000. The expected net incremental cash flows are given below:

Year	Machine A	Machine B
1	35,000	25,000
2	45,000	35,000
3	55,000	45,000
4	35,000	65,000

The company's cost of capital is 6 per cent per annum. Calculate the NPV of each machine. Indicate which machine should be purchased on the basis of NPV method of ranking investment proposal.

Solution. The calculation of NPV is shown below:

Year End	PV Factor @ 6%	Machine A		Machine B	
		Cash Flow	Present Value	Cash Flow	Present Value
1	0.943	35,000	33,005	25,000	23,575
2	0.890	45,000	40,050	35,000	31,150
3	0.840	55,000	46,200	45,000	37,800
4	0.792	35,000	27,720	65,000	51,480
Total			1,46,975		1,44,005

In both the cases the total present value of all the cash inflow is less than the total cash outflow of Rs 1,50,000 and there is no need to subtract the cash outflow as the money is immediately spent. Comparing the two NPV, the NPV of machine A is greater, therefore it must be purchased.

Example 12.5. A company is deciding to choose between two mutually exclusive projects A and B. Project A requires an initial investment of Rs 4,00,000 and is expected to generate a cash flow of Rs 1,40,000 per annum for 4 years of its life. Project B requires Rs 4,50,000 and has a life of 7 years and is expected to generate a cash flow of Rs 1,00,000 per annum. Which proposal should be accepted? Assume a 6 per cent rate of interest.

Solution. The NPV in both the cases can be calculated as follows:

Project A : Given $n = 4$, $i = 0.06$, then PV factor $= 3.4651$

Then NPV $(A) = 1,40,000 \times 3.4651 - 4,00,000 = $ Rs 85,114

Project B : Given $n = 7$, $i = 0.06$, then PV factor $= 4.9173$

Then NPV $(B) = 1,00,000 \times 4.9173 - 4,50,000 = $ Rs 41,730

Since NPV $(A) >$ NPV (B), project A should be chosen based on the NPV criterion. For a more valid comparison, the life span of two projects must also be equated. This can be done by calculating their annual annuity. For projects A and B,

Project A : Equivalent annual annuity $= 85,114/3.4651 = $ Rs 24,563.21

Project B : Equivalent annual annuity $= 41,730/4.9173 = $ Rs 8,492.58

Since the value of project A is more, it will therefore contribute more to the maximization of the owner's wealth and should be chosen.

Remark: When life span of two or more mutually exclusive projects is different, such a conversion is essential. In case the projects are independent, such a conversion is not required.

12.7.3 Benefit-cost Ratio (BCR)

This method is an improved version of the NPV method and can be defined in *two* ways:

1. BCR = PVB/I

where PVB = present value of all future cash flow $= \sum_{t=1}^{n} \dfrac{R_t}{(1+r)^t}$; I = initial capital investment;

t = operating n = operating life of the project; R_t = net cash flow for the year t.

2. NBCR $= \dfrac{\text{NPV}}{I} = \dfrac{\text{PVB} - I}{I} = \dfrac{\text{PVB}}{I} - 1$

where NBCR = net benefit-cost ratio and NPV = net present value.

The following decision rules are adopted for accepting or rejecting a project based on BCR criterion:

When	BCR	or	NBCR	Rule
	> 1		> 0	Accept
	= 1		= 0	Indifferent
	< 1		< 0	Reject

Advantages

1. When the initial money available to spend in the current period is limited, the BCR criterion may rank projects correctly in the order of decreasing efficient use of capital.
2. Under unconstrained conditions, the BCR will accept or reject a project as per the NPV criterion.

Drawbacks

1. It does not provide means for aggregating several smaller projects into a package that can be compared with a large project.
2. When cash outflow occurs beyond the current period, the BCR criterion is not suitable for selecting a project.

12.7.4 Internal Rate of Return (IRR)

In IRR method (or discounting cash flow method), the discount rate is not fixed and is varied till the NPV becomes zero. The discount rate at which the NPV becomes zero is known as IRR. The discount rate can be calculated by the expression

$$\sum_{t=1}^{n} \frac{R_t}{(1+r)^t} = 0$$

where R_t is the net cash flow for the year t; r, the discount rate or internal rate of return; and n, the operating life of the project.

The IRR $(= r)$ so calculated is compared with the required rate of return, and if IRR is greater than the required rate of discount, then the project is accepted, otherwise rejected. Hence, the required rate of return is that minimum return which the owner of the firm expects to earn on the project.

Advantages

1. It ranks the projects according to their NPV/IRR. A project with higher IRR is selected from among several projects.
2. It considers the cash flow stream in its entirety.

Drawbacks

1. The IRR value cannot distinguish between lending and borrowing and, therefore, a high IRR need not necessarily be a desirable yardstick for selecting a project.
2. It may not be rigidly defined.

Example 12.6. A company is trying to decide which of the two machines, A or B, to purchase. Each will involve an investment of Rs 10,000. The expected net incremental cash flow is given below:

Year	Machine A, Rs	Machine B, Rs
1	5,000	2,000
2	4,000	3,000
3	2,000	5,000
4	2,000	4,000

The company's cost of capital is 10 per cent. Calculate IRR of machine A.

Solution. The IRR of machine A will be calculated as follows:

$$\frac{5,000}{(1+IRR)^1} + \frac{4,000}{(1+IRR)^2} + \frac{2,000}{(1+IRR)^3} + \frac{2,000}{(1+IRR)^4} = 10,000$$

Here the unknown value of IRR can be determined as follows:

(*a*) Find the average cash flow, i.e., $R_t = (5,000 + 4,000 + 2,000 + 2,000)/4 = $ Rs 3,250

(b) Divide the initial investment outflow by the average cash flow of (a), i.e., 10,000/3,250 = 3.0769.

(c) Locate the nearest PV factor from the row appropriate to the number of years from table of 'Present value of an annuity of Re 1 per period for n period.' This will give approximate IRR. For $n = 4$, it is 3.102 at 11 per cent. This means that the starting IRR may be taken as 11 per cent.

(d) Using IRR obtained in (c), the present value of cash flow is calculated as shown below:

Cash Flow	PV Factor @ 11%	Present Value
5,000	0.9009	4,504.5
4,000	0.8116	3,246.4
2,000	0.7312	1,462.4
2,000	0.6587	1,317.4
Total		10,530.7

Since the present value of cash inflow is more than the outflow, therefore the discount rate should be increased. For PV factor at the rate of 12 per cent and 13 per cent, the present value of cash inflow is Rs 10,347.9 and Rs 10,170.2, respectively. However, at 14 per cent discount rate, the present value of cash inflow is Rs 9998.2, which is very close to Rs 10,000. Hence, the machine A has an IRR (almost) equal to 14 per cent at which NPV becomes zero.

Self-assessment Questions Set-I

1. Elaborate the concept of Project Management. Name the different types of organizational levels that can be adopted in the field of project management.

2. Define the term 'Project'. Enumerate the different types of business ideas for capital expenditure.

3. Define the term 'Project' and distinguish it from various similar terms in its family tree.

4. Discuss the various types of industrial projects.

5. Discuss in detail various phases in the life cycle of a project.

6. Name the various activities associated with implementation phase of the project life cycle.

7. Discuss various steps that are to be followed in the project management approach.

8. Name the specific techniques used for completing various phases of a project life cycle.

9. What is a 'Feasibility Report'? What types of data is required for its preparation?

10. What type of information is required for market and demand analysis?

11. What aspects are considered in technical analysis?

12. What considerations influence the choice of location for a plant?

13. What are the components of cost of projects? Discuss them in detail.

14. Describe the various sources of finance that may be used to meet the cost of a project.

15. Discuss briefly the working of at least two Indian and foreign financial institutions.

16. What are the major activities of financial institutions in India?

17. (a) What assumptions underline break-even analysis?

(b) Discuss the algebraic analysis of cost-volume-profit relationship.

(c) What is P/V ratio? What does it measure and how is it useful?

18. What do you understand by terms such as 'term finance' and 'finance structure of a firm'.

19. What methods are used for assessing the economic viability of a project and what is the rationale underlying these methods'?

20. Caravan Company sold 1,00,000 units of its product at Rs 20 per unit. Variable cost is Rs 14 per unit (manufacturing cost of Rs 11 and selling cost of Rs 3). Fixed cost is incurred uniformly throughout the year and it amounts to Rs 7,92,000 (manufacturing cost of Rs 5,00,000 and selling cost of Rs 2,92,000). There are no inventories at the beginning or end of the accounting period.

With this information, you are required to determine (i) break-even level for this product, (ii) the number of units that must be sold to earn an income of Rs 60,000 (before income-tax deduction), (iii) the number of units that must be sold to earn an after tax profit of Rs 90,000 (assuming a tax rate of 50 per cent), and (*iv*) the break-even point for this product after a 10 per cent increase in wages and salaries (assuming labour cost is 50 per cent of variable cost and 20 per cent of fixed cost).

[Ans: (*i*) 132,000 units, (*ii*) 142,000 units, (*iii*) 162,000 units, (*iv*) 147,156 units].

21. Shri Synthetics Ltd. has an installed capacity of 10,000 units per annum. They are operating at about 35 per cent of the installed capacity. For a certain year they have budgeted as follows:

Production/sales = 8,000 units;   costs: Direct material = 16 crore

                                     Direct labour = 1.2 crore

                                     Factory expenses = 1.6 crore

                                     Administrative expenses = 0.4 crore

                                     Selling expenses = 0.4 crore

and profit = 2 crore.

Factory expenses as well as selling expenses are variable to the extent of 20 per cent. Calculate the break-even point as percentage of installed capacity.

22.   (*a*) National Company Ltd. manufactures and sells four types of products under the brand names ACE, UTILITY, LUXURY and SUPREME. The sales-mix in value comprises:

Brand	Percentage
ACE	33.33
UTILITY	41.67
LUXURY	16.67
SUPREME	8.33
	100

The total budgeted sale (100 per cent) is Rs 6,00,000 per month. The operating costs are

ACE	:	60 per cent of selling price
UTILITY	:	68 per cent of selling price
LUXURY	:	80 per cent of selling price
SUPREME	:	40 per cent of selling price

The fixed costs are Rs 1,59,000 per month. Calculate the break-even point for the products on an overall basis.

(*b*) It has been proposed to change sales-mix as follows; the total sales per month remains Rs 6,00,000:

Brand	Percentage
ACE	25
UTILITY	40
LUXURY	30
SUPREME	5
	100

Assuming that this proposal is implemented, calculate the new break-even point.

[Ans: (*a*) Rs 4,54,285.71 (*b*) Rs 5,00,000].

23. The Super Cement Company produces a special kind of cement which is packed and sold in bags of 20 kg. During the previous month its revenue and cost patterns were as follows:

Selling price per bag	:	Rs 50
Variable cost per bag	:	Rs 26
Fixed costs	:	Rs 10,000
Quantity	:	Rs 3,500 bags

Consider each of the following separately:

(*a*) What is the break-even quantity?

(*b*) Assuming a 10 per cent increase in production volume, what is the percentage change in profits'?

(*c*) Assuming a 10 per cent increase in selling price, what is the new break-even point?

(*d*) Assuming 9 per cent increase in fixed cost, what is the new break-even point?

(*e*) Assuming that the variable cost increases by Rs 20 per bag, what is the new break-even point?

24. The Zenith Corporation is considering a capital investment of Rs 12,00,000 in a project, which is expected to yield the following cash flows:

Year	:	1	2	3	4 to 7	8
Cash inflow ('000 Rs)	:	150	180	160	140	190

If the required rate of return is 13 per cent, determine (a) NPV of the project, and (b) IRR of the project. Is the proposal an acceptable one?

25. The cash flow streams for four alternative investments A, B, C and D are:

Year	A	B	C	D
0	– 2,00,000	– 3,00,000	– 2,10,000	– 3,20,000
1	+ 45,000	+ 45,000	+ 90,000	+ 2,00,000
2	+ 45,000	+ 35,000	+ 55,000	+ 25,000
3	+ 45,000	+ 35,000	+ 60,000	–
4	+ 45,000	+ 25,000	+ 55,000	–
5	+ 45,000	+ 25,000	+ 45,000	+ 50,000

Calculate the payback period, net present value and internal rate of return for the four alternatives. Which one would you choose and why?

26. (a) What are the accept/reject criteria for the net present value and internal rate of return method of project evaluation?

   (b) Broken-Hill Proprietary Ltd. is considering the following two mutually exclusive projects:

   Project X : Initial cost Rs 2,00,000; Rs 30,000 per year after tax inflow for 10 years

   Project Y : Initial cost Rs 2,00,000; Rs 18,000 per year after tax inflow for 20 years

   (i) Compute the net present value for each project;

   (ii) Compute the internal rate of return for each project;

   (iii) Rank the two projects according to the above criteria and pronounce your judgement.

27. A company is considering two mutually exclusive projects. The initial investment required for both the projects is Rs 10,00,000 each. The project has a life of 5 years and uses straight line method of depreciation. The required rate of return is 15 per cent and the company pays 50 per cent tax. The cash inflow before depreciation and taxation are:

Year	Project A	Project B
1	7,00,000	8,00,000
2	8,00,000	6,00,000
3	8,00,000	10,00,000
4	9,00,000	7,00,000
5	6,00,000	6,00,000

Which project is acceptable under NPV and IRR methods?

28. A firm is considering the introduction of a new product which will have a life of five years. Two alternative methods of promoting the product have been identified:

Alternative 1: This will involve employing a large number of agents. An immediate expenditure of Rs 5,00,000 will be required to advertise the product. This will produce net annual cash inflow of Rs 3,00,000 at the end of the five years. However, the agents will have to be paid Rs 50,000 each year. On termination of the contract at the end of the fifth year, the agents will have to be paid a lumpsum of Rs 1,00,000.

Alternative 2: Under this alternative, the firm will not employ agents but will sell directly to the consumers. The initial expenditure on advertising will be Rs 2,50,000. This will bring in cash inflow of Rs 1,50,000 at the end of each year. However, this alternative will involve out-of-pocket cost for sales administration to the extent of Rs 50,000. The firm also proposes to allocate fixed cost worth Rs 20,000 per year to this product, if this alternative is pursued.

   (a) Advise the management as to the method of promotion to be adopted; and

   (b) Define the internal rate of return. Calculate the internal rate of return for Alternative 2. You may assume that the firm's cost of capital is 20 per cent per annum.

29. Consider the following proposed investments with the indicated cash flow:

Investment	Initial Outlay (Rs '000)	Year End Cash Flow		
		Year 1 (Rs '000)	Year 2 (Rs '000)	Year 3 (Rs '000)
A	200	200	0	0
B	200	100	100	100
C	200	20	100	300
D	200	200	20	20
E	200	140	60	100
F	200	160	160	80

Rank the investment deriving the NPV using a discount rate of 10 per cent and state your views.

12.8 Project Implementation

Once a project has been selected, objectives defined, a project manager appointed and the zero-date fixed, the focus shifts to its implementation. This involves the completion of numerous activities by employing various resources such as men, machine, material, money and time so that the project on paper is translated into reality.

The proper planning, scheduling and control of all activities of a project, given their interrelationships and constraints on availability of resources, is done by the project manager by seeking help from internal and external resources.

Figure 12.3 illustrates the various stages of implementation phase of the project. The implementation phase begins with the 'project brief' and ends with the 'project handed over' in the complete form to the operating group, which will commission the completed plant.

Authorization
↓
Project Brief (or Manual)
↓
Project Organization Planning
↓
Project Technological Planning
↓
Construction of Infrastructure
↓
Project Integration
↓
Project Handover → Operations

Fig. 12.3   Stages of project implementation

12.8.1 The Project Brief

The project brief is a mechanism of the implementation phase in the form of either a standard document or a specific memorandum, also called the *project charter*, issued by the authorization group. The project brief contains the following:

    (a) A set of instructions—project scope, goals, name of the project manager and his authority;

    (b) Information such as target dates, cash release schedules, etc. which may be needed to clarify what has to be done; and

    (c) A letter authorizing the use of internal and external resources to a certain limit.

12.8.2 Project Organization Planning

After getting the green signal from the authorization group, the project manager takes charge. The framework of operation, if not available from previously executed comparable projects, must be quickly established by adjusting the available manpower from previous phases of the project.

The main segments of project organizational planning are enumerated below:

Project Organization

The project manager's authority *vis-a-vis* his position—to whom he reports, who reports to him, can be demonstrated by organizational charts. However, it will also depend upon the manner in which the project is to be carried out. For instance, a project manager may have to discharge his duties as a line manager with specialist staff directly responsible to him or he may have to coordinate with the other staff who are answerable to their own functional managers.

Project manager as a staff assistant to the chief executive. Figure 12.4 shows the position of a project manager where his job is only to collect and communicate information about the progress of the project to the chief executive. On his part, the project manager neither takes any decision for the project nor provides any staff service to various functional managers responsible for making decisions for the project. He, however, may influence some decisions taken either by the chief executive or by the functional managers.

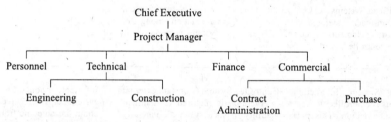

Fig. 12.4 Project manager as a staff assistant to chief executive

Project management as a specialized staff function. Figure 12.5 shows the position of the project management division where the project manager will be equipped with project management tools and techniques and provide schedules, budgets and information to other functional divisions who will execute the project. In addition to this, he can also carry out service activities such as collecting and transmitting data, maintaining records, measuring progress, analysing progress and preparing progress reports, and maintaining communication link between various functional divisions, and between the company and other outside agencies.

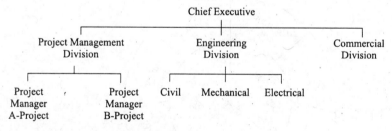

Fig. 12.5 Project management as a specialized staff function

In this position, the project manager neither takes any decision for other participating functional departments nor does he direct these departments to coordinate. He, however, can always advise these departments, but the veto power lies with the respective department.

Project Systems Definition

This is the specification of all administrative procedures and systems related to the project. It establishes a pattern of information flow and a manner of coordination within which each functional group or specialist manpower is integrated to achieve the overall project objectives. Here particular attention is given as to how project reporting and control in terms of time and money should be taken care of.

Distinction between System and Procedure

A *business system* refers to the combination of physical systems such as the man-man system, man-machine system, machine-machine system. Such systems are essential for implementing any phase of a project. An example of such a system is the purchase system which involves purchase officers, vendors, specifications, materials, purchase orders and conditions of purchase.

A *procedure* is a pre-determined sequence of tasks for carrying out the recurring work of a system, uniformly and consistently. For example, in a purchase system, procedures for selecting vendors, evaluation of purchase offers, and release of orders need to be developed.

Class of Systems

The broad categories of systems are shown below in the chart:

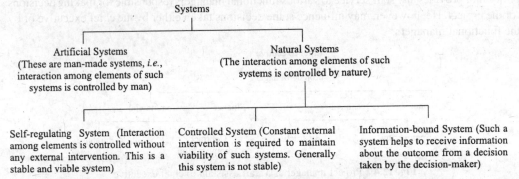

The following *three* steps are essential to design project management system:

(*a*) Conceiving a total physical system and its natural modules;

(*b*) Identifying interrelationship between natural modules; and

(*c*) Developing a control system using information as a media for self-control and forced control of the entire project.

The conceptual design model of a project management system is shown in Fig. 12.6.

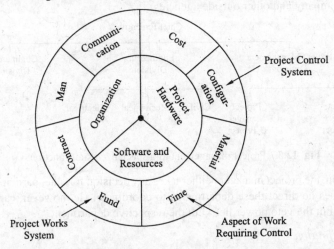

Fig. 12.6 Conceptual design model of a project management system

The important elements of the project management system are as follows:

1. Project Work System (Fig. 12.6): This represents the overall view of three systems—organization system, project hardware system and software and resources system. If individuals in each of these systems are concerned only with their function, then outside intervention will be required to coordinate their work. Better coordination in terms of effective project implementation plan can be done by developing a work breakdown structure (WBS).

2. **Work Breakdown Structure:** It is the technique of breaking down a work into its components and simultaneously establishing interrelationship among the components. The WBS, therefore, enables the integration of people, hardware and software into a total project work system, and at the same time establishes a hierarchy of the three systems.

The work can be broken down by using (*i*) *hardware-oriented approach* in which the overall system is broken down first into individual systems, followed by sub-systems and finally into various individual elements. This is done in a particular hierarchy. The codification of individual systems, their sub-systems and then the various elements helps the project manager in evaluating the overall project work system in terms of time, cost, and in assessing the accountability of performance; (*ii*) *agency-oriented approach* if the project is to be completed with the help of various execution agencies (Fig. 12.7 shows the linkage between execution agencies, hardware and software; and (*iii*) *function-oriented approach* in which work is distributed as per specialization in a particular trade, as shown in Fig. 12.8. This approach is normally practised by contractors to get the work done.

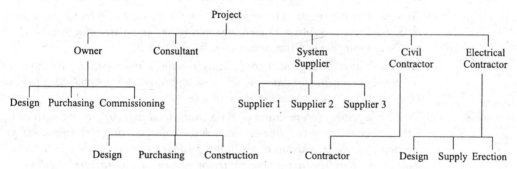

Fig. 12.7 Agency-oriented approach to WBS

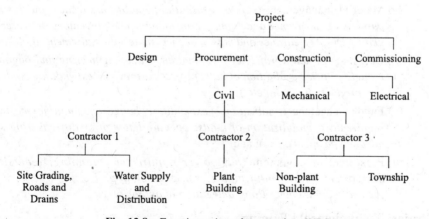

Fig. 12.8 Function-oriented approach to WBS

3. **Project Execution Plan (PEP):** This is an exercise of matching project hardware and software with the organization system so as to achieve a viable work system. It includes the following four sub-plans:

    (*i*) **Contracting plan:** Awarding contracts when the owner's company does not have in-built competence;

(*ii*) **Work package plan:** In the course of dividing a project into systems and sub-systems, a stage is reached where division into components will strip it of its multidisciplinary character. At this stage such work can be grouped together in order to form a viable contract. The identification of such work elements and grouping them together for execution is called a work package. Such work packages ensure a close adherence to time, cost and technical performance targets.

(*iii*) **Organization plan:** In order to protect the interest of the project, the owner can intervene in *three* ways: (*a*) Coordinating various agencies responsible for project execution; (*b*) Activating and motivating the agencies so that each one performs as they should; and (*c*) Assisting agencies in solving their problems in certain critical areas.

(*iv*) **Systems and procedure plan:** In order to avoid conflict and overlapping in day-to-day operation of a system, the management of a project has been divided into *eight* sub-systems. All these sub-systems have to operate within their own jurisdictions. These sub-systems along with their jurisdictions are:

(*a*) Contract management (*setting conditions of contract; tendering and its evaluation and award; assigning an agreement; measurement of completed work; billing and payment; work inspection and acceptance; taking over of completed work*);

(*b*) Configuration management (*procedure for finalization of project scope in terms of WBS; basic engineering package; engineering design basis; value engineering; quality assurance and inspection; technical audit, etc.*);

(*c*) Communication management (*organizing meetings and recording its minutes; developing procedure for data logging; making presentations; conducting project workshops; control-room maintenance*);

(*d*) Time management (*preparation of WBS, work-load assessment and numbering work packages; project schedules including resources; progress measurement; revision of project schedules; obtaining feedback and updating of schedules; evaluation of bids to assess capability of vendor or contractors to adhere to schedules; audit; work tracking and day-to-day follow-up*);

(*e*) Material management (*vendor evaluation; quality assurance and inspection; purchasing; insurance and claims; store management; inventory status reporting; getting DGTD clearance and import licence; material requirements and planning*);

(*f*) Cost management (*project cost estimation; value engineering and ongoing cost reduction; price evaluation of bids; project cost review; expenditure control; cost and productivity audit, etc.*);

(*g*) Fund management (*finalization of expenditure; budget and audit; forecasting fund requirement; mobilization of funds; opening letter of credit; ensuring security advance payments, etc.*); and

(*h*) Personnel management (*manpower requirement planning; requisitioning manpower; recruitment; training or orientation of project staff; performance or job evaluation; counselling; delegation of authority; etc.*).

12.8.3 Project Technological Planning

This stage of the implementation phase is concerned with engineering and design. The project technical objectives are defined and developed in detail. The technological planning can vary from a repeated project to a new project. The *four* phases of technological planning are explained below:

1. **Process Definition:** The inputs and outputs for the plant are clearly specified in the project intent. Such requirements are depicted using standard diagrams like flow diagrams (chemical industry), process charts (engineering industry) or circuit diagrams (electronics industry). The

use of such diagrams enables the project executors to describe the overall pictorial view of the project content and facilitates in assessing the interaction effects of various sections of the project.

2. **Process and Engineering Design:** The functional and engineering design of all project constituents can either be carried out by the firm itself or contracted to consultants or suppliers. If responsibility is given to outside agencies, then the task of design verification or approval lies with the firm.

   The design activity includes both drafting and construction of models. This activity ranges from the technological assemblage of major units to small components.

3. **Specifications:** In the context of a production plant project, a statement is made stating the expected attributes and performance of an item in terms of its size, output rate, operational speed, accuracy, reliability, etc. In other words, specifications set the profile for technical requirements. The design requirements need to spell out matters related to construction, and features of the item which are necessary for operation, safety and maintenance. A separate specification sheet needs to be prepared for installation, site construction work, acceptance tests, etc.

4. **Equipment Selection:** Technical specifications of equipment are required to streamline the selection process. The selection process of equipment must ensure the chosen profile for equipment. The profile of an equipment may be constructed in terms of primary attributes (attributes which cannot be negotiated or compromised) and secondary attributes (attributes which are desirable but not necessary and are guided by the price factor).

Procurement

Procurement is concerned with the purchase of the required material, machinery and equipment within the specifications, and with the hiring services of external agencies on contractual basis. The procurement normally accounts for 80-90 per cent of the project cash outflow, and thus calls for strict vigilance and integration with the overall project system.

12.8.4 Construction of Infrastructure

At the end of all relevant planning activities, construction becomes a meaningful activity. Construction activity includes construction of buildings and related activities, ranging from the trial test boring on a 'greenfield' plant site, to the final landscaping, installation of equipment in specified positions, road diversions, setting up site workshops, canteens, offices, recreation rooms, etc.

The success of this stage of implementation depends mainly on effective site management and other predecessor stages of implementation.

12.8.5 Project Integration

This stage of implementation is a natural extension of the construction stage in the sense that after having erected structures of buildings, some more work like electric fittings, telephone wiring, plumbing, etc. is still required to make the building meaningful for occupation. Similarly, after completing all types of installation, the building would need to be integrated into an overall production unit.

12.8.6 Project Handover

At this stage, the plant is handed over to the operating management by the project management group. However, the operational staff begin working with the project management groups as soon as plant gets nearer the operational state [in order to get themselves acquainted, with the plant]. In a few cases, the plant is not handed over completely in one instalment. First, the operating staff move in and begin testing various devices. During this time, the project management group observe carefully the testing exercise. Certain documents such as drawings, circuits, maintenance manuals, etc. are also handed over along with the building, plant, spares and accessories.

12.9 Project Planning, Scheduling and Monitoring

A project involves a large number of activities. Constraints and resources cannot be visualized easily and, therefore, the project calls for formal planning, scheduling and monitoring. For *planning*, the focus is on the questions: '*What is to be done*'? '*How is it to be done*' and '*Who is to do it*'? For *scheduling*, the focus is on the questions: '*When is it to be done*' and '*How much is to be done*'? For *monitoring*, the focus is on the questions: '*How much has been done*' and '*What needs to be done*'? From these questions under three different heads, it is clear that the project management calls for developing a team approach to get the work done through harmonious group effort. This could be achieved by adopting the 7-C model, i.e., *conceiving, concurring, committing, communicating, coordinating, counselling and controlling*.

12.9.1 Planning

Functions of Planning

The following are the functions of the project planning aspect of management:

  (*a*) Providing the basis for organizing the work to be undertaken and assigning responsibility to complete the work to execution groups;

  (*b*) Evolving a consensus on actions to be taken by individuals and execution groups;

  (*c*) Developing a sense of urgency and time consciousness among the people at work; and

  (*d*) Providing a foundation for project scheduling, monitoring and control.

Areas of Planning

  1. **Planning the project work:** (*a*) Listing the activities to be completed; (*b*) Deciding the sequence in which activities listed in (*a*) are to be taken up; and (*c*) Deciding the date and time for start and completion of each activity.

  2. **Planning the resource:** Approving the list of resources (machine, material, money, etc.) date by date for completion of activities listed earlier.

  3. **Planning the manpower and organization:** The manpower (managers, technologists, manual labour, etc.) needed at every stage of the project is estimated and the responsibility for carrying out the project is assigned.

  4. **Planning the information system:** The information system is defined to keep the project manager upto date about the progress of the project and to assist him in monitoring the project.

  From the above discussion, it appears that the purpose of planning is understood to be achieved as soon as the project work system is conceived and everyone involved is made to agree on the actions to be taken.

12.9.2 Scheduling

After the planning phase of the time management of the project is over, there comes a scheduling phase. The purpose of scheduling is to make commitment and then communicate the same to all concerned in order to ensure coordination through a self-regulating mechanism.

Basic Issues in Scheduling

The issues involved in the process of perfect scheduling which would answer the questions as to '*when a particular work is to be done*' and '*how much is to be done*' are as follows:

  (*a*) Objective to be achieved;

  (*b*) Work involved at various stages;

  (*c*) Various activities to be completed and their sequence;

  (*d*) Time required to complete each activity; and

  (*e*) Resources available and the various constraints.

All these five issues involved in the process of project scheduling are interdependent and therefore there is a need to study their linkages and possible impact on each other. Figure 12.9 represents the linkage of these issues and the zone of consideration for the preparation of a project schedule.

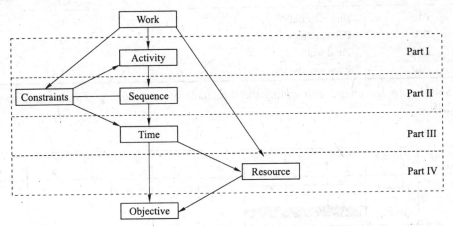

Fig. 12.9   Issues of project scheduling process

The issues listed earlier arise because some kind of work is to be executed. This work involves identification of activities, and activities involve sequence. Since there may be a number of activity sequence combinations, a combination is chosen which shows the minimum completion time within existing constraints. Also, among various trade-offs between time and resource, the choice should be governed by the objective to be achieved.

From Fig. 12.9 it is clear that a final project schedule preparation calls for careful evaluation of several combinations of *activity, sequence, resource* and *time* to complete the defined *work* in relation to defined *objective* and *constraints*. The project schedule document chosen in this manner must contain (*a*) a list of all activities to be completed, (*b*) optimal *sequence* in which *activities* are to be taken up, (*c*) decided *date* and *time* for start and completion of each *activity*, and (*d*) a list of resources required date by date for completion of activities.

12.9.3 Network Techniques for Project Scheduling

Once a project is selected, the focus shifts to its execution. This involves the completion of a large number of project components (called activities) through the use of various resources—men, machine, material, money, time, etc. These activities are interrelated because of physical, technical, and other considerations.

For proper planning, scheduling and control of these activities, given their interrelationships and resource constraints, the following *two* techniques have been found quite useful:

1. Bar or Gantt charts, and
2. Network Analysis Techniques (PERT/CPM).

Bar or Gantt Chart

During World War I, an American, Henry Gantt, designed the bar chart as a visual aid for planning and controlling his projects. In recognition of his contribution, such bar charts often bear his name.

In these charts, time is usually represented in terms of hours/days/weeks/months along the horizontal axis (*x*-axis), and various operations/activities are represented along the vertical axis (*y*-axis). The duration of each activity is represented by bars drawn against each of the activities or jobs. The length of the bar is proportional to the duration of the activity, where the beginning of the bar indicates the starting date and the end, the finishing date of the concerned activity.

Example 12.7. Draw a bar chart for the work of decorating the drawing room of a house. The list of activities involved in this project are as follows:

Activity number	Description	Duration (days)	Timing (day)	
			Start	Finish
010	Buy material	3	0	3
020	Paint ceilings	5	3	8
030	Paint walls	5	3	8
040	Paint woodwork	6	3	9

Solution. A bar chart, representing the time-table of operations given above, is shown in Fig. 12.10.

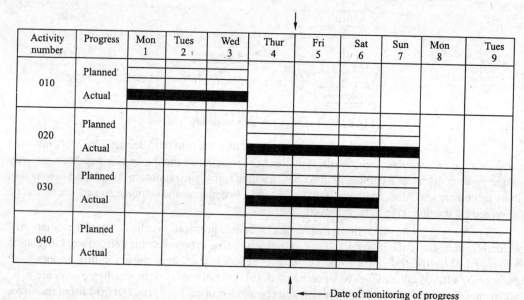

Fig. 12.10 The Gantt chart

Once the project has started, the next function is to show how the work is actually progressing. This is achieved by drawing a second line (or bar) above, inside or below the original bar to compare the planned work with the actual output.

Progress of an activity can be presented either as a percentage-completed or as a duration of the remaining activity, For example, for the decorating project, actual progress at the end of day 4 was reported as follows:

Activity Number	Percentage Complete	Remaining Duration
010	100	0
020	80	1
030	60	2
040	50	3

The planned activity chart is shown in Fig. 12.10. This type of presentation enables the project manager to see immediately the status of all activities.

The next step is to analyse the progress:

• Activity 010 should have been completed and is finished;

- Activity 020 should have been started and 20 per cent completed but it is actually 80 per cent complete. This means the activity is 3 days ahead of planned progress;
- Activity 030 should have been started and 20 per cent completed but it is actually 60 per cent complete. This means the activity is 2 days ahead of planned progress; and
- Activity 040 should have been started and 20 per cent completed but it is actually 50 per cent complete. This means the activity is 3 days ahead of planned progress.

Advantages and Disadvantages of Gantt Chart

The advantages of Gantt chart may be summarized as follows:

- Easy to assimilate and understand.
- Displays activity progress very clearly and simply.
- Useful for forecasting the resource requirement.

The disadvantages of Gantt chart may be summarized as follows:

- It does not explicitly indicate sequencing and interrelationships between activities.
- It is not suitable for multiple decision-making on a logical sequence of activities, time and resources.

Network Analysis Techniques

There are two basic network analysis techniques: PERT (Programme Evaluation and Review Technique) and CPM (Critical Path Method). Both of these techniques originated in the USA. CPM originated in 1957 in the industrial sector in connection with the scheduling of the shutdown of Du Pont's chemical plant, whereas PERT originated at about the same time in connection with the development of 'Polaris' ballistic missile project of the US military.

The network analysis technique provides a graphical method of representing the work plan in the form of arrow diagrams and allows their numerical analysis to obtain information of interest. An arrow diagram can be defined as a network in which arrows represent operations/activities that have to be performed. The arrangement of arrows shows the sequence as well as the interdependence between various activities required to be performed for executing a project (Fig. 12.11).

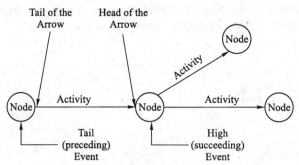

Fig. 12.11 Activities and events in an arrow diagram

Activity

It is a distinct operation or element of work that has to be performed. In an arrow diagram, the arrow represents an activity, the tail represents the start of the operation and head, the completion. A single activity cannot be represented by more than one arrow. The duration of the activity completion along with its name may be written over the arrow itself. An activity which does not consume time or resource is called *dummy activity* and is represented by a *dashed arrow*.

The length and orientation of the arrow are not important. The length of an arrow has no relationship with the duration of an activity.

Event

An event represents a specified instant or point of time during the execution of the job. An event marks the start or finish of an activity or a group of activities.

Events are usually represented by circles, but other shapes such as square, rectangle, oval, etc. could equally serve the purpose. Event numbers are written within the circles and must not be repeated.

Rules for Network Diagram Construction

The rules to be followed while constructing the network diagram are summarized below:

1. Each activity must start and end in a node. An activity having a preceding event, *i*, and a succeeding event, *j*, is also represented as (*i*, *j*).
2. Each activity must be uniquely defined:
   (*a*) Only one activity can span across a pair of events;
   (*b*) An event number should not be repeated. Events must be numbered in such a way that the number at the head event is higher than the number of the corresponding tail event.
3. (*a*) There should be no loops in the network diagram (Fig. 12.12); and
   (*b*) If an activity has the same preceding and succeeding events (Fig. 12.13), then such a situation is not permissible.

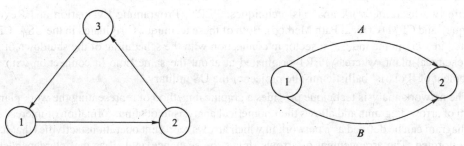

Fig. 12.12   Loop in the arrow diagram   **Fig. 12.13**

To ensure that each activity is uniquely defined, it is necessary to introduce a dummy activity to conform to the rules of network diagram construction (Fig. 12.14).

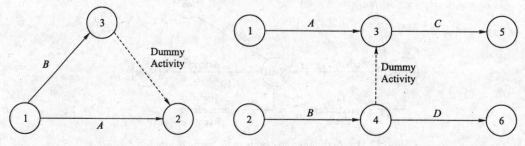

Fig. 12.14   Use of the dummy activity   **Fig. 12.15**   Another use of the dummy activity

A dummy activity is also used to represent a constraint necessary to show the proper relationship between activities as shown in Fig. 12.15.

4. The logic of interrelationship between various activities in a network is governed by the following rules:
   (*a*) An event cannot 'occur' until all the activities leading into it have been completed; and
   (*b*) No activity can commence until its tail event has 'occurred'. This means that an activity cannot start unless all preceding activities, on which it depends, have been completed.
5. Dummy activities also follow the dependency rules 4 (*a*) and (*b*) just like the other activities.

6. As per convention, the numbering of events is done from left to right and from top to bottom. The project completion time flows from left to right.

Example 12.8. Construct a network diagram based on the activity list and preceding activities:

(a) Activity   :   A   B   C   D   E   F   G   H   I   J   K

Preceding activity :   —   —   A   B   C   B   C, D   G, F   E   H, I   J

(b) Activity   :   A   B   C   D   E   F   G   H   I   J   K   L

Preceding activity :   —   —   —   B, C   A   C   E   E   D, F, H   E   I, J   G

Solution.

(a)

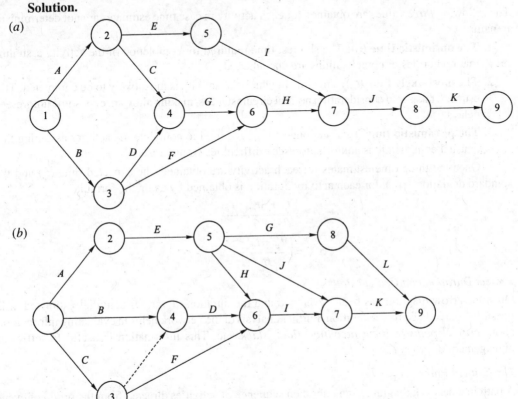

(b)

Difference between PERT and CPM

The use of either technique is based on individual characteristics. The main difference between these two techniques lies in the way activity time durations are addressed. The accuracy of an activity's time estimate usually depends on the information available from previous projects. If an activity has been performed before, its duration can be more accurately predicted. However, activities of a new work, which are difficult to measure or are dependent on other uncertain variables, may have a wide range of possible time durations.

CPM is best utilized for repetitive and non-complex projects where time estimates can be made with some measure of certainty, *e.g.*, a construction project. PERT, on the other hand, is useful for non-repetitive and complex projects in which activity time estimates may vary over a range of possibilities, *e.g.* a research project. Furthermore, PERT is considered to be event-oriented whereas CPM is activity oriented.

PERT technique has been developed to apply a statistical treatment to the possible range of activity time durations. The range of activity times is expressed in terms of three time estimates.

These three time estimates are imposed on a normal distribution to calculate the activity's expected time.

CPM has been developed to take care of the time-cost trade-off dilemma often presented to project managers. This technique enables the project manager to understand the effect of various project time cycles on direct and indirect cost. Obviously, compressing the project duration will reduce indirect costs, but may increase direct costs. This technique is often called *project crashing* or *acceleration technique.*

Activity Time Estimation

The following *three* values are obtained for each activity in case time estimates are not deterministic in nature:

1. **The optimistic time (t_o):** The shortest time required for completion of the activity assuming that no hurdles or complications are encountered.

2. **The most likely time (t_m):** The time in which the activity is most likely to be completed. This estimate takes into consideration normal circumstances, making allowance for some unforeseen delays.

3. **The pessimistic time (t_p):** The longest time required to complete the activity assuming that unusual complications and/or unforeseen difficulties would arise.

Once the three time estimates for each activity are obtained, the expected time (t_e) and the standard deviation (σ_{te}) for each activity duration is obtained by using the formula

$$t_e = \frac{t_o + 4t_m + t_p}{6}$$

and

$$\sigma_{te} = \left(\frac{t_p - t_o}{6}\right).$$

Project Duration and Critical Path

Once the arrow diagram has been developed and the duration of various activities estimated, it is possible to calculate project duration. Further analysis of the network helps in evaluating information about *critical paths, critical activities, float, slack,* etc. This information is useful for efficient management of projects.

The Critical Path

A path in a network diagram is an unbroken sequence of activities directed from the origin of event (or node) to the terminal event. The longest (a path along which it takes the longest to traverse) continuous chain of activities through the network, starting from the first event to the last event is called the *critical path.*

The activities lying on the critical path are called *critical activities,* which govern the completion of the project. Any delay in their execution would result in delay in overall completion of the project.

Critical Path Calculations

In order to identify the critical path from among several possible paths in a network diagram, the calculation of *earliest expected completion time of events* (T_E) and the *latest allowable time* or *latest finish time of events* (T_L) is done.

$$T_{E_j} = \max \{T_{E_i} + d_{ij}\}$$

where E_i = earliest expected completion time of tail event i ($< j$); d_{ij} = expected completion time of activity (i, j)

$$T_{L_i} = \min \{T_{L_j} - d_{ij}\}$$

where T_{L_i} = latest finish time of event i ($< j$).

The earliest expected completion time of events is computed moving from the initial event to the end event and adding at each stage the duration of the activity to the T_E value of the preceding event. This operation is known as *forward pass*.

Similarly, the latest finish time of events is computed moving from the end event to the initial event and subtracting at each stage the duration of the activity from T_L value of the succeeding event. This operation is known as backward pass.

The critical path is identified by the values of T_E and T_L of each event. The critical path is obtained by connecting all events in a continuous chain, where $T_L = T_E$.

Float and Types of Float

Activities that are not critical are called *non-critical activities*. These activities have a certain amount of *spare time* or *float available*. This float could be positive or negative. Thus, non-critical activities can be delayed or advanced (depending on the extent of float availability) without affecting the overall completion date.

The calculation of float is necessary to ensure rational allocation of resources to various activities. There are three types of floats:

1. *Total float*. It is obtained by the total time which is available for performing an activity *minus* the duration of the activity.

$$\text{TF} = (T_{L_j} \text{ of head event} - T_{E_i} \text{ of tail event}) - d_{ij} \ (i < j).$$

2. *Free float*. This is part of the total float which does not affect the subsequent activities.

$$\text{FF} = (T_{E_j} \text{ of head event} - T_{E_i} \text{ of tail event}) - d_{ij}$$

3. *Independent float*. The float of an activity which neither affects the predecessor nor the successor activities is called *independent float*.

$$\text{IF} = (T_{E_j} - T_{L_i}) - d_{ij}$$

Slack

The word 'float' is commonly used for activity oriented networks. Slack indicates latitude in terms of time available for various events in event oriented networks.

Since events have both T_E and T_L-values, therefore slack is given by the difference between these times. Thus slack could be positive or negative depending upon whether the latest finish time, T_L, is later or earlier than the earliest finish time, T_E of an activity respectively. Further, as the form slack is associated with events, each activity will have two slacks *head slack* and *tail slack*. Hence, from definitions of floats, we have

Total float = Free float + head slack

Also,   Free float = Independent float + tail slack.

Time-cost Trade-off

For crashing the project duration, an incremental cost is calculated. This cost is the measure of cost-per unit-time reduction and provides a convenient measure for comparing activities in time reduction analysis. It is calculated as follows:

$$\text{Incremental cost slope} = \frac{\text{Crash cost} - \text{Normal cost}}{\text{Normal time} - \text{Crash time}} = \frac{\Delta C}{\Delta T}$$

For each iteration of the network, only critical activities have to be crashed. The activity to be crashed is one for which incremental cost is minimum. If there is single critical path, then continue to reduce the activity time to the maximum allowable reduction until another path becomes critical. But if there is more than one critical path, then make a comparison between an activity or any combination of activities on all critical paths which will reduce all critical paths.

Example 12.9. Consider a project, given the following activities and their time estimates:

Activity	Predecessor	Time (days)		
		t_o	t_m	t_p
A	—	2	4	6
B	A	8	12	16
C	A	14	16	30
D	B	4	10	16
E	C, B	6	12	18
F	E	6	8	22
G	D	18	18	30
H	F, G	8	14	32

(a) Draw an arrow diagram for the project,

(b) Identify the critical path and compute the expected project completion time; and

(c) What is the probability that the project will require 75 days?

Solution. The expected time and variance of each activity is calculated in the following table:

Activity	Predecessor	Estimated Time			Expected Time (t_e)	Variance (V_{te})
		t_o	t_m	t_p	$= \dfrac{t_o + 4t_m + t_p}{6}$	$= \left(\dfrac{t_p - t_o}{6}\right)^2$
A	—	2	4	6	4	4/9
B	A	8	12	16	12	16/9
C	A	14	16	30	18	64/9
D	B	4	10	16	10	4
E	C, B	6	12	18	12	4
F	E	6	8	22	10	64/9
G	D	18	18	30	20	4
H	F, G	8	14	32	16	16

(a) Making use of the given information, the network diagram is given in Fig. 12.16. For the critical path, first calculate the earliest expected event time (T_E) and the latest finish time (T_L) for each event.

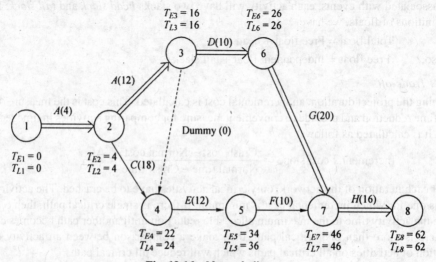

$T_{E3} = 16$
$T_{L3} = 16$

$T_{E6} = 26$
$T_{L6} = 26$

$D(10)$

$A(12)$

$A(4)$

Dummy (0)

$G(20)$

$T_{E1} = 0$
$T_{L1} = 0$

$T_{E2} = 4$
$T_{L2} = 4$

$C(18)$

$E(12)$

$F(10)$

$H(16)$

$T_{E4} = 22$
$T_{L4} = 24$

$T_{E5} = 34$
$T_{L5} = 36$

$T_{E7} = 46$
$T_{L7} = 46$

$T_{E8} = 62$
$T_{L8} = 62$

Fig. 12.16 Network diagram

(b) The path, called *critical path*, where T_E and T_L values are equal, is shown by the double lines in the diagram.

The critical path is, *A–B–D–G–H* (or 1–2–3–6–7–8) and the expected project completion time is $4 + 12 + 10 + 20 + 16 = 62$ days.

(c) The probability that the project will require at least 75 days for its completion is given by

$$Z = \frac{\text{Desired time} - \text{Expected time}}{\sqrt{\text{Variance}}}$$

The variance of the project length is given by

$$V_{t_e} = \frac{4}{9} + \frac{16}{9} + 4 + 4 + 16 = 26.2$$

Then

$$Z = \frac{75 - 62}{\sqrt{26.2}} = 2.54$$

and, therefore,   Prob $(x \geq 75)$ = Prob $(Z > 2.54)$

$$= 0.9944 \text{ (refer normal distribution table)}$$

Example 12.10. Consider a project, given the following activities and their time estimates:

Activity	Expected Time (days)	Activity (days)	Expected Time (days)
1-2	4	5-6	4
1-3	1	5-7	8
2-4	1	6-8	1
3-4	1	7-8	2
3-5	6	8-10	5
4-9	5	9-10	7

(a) Draw the network;

(b) Identify the critical path for monitoring the project; and

(c) Calculate total float and free float for each activity.

Solution: (a) Based on the information, a network diagram is shown in Fig. 12.17.

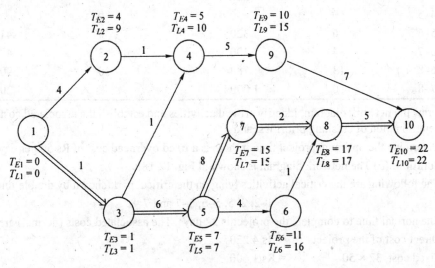

Fig. 12.17

(b) The critical path in Fig 12.17 is shown by double lines. The resulting path is: 1–3–5–7–8–10. The total project duration is 22 days.

(c) Calculations for total floats and free floats are shown in the table below:

Activity	Duration (days)	Total $(T_{L_j} - T_{E_i}) - d_{ij}$	Free $(T_{E_j} - T_{E_i}) - d_{ij}$
1–2	4	$(9-0)-4=5$	$(4-0)-4=0$
1–3	1	$(1-0)-1=0$	$(1-0)-1=0$
2–4	1	$(10-4)-1=5$	$(5-4)-1=0$
3–4	1	$(10-1)-1=8$	$(5-1)-1=3$
3–5	6	$(7-1)-6=0$	$(7-1)-6=0$
4–9	5	$(15-5)-5=5$	$(10-5)-5=0$
5–6	4	$(16-7)-4=5$	$(11-7)-4=0$
5–7	8	$(15-7)-8=0$	$(15-7)-8=0$
6–8	1	$(17-11)-1=5$	$(17-11)-1=5$
7–8	2	$(17-15)-2=0$	$(17-15)-2=0$
8–10	5	$(22-17)-5=0$	$(22-17)-5=0$
9–10	7	$(22-10)-7=5$	$(22-10)-7=5$

Example 12.11. The following table gives data on normal time and cost and crash time and cost for a project.

Activity	Normal Time (days)	Normal Cost (Rs)	Crash Time (days)	Crash Cost (Rs)
1–2	3	300	2	400
2–3	3	30	3	30
2–4	7	420	5	580
2–5	9	720	7	810
3–5	5	250	4	300
4–5	0	0	0	0
5–6	6	320	4	410
6–7	4	400	3	470
6–8	13	780	10	900
7–8	10	1,000	9	1,200

(a) Draw the network diagram, identify critical activities and establish the associated costs for the determination of crashing priorities; and

(b) Determine the optimum project time if there is a fixed overhead cost of Rs 50 per day.

Solution. (a) The network diagram is shown in Fig. 12.18.

The following are the critical activities lying on the critical part (shown by double lines):

1–2, 2–5, 5–6, 6–7 and 7–8.

The normal time to complete the project is 32 days. The associated costs (normal) are:

Direct cost of the project   = Rs 4,220
Fixed cost, 32 × 50   = Rs 1,600
Total normal cost   = Rs 5,820

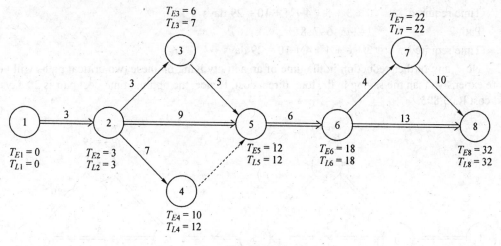

Fig. 12.18

(b) *Crashing of activities.* The lowest incremental cost incurred for any activity along the critical path is 2-5 and 5-6. Therefore, crashing of activities is done one by one.

Critical Activity	Incremental Cost (Rs)
1–2	$\dfrac{400-300}{3-2} = 100$
2–3	$\dfrac{30-30}{3-3} = 0$
2–4	$\dfrac{580-420}{7-5} = 80$
2–5	$\dfrac{810-720}{9-7} = 45$
3–5	$\dfrac{300-250}{5-4} = 50$
4–5	—
5–6	$\dfrac{410-320}{6-4} = 45$
6–7	$\dfrac{470-400}{4-3} = 70$
6–8	$\dfrac{900-780}{13-10} = 40$
7–8	$\dfrac{1,200-1,000}{10-9} = 200$

The duration of activity 5–6 can be reduced by 2 days and of activity 2–5 maximum by 1 day. The new network will be as follows.

The duration of the project now reduced to 29 days at an incremental cost by Rs 135 (3 days × cost Rs 45 each). Therefore, total new project cost is:

Direct cost   = Rs (4,220 + 135) = Rs 4,355
Fixed cost   = 29 × 50 = Rs 1,450
Total cost   = Rs 5,805

With this reduction of 3 days, we have two critical paths in the network diagram:
Path 1   : 1–2–3–5–6–7–8

Time required   : $3 + 3 + 5 + 4 + 4 + 10 = 29$ days
Path 2   : 1–2–5–6–7–8
Time required   : $3 + 8 + 4 + 4 + 10 = 29$ days.

Now, any further reduction in the time of an activity lying on these two critical paths will be more expensive than the saving in the total direct cost. Hence, the optimal time-cost pair is 29 days, and cost Rs 5,805.

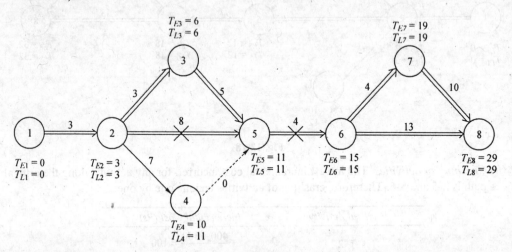

Example 12.12. The time required to complete each of eight jobs on two machines are shown below. Each job must follow the same sequence, beginning with machine *A* and moving to machine *B*. Determine the optimal sequence and show the resultant sequence on a time chart and find the idle time for machine *B*.

Job	Time, hr	
	Machine A	Machine B
1	16	5
2	3	13
3	9	6
4	8	7
5	2	14
6	12	4
7	18	14
8	20	11

Solution. The optimal sequence is as given below:

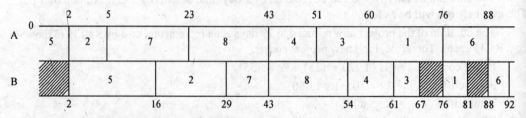

As per the above table, optimal sequence is 5–2–7–8–4–3–1–6. .

The path is

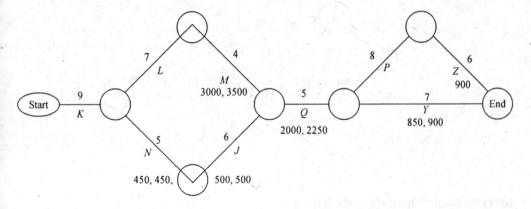

Project duration is 39 weeks.

Project duration, week	Shortest Activity	Crash cost
39	–	0
38	Z	90
37	N, L	170
36	Q	200
35	Q	225
34	M, N	345

It is required to stop here. Additional crashing cost will cost more.

Example 12.13. The data for a simple construction project are as given below:

Activity	Immediate Processor(s)	Time (days)		Direct-cost, Rs	
		Normal	Crash	Normal	Crash
A	—	4	3	60	90
B	—	6	4	150	250
C	—	2	1	38	60
D	A	5	3	150	250
E	C	2	2	100	100
F	A	7	5	115	175
G	D, B, E	4	2	100	240

Indirect costs are Rs 40 per day.

(a) Draw an arrow diagram for the project;

(b) Find all the paths in the project along with their normal and crash times;

(c) Find the crashing costs for each activity on a per day basis; and

(d) Determine the project duration that will return the minimum total project cost by appropriately crashing the project.

Solution. (*a*) The arrow diagram is given by

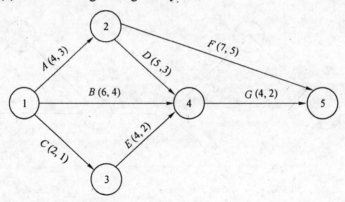

(*b*) Paths and their normal and crash times are:

Path	Normal Time	Crash Time
1–2–5	11	8 (critical)
1–2–4–5	13 (critical)	8 (critical)
1–4–5	10	6
1–3–4–5	8	5

(*c*) Crashing cost per day $= \dfrac{\text{Crash cost} - \text{Normal cost}}{\text{Normal time} - \text{Crash time}}$.

Hence,

Activity	Node	Crashing cost per day
A	1–2	30
B	1–4	50
C	1–3	22
D	2–4	50
E	3–4	—
F	2–5	30
G	4–5	70

(*d*) Crashing the project:

Crashing	Options	Cost (Rs)	Decision	Project Duration	Critical Path
First	(*i*) 1–2	30	Crash 1–2	12	1–2–4–5
	(*ii*) 2–4	50			
	(*iii*) 4–5	70			
Second	(*i*) 2–4	50	Crash 2–4	11	1–2–4–5
	(*ii*) 4–5	70			
Third	(*i*) 2–4	50	Crash 2–4	10	1–2–5
	(*ii*) 4–5	70			1–2–4–5
					1–4–5
Fourth	(*i*) 2–5, 4–5	100	Crash 2–4, 4–5	9	1–2–5
					1–2–4–5
					1–4–5
Fifth	(*i*) 2–5, 4–5	100	Crash 2–5, 4–5	8	1–2–5
					1–2–4–5
					1–4–5

Project Duration	Direct Cost			Indirect Cost	Total Cost
	Normal	Crashing	Total	Rs 40/day	
13	713	0	713	520	1,233
Min. 12	713	30	743	480	1,223
11	713	80	793	440	1,233
10	713	130	843	400	1,243
9	713	230	943	360	1,303
8	713	330	1043	320	1,363

As can be seen, the minimum project cost of Rs 1223.00 is for a project duration of 12 days.

12.9.4 Categories of Project Schedules

The process of project scheduling is not classified by the techniques used but categorized on the basis of purpose of schedules. Schedules are broadly classified into *three* categories:

Category	Description of Schedules	Purpose of Schedules
I	System (or overall or master) schedule	To fix a project completion target, and individual sub-system completion targets. This will require sequence and interrelationship to be established between various systems comprising utilities, processes, and resources (internal and/or external). In other words, an integration between inputs-outputs and resources is required in the context of the whole project to achieve the overall objective of the project.
II	Resource schedules or Agency schedules or Functional schedules	To mobilize resources (money, manpower, machine, material, etc.) and their commitment so as to get maximum throughput with minimum commitment of resources. Also, agency/functional schedules are prepared for internal and external agencies involved in project execution.
III	Input-output schedules or Production schedules or Work schedules	To check the output of internal and external agencies in terms of physical items (drawings, orders, equipment, approach roads, etc.) or activities and target dates fixed for each.

Scheduling techniques discussed earlier along with management levels and categories of schedules can be grouped into a pyramid structure according to the importance of their usages as shown in Fig. 12.19.

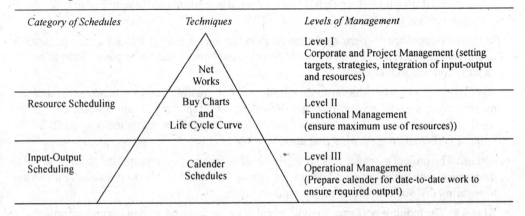

Fig. 12.19 Hierarchy of schedules, techniques and management

12.9.5 Monitoring

The process of monitoring ensures some real and positive action apropos various categories of schedules developed during scheduling by way of holding counselling sessions. Thus, monitoring is a kind of action, small and routine in nature, which generates a series of one time actions, both small and big, and ends up in bridging the gap between achievement and targets.

Three broad categories of schedules form the main monitoring categories against which performance needs to be measured, reviewed and reported to the project manager. However, what is to be measured, reviewed and reported will depend on who is to take action and what action he is likely to take. Usually the project managed by an organization has its various levels of management. These levels have different duties to discharge and take different types of action which fall under their jurisdiction. Therefore, monitoring, which has to be done under different categories of schedules, has to be streamlined in such a manner so as to cater to the need of various levels of management.

Steps in Monitoring and Role of Monitor

1. **Setting the environment:** The project monitor exercises the authority of the project manager to discharge certain outline tasks. The role of monitor is well defined, known and accepted by all the participating agencies whose activities are being monitored.

2. **Setting performance standards:** The project monitor, on behalf of the project manager, sets systems and procedures for monitoring the project and obtains commitment from participating agencies in respect of the same. He also reviews performance in terms of time schedule, budget and quality of the project against given standards. These standards are also known to all and accepted by the concerned groups.

3. **Measuring:** The project monitor keeps a close watch on the progress of activities by way of collecting information regarding 'what has been done' with respect to 'what should have been done.' He then quantifies the same for comparison with targets. For this, he gets regular feedback on achievements, measures the same and compares these with the set targets. If such targets are not met, he takes remedial actions. In fact, continuous feedback, measurement and comparison of achievements restricts non-permissible activities.

4. **Reviewing:** In case non-permissible activities are discovered by the monitor, he may take the following actions:

   (*a*) Interact with the defaulting agency pointing out deviations from the expected targets;

   (*b*) Find reasons for such non-permissible activities or deviations having occurred, as well as when and how such deviations are likely to be corrected; and

   (*c*) Take a decision whether such deviations could be permitted to continue or not, in view of the reasons found out in (*b*).

   In case deviations are not permitted, then the monitor holds meetings with the concerned agency or carries out fresh studies with a view to working out 'what needs to be done', so as to ensure an early solution to the problem.

5. **Reporting:** If an early solution to the problem is not possible due to some reasons, then the monitor reports to the project manager. However, such reporting is rare because the agency itself is inclined to resolve defaults in view of the recognition of authority enjoyed by the monitor on behalf of the project manager.

6. **Action:** The project manager acts promptly on all unresolved issues reported to him and holds discussions with the monitor and defaulting agency for quick solution to problems, with a view to ensuring that such problems do not recur in future.

   Remark: The monitor performs steps 3, 4, and 5, i.e., measuring, reviewing and reporting, and thus these steps constitute *monitoring*.

A schematic diagram depicting the linkage between the control process of monitoring (measuring, reviewing and reporting), monitoring heads and different levels of management is shown in Fig. 12.20.

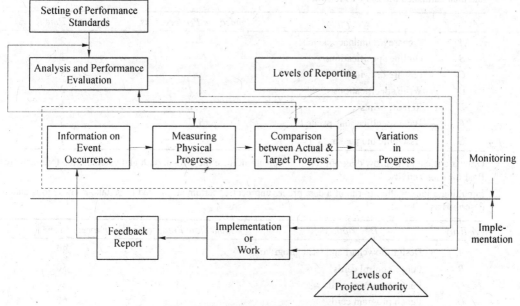

Fig. 12.20   Project monitoring system

Self-assessment Questions Set-II

1. What do you understand by Gantt charts? How are these prepared?
2. Describe briefly the background leading to development of CPM and PERT.
3. In what ways do the network analysis techniques help the project management?
4. What are the conventions usually followed in drawing arrow diagrams?
5. What main aspects need to be remembered while drawing arrow diagrams?
6. What is float? What are the different types of floats?
7. What is slack? How do you distinguish between slack and float? Give the relationship between the two, if any.
8. What are the three time estimates needed for PERT analysis and what do they represent? Show how you would use these estimates to compute the expected activity time and the variance in activity time.
9. "PERT provides the framework for describing, scheduling and then controlling a project." Discuss.
10. What are the main differences between PERT and CPM?
11. A company manufacturing plant and equipment for chemical processing is in the process of quoting a tender called by a public sector undertaking. Delivery date once promised is crucial and penalty clause is applicable. The winning of tender also depends on how soon the company is able to deliver the goods. The project manager has listed the activities in the project as under:

Activity	Predecessor	Activity time (weeks)
A	—	3
B	—	4
C	A	5
D	A	6
E	C	7
F	D	8
G	B	9
H	E, F, G	3

(a) Find the delivery week from the date of acceptance of quotation; and

(b) Find the total float and free float for each of the activities.

12. An architect has been awarded a contract to prepare plans for an urban renewal project. The activities of the job and their estimated times are as follows:

Activity	Description	Immediate Predecessors	Expected Time (days)
A	Prepare preliminary sketches	—	2
B	Outline specifications	—	1
C	Prepare drawings	A	3
D	Write specifications	A, D	2
E	Run off prints	C, D	1
F	Have specifications printed	B, D	3
G	Assemble bid packages	E, F	1

Draw a critical path arrow diagram for this project, indicate the critical path and calculate the total and free float for each activity.

13. In putting a job together to run at a data processing centre, certain steps need to be taken. These jobs can be described as follows:

Activity	Description	Immediate Predecessors	Expected Time (min)
A	Design flowchart and write program	—	180
B	Punch control cards	A	30
C	Punch comment cards	A	20
D	Punch program cards	A	60
E	Obtain brown folder	B, C, D	10
F	Put deck together	B, C, D	20
G	Submit deck	E, F	10

Draw an arrow diagram and identify the critical path. What is the minimum time of completion?

14. For the data given in the table below, draw the network. Crash systematically the activities and determine the optimal project duration and cost.

Activity	Normal		Crash	
	Time (days)	Cost (Rs)	Time (days)	Cost (Rs)
1–2	8	100	6	200
1–3	4	150	2	350
2–4	2	50	1	90
2–5	10	100	5	400
3–4	5	100	1	200
4–5	3	80	1	100

Indirect cost = Rs 70 per day.

15. The following table gives data on normal time and cost and crash time and cost for a project:

Activity	Duration (weeks)		Total Cost (Rs)	
	Normal	Crash	Normal	Crash
1–2	3	2	300	450
2–3	3	3	75	75
2–4	5	3	200	300
2–5	4	4	120	120
3–4	4	1	100	190
4–6	3	2	90	130
5–6	3	1	60	110

(a) Draw the network and find the critical path and the normal project duration;

(b) If the indirect cost is Rs 100 per week, find the optimal duration by crashing and the corresponding project cost; and

(c) With the crash durations indicated, what would be the minimum crash duration possible, ignoring indirect cost?

16. Following network and activity times are given:

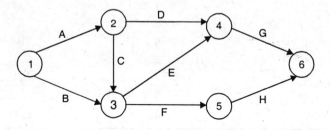

Activity	Optimistic Time	Most Likely Time	Pessimistic Time
A	6	7	14
B	8	10	12
C	2	3	4
D	6	7	8
E	5	5.5	9
F	5	7	9
G	4	6	8
H	2.5	3	3.5

(a) Calculate the expected time and variance for each activity; (b) draw the critical path; (c) time to complete the project; (d) probability that the project will be completed within 25 days. **Hint.** (a) Expected time and variance for each activity are:

Activity	Expected Time	Variance
A	8	1.78
B	10	0.44
C	3	0.11
D	7	0.11
E	6	0.44
F	7	0.44
G	6	0.44
H	3	0.03

(b) Critical path $= A - C - E - G$; (c) Duration to complete the project along the critical path $= 8 + 3 + 6 + 6 = 23$ days; (d) Probability of completion of project in 25 days.

Standard deviation of critical path $= \sqrt{1.78 + 0.11 + 0.44 + 0.44}$

$= 1.664$

$Z = 25 - 23/1.664 = 1.2$

$P(1.2) = 0.885$

17. A project has been defined to contain the following list of activities along with their required times for completion:

Activity	Time, days	Immediate Predecessor(s)
A	1	—
B	4	A
C	3	A
D	7	A
E	6	B
F	2	C, D
G	7	E, F
H	9	D
I	4	G, H

(*a*) Draw the critical path;   (*b*) Show the early start and finish times; (*c*) Show the critical path; and   (*d*) what would happen it activity F was revised to take four days instead of two?

Hint. (*a*) & (*b*): Critical path and early start and finish times are:

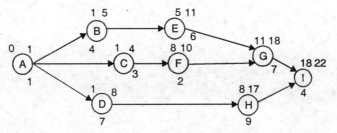

(*c*) Critical path: A – B – E – G – I
(*d*) New critical path: A – D – F – G – I. Time of completion is 23 days.

18. A project consists of eight activities as given below:

Activity	Duration, days	Immediate Predecessor (s)
A	1	—
B	3	A
C	5	—
D	3	B, C
E	1	D
F	12	—
G	3	E, F
H	1	G

(*a*) Draw the project network diagram. Find the critical path and the project completion time, and (*b*) If the activity F is now completed in 8 days, what would be the critical path and the project completion time.

Hint. The project network diagram is:

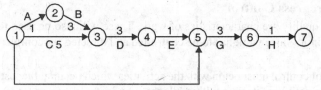

Three paths are: A – B – D – E – G – H   = 12 days
                    C – D – E – G – H = 13 days
                    F – G – H = 16 days (largest)

Hence, critical path is F – G – H, and project completion time is 16 days.

(*b*) If activity F takes 8 days, path F – G – H = 12 days. Hence, path C – D – E – G – H = 13 days is the largest and will be the new critical path. Therefore, new project completion time = 13 days.

12.10 Project Control

The aim of monitoring is to ensure adherence to targets. When, as a result of monitoring, a work package is carried out as per pre-determined standard, then the work package is said to be under control.

Control, however, is not the action itself. It is the presence of a force which ensures adherence to a pre-determined target or standard through overt or covert actions. The covert actions include setting up objectives, organization, schedules, budget, systems and procedures whereas overt actions include all those actions—measuring, reviewing and reporting—that are taken as a result of monitoring. For example, a project manager may find that an operation has been delayed due to delayed supply of an equipment. Now, if he decides to establish control, he may ask the vendors to submit detailed schedules, and insist for frequent reporting. In this case, control is said to have been exercised through covert actions. In case the project manager decides to take corrective action on the basis of reports or review from the agency at work, the control is said to have been exercised through overt actions.

Irrespective of the kind of approach to control, the essence of control is action. Monitoring being action-oriented, it supplements and leads to control and control in turn leads to achievement of objectives. Thus, a project has to be steered in the direction of its objectives using certain devices (organization, schedules, budget, systems and procedure) of control.

The following topics are discussed to highlight the scope of project control:

1. Scope/Progress Control
    (*a*) List of activities,
    (*b*) Progress measurement, and
    (*c*) Expediting and follow-up.
2. Performance Control
    (*a*) Change control, and
    (*b*) Quality assurance plans.
3. Schedule Control
    (*a*) Predictive schedule control,
    (*b*) Preventive schedule control, and
    (*c*) Schedule status reviews.
4. Cost Control
    (*a*) Cost control stages,
    (*b*) Cost control methods, and
    (*c*) Cost status reports.

12.10.1 Scope/Progress Control

The time, cost and quality are characteristics of work. These will also be used to control variations within a specified limit. Since work has to be controlled and directed for completion, no lapse at this end is acceptable.

The process of control must begin with the activities which occur at the last level of WBS. The completion of these activities in time within allocated budget and according to the set quality will lead to the completion of activities at the next higher level of WBS, and ultimately of the whole project itself.

1. **List of activities:** All agencies involved in the project must first submit the detailed list of activities to be performed at the lowest level of WBS before the start of the stage of progress control. Then total quantum of work and effort required for completion of these activities are estimated. This list can also be used for the following purposes:

   - To exercise functional control over activities, i.e., elimination of these activities which require undue amount of time and effort but do not contribute to value;
   - To exercise scope/control over activities, i.e., an approved list of activities, also called the *work order,* should not include any activity which may affect progress of work, cost and time of completion; and
   - To exercise progress/control over activities, i.e., to keep record of what has been done and what remains to be done. The last activity relates to progress control.

2. **Progress measurement:** The concept of progress measurement stresses upon the physical progress and not upon the efforts or money spent. The physical progress can be calculated by dividing the total scope of work into measurable activities. Each activity is further divided into job steps. Each of these steps has a certain pre-determined percentage of progress which is measured towards the end of a job step. When all job steps of an activity are completed, the activity is said to be completed.

At each WBS level, the activities and their job steps needed to complete them may not require the same amount of effort and cost. Thus, to calculate the overall progress, the weightage to each WBS level is assigned in proportion to the cost contribution each level has towards the total cost of project. The weightage factor can be decided based upon the manhours required for each activity.

A project has to pass through various stages before completion. Three major phases of the project life may be:

   (*a*) Design and engineering phase;

   (*b*) Procurement of material equipment phase; and

   (*c*) Construction phase.

The present practice of measuring the progress may vary from firm to firm. However, few common methods are:

(*i*) Percentage Design Progress $= \dfrac{\text{Actual manhours spent as on date}}{\text{Estimated manhours}} \times 100 = D\%.$

(*ii*) Value of Material received on Site

$\qquad\qquad = \dfrac{\text{Percentage progress on value basis as on date}}{\text{Total value of material to be purchased}} \times 100.$

(*iii*) Percentage Progress on Efforts Basis $= \dfrac{\text{Manhours spent as on date}}{\text{Estimated procurement manhours}} \times 100.$

The progress of the project on a given date depends upon the progress made in various phases comprising the project. The complete progress for the total project can be worked out as follows:

$$\text{Total Project Progress} = \dfrac{p_1\,w_1 + p_2\,w_2 + p_3\,w_3}{w_1 + w_2 + w_3} = P\%$$

where p_1, p_2 and p_3 are the percentage progress made in each phase of the project and w_1, w_2, and w_3 are the weightages assigned to each phase. In general,

$$P\% = \sum_{i=1}^{n} p_i \, w_i \bigg/ \sum_{i=1}^{n} w_i$$

where $\sum_{i=1}^{n} w_i = 1$.

3. **Expediting and follow-up:** The process through which progress is ensured is called *expediting* and *follow-up*. Expediting acts as an external force to do work on a project towards its completion. However, the rate of progress may not be taking place in the desired manner or direction, and thus it calls for a *follow-up* of all commitments on a day-to-day basis or at some suitable intervals till the project is completed.

Expediting of a project is done not only by exerting pressure to hasten things but also by a continuous review of progress of the project and holding joint meetings of various agencies (*i*) to review progress, (*ii*) to know reasons for lack of progress, and (*iii*) to know the availability of resources at different workplaces, etc.

The actions and commitments taken during such meetings are recorded in the form of 'minutes of meeting' (MOM). The commitments in MOM are used later to carry out follow-up at specified intervals for ensuring desired progress.

Line of balance chart (LOB) is also used to compare commitments with the actual progress. LOB facilitates reading minimum progress required to be achieved at various phases of the project, and if not achieved it then indicates the workplaces where attention is required to be given.

12.10.2 Performance Control

Performance control is important because non-performance of any project is criticized by the society as well as by the operating personnel. Before exercising performance control it is essential to identify performance parameters and ensure right specifications, selection of right vendors/contractors, and right contractual stipulations regarding warranties (quality or performance the purchaser has a right to rely upon) and guarantees (obligations on the part of seller, contractor or manufacturer in the event of goods found defective or not meeting standards of performance).

Few critical parameters of performance control are: output, raw materials, and power consumption per unit of production. The plant design and specifications must be made in accordance with performance requirements.

To accommodate normal variations, control limits like *upper control limit* (UCL) and *lower control limit* (LCL) can also be introduced in view of non-adherence to exact performance measures. Thus, if performance stays within the control limits at various stages of development of the project then it will be considered under control.

1. **Change control procedure:** Any change in the pre-specified procedure or schedule is not allowed unless the project manager has been informed. To prevent such tendency of making changes, a system of regular reviews and checks must be instituted into the project management system. A system which ensures faithful transformation of design and specification into the job or product comprises *periodic review meetings* and *quality control*. Periodic review meetings are held to check and ensure that no change is made in the specification without proper authorization while quality control helps to ensure that product conforms to the specifications.

Sometimes it becomes essential to make changes due to compelling circumstances such as the availability of new technology, raw material, etc. In such circumstances, a change control system acts to record changes, examine changes requested by different agencies in the light of repurcussions on time, cost and performance schedules. Only after a careful study such changes should be allowed for implementation.

2. **Quality assurance plan:** Beside guarantee, the vendor is also asked to submit a quality assurance plan. This plan contains the list of all activities to be performed by the vendor's own quality control department and documentation to be maintained for review by the owner's inspection group at the vendor's place or by a third-party inspection agency. The inspection group has the authority to stop production in case of non-performance. Only after necessary rectification, the product will be allowed to be released for sale.

12.10.3 Schedule Control

Schedule control is exercised to ensure compliance with time schedule for the project. Schedules are prepared to provide a basis for direction, communication, coordination and progress control. In a given project, input for one group has to come from the output of another. Thus, to ensure even progress of each agency's work, continuous monitoring and control of project become essential which helps in adherence to the project schedule.

1. **Predictive schedule control:** Schedule control starts with the feedback of project completion activity. If this report indicates any possibility of delay in the project completion, then immediate investigations are ordered to find ways and means of bringing the project back to schedule. The ways and means suggested may include changes of engineering nature such as change in scope, cost, specifications, etc. (all to be processed through *change in order procedure* for implementation) as well as administrative changes such as more working hours, new working methods or simplifications, vigorous follow-up, etc. Such type of schedule control is known as predictive schedule control.

2. **Preventive schedule control:** The feedback report submitted to the project manager about the project completion may show a rosy picture. All those areas which normally delay a project need special attention and corrective action in advance.

Delay usually occurs more in the beginning of a project than towards the end. The delay towards the end is usually a hangover of the past. Thus, schedule control must start before and immediately after the zero-date.

The following is a list of a few important activities and/or areas which invariably cause delay and hence should be properly followed up to prevent delay:

  (a) Finalization of designs, specifications, etc.;
  (b) Short-listing of vendors, contractors;
  (c) Deciding purchase and contract procedures, overall project layout and project coordination procedure;
  (d) Finalization of task lists and operating level schedules;
  (e) Import licence;
  (f) Release of funds from financial institutions; and
  (g) Delivery of equipment and machinery.

12.10.4 Cost Control

Cost is one of the parameters, which reflects performance in all areas. Thus, the objective of cost control should be to monitor all cost components and ensure completion of the project at an optimal cost without lowering performance. The keys to effective cost control are detailed engineering design (an expenditure at the initial phases of the project) and commitment to control.

1. **Cost control stages:** There are three basic elements of cost—hardware cost, software cost and time induced cost. Hardware cost comprises of design and engineering and, therefore, can be controlled through these two aspects. Software cost comprises of systems and procedures and, therefore, can be controlled through them. Time-induced cost can be reduced by effective

scheduling and monitoring. Out of these three types of cost, the hardware cost forms a major part of the total cost. Since hardware cost is incurred before the zero-date of the project, more attention must be given towards such costs.

A few stages for ongoing cost control through design and engineering are listed below:

(*a*) Finalization of system design;

(*b*) Purchase/tender specifications;

(*c*) Review of vendor drawings; and

(*d*) Finalization of construction drawings.

2. **Cost control methods:** Value engineering is one of the methods which could be applied to reduce cost even before the finalization of the basic package or before the zero-date. Methods which can be used at different stages of the project for cost control are listed below:

(*a*) At zero-date;

(*b*) During detailed engineering;

(*c*) During procurement and sub-contracting; and

(*d*) During construction.

3. **Cost status reports:** A format indicating headwise budget may be used to administer the cost control system and the same must be reviewed first after the design, and then after commitment of expenditure and finally after actual expenditure. Every effort should be made to reduce cost using value engineering approach where there is a scope, specially during design and ordering stages.

An approach, called ABC (Always Better Control), may be used for selecting items for value analysis. In ABC analysis, items are classified into three categories *A*, *B* and *C* on the basis of estimated cost, and their representation in total number of items may be as follows:

Class	% of Total Items	% of Total Project Cost
A	10–20	70–85
B	20–30	10–25
C	60–70	5–15

However, the actual break points between these three categories are likely to vary depending upon complexity of the individual project and business.

12.11 Project Evaluation

The time and content of an evaluation is often determined outside the project or programme management. The evaluation is often considered as a control imposed on management. It helps to analyse the project and improve its management. Figure 12.21 shows the activities for those concerned with the project outcome and its evaluation.

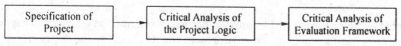

Fig. 12.21 Project outcome and its evaluation process

12.11.1 Major Problems of Evaluation Efforts

Definition of Evaluation

Evaluation, in its general sense, is used to describe a systematic framework to collect and analyse information on events associated with the implementation of the project with a view to improving upon its management. From this definition, some characteristics can be derived:

(*a*) Evaluation relates to management; and

(*b*) Management implies a certain amount of planning.

Utility of an Evaluation System

The purpose of evaluation is to improve the management system by (*a*) providing timely information on the success/failure of policy programmes and projects, and (*b*) assuring that the information is used by the decision-makers. This is possible only if the following conditions are fulfilled:

(*i*) The impact of the project is defined in measurable terms;

(*ii*) The information collected truly reflects the degree of attainment of the project's objectives;

(*iii*) There is an understanding of how the project's input and output are related to the project purpose; and

(*iv*) It is known for what type of decisions the information will be used and its relative importance in the decision-making process.

12.11.2 Types of Evaluation

All activities providing information for the measurement of projects are summed up in the term *evaluation*. There are different types of evaluation, and each of these has its own purpose and requirements. The task of setting up an evaluation system is to choose the ones, from among different evaluation types, which are adaptable to the information needs and the capacity of the project management.

Purpose of Evaluation

The evaluation intends to determine the type of data to be collected, degree of reliability and, therefore, the design of the evaluation and the significance and conclusiveness of the information collected.

The criterion to choose, from among different types of evaluation, concerns the potential of the evaluation to improve the project management and whether the information collected is relevant or can be obtained given the constraints under which the project is being executed.

A typology based on the purpose of evaluation is, therefore, necessary in attempting to discuss the 'worth' of various types of evaluation.

Accounting and Auditing

These are traditional means of ensuring that funds are spent in the manner these have been authorized and such spending complies with the administrative regulations. Since such regulations are administrative rather than management tools, these cannot be considered as types of evaluation.

Project Reporting System

The traditional reporting systems limit themselves to the financial and physical implementation of the project. Since these are administrative control devices, therefore these cannot be considered as types of evaluation. However, in a modern management system, project reporting is an integral part of the monitoring exercise.

Monitoring

The monitoring exercise is expected to provide necessary information on 'what is happening' (not only on the project itself but also on the environment and its effects on the target group) in order to assess progress towards achievement of the project objective. The results of monitoring are used (*a*) by the project management to know where the project stands; and (*b*) by the funding agency as an information tool to assess the project performance.

Process Evaluation

The process evaluation (also known as formative, developmental or ongoing evaluation) is expected to provide information on 'why it is happening (or why it is not happening)' in order to serve the operational needs of project personnel. While monitoring is a continuous exercise, process evaluation is an *ad hoc* attempt to solve a specific problem.

The process evaluation is particularly used (*a*) in experimental projects where little is known about how to produce the desired effects; and (*b*) to improve the performance of flexible treatments at relatively minor cost prior to dissemination.

Implementation Evaluation

The implementation evaluation, a control device, is used by the chief executive to determine whether the individual project has been executed according to the guidelines. He attempts to find out '... what transpires at the point of execution.'

Impact Evaluation

The impact evaluation (also called *ex-post evaluation*) attempts to identify all the effects of a project whether anticipated or not. It not only measures the effects of a project, but also attempts to validate or invalidate the logic of the project, i.e., hypotheses (or assumptions) that are linking the project's input to output, output to purpose and purpose to objective. Thus, impact evaluation has *four* goals:

(*a*) Identify whether the stated goals have been achieved;
(*b*) Attribute identified effects to the programme, i.e., rule out rival hypotheses by circumstantial evidence;
(*c*) Determine conditions under which project is most effective; and
(*d*) Delineate any unanticipated consequences or side effects of the implementation programme.

The *impact evaluation* is different from *process evaluation* and *monitoring* in regard to the following:

1. Impact evaluation is done at the end of the project or sometime after the end of the project. However, it does not mean that it is planned and executed at the end of the project. It requires information on the situation at the beginning of the project and during its execution. The decision whether to undertake an impact evaluation or not should, therefore, be taken at the beginning of the project.

2. Impact evaluation enquires about the question: 'what has happened' and 'why it has happened?' Since it attempts to attribute effects to the programme, it necessarily includes an implementation evaluation. It is obviously important to know what kind of programme has (or has not) produced the measured effects. An impact evaluation without an implementation evaluation risks attributing effects to a treatment that never existed or attributing the failure of a programme to the content of the programme rather than to its faulty execution.

3. Impact evaluation provides information to the chief executive or owner, and not to the project manager.

Evaluation Research

It is a scientific activity designed to assess the operation and impact. Evaluation research and impact evaluation enquire about the same set of questions. However, these differ in terms of methodology and thus in the degree of confidence one can put into the result of the evaluation. The evaluation research rules out rival hypotheses by the use of statistical methods to arrive at a definite conclusion concerning the value of a given policy action.

The different types of evaluation and their characteristics are summarized in Table 12.3.

Table 12.3 Types of Evaluation and their Characteristics

Type of Evaluation	Characteristics			
	Purpose	Timing	Type of Information	Expected Results
Accounting and auditing	Control	Accounting; continuous auditing; periodical	Financial	Improved financial administration

Contd...

Type of Evaluation	Characteristics			
	Purpose	*Timing*	*Type of Information*	*Expected Results*
Reporting (Traditional)	Control	Periodical	Input/output	Improved administration of products and services
Reporting/ Monitoring	Determine what is happening	Continuous	Input/output purpose, inter-vening variables	Improved management of projects
Process evaluation	Determine why it is happening	*Ad hoc* or periodical	Input/output process; purpose	More efficient manage-ment of project components
Implementation evaluation	Determine exe-cution of project components	Periodical	Input; process	Improved management of content of project activities
Impactor ex-post evaluation	Determine effects of project	Data collection: beginning/end of project analysis: end of project	Input/output purpose, goal, hypotheses	Improved programmed management
Evaluation research	Determine effects of policy	Data collection: periodical analysis end of project	Input/output purpose goal, hypotheses	Improved policy manage-ment and planning

12.11.3 Setting up an Evaluation System for an Agency

The specific steps and results of setting up an evaluation system for an agency are outlined as follows:

Analytical Steps	Product
1. *Analysis of management structure*	
Decision-making procedure	Diagram
↓	
Information needs	Preliminary theoretical list of information requirement
↓	
Capacity of information collection	Feasible list of information requirements
2. *Scrutiny of information users*	
Willingness to use information	Feasibility list of useful information require-ments
↓	
Timing of information needs	Feasible list of useful information that can be made available when needed
↓	
Acceptability of the presentation of information	Reporting system for the information
3. *Scrutiny of uses of information*	
• Importance of information for decision	
• Importance of decision for programme	Required accuracy of information
	↓
• Information collection capabilities	Feasible accuracy of information
4 *Choice of an evaluation programme*	
• Comparison: needs and resources	List of programmes and projects to be evaluated
• Comparison of different types of evaluation	Type of evaluation design appropriate for specific information needs

12.11.4 Setting up an Evaluation System for a Specific Project

Once it has been decided that a specific project should be evaluated, the following information will determine the type of evaluation system chosen:

1. What should be measured?
2. For whom should it be measured?
3. For what should it be measured?
4. How should it be measured?
5. How should the data be collected?
6. When and in which form is the information needed?
7. Who collects, analyses and presents the information?

The summary of the analytical steps and their results in setting up an evaluation system for a specific project is as follows:

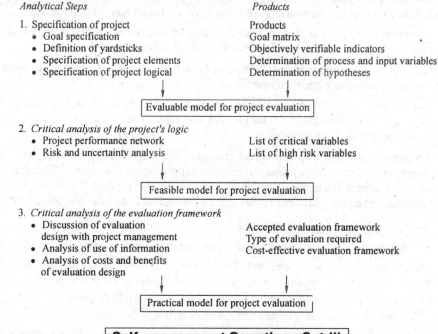

Analytical Steps	Products
1. Specification of project	Products
• Goal specification	Goal matrix
• Definition of yardsticks	Objectively verifiable indicators
• Specification of project elements	Determination of process and input variables
• Specification of project logical	Determination of hypotheses

Evaluable model for project evaluation

2. *Critical analysis of the project's logic*
   • Project performance network — List of critical variables
   • Risk and uncertainty analysis — List of high risk variables

Feasible model for project evaluation

3. *Critical analysis of the evaluation framework*
   • Discussion of evaluation design with project management — Accepted evaluation framework
   • Analysis of use of information — Type of evaluation required
   • Analysis of costs and benefits of evaluation design — Cost-effective evaluation framework

Practical model for project evaluation

Self-assessment Questions Set-III

1. What are the various stages of project implementation phase of a project?
2. Explain the possible places of a project manager in the project organization and also the range of his authority.
3. What is a project system? Explain various types of sub-systems of a project system.
4. What are the elements of the project management system?
5. What do you understand by the terms planning, scheduling and monitoring in the context of project management?
6. What are the basic issues involved in the process of project scheduling?
7. Name the various techniques of project scheduling and also highlight their salient features.
8. Distinguish between different categories of project schedules and their hierarchy with techniques and levels of management.
9. Explain in detail various steps involved in monitoring and the role of a monitor.
10. What do you understand by project control?
11. Name and discuss various aspects of project control.
12. Consider a project involving repair of an existing building. Discuss the steps involved in project formulation and implementation strategies.
13. How is a project network used for monitoring, control and evaluation?
14. Prepare a flow diagram of various activities concerned with the project outcome and its evaluation.
15. What are major problems associated with the project evaluation efforts?
16. Discuss various types of project evaluations and their characteristics.
17. What are the analytical steps involved in the process of setting up an evaluation system?

12.12 Computer Aided Project Management

When the size of the project increases, it becomes difficult and at times even impossible to plan, schedule, budget and control project activities using manual techniques. Hence, for large projects the task is made easier with the use of computers. It is, therefore, necessary to have computerized project management system (CPMS) for projects of bigger size and complex nature. The advantages of using CPMS are as under:

- A CPMS can analyse the problem at a very high speed as compared to manual analysis. Because of its high speed, any number of permutations and combinations can be handled with ease which cannot be done manually. For example, sensitivity analysis of profitability estimate can be done using computers by varying the different parameters and studying their impact on profit. Carrying out such an analysis manually is very difficult and tiresome task.

- Since computers can store and process large volumes of data, CPMS is best suited for large and complex projects that require handling and analysis of voluminous data.

- Accuracy of results produced by CPMS can be relied upon while there is an element of committing mistakes in manual computations.

- A CPMS reduces the human resource requirements considerably. A well versed computer programmer can replace many of the clerical and support staff and thus CPMS improves efficiency and economy of projects.

- Since a project manager, who is in direct control of the project, can himself directly interact with computers and analyse the problem rather than depending upon too many of his subordinates, he can plan properly and arrive at optimum decisions. It also relieves the project manager of daily routines and makes more time available at his disposal so that he can plan and act efficiently.

12.12.1 Project Management Softwares

Some of the common, but essential requirements of project management softwares are as under:

- The project management software should be able to handle multiple projects together. In other words, it should have the capacity to integrate the different projects that are in progress at the same time and to produce consolidated reports of all the on-going projects.

- It should support a variety of graphs and reports in different formats.

- It should have filtering capacity to extract a set tasks and milestones from a scheme for the purpose of analysis and for producing the required reports.

- It should support a range of file formats for importing and exporting data.

  Some of the desired features of project management softwares are as under:

- The project management software should be, as far as possible, one that is compatible with the software currently being used by the organization.

- It should be easy to learn and easy to implement.

- It should have extensive on-line help so that the learner will gain confidence in putting the software to use without apprehension.

- It should have the capacity to solve a wide range of problems.

- It should have the capacity to produce the reports required by the management and in the desired format.

- As far as possible, it should have the facility to operate on the existing network environment.

12.12.2 Software Packages for CPMS

The first project management software tools were developed in the late 1960s. The early software tools developed were mainly for the mainframe computers. During the 1970s and 1980s project management software packages suitable for microcomputers were developed and by 1990 there were over 100 project management software packages available for use. Though there are many software packages available today, only a few are widely used since many project management software packages are not comprehensive in their coverage, but were mainly meant for specified project management areas. Some of the popular software packages used in project management are as under:

Microsoft Project
Harvard Total Project Manager
Project Planner
PRISM
YOGNA
INSTA PLAN
Quick Net
PC-projaks
Proman
Project Scheduler 8

PRISM, the software package developed by Tata Consultancy Services and INSTA PLAN, the package developed by WIPRO, are popular among Indian project managers.

PRISM determines the sequence of activities and the duration within which each activity must be completed in order to meet a given project schedule. For a given budget, PRISM can determine the minimum time within which the project must be completed. The details of all the available resources can be fed into a resource pool. PRISM automatically schedules activities based on the resource requirement of each activity and referring to the resource pool for the availability of resources. PRISM provides many pre-designed reports like the list of critical activities, the list of activities that are currently in progress, variations in the duration of activities completed so far, activities that lag behind the schedule and many other useful reports. PRISM also supports a powerful graphic generator that provides the user with many useful charts like Bar chart, time-cost trade off curves, resource histograms, cash flow graphs, network diagrams, etc.

INSTA PLAN provides project planning facilities and also has presentation features.

It provides four types of reports and three types of presentation charts. INSTA PLAN is gaining acceptance because of its simplicity for use.

12.12.3 Microsoft Project 2000

Microsoft Project is the most popular among the available project management software packages. Project 2000 software supports many project management areas like scheduling, budgeting, resource management, charting, performance monitoring, risk management, analysis, reporting and communication.

Project 2000 also offers the facility to manage multiple projects. It also provides for sharing of resources between the projects and export/import of project data among the multiple projects being handled.

The various features and facilities available in Project 2000 package are explained below.

Gantt Chart

A Gantt chart shows the sequence of activities. While a traditional Gantt chart shows the relationship between various activities by way of a bar diagram. Project 2000 uses a modified Gantt chart that includes links to show the relationship between the activities. Adding link lines to Gantt chart clearly indicates the series and parallel relationship between the activities (Fig. 12.22).

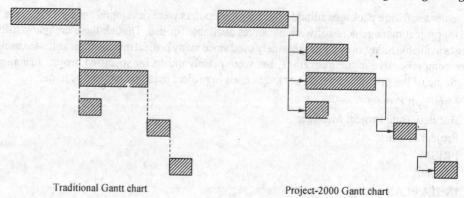

Traditional Gantt chart   Project-2000 Gantt chart

Fig. 12.22

Project Baseline

Any project plan is finalized after a lot of deliberations, corrections, modifications and revisions. Once the project plan is finalized, it is to be 'stored' as a reference. Project 2000 uses a 'baseline' for storing the project plan. A baseline is a project plan containing the original estimates for tasks, resources, assignments and costs. Data as per the plan like start and finish dates of tasks, duration of tasks, splits in tasks, costs of tasks, etc. are captured in a baseline. Once a baseline is formed and stored, it is used as a reference for comparing the actual progress with the planned progress. The comparison can be made either in terms of cost or in terms of time.

Splitting Tasks

When a project is under implementation, a task may need to be splitted. Suppose a person, who is attending a particular ask, requiring two months duration, goes on leave after one month. Instead of waiting for one month till the person rejoins, the task can be split so that a portion is completed before the person goes on leave and the remaining portion after the person rejoins the team. The rest of the tasks can be accordingly realigned provided that such splitting of a task does not bring forth any error in the logical sequence of tasks. Project 2000 provides facilities for splitting tasks and revising the project schedule suitably.

Schedule Processing (or relating tasks with one another)

Tasks in a project are to be properly linked. Once proper link is established between the different tasks, the project schedule can be altered suitably whenever there are changes in the start/completion time(s) of some of the tasks. Project 2000 links the tasks by establishing the relationship between the different tasks. When tasks are linked, the task that must be started or completed first is called the predecessor and task that depends on the predecessor is called the successor. Project 2000 uses the following relationships for linking the tasks:

- Finish-to-start
- Start-to-start
- Finish-to-finish
- Start-to-finish

The finish-to-start relationship is the default relationship in Project 2000, since it is the relationship most commonly come across. If there is a finish-to-start relationship between two tasks, one task cannot start until another task finishes. A start-to-start relationship is one in which one task cannot start until another task starts. A finish-to-finish relationship is one in which one task cannot finish until another task finishes. In a start-to-finish relationship, the finish date of one task depends on the start date of another task. The relationship between the different tasks of a project is to be carefully studied before establishing the links. Any error in establishing the links properly will result in faulty scheduling logic and the results will be wrong. Links between the different tasks can be established in Project 2000 using any one of the following facilities available:

1. Toolbar or menu commands.
2. Task information dialog box or task tables.
3. Drag and drop using the mouse.

Project 2000 also provides facilities for modifying the task relationships. It may be likely that the task relationship is not correctly established for all the tasks at the first instance itself, especially for bigger projects. Further, when a task is removed or a new task is inserted or a task is moved, Project 2000 automatically repairs the broken links created due to such modifications when 'Autolink' option is enabled.

Project Cost Estimation

Project 2000 arrives at the project cost by arriving at the costs of individual tasks indirectly. Every activity consumes resources. Costs are assigned to resources and resources are in turn assigned to tasks. Cost of a task is arrived at by the software by multiplying the resource required to complete a task with the cost of the resource. A resource pool is created that includes all the resources used in the project. Resources are grouped into two categories, *viz.*, work resources and material resources. Work resources are the people and equipment assigned to a task. Material resources are supplies, stock and other consumable items used to complete the tasks. Details about the work resources and material resources are entered in the 'Resource Sheet'. The resource sheet contains, *inter alia*, fields like resource name, resource type (work or material), standard rate, etc. Apart from creating a resource pool, the resource must be assigned to tasks so that cost of each task can be arrived at. 'Resource assignment' relates a task to the resources responsible for the task. Resources can be assigned to tasks by using the 'Assign Resources Dialog Box' or by using the 'Task Form'

After tasks, resources and their costs and resource assignments are entered. Project budget (i.e., estimated project cost) can be arrived at easily.

Monitoring the Progress of Project (Earned value analysis)

Project 2000 includes tools for Earned Value Analysis, also called BCWP (Budgeted Cost of Work Performed) analysis. Earned Value Analysis measures key performance indicators and compares them to the baseline parameters. The difference (or variance) between the baseline and actual performance can be calculated which indicates whether the project is being implemented as planned. Project 2000 can measure both cost variance (the difference between the task's planned cost and actual cost) and schedule variance (the difference between the actual progress and the scheduled progress of a task).

For calculating the variance, the upto date progress of the project is to be entered into the package. Project data can be updated using 'Tracking Table' in the 'Task Sheet View'. This table contains fields like actual start date, actual finish date, percentage of actual completion, actual duration, remaining duration, actual cost and actual work. Once all the required data on the actual progress of the project are entered, Project 2000 can calculate the variances. Variances can be viewed by switching to 'Tracking Gantt View' and selecting 'Variance Table'. The variance table gives the baseline data and the variances of all tasks.

'Earned Value Table' of Project 2000 gives the following estimates at any point of time:

BCWS : Budgeted Cost of Work Scheduled
BCWP : Budgeted Cost of Work Performed
ACWP : Actual Cost of Work Performed
SV : Schedule Variance [BCWP-BCWS]

CV   : Cost Variance [BCWP-ACWP]

EAC   : Estimate at Completion (i.e., the estimate of cost if the remainder of the task's work is completed as budgeted)

BAC   : Baseline cost at Completion

VAC   : Variance at Completion (BAC-EAC]

Using the above information furnished by Project 2000, two important indices can be calculated, *viz.*,

Schedule Performance Index (SPI)   : BCWP/BCWS

and

Cost Performance Index (CPI)   : BCWP/ACWP

When SPI is greater than 1, the actual cost incurred is more than the budgeted cost; when CPI is greater than 1, the actual cost incurred is less than the budgeted cost.

Resource Levelling

Project 2000 provides two options for resource levelling. Resource levelling can be done within a specified range of dates or for the entire project. Project 2000 allows two methods of levelling, *viz.*, 'automatic' and 'manual' levelling. When automatic levelling option is chosen, the project will adjust tasks as soon as a task is changed or assigned a resource that results in over allocation, i.e., the software checks for over allocation after each entry. Hence, choosing automatic levelling option will slow down the overall performance of the software. If manual option is chosen, the discretion to level the resources is given to the project manager. When he chooses to level the resources, he can open 'Resource Levelling Dialog Box' and click 'Level now' to level the resources.

Project 2000 will not delay tasks that have the following constraints:

• Must finish on

• Must start on

• As late as possible (for projects scheduled from the start date)

• As soon as possible (for projects scheduled from the finish date).

It may be noted that when the constraint 'Must finish on _____' is not given to any of the tasks, it means that there is no constraint on project completion time. In this case, the resource allocation will be optimum and the resource allocation will amount to 'resource smoothing'.

Before using Project 2000's levelling feature, the constraints and priority settings for the critical tasks are to be defined. Priority setting for tasks can be given in the range 0 to 1000. If a task is set a priority of 1000, Project 2000 will not delay this task.

Resource Pool

A resource pool is a project file that contains resource information of an organization. The main idea behind creating a resource pool is to facilitate sharing of resources among multiple projects. When an organization handles multiple projects at a time, it becomes efficient to distribute resource from the resource pool instead of allocating resources for the individual projects exclusively. The multiple projects that are under implementation/to be implemented can be assigned priority, by assigning a number from 0 to 1000 in order to rank them in the order of their relative importance. A project that is given the highest priority (i.e., assigned the highest number) will receive top consideration while allocating resources from the resource pool; projects with lower priority will receive lower consideration while allocating resources. This arrangement will help to handle situations in which there is a conflict for resource sharing among the multiple projects.

PERT

Three time estimates are used in PERT, *viz.*, the optimistic time, the pessimistic time and the most likely time. The three time durations are weighted and averaged to determine the expected duration of the tasks. Weights are to be assigned to three time estimates so that Project 2000 can arrive at the expected time of the tasks and use the same in PERT calculations. The default settings for weights are as under:

Optimistic : 1

Expected : 4

Pessimistic : 1

[Project 2000 uses the term 'Expected' time for the 'Most Likely' time].

The above default settings for the weights of the three time estimates are based on the assumption of normal distribution for the time estimates. If there is evidence that the distribution of time estimates will not follow normal distribution, the weights can be altered. Project 2000 permits allocation of different weights by the user depending on his perception of the distribution of time estimates. For example, the user can alter the weights for three time estimates as under:

$$\begin{array}{l} \text{Optimistic : } 0.50 \\ \text{Expected : } 4.00 \\ \text{Pessimistic : } 1.50 \end{array}\Bigg\} \text{ (or) } \begin{array}{l} \text{Optimistic : } 1.50 \\ \text{Expected : } 4.00 \\ \text{Pessimistic : } 0.50 \end{array}\Bigg\} \text{ (or) } \begin{array}{l} \text{Optimistic : } 0.40 \\ \text{Expected : } 3.60 \\ \text{Pessimistic : } 2.50 \end{array}\Bigg\} \text{ etc.}$$

After three time estimates and their weights are fed in, Project 2000 provides views of Gantt and expected Gantt chart can be seen. Critical path can be viewed by choosing 'View' menu and further choosing 'Network diagram' from 'View' menu. Project 2000 also provides filter facility to view network diagram. When the filter facility is used, the network diagram will display only the critical tasks on the screen that require the attention of the project manager.

Reports

Project 2000 provides the following built-in reports:

- Overview reports
- Current activity reports
- Cost reports
- Assignment reports
- Workload reports.

Overview reports: An overview report provides an overview of the following aspects of the project at a fixed point in time:

1. Project summary. [This report compares the actual dates, duration, work, total costs and task status with the project baseline].

2. Top level tasks. [This report provides the name, duration, start date and finish date for the highest level tasks and summary tasks, based on the outline].

3. Critical tasks. [This report provides the start and end dates for all critical tasks, including the preceding and succeeding tasks for each critical task].

4. Milestones. [This report shows the milestone tasks sorted in ascending order by start date; the sort order can also be changed by the user. **Note:** Milestones are tasks that usually have no duration and mark the completion of a significant phase of the project].

Current activity reports: The current activity reports are task-focused reports. If desired, the user can add resource information to these reports by customizing the reports. Project 2000 provides the following reports under this head:

1. Unstarted tasks. [This report shows that tasks that have not yet begun. The immediate predecessors of such tasks are also given].

2. Tasks starting soon. [This report gives the tasks that are scheduled to start within the date chosen by the user].

3. Tasks in progress. [This report shows the tasks that have already started. The resource information associated with these tasks are also given].

4. Completed tasks. [This report shows the tasks that have been completed. The start and finish dates of the completed tasks are also given].

5. Should have started tasks. [This report shows the tasks that should have started by the time chosen but have not yet started].

6. Slipping tasks. [This report shows the tasks that have been rescheduled beyond the baseline start date].

Cost reports: Cost of project is a main consideration for the project manager. A project might have been completed within the pre-planned completion date. However, if the cost of completion had doubled as compared to the budgeted cost, there is no merit in having completed the project in time. Thus, cost reports help the project manager to identify the deviations in cost and provide an opportunity to correct the discrepancies in order to contain the cost.

Project 2000 provides the following reports under this head:

1. Cash flow. [This report shows the weekly cost of the project, giving the break-up details of the cost of different tasks. The report can be customized to show different time units, say, in terms of monthly cost, biweekly cost, etc.].

2. Budget. [This reports shows the actual cost vs. the budget cost per task].

3. Overbudget tasks. [This report shows the tasks whose actual costs have exceeded the baseline costs].

4. Overbudget resources. [This report shows the resources whose actual costs have exceeded the baseline costs].

5. Earned Value. [This report shows how much of the budget should have been spent by this time (i.e., as of current date) based on total work and resource costs].

Assignment reports: Resource reporting is the focus of the assignment reports. Project 2000 provides the following reports under this head:

1. Who does what. [This report shows each resource and the tasks assigned for each resource].

2. Who does what when. [This report shows each resource and the tasks assigned for each resource along with a calender showing the daily work assigned for each task].

3. To do list. [This report shows the list of tasks for the chosen resource along with start and finish dates, duration, predecessor task and other assigned resources. If a task has already been completed, it is checked off in the report].

4. Overallocated resources. [This report shows the list of overallocated resources with their assigned tasks, including start and finish dates, duration and delay].

Workload report: There are two forms of workload reports, *viz.*, the task usage report and the resource usage report. The task usage report lists the tasks and their assigned resources in the first column. The rest of the columns are dates in increments of one week. Under the date columns, the work scheduled for each task and for each resource are displayed. The resource usage report is similar to 'Who does what when' report.

12.12.4 Enterprise-wide Project Management

It is a web based project management system in which multiple project summaries are monitored from one central location. It allows for collaborative planning among project managers and project executives, thus facilitating web based resource management and reporting. '*Microsoft Project Central*' and '*Project Communicator*' are the two popular web based project management software tools. The interaction between the project manager and different project teams located at different locations is achieved through web.

The project manager prepares project schedule, resource allocation plans, etc., with the help of a project management software and put the data on the internet server. The team members, who are incharge of actual execution of projects at different locations, access the web site and collect the required data sent by the project manager. The team members submit actual work times, actual resource requirements, etc. back to the project manager through the internet server. The project manager accesses the responses from the team members, revises his estimates if need be, and re-submit the revised plan of action. Thus, the system provides for continuous interaction between the different personnel involved in project execution at different project sites, which helps in better monitoring and efficient utilization of resources.

12.12.5 Spread Sheets for Financial Projections

Spread sheet packages like Lotus-123 and MS Excel help in developing financial projections like profitability estimates, cash-flow estimates, break even estimates, etc. The design of spread sheet software, that provides cells in which formulae and functions can be embedded, is best suited for easily developing software packages for financial projections. The greatest advantage of a spread sheet package is that it helps in carrying out sensitivity analysis of financial projections. Any or all of the parameters used in financial projections can be altered and the variations in the results can be studied. Such 'what-if' analysis can be done using other software packages only with a great level of programming skills. Spread sheet also supports a variety of graphical views which can be used to depict the financial projections in graphical form.

12.13 Some Essentials in Project Management

Bank Guarantee: 'Bank guarantee', as the word implies, is an assurance given by the bank. In any transaction, there are two parties, the seller and the buyer. The bank may offer its guarantee either on behalf of the seller or on behalf of the buyer as the situation demands. A more precise definition of 'bank guarantee' is that it is a contingent contract in which the bank agrees to fulfil certain obligations upon happening of some event; the contingent contract becomes a full fledged contract upon happening of the event which is the subject matter of the contract. Banks charge a guarantee fee from their customers on whose behalf they offer their guarantee.

Bank guarantee can be broadly grouped into *three* types. They are:

- Financial guarantee
- Performance guarantee
- Deferred payment guarantee.

Financial guarantee: When a bank gives financial guarantee on behalf of its customer, the bank undertakes to discharge some monetary obligation of its customer. Examples of financial guarantee include the guarantee given by the bank to a civil engineering contractor to deposit Earnest Money Deposit (E.M.D.) for participating in tenders. As per the tender procedure, the E.M.D. deposited by the successful tenderer is retained and the E.M.D deposited by all other tenderers, who are unsuccessful, will be refunded. Hence, it will be advantageous for a civil contractor who is bidding for a contract to give bank guarantee instead of depositing E.M.D. in cash as depositing of E.M.D. in cash will affect the liquidity position of the contractor. Similarly situations arise in meeting the monetary obligations of courts, custom departments, income-tax department, etc.

Performance guarantee: These are the guarantees issued by a bank for the performance of a specific contract or obligation. In case of non-performance of the contract/obligation (by the bank's client on behalf of whom the bank has given its guarantee), the bank is required to compensate the losses incurred due to the non-fulfilment of the contract/obligation. For example, when an entrepreneur approaches a bank/financial institution for term loan for the purchase of a capital equipment and if the bank/financial institution is not familiar with the equipment supplier or with the equipment and also in cases where the success of the project mainly depends upon the correct performance of the equipment, the bank/financial institution may prefer to take suitable precautions and may insist the equipment supplier to give a performance guarantee. The performance guarantee might contain conditions like achievement of rated output of the equipment, quality of output as per the prescribed specifications, etc. In case the capital equipment does not give the required performance as per terms of the guarantee, the guarantee can be invoked (by the purchaser or by the bank/financial institution as the case may be) and once the guarantee is invoked, the guarantor (i.e., the bank that has offered its guarantee in favour of the equipment supplier) is required to make good the loss due to equipment's underperformance, as per the terms stipulated in the performance guarantee.

Deferred payment guarantee: As the name implies 'deferred payment guarantee' is a guarantee given by a bank for the deferred payment. When an entrepreneur is in need of a capital equipment and if the supplier of the capital equipment is prepared to supply the equipment on deferred payment basis on the strength of a bank guarantee in his favour, the purchaser of the equipment arranges for a bank guarantee in favour of the supplier. (Of course, the buyer of the equipment might pay outright the cost of the equipment if he has cash in hand and the question of deferred payment arises only when the buyer is short of the required money). The banker guarantees deferred payment by the purchaser of the equipment as per the terms of the deferred payment agreement between the seller and the buyer. If, for example, the cost of the capital equipment is Rs 50 lakhs and if the supplier demands an immediate payment of Rs 10 lakhs and expects the balance amount of Rs 40 lakhs to be paid in 20 monthly instalments of Rs 2 lakhs each along with monthly interest on the balance amount payable at the rate of 15% per annum, the buyer of the equipment arranges for a guarantee to suit the terms of the repayment. By giving the guarantee, the banker guarantees the supplier of the equipment, payment of the deferred instalments by the buyer. In case the buyer fails to pay the stipulated deferred instalments to the seller and if the seller invokes the guarantee, the banker is under obligation to pay to the equipment supplier as per the terms of the deferred payment guarantee.

BOOT (Build, Own, Operate, Transfer) Projects: BOOT project have their origin in Turkey, where the formula for building up of mega projects was tried in 1980s. There are two parties to a BOOT project, *viz.*, the principal project promoter (usually, the Government) and a private participant. The private participant arranges the finance required for the project, build the project and maintain the project during the contracted period. Finally, the private participant transfers the project to the principal at no cost. During the contracted period, the private participant owns and operates facilities and tries to recover his investment, cost of investment, maintenance expenses and also earn profit on his investment.

The contract between the principal and the private participant is known as the *concession agreement*. All the terms of the contract, like the concession offered by the principal, the role of the private participant, the terms of financial arrangement, construction, maintenance, revenue realization, termination of the contract, etc. as contained in the concession agreement. Highways, bridges, water supply lines, gas/oil pipelines, hydroelectric power stations, etc. are some of the projects suitable for BOOT arrangement. The land required for such projects are normally acquired by the Government (the principal) and offered to the private investor for the construction of the project as per the terms of the concession agreement.

The period of contract (after which the private participant is to handover the project to the principal) is generally very high ranging from 20 to 40 years or even more, depending on the pay-back period of the project. The payback period of such projects are normally very high in view of the huge investment required and comparatively lower returns on the investment.

BOOT projects are useful for the development of infrastructure of a country. Without such an arrangement, neither the Government will have the required resources and inclination to build such projects nor the private entrepreneurs will take up such projects.

Some of the other variants of BOOT projects are as under:

BOO (Build, Own, Operate) projects: The private investors execute the project, own and operate the infrastructural assets created for the whole life. Since the private investors become the sole owners and operators of the assets, they can even mortgage the assets to banks/financial institutions and arrange for the finance required to build the project.

BOLT (Build, Operate, Lease, Transfer) projects: The private investors build and operate the project for a specified period of time. After the end of the pre-fixed period, they handover the project to the Government (the principal) on lease. The Government, which takes over the project in the capacity of lessee, pays periodical lease rentals to the private investors for the rest of the life of the project.

There are also some other variants of BOOT projects like BTO (Build, Transfer, Operate), BRT (Build, Rent, Transfer), BOD (Build, Operate, Deliver), BOOST (Build, Own, Operate, Subsidise, Transfer), etc.

Choice between mutually exclusive investments of unequal life: Mutually exclusive investments are those out of which only one can be chosen. Suppose one wants to purchase a car. There are so many models and varieties of cars available. But the requirement is to purchase only one car. The choice is made by comparing the pros and cons. Similarly when a choice is to be made from a few mutually exclusive investment options of equal life, the problem is a simpler one. The present value of costs associated with the available investment options can be studied and the choice can be made by choosing the investment option for which the present value of costs is minimum. The problem gets little complicated if the lives of the projects (i.e., investments) are unequal

Self-assessment Questions Set-IV

1. What do you understand by computerized project management system? Outline the advantages of using CPMS.
2. Explain the essential requirements of project management softwares. Also, mention its desirable features.
3. What are the important software packages used in project management?
4. Explain various features and facilities available in Project-2000 package.
5. How are multiple project summaries monitored from one central location? Explain with the help of a net diagram.
6. Write short notes on the following:
   (a) Bank guarantee,
   (b) Financial guarantee,
   (c) Performance guarantee,
   (d) Deferred payment guarantee, and
   (e) BOOT, including BOO and BOLT.

Information Technology and Management

13.1 Introduction

The term 'information technology' (IT) was coined during the late 1970s. It refers to information handling through the computer-based technology. Grauer (2000) categorizes the application of IT into seven main areas: information systems; personal computing; science and research; process/device control; education; computer-aided design (CAD), and artificial intelligence. Technology benefits are many such as cost savings, improved productivity, enhanced customer service, company-wide knowledge base, increased employee involvement in decision-making and improved quality of work life. However, disadvantages of technology are initial cost outlay, time tag between outlay and benefits, job displacement, increased employee isolation, and opportunities for fraud and other related activities. The twenty-first century witnessed advances from an age of automation to an era of digitisation (built on zeros and ones). It started with computer technology which changed from mainframe to personal computer to net personal computers. Along with these changes, there were changes in softwares. As network started, there was a convergence of telecom with computers. The nature of data transmission using telecom and subsequent development of wireless phone and mobile have revolutionised the information processing system.

Similarly there is a shift in business models to move beyond automation to innovation. The potential of information systems (IS) is to exploit the power of people's creativity. Feraud (1999) suggested the cascade model of the evolution of information management. The adoption of IT consists of a series of jumps. They are:

- As the organization faces an information-processing crisis, it adopts the IT solution.
- Then the organization tries to build its IT competence through trial and error.
- Next jump is to expand the scope of IT.
- Final jump is to use IT to drive the strategy and have a competitive advantage.

Emerging economic trend is based on several layers such as social organization, enterpreneurship, knowledge creation, workforce skillsets, infrastructural tools, and natural resources. The important change in the third industrial revolution is occurring in retailing. It is moving from national to global and this transition is more turbulent than earlier industrial revolutions.

13.2 Information

The nature and scope of information required by managers at different levels in an organization varies considerably. Organizations require different types of information systems to meet their needs. Therefore, information can be defined as the data which is organised and presented at a time and place so that the decision-maker may take necessary action. In other words, information is the result/product of processing data. The conversion process of data into decision is shown in Fig. 13.1.

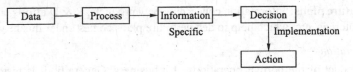

Fig. 13.1 Conversion of data into decision

From Fig. 13.1, it is seen that information consists of data that has been retrieved, processed or otherwise used, for informative or inferential purposes, arguments, or as a basis for forecasting. For example, some supporting documents, ledgers and so on, which comprise source material for profit and loss statements, may be used by the decision-maker for profit planning and control, or for other decision-making purposes. In fact, the relation of data with information is that of raw material to finished product. As mentioned earlier, information resources could supplement the existing list of 5 Ms by introducing messages and moments in the context of information resource management. Information resources (in the sense of stored data of all types) are reusable.

Information contains an element of surprise, reduces uncertainty and triggers off action. It carries messages and when perceived by the recipients via any of the senses, it increases their state of knowledge or intelligence.

For planning information, requirements of decision-makers can be classified into three broad types as enumerated below:

Environmental Information

Environmental information requirement can be further classified and described as follows:

1. **Government policies:** Information about Government policies or financial and tax affairs, political stability, etc. is required and may have a significant effect on future planning decisions.
2. **Economic trends:** It includes information about (*a*) economic indicators like employment, productivity, capital investment; (*b*) prices and wage levels which affect all organizations regardless of product or services; and (*c*) GNP level, trend and consumer disposable income.
3. **Technological environment:** The information on technological changes or advancements is necessary for forecasting such changes in the firm and their probable effects on the same. It is also desirable to assess the effect of technical changes on new products and processes.
4. **Factors of production:** These include information about the source, cost, location, availability, accessibility and productivity of the major factors of production such as (*a*) labour; (*b*) materials and spare parts; and (*c*) capital.

Competitive Information

Competitive information requirement can be classified and described as follows:

1. **Industry demand:** This refers to the demand forecast of the industry for the product manufactured or about the area in which the firm is operating.
2. **Firm demand:** This implies assessment of the firm's capabilities, activities and potentialities to meet demand relative to the capabilities and actions of the competing firms.
3. **The competition:** This includes information about competing firms for forecasting own product demand and making decisions and plans to achieve the forecast. Such information falls into *three* categories:
   (*a*) **Past performance:** It encompasses information concerning profitability, return on investment, market share, etc. which helps to provide a yardstick for setting performance objectives for future;
   (*b*) **Present activity:** Under this heading comes information concerning competitor's price strategies, advertising campaigns, product mix, changes in distribution channels, etc. which help to evaluate one's own weaknesses or strengths; and

(c) **Future plans:** Information concerning new products, R & D efforts, availability of raw materials, etc. which help to decide future plans comes under this head.

Internal Information

It is the by-product of the normal operations of a business. Generally, it is historical or static in nature; it is after the fact data.

Internal information is aimed at identification of the firm's strengths and weaknesses. It includes the following:

1. **Sales forecast:** Since all other internal plans of the firm are guided by the sales plan, it is consi-dered as the dominant premise internal to the firm.

2. **The financial plan:** Information on financial or budget plan is important because it represents a quantitative and time bound commitment about the allocation of total resources (workers, plant, materials, overheads, administrative expenses) of the firm. It provides information about a number of sub-plans of the firm and it acts as an important link between all activities of the firm.

3. **Supply factors:** Information concerning availability and limitations of certain supply factors such as labour, capital, plant and equipment is important as these factors play a vital role in developing the financial and subsidiary plans for achieving firm's objectives.

4. **Policies:** Long-term basic policies on product range, marketing, finance and about personnel do not permit flexibility in developing alternative courses of action in the short run.

13.2.1 Information Needs and Its Economics

The availability of information to management at various levels has improved due to *three* reasons:

1. **Development of telecommunications:** The information flow has been accelerated with developments in communication technology like radio telephoney, microwave communication, laser communication and satellite communication.

2. **Processing of data with computer:** The accessibility of information has been considerably improved as a computer can readily scan the available stored data to provide the required information.

3. **Video technology:** Video technology permits the recording of activities on video cassettes and video discs. By combining the functions of TV set and a computer it is possible to produce a video text which can be a storehouse for handy information.

Table 13.1 summarizes the information needs at various levels of management. All managers, whatever be their level in an organization, are engaged in making decisions. It is only in the degree, influence and time-span that decisions made at various levels of management differ.

13.2.2 Information Classification

The information obtained and used in the organizations can be classified into *five* categories:

1. **Action vs. non-action information:** The information (or data) lying unnoticed is called non-action information, but the same information (or data) when processed and used in some context by the recipient is called *action information*.

2. **Recurring vs. non-recurring information:** Information which is generated at regular intervals of time is called recurring (or repetitive) information. A particular type of information which is arrived at through some special kind of study and which helps in management decision is called *non-recurring (or non-repetitive) information*.

3. **Documentary vs. non-documentary information:** Information which is available in some docu-ment form, i.e., either in some written form or on microfilms, magnetic tapes, floppy disks, etc. is called *documentary information*. All other information is categorised as *non-documentary (or oral)*.

Table 13.1   Information Needs at Various Levels of Management

Level of Management	Management Population in %	Extent of Organization	Time Period	Nature of Decisions	Financial Powers	Nature of Information
Top Level	5 (approx.)	Whole organization	Long term	Selection of top personnel, policy approvals, emergency decisions	Extensive	Sporadic and one-shot
Middle Level						
(a) Staff	10 to 20	Whole organization	Long term	Formulation of policies, framing of rules and procedures	Limited	Periodic information for special policies, procedures, etc.
(b) Line		A division of the organization	Medium term	Actual supervision of operations	Limited to his divisional require- ments	Operational (may be on daily basis)
Junior Level	70 to 80	Normally a small unit of the organization	Short term	Initially involved in day-to-day operations, rather lmited freedom	Very limited	Operational, instantan- eous, on-line

4. **Internal vs. external information:** The distinction is obvious. Managers at different hierarchies in the organization require different combinations of internal and external information.

5. **Historical information vs. future projections:** Here again the distinction is obvious because historical information would be futile unless it can be used for future projection.

13.2.3 Information Characteristics or Value

The value of information for a successful functioning of any organization is now well recognised. The vital role of information as a link in the business system is shown in Fig. 13.2.

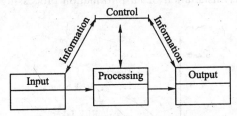

Fig. 13.2   Role of information as a link in the business system

With business activities becoming more and more complex, the value of information is now vital, and hence greater managerial skill is required to perform the increasing range of business activities.

The information to be of 'value' must possess certain desirable quantitative and descriptive characteristics. The primary characteristics which an information must possess are: (*i*) Relevance; (*ii*) Availability; and (*iii*) Timeliness. Besides, certain desirable and necessary variable attributes of information are objectivity, sensitivity, comparability, consciousness and completeness. This information must be of quality. Since information is a critical organizational resource, low quality information has an adverse effect on organizational performance. The quality of information is determined by how it can motivate human action and contribute to effective decision-making. The measures of quality of an information are as follows:

1. **Accuracy:** The degree of accuracy of an information depends upon the truthfulness with which data is collected either from primary or secondary sources. The information must be a true reflection of the situation; otherwise decision are bound to be incorrect and may lead to disastrous consequences.

2. **Form:** The information value increases if the form in which it is to be supplied matches the requirements of the decision-maker. For example, if a decision-maker requires information on sales pattern in a graph form, then he appreciates receiving such information (or data) in a graphical form rather than in a tabular form.

3. **Relevance:** The available information needs to be updated all the time so that it could match its current utility. For example, in a service organization, new data regarding improvement in the service keeps coming in most of the time. Therefore, processing continues to take place so that updated information is available all the time.

4. **Timeliness:** The information should be available when required. Delayed information has less value as a resource.

5. **ABC nature of information:** Sometimes internally generated information can be categorised as follows based on its availability, cost and dependence:

   Four basic principles of information management are:

   Data + Relevance + Purpose = Information

   Information + Insight = Understanding

   Understanding + Communication = Intelligence

   Intelligence + Action = Effectiveness.

13.2.4 Business Risk due to Information Gap

Generally decisions are made in the absence of adequate information because efforts to get the required information are either tedious or too costly. Sometimes there is no knowledge of the availability of required information, and often it is not available in the form needed.

The risk of taking wrong decisions is minimized by maximizing the availability of the needed information as shown in Fig. 13.3. The availability of perfect information to minimize the risk element of business call for proper installation of an information processing system at the appropriate position.

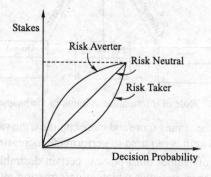

Fig. 13.3   Business risk in terms of information gap

A few observations can be made on Fig. 13.3.

(*a*) With the increase in efforts of information collection (time and money), the probability of availability of information is increased;

(*b*) With the increase in availability of information about a particular business activity, the business risk is minimized; and

(*c*) In spite of all-out efforts for information collection, the importance of availability of information does not increase beyond a limit. Hence, it is necessary for a manager to know the limits of information availability in a given situation.

13.2.5 Information from Data

Data Life Cycle: Data has its own life cycle. The following aspects of the data life cycle are important in the development, design and operation of the information system:

1. **Generation of data:** This may take place internally and/or externally by the occurrence of an event in a business organization such as sales slips, personnel forms, purchase orders, etc.

2. **Manipulation of data:** Manipulation of data involves addition, subtraction, multiplication, division, etc., based on certain formulae. This includes, for example, preparing pay slips for employees, bills of customers, determining optimal product-mix, economic order quantity, aggregate production planning, etc.

3. **Storing/retrieving and reproduction of data:** The generated data is *stored* in a document in devices such as magnetic disks and tapes. The stored data is *retrieved* by searching for specific data elements from the device on which it is stored. The retrieved data may be *reproduced* or converted to a different form of storage by preparing documents, reports, etc. The data life cycle is shown in Fig. 13.4.

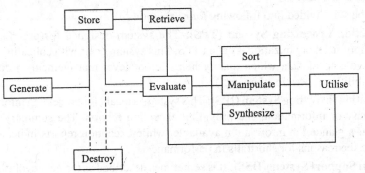

Fig. 13.4 Data life cycle

Data Processing Methods

Before the evolution of computers, data processing consisted of manual procedures whereby data operations were performed by hand with the aid of basic devices such as a pencil, paper, slide rule, etc. Then came the electro-mechanical method which is actually a symbiosis of man and machine. This was followed by the use of typewriters, cash registers, time clocks, etc.

The punched card equipment method came into use along with the 'unit record system', the principle being that data concerning a person, object, or event is normally punched (recorded) on a card. A number of cards placed logically and sequentially in a deck was termed a 'file'. There was considerable reduction in manual intervention. After the development of the electronic computer, a single machine became capable of performing most of the data operations without intermittent human intervention. Today, data processing is generally assumed to be *electronic data-processing* (EDP). Initially, computer systems were used in many organizations to perform essentially the *automatic data processing* (ADP). Recent technological developments, especially in the field of electronics, have reduced the cost and size of a computer. Thus, organizations of almost any size can benefit now by using computer data processing.

13.3 Management Information System

Management Information System (MIS) is an integrated man-machine system which collects, maintains, correlates and selectively displays information in the proper time frame consistently, to meet the specific needs of various levels of management, in order that decisions could be made and action taken for fulfilling the objectives of an organization. In other words, it is a system which (*i*) provides information to support managerial functions (planning, control, organising, operating); (*ii*) collects information systematically and routinely in accordance with a well defined set of rules; and includes (*iii*) files, hardware, software and operations research models of processing, storing, retrieving and transmitting information to the users.

An effective MIS has the following objectives:

1. **Facilitate** the decisions-making process by furnishing information in the proper time frame. This helps the decision-maker to select the best course of action.

2. **Provide** requisite information at each level of management to carry out their functions.

3. **Help** in highlighting the critical factors to be closely monitored for successful functioning of the organization.

4. **Support** decision-making in both structured and unstructured problem environments.

5. **Provide** a system of people, computers, procedures, interactive query facilities, documents for collecting, storing, retrieving and transmitting information to the users.

13.3.1 Categories of MIS

The MIS can be sub-divided into following *four* categories:

1. **Transaction Processing System (TPS):** The system designed for processing day-to-day transactions in an organization is called TPS. This system deals with collecting and processing a large volume of data which mainly helps junior level management in discharging their responsibilities (operational control).

2. **Information Providing System (IPS):** This system is meant for processing information, making a summary of information, and providing exception reports, The summary reports help in giving at a glance the information available, while exception reports indicate deviations (if any) and the reasons for shortfalls in performance,

3. **Decision Support System (DSS):** It is sometimes described as the next evolutionary step after MIS. It helps in improving the analytical capability of the decision-maker by creating an interactive model of the real-life situation.

4. **Programmed decision-making system:** The word 'program' is derived from the jargon of the computer field, where it is defined as a plan for the automatic solution of a problem. Programs are simply a string of instructions to accomplish a job or a task. In this information age, the systems for programmed decisions are created so that decisions are made by the system rather than a person.

13.3.2 MIS and Organization Structure

Organization structure and information needs are inseparably linked like the human anatomy (as organization structure) and the nervous system (as information system). The knowledge of organization structure and proper record of delegation of authority within the organization are prerequisites of MIS. This actually helps in defining authority and responsibility, demarcating decision-making areas, and measuring objectives of each sub-system (or unit). The outline of the design of an MIS for any organization is shown in Fig. 13.5.

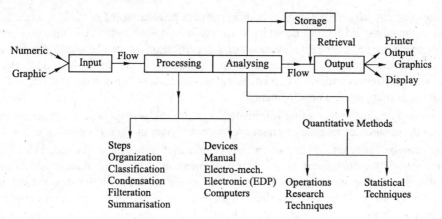

Fig. 13.5   Organization of an MIS

13.3.3   Location of MIS in a Business Organization

Different business organizations follow different procedures in locating an information centre in the organization. Three forms of organizations of MIS /Data Processing (DP) set-up are generally known. These are as follows:

1. **As part of financial department:** In this case, DP personnel, headed by a DP Manager, are placed under the charge of the financial controller or the chief accounts officer. This is so because historically financial applications were the first to be computerised and systematised.

2. **DP organization under a separate direction (MIS):** Sometimes other names such as director (management services) or director (data processing) are also used. In this form of organization, the DP Manager or the Director of MIS enjoys a status equal to the Financial Controller or the Chief Accounts Officer or any other chief of the functional divisions. This kind of organization is adopted by companies, who recognise data processing and systems design as important functional areas.

3. **DP organization as a separate company:** This kind of organization, followed largely by the consultancy units or subsidiaries of conglomerate of companies, is useful for the speedy and rapid growth of systems design and other related data processing activities both with respect to internal applications as well as external consultancy.

13.3.4   Characteristics of MIS

Some important features of MIS are summarized as follows:

1. **Management-oriented:** The system is designed from the top downwards. It does not mean that the system is designed to provide information directly to the top management. Other levels of management are also provided with relevant information. Here management orientation of MIS implies that the development of information system efforts should start from an appraisal of management needs and overall business objectives.

   For example, in the marketing information system, the activities such as sales-order processing, shipment of goods to customers and billing for the goods are basically operational control activities. This information can also be tracked by a salesman to know the sales territory, size of order, geography and product line, provided the system is designed accordingly. However, if the system is designed keeping in mind the top management, then data on external competition, market and pricing can be created to know the market share of the company's product and to serve as a basis of a new product or market-place introduction.

   In brief, the information system can be geared initially to provide information to middle and junior management levels, without reducing the possibility of integration into a strategic planning sub-system for top management.

2. **Management directed:** Because of management orientation of MIS, it is necessary that management should actively direct the system development efforts. A one time involvement is not enough. To ensure the effectiveness as per specifications of the designed system, continued review by the management is a must. In other words, the management should be responsible for setting system specifications, and it must play a vital role in the subsequent trade-off decisions that occur in the system development.

For example, in the marketing information system, the management must determine what sales information is necessary to improve its control over marketing operations.

3. **Integrated:** The word 'integration' means that the system has to be wholistic in its approach, to cover all the functional areas of an organization so as to produce more meaningful management information, with a view to achieving the objectives of the organization. It has to consider various sub-systems, their objectives, information needs, and recognise the interdependence that these sub-systems have amongst themselves, so that common areas of information are identified and processed without repetition and overlapping. In other words, an integrated system that blends information from several operational areas is a necessary element of an MIS.

For example, in the development of an effective production scheduling system, a proper balance amongst the following factors is desired: (*i*) set-up costs; (*ii*) manpower; (*iii*) overtime; (*iv*) production capacity; (*v*) inventory level; (*vi*) money available; and (*vii*) customer service. Ignorance regarding any of these factors would lead to a sub-optimal solution.

4. **Common data flows:** Because of the integration concept of MIS, common data flows concept avoids repetition and overlapping in data collection and storage, combining similar functions, and simplifying operations wherever possible. However, it may be better to live with a little duplication to ensure system's acceptability and workability.

For example, in the marketing operations, orders received for goods become the basis of billing of goods ordered, setting up of the accounts receivable, initiating production activity, sales analysis and forecasting, etc.

5. **Heavy planning element:** An MIS cannot be established overnight. It takes 3 to 5 years or even more to establish it properly in an organization. Hence, long-term planning is required for MIS development to fulfil the future needs and objectives of the organization. The designer of an MIS must ensure that it should not become obsolete before it actually gets into operation.

An example of such a feature of MIS may be seen in a transportation system where a highway is designed not to handle today's traffic requirements but to handle the traffic requirements five to ten years hence.

6. **Sub-system concept:** Even though the system is viewed as a single entity, it must be broken down into meaningful sub-systems that can be implemented one at a time. The division of an MIS into various sub-systems opens a way for this phasing plan. In Fig. 13.6, various systems have been shown, which in turn can be broken into additional sub-systems to delimit boundaries to the problems.

7. **Flexibility and ease of use:** While building an MIS system all types of possible means which may occur in future are added to make it flexible.

A feature that often goes with flexibility is the ease of use. The MIS should be able to incorporate all those features that make it readily accessible to a wide range of users with easy usability.

13.3.5 Classification of MIS

According to Mason, the MIS can be divided into *four* categories:

1. **Data bank information system:** In this system, the link between the information system and the user is assumed to be weak. This type of system is more useful for unstructured decisions.

The information system collects, classifies and stores data which may be useful to the user. The user makes request for data as per his need and determines the cause and effect in view of the actions, and makes judgement as to which outcome is suitable. The data does not help the user in making predictions or decisions, however, the nature and availability of data itself tend to suggest certain desirable alternatives to the user. The data bank information system is shown in Fig. 13.6.

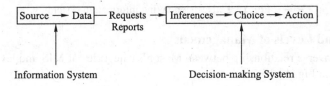

Fig. 13.6 Data bank information system

2. **Predictive information system:** This class of system is an extension of the data bank information system. In this system, prediction and inference-making occurs when processing by the information system passes from basic data to conclusions about the source.

The decision-making system (or user) asks as to 'what if' certain actions are taken. In response to such enquiries, the information system responds in the vein of 'if' user goes for action 'then'. This is what he can expect, will occur. Here the outcome is not evaluated.

This class of MIS is helpful when decisions are semi-structured (relationship between input and output is either deterministic or probabilistic, but mathematical optimization is possible in the absence of unrealistic assumptions). Ultimately decisions are taken based on predictions that the user receives. The predictive information system is shown in Fig. 13.7.

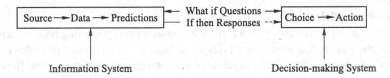

Fig. 13.7 Predictive information system

3. **Decision-making information system:** In this system, an organization's value system and criteria for choice are incorporated. This level of MIS is useful for structured decisions (Fig. 13. 8).

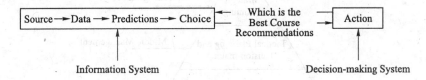

Fig. 13.8 Decision-making information system

Optimization methods such as 'operations research' and 'cost effectiveness' are examples of this MIS system. The solution offered by such models with a specific objective function (for ranking outcome from each alternative course of action) and a set of constraints (for specifying functional relationship amongst various resources) recommend a single course of action for optimizing the policy. The decision-maker, however, may not act on the recommendation.

4. Decision-taking information system: In this system (Fig. 13.9), the information system and the user are assumed to be one. For example, a purchase order is released automatically when an inventory level reaches or goes below the reorder point or sends reminders to vendors to supply goods when supply is overdue.

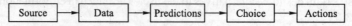

Fig. 13.9   Decision-taking information system

13.3.6 MIS and Levels of Management

There exists an inverse relationship between Mason's categories of MIS and levels of management (TMJ) as shown in Fig. 13.10.

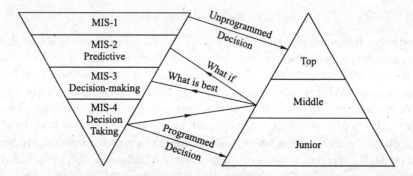

Fig. 13.10   Inverse relationship

Levels of Management Activities

Different management activities will have different information processing requirements. As shown in Fig. 13.11, the transaction processing (viewed as base of the pyramid) provides the base for all the activities. This base is significant in terms of processing time and number of files compared to strategic planning. The top portion of the pyramid requires more outside information, which is generally less structured, and the decision process at this level will be more non-programmed. The lower portion of the pyramid tends to be more structured, precise, current and repetitive data.

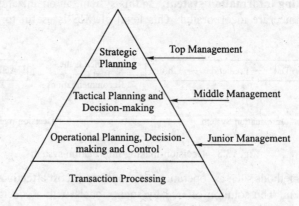

Fig. 13.11   Pyramid structure of MIS

Table 13.2 shows the information requirement for different levels of management activity in the case of some selected information characteristics.

Table 13.2 Information Requirement for Different Levels of Management in the case of some Selected Information Characteristics

Information Characteristics	Strategic Planning	Management Control	Operational Control
Volume	Low	Intermediate	High
Source	Significant amount from external source	Mostly internal	Entirely internal
Scope	Very wide	Intermediate	Well-defined, narrow
Level of aggregation	Aggregate	Intermediate	Detailed
Time horizon	Future	Present	Historical
Currency	Quite old	Intermediate	Highly current
Accuracy	Low	Intermediate	High
Frequency of use	Infrequent	Intermediate	Very frequent

13.3.7 Design of an MIS

While designing an MIS, a general approach has to be followed so that a suitable system can be devised to cater to the needs of different organizations as per their functions and decision-making requirements. Irrespective of the organization in question, the data gets generated at various levels of the management. These data when processed and analysed become information which, when properly communicated in time to the decision-maker, helps in making decisions and undertaking actions.

The following steps are generally taken in the design of an MIS (Fig. 13.12).

1. **Identifying information needs at all levels of management:** There are problems in every growing business organization, but most of the time a clear definition of problems and a priority system for their solution is not known. Thus, as a first step in MIS design, the management should identify, in detail, the problems to be solved.

   The mission statement for the business as a whole leads to objectives for the general business and these objectives help in framing various plans. Each of these business objectives and plans need some kind of feedback (or information). These information needs are actually the problems, to be solved by the MIS function.

   The following steps are necessary to initiate the design process and are repeated until the information requirement and the problem to be solved are fully understood:

   (a) Initiating the information need;

   (b) Asking questions about the need;

   (c) Suggesting interpretations of that need;

   (d) Detailing the original statement; and

   (e) Reviewing with the management the more detailed statement of the need.

2. **Listing objectives of MIS and anticipated benefits:** The users must define system objectives in terms of information demands and not in terms of satisfaction of demands that are not related to an objective. For example, in several government departments, prior to the designing of an information system, the system objective was the automation of hundreds of reports without looking at the management of tasks related to functional or resource system represented by the report. These are training needs, employee relations, safety, recruitment, staffing. Such attention is possible only by automation of records or processing of existing data, otherwise the true objectives of the organization represented by the system are overlooked.

   The system objective should be defined in terms of what a decision-maker can do and how effectively he would be able to function after his information requirements have been complied with. The basic questions asked, while listing down the objectives of the MIS system design, are: (*i*) What is the purpose of the system? (*ii*) Why is it needed? (*iii*) What is it expected to do? and (*iv*) Who are the users and what are their objectives?

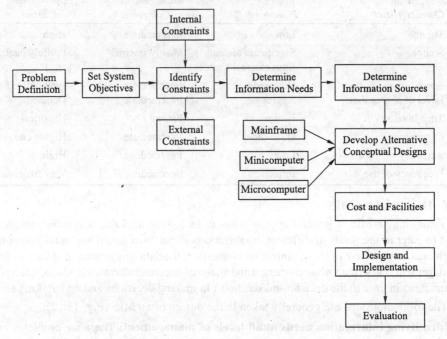

Fig. 13.12   MIS design

Obviously, the objectives of the MIS system design have to match with the objectives of the organization. However, a common fallacy in stating objectives of the MIS system is to emphasize these in vague terms: reduce costs, improve efficiency, keep accurate records, meet customer demands and meet the production schedule.

A few more examples of the fallacy and vagueness in stating objectives of the organization and hence that of the MIS system design are given below: a university vice-chancellor may state his objective as to 'provide quality education'; whereas a minister may claim it to be to 'provide more jobs for the unemployed'. In both the cases, the objective so stated is not enough to provide a measure of performance of the system or to design an information system to help achieve the objective.

3. **Identifying systems constraints (internal and external):** The systems constraints are also called *problem boundaries* or *restrictions* under which objectives may be achieved. These constraints (or limitations) in the design of the system are the creation of the manager-user or the designer himself, because of his limited freedom of action in designing a system to achieve the objectives.

   The internal constraints are viewed in terms of (*i*) top management support, (*ii*) organizational policy; (*iii*) personnel needs (manpower) and availability; (*iv*) cost and resource; and (*v*) acceptance (resistance in the acceptance of computerized MIS are: economic threat, threat to status, threat to ego, etc.).

   The external constraints are mainly concerned with the customer. Ordered entry, billing and other systems that interface with the systems of the customer must be designed with the customer's need in mind. In addition to this, a variety of other external constraints exist, i.e., Govt. (central or state) restrictions on the processing of data, unions, suppliers, etc.

4. **Determining information needs and resources:** The system design must begin with determining the real information needs of the management: information that can increase the perception of managers in critical areas such as problems, alternatives, opportunities and plans. In other words, if a decision-maker can define his objectives and spell out the items of information that are needed to attain the objectives, then he or she is at least half-way home in systems design.

A decision-maker needs information for a variety of reasons concerned with the management process. The type of information which is required at various times and for various purposes depends on two factors: (*i*) Personal managerial attitudes, *e.g.*, knowledge of information systems; managerial style; perception of information needs, etc. of the individual manager; and (*ii*) Organizational environment (nature of the company; level of management; structure of the organization, etc.).

After estimating the need of information and clearly defining the objectives, the next step in MIS system design is to determine the sources of information. The sources of information may be categorized as follows: (*i*) *Internal sources*. It is in the form of written materials—file records, memoranda and letters, reports containing information about the existing system, etc.; (*ii*) *External sources*. It may be in the form of trade and Govt. publications; personal interviews of managers and personal interaction with decision-makers.

Information needs and sources of a few sub-systems may be stated as follows:

Sub-system		Information
Inventory	need :	Items falling below minimum inventory level
	source :	Stock level determination sub-system compares current balance against minimum inventory level
Production Control	need :	Cost variance over or under 5 per cent
	source :	Integration of costing with manufacturing applications—shop control, stores requisitioning, manpower availability, etc.
Purchasing	need :	Performance of individual vendors
	source :	Comparison of prices, quality, lead time with predetermined standards.

5. **Developing alternative conceptual design and selecting one:** The conceptual design of MIS is considered as a skeleton of the MIS, which guides and restricts the form of the detailed design. The concept of design of an MIS consists of: patterns of information flow; channels of information; and role of decision-makers and competitors.

The alternative concepts of a system can be evaluated on the basis of the following:

(*a*) Compare anticipated performance of the conceptual design with respect to objectives of the system developed earlier;

(*b*) For quantified comparison amongst systems, prepare a preliminary cost-effectiveness data for the system;

(*c*) Examine the quality of databases and information to be made available. Study the number of operations, dispersions and duplication of files, and potential breakdown points; and

(*d*) Expand the conceptual designs in greater detail if none of these provide a preferred design.

6. **Preparing the conceptual design report:** The conceptual design report is a proposal prepared for the expenditure of funds and possible changes in the organizational set-up. Since this report is submitted to management, it must contain the summary of problems that necessitate

the system, the objectives, the general nature of the system, reasons why this concept was selected over others, and time and resources required to design and implement the system.

Along with this summary, a separate report about the performance specifications of the system may also be submitted. The performance specifications describe the functions which must be performed by the system, and provide the yardstick for its assessment.

13.3.8 Implementation of MIS

Before installing a new MIS in any organization, it is desirable to know whether there is already an old MIS in operation. If so, then the old system is allowed to operate parallely till the new system is fully in operation. This arrangement will be helpful in examining the relative advantages of the new system over the old one.

The implementation plan involves the following steps:

1. Preparing organizational plans.
2. Planning of work flow.
3. Training of personnel.
4. Development of software.
5. Acquiring computer hardware.
6. Designing the format for data collection.
7. Construction of data files.
8. Operation of old and new systems in parallel.
9. Phasing out the old and inducting the new system.
10. Evaluation, maintenance and control of the new system.

The outline of implementation phase of an MIS is shown in Fig. 13.13.

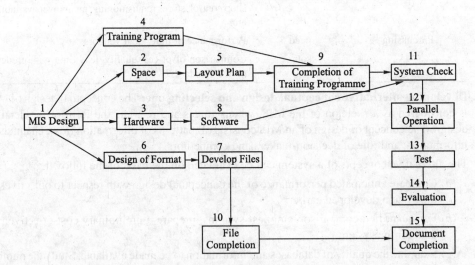

Fig. 13.13   Steps of implementation of an MIS

13.3.9 Disadvantages of Information Systems

Many benefits can be derived from information systems and technologies by the organizations. However, at times, the same systems and technologies can have negative effects on people and organizations. Therefore, it is utmost essential that organizations take all possible precautions to ensure that information systems will not hinder their growth and progress. Following disadvantages are likely to be there from information systems:

1. **'Deskilling' of workers:** Introduction of new technologies, especially for automation, sometimes render obsolete the existing skills of some workers. Many industries such as the automobile, steel, insurance industries, banks, have gone through periods of massive layoffs because of intense automation efforts. Therefore, while computerisation can increase operational efficiency and improve profits, sometimes it is also the root cause of workforce reduction.

2. **Information overload:** Generation of excessive amounts of information can overwhelm managers who must digest it and use it to make decisions. At times, this improvement also has its downside.

3. **Employee mistrust:** Employees sometimes fear that computers will eventually replace them. They may view information systems with skepticism, unless they are assured that their jobs are not in danger.

4. **Increased competitive pressure:** There is increased pressure on small and medium-scale industries, failing which they are steadily being pushed out of the marketplace by larger companies.

5. **Disenchantment with IS:** Many organizations are unable to value the information systems and technologies to their organizations *vis-a-vis* the return on investment. In coming years, the MIS will experience close scrutiny of its abilities to deliver on its promises.

6. **Security breaches:** When organizations introduce new and sophisticated technologies, they must also find new ways to protect these assets from theft, pilferage, and security breaches. Therefore, computers and information systems actually increase the operating costs of an organization.

13.3.10 Approaches of MIS Development

Generally, following *seven* approaches are used for developing MIS:

1. **Top down approach:** This approach develops a corporate plan as a guide for designing the information system. Here top management takes the lead in formulating objectives, policies and plans and communicates them down the line to middle and supervisory management for translating them into reality.

2. **Bottom up approach:** It consists of following *five* steps: (*a*) Individual functional applications are planned separately consisting of transaction processing, updating of files md simple reports; (*b*) Files of various functional applications are integrated by means of indexing and chaining into a database; (*c*) Various functions are added to operate on the database at management control level; (*d*) Integration of models into a model base having a wide variety of analysis, decision and planning models; and (*e*) Strategic planning data and planning models are added to the information system.

3. **Integrative approach:** This approach permits managers at all levels to influence the design of MIS. Here evaluation, modification and approval of top management continues till a final design is acceptable to all levels.

4. **Traditional approach:** Here activities are performed in sequence. Each activity is undertaken only when the previous activity is completed. Managers and users consider and review the work performed by MIS professionals during each stage of processing, in order to ensure accuracy and completeness.

5. **Prototyping approach:** In order to avoid any possible delay, prototyping approach is used. The goal is to develop a small or pilot version, called a prototype, which is built quickly and at lesser cost with the intention of modifying it when need arises.

6. **End user development approach:** With the increasing availability of low cost technology, end user development is popular in many organizations. Here the end user is responsible for system development.

7. **Systematic approach for development in small organizations**: Since fewer MIS professionals shall be working with variety of responsibilities, they have little time to develop new systems for users. In a very small organization, no MIS professional will exist. This does not mean that they cannot develop management information systems. They develop systems using the following steps:

(*a*) Identify requirements.

(*b*) Locate, evaluate and secure software development.

(*c*) Locate, evaluate and secure hardwares.

(*d*) Implement the systems.

13.3.11 Constraints in Developing an MIS

Following are the constraints in developing an effective MIS:

1. No management system to build upon.
2. No clear definition of mission and purpose.
3. No objectives for the company.
4. Lack of management participation.
5. Misorganization.
6. Over-reliance on the consultant/manufacturer.
7. Communication gap.
8. Performance of key people.

13.3.12 MIS and Use of Computer

Following are the main advantages of using computer technology in MIS:

1. Expanding scope for using information system.
2. Enhancing speed of processing and retrieval of data.
3. Widening the scope of analysis.
4. Increasing complexity of system design and operation.
5. Integrating different information sub-systems.
6. Increasing the effectiveness of information system.
7. Extending more comprehensive information to business managers.

13.3.13 Limitations of MIS

Following are the main limitations of MIS:

1. MIS cannot replace managerial judgement in decision-making. It is merely an effective tool for the managers in decision-making and problem-solving.
2. The quality of output of MIS is directly proportional to the quality of input and processes.
3. MIS cannot provide tailor-made information packages. It is required to analyse the available information before decision-making.
4. In a fast changing and complex environment, MIS may not have enough flexibility to update itself quickly.
5. MIS takes only quantitative factors into account.
6. MIS is less useful for making non-programmed decisions.
7. MIS is less effective in organizations where information is not being shared with others.
8. MIS is less effective due to frequent changes in top management, organizational structure and operational staff.

13.4 Decision Support System

Decision Support System (DSS) is an outcome of MIS, providing support for management at operational control, management control, and strategic planning. The emphasis is on 'support' rather than on automation of decisions. DSS allows the decision-maker to retrieve data and test alternative solutions during the process of problem-solving. In 1984, Freyenfeld proposed the following empirical definition of DSS based on discussion with some 30 suppliers, users and academic organizations:

"A decision support system is an interactive data processing and display system which is used to assist in a concurrent decision-making process, and which also conforms to the following characteristics: (*a*) It is sufficiently user-friendly to be used by the decision-maker(s) in person; (*b*) It displays its information in a format and terminology which is familiar to the user(s); and (*c*) It is selective in its provision of information and avoids its user(s) in information overload.

Another definition of a decision support system is: 'A set of well-integrated, user-friendly, computer-based tools that combine data with various decision-making models—quantitative and qualitative—to solve semi-structured and unstructured problems.'

Initially G. Anthony Gorry and Michael S. Scott Morton felt a need for a framework to channel computer applications toward management decision-making and developed a grid, known as the *Gorry and Scott Morton grid* (Fig. 13.14). The grid is based on Simon's concept of programmed and non-programmed decisions and Robert N. Anthony's management levels. The decision types are described in terms of problem structure, ranging from structured to semi-structured to unstructured. A fully *structured problem* is one in which the first three of Simon's phases—intelligence, design and choice—are structured. The decisions are routine and straightforward. By following a set of pre-established steps, a solution to the problem can be found. Such a problem does not require intuition or judgement. Therefore, the system returns the same solution every time. An *unstructured problem* is one in which none of the three phases is structured. The decisions are unique and non-repetitive. Because they require intuition, experience and judgement, there may be no one 'best' solution and solutions may differ from one decision-maker to the other. A *semi-structured problem* is one in which one or two of the phases are structured. The decisions in this category fall somewhere between structured decisions, which are routine and repetitive, and unstructured decisions, which are unique and non-repetitive.

Management Levels			
	Operational Control	Management Control	Strategic Planning
Structured	Accounts Receivable	Budget Analysis— Engineered Costs	Tanker Fleet Mix
	Order Entry	Short-term Forecasting	Warehouse and Factory Location
	Inventory Control		
Semi-structured	Production Scheduling	Variance Analysis— Overall Budget	Mergers and Acquisitions
	Cash Management	Budget Preparation	New Product Planning
Unstructured	PERT/COST Systems	Sales and Production	R&D Planning

Degree of Problem Structure (row label on left axis)

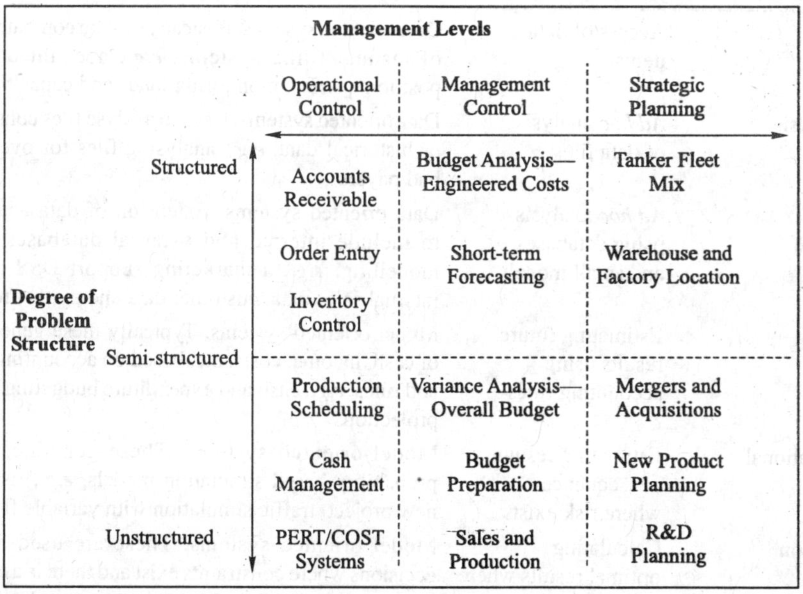

(*Source:* G. Anthony Gorry and Michael S. Scott Morton. 'A Framework for Management Information Systems', *Sloan Management Review*, 13 (Fall 1971), 55-70).

Fig. 13.14   Gorry and Scott Morton grid

Gorry and Scott Morton entered types of business problems into their grid. For example, accounts receivable is solved by managers on the operational-control level making structured decisions. R&D planning is accomplished by strategic planning managers making unstructured decisions.

The horizontal dotted line through the middle of the grid is significant. It separates the problem that had been successfully solved with computer assistance from those problems that had not been subjected to computer processing. The upper area was named *structured decision systems* and the lower area was named decision support systems.

DSS are especially useful for semi-structured problems where problem-solving is improved by interaction between the manager and the computer system. The emphasis is on small, simple models which can easily be understood and used by the decision-maker. Examples of semi-structured decisions are: planning a mix of investments for a portfolio, looking at the financial implications of various ways of financing a short-term cash flow deficit, consideration of alternative production and pricing policies, assessing the impact of potential future changes in exogenous variables such as interest rates, analysis of the credit-worthiness of corporate clients, and assessing the likely impacts of departmental reorganization.

In essence, there are *three* objectives that a DSS should achieve. These are: (*a*) Assist managers in making decisions to solve semi-structured problems; (*b*) Support the manager's judgement rather than try to replace it; and (*c*) Improve the manager's decision-making *effectiveness* rather than its efficiency.

13.4.1 Classifications of DSS

Steven L. Alter (1976) developed a taxonomy of DSS, by conducting a study of 56 DSS in use in organizations, based on the degree to which the system outputs can directly determine the decision. The resulting classification of system types is summarised in Table 13.3.

Table 13.3 Classifications of DSS

DSS Classification	Type of Operation	Examples and Comments
File Drawer Systems	Access of data items	Data oriented systems. Basically on-line computerised versions of manual filing systems, *e.g.*, account balance, stock position queries, monitoring loads and capacities.
Data Analysis Systems	*Ad hoc* analysis of data files	Data oriented systems. Used to analyse files containing current or historical data, *e.g.*, analysing files for overdue account, bad payers.
Analysis Information System	*Ad hoc* analysis using databases and small models	Data oriented systems. Extension of data analysis systems to include internal and external databases with limited modelling, *e.g.*, a marketing support DSS could include internal sales data, customer data and market research data.
Accounting Models	Estimating future results using accounting rules	Model oriented systems. Typically these generate estimates of cash, income, costs, etc. based on accounting relationships and rules, *e.g.*, cash and expenditure budgeting, balance sheet projections.
Representational Models	Estimating results, consequences where risk exists	Model oriented systems. These generate results using probability based simulation models, *e.g.*, risk analysis for new project, traffic simulation with variable flows.
Optimisation Models	Calculating optimal results where constraints exist	Model oriented systems. These are used for structured decisions where constraints exist and there is a clear objective, *e.g.*, machine loading, material usage, production planning.
Suggestion Models	Producing suggested results where decision rules are known	Model oriented systems. These compute suggested decisions for semi-structured problems. Expert systems are one of the tools, *e.g.*, credit authorisations, insurance rate calculations.

13.4.2 Characteristics of DSS

- The computer must support the manager but not replace his/her judgement. It should, therefore, neither try to provide the 'answers' nor impose a predefined sequence of analysis.
- The main payoff of computer support is for *semi-structured* problems, where parts of the analysis can be systematised for the computer, but where the decision-maker's insight and judgement are needed to control the process.
- Effective problem solving is *interactive* and is enhanced by a dialogue between the user and the system. The user explores the problem situation using the analytic and information-providing capabilities of the system as well as human experience and insights.

13.4.3 Components of a DSS

There are *three* main software components of a DSS. There are: *a database management system* (DBMS), a *model management system*, and *support tools*. Data in the DSS database are managed by the DBMS, which covers compilation of data, manipulation of data, data generation, updating, data maintenance, and dissemination of data. Model management system stores and accesses models that managers use to make decisions. Such models are: statistical models, production models, marketing models, human resource models, financial and accounting models, and strategic models. These models are extensively used in different functional areas of a business. Support tools—online help, pull-down menus, user interfaces, graphical analysis, error-correction mechanisms—facilitate users interactions with the system. In such an environment, good interfaces can make or break the system.

13.4.4 Functions of a DSS

There are *five* functions of a DSS facilitating managerial decision-making. They are:

- Model building
- 'What-if' analysis
- Goal seeking
- Risk analysis
- Graphical analysis.

Model building allows decision-makers to identify the most appropriate model for solving the problem at hand. It takes into account input variables, interrelationships among the variables, problem assumptions and constraints. For example, a marketing manager of Videocon is charged with the responsibility of developing a sales forecasting model for colour TV sets. A model builder uses a structured framework to identify variables like demand, cost and profit, analyse the relationships among these variables, identify the assumptions, if any (*e.g.*, assume the prices of raw materials will increase by 5% over the forecasting period), and identify the constraints, *viz*, the production capacity of the plant. All this information are then integrated by a system into a decision-making model, which can be updated and modified whenever required.

'What-if' analysis is the process of assessing the impact of changes to model variables, the values of the variables, or the interrelationships among variables. This helps managers to be proactive, rather than reactive, in their decision-making. This analysis is critical for semi-structured and unstructured problems because the data necessary to make such decisions are often either not available or imcomplete. Hence, managers normally use their intuition and judgement in predicting the long-term implications of their decisions. Managers can prepare themselves to face a dynamic business environment by developing a group of scenarios (best-case scenario, worst-case scenario and realistic scenario). Spreadsheet packages, such as Excel and Lotus 1-2-3, have 'what-if' applications.

Goal seeking is the process of determining the input values required to achieve a certain goal. For example, house buyers determine the monthly payment they can afford (say, Rs 7,000) and calculate the number of such payments required to pay the desired house.

Risk analysis is a function of DSS that allows managers to assess the risks associated with various alternatives. Decisions can be classified as low-risk, medium-risk, and high-risk. A DSS is particularly useful in medium-risk and high-risk environments.

Graphical analysis helps managers to quickly digest large volumes of data and visualise the impacts of various courses of action. First, the Lotus system enabled users to easily display and print information in a graphic form. S L Jarvenpaa and G W Dickson (1988) studied the relative advantages and disadvantages of tabular and graphic output. They recommended the use of graphs when:

- Seeking a quick summary of data.
- Detecting trends over time.
- Comparing points and patterns at different variables.
- Forecasting activities.
- Seeking relatively simple impressions from a vast amount of information.

The researchers suggest that a tabular presentation be used when it is necessary to read individual data values.

Jarvenpaa and Dickson also offered the following tips when choosing between the various types of graphs:

- Line or bar charts are preferred for summarising data.
- Grouped line or bar charts are good for showing trends over time.
- Grouped bar charts are better than pie charts for presenting parts of a whole.
- Grouped line or bar charts are good for comparing patterns of variables.
- Use horizontal rather than vertical bars when comparing variables.
- Use single-line or bar charts to compare individual data points between variables.
- Put data values on the top of the bars in a bar chart for easier reading.

Spreadsheets have sophisticated graphical analysis capabilities. For example, Microsoft Excel gives the user a wide choice of graphs and charts in many colours and patterns.

13.4.5 Development of DSS

The development of a decision support system is determined by the types of information and the facilities needed for taking the decision. Decision support systems are developed using programming languages or produced by packages specially incorporating decision support development tools.

Conventional high-level languages, such as C^{++} and BASIC, can be used to develop DSSs. They are extremely flexible. However, DSSs using these languages involve a lengthy analysis and design phase. Fourth-generation or very high-level languages are more appropriate. They are particularly useful as they are generally database-oriented. This is important for those systems that rely on data retrieval and analysis for decision support. An example of a prominent fourth-generation language is SQL, which can be used on many relational database systems such as ORACLE. The selection of a language depends on factors such as:

- Availability of language and support for it.
- Experience of developers with various languages.
- Amount of manipulation vs. presentation of data.
- Need to document and maintain the program.
- Frequency of use and number of users.

The advantages of using programming languages are that:

- Applications development is speedy.
- Many are end-user orientated.
- They are more likely to be declarative rather than procedural.

In general, there are *three* methods for developing DSS:

1. DSS generator.
2. DSS shells.
3. Customer made software.

DSS Generator

A DSS generator is comprised of programs such as data management tools, electronic spreadsheets, report generators (user-friendly programs that allow decision-makers to produce customised reports), statistical packages, graphical packages, query languages, and model-building tools, that help in the development of a DSS. Some known DSS generators are FOCUS, Excel, and Lotus 1-2-3.

DSS Shell

A DSS shell is a program used to build a customised DSS. Shells eliminate the need for developing the DBMS, model management system, and user interfaces, because skeletal versions of these modules are already available in the shell. A user can simply connect the shell with the appropriate external and internal databases and input the appropriate models in order to have a fully functional DSS.

System development can proceed at a rapid pace because of availability of basic versions of the DBMS, the model management system, and the set of interfaces in the shell. Shells have become user-friendly, allowing even users with little or no programming background to develop fairly sophisticated systems. The main disadvantage of a shell is that it may have to be customised to meet the needs of the decision-maker or the user may have to adopt the problem to the tool.

A DSS, called Advia, assists entrepreneurs in developing a plan, analysing the marketing and financial aspects of their businesses, and implementing it. This DSS has two components—Manage and Decide. *Advia Manage* is a financial model that allows managers to forecast income statements, project operating cash flow, automatically create forecasted balance-sheets, and analyse key financial data and ratios. *Advia Decide* is designed to analyse market issues such as the status of our organization in the market, aims of our organization in the next five years, and how do we get there? Advia Decide has two components: Situation Analysis and Vision. Some questions asked by the system from the user are structured whereas other questions are open-ended, allowing the user to provide input in a variety of ways. Depending on the size of the company and the amount of information available, a single session with Advia can last 5 to 6 hours. The output of this DSS is a first draft of a business plan, along with some interesting and useful insights about the company's market possibility and strategy.

The second module, Advia Manage, is designed to assist users through complex financial decision-making processes and has two components: Forecast and Tracking. Many CEOs of small firms struggle to assess the performance of their firms. Advia provides an objective framework to help each of them evaluate his/her firm and its performance.

Custom-made Software

Custom-made software is designed and developed by an organization, who is committed to DSS technology but cannot find a suitable generator or shell. The software is developed using a procedural language, such as C, or a 4GL, such as FOCUS. Organizations may also choose to combine shells and customised software.

The primary disadvantage of this approach is that the system may be expensive and time-consuming to develop, and organizations may run into unexpected bottlenecks and cost overruns.

13.4.6 Group Decision Support Systems

The decision support systems considered so far have been concerned with computerised support for an individual taking a decision characterised as semi-structured or unstructured. Many decisions taken within an organization are not by a single individual but as a result of group deliberations.

Group Decision Support Systems (GDSS) are computer-based information systems that facilitate the free flow and exchange of ideas and information among group members while maintaining their anonymity. Other terms have also been coined to describe the application of information technology to group settings. These terms include group support system (GSS), computer-supported cooperative work (CSCW), computerised collaborative work support, and electronic meeting system (EMS). The software used in these settings has been given the name *groupware*.

Groups typically consist of less than 20 people, who arrive at decisions through communication. The communication serves to share information and implement the decision-taking process. The decision may be taken by vote but is more often by negotiation, consensus, or preference ranking.

Three types of computer-based support are available:

1. **Decision networks:** This type allows participants to communicate through networks with each other or with a central database. Applications software may use commonly shared models to provide support. The commonest implementation is using a local area network and micro-computers. The technology filters out many of the typical group dynamics of a participative meeting.

2. **Decision room:** Participants are located in one place—the decision room. The purpose of this is to enhance participant interaction and decision-making by computerised support within a fixed period of time using a facilitator. Specific computer-based tools are provided (Fig. 13.15).

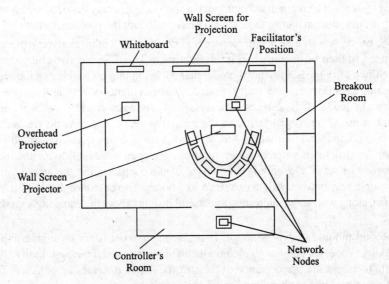

Fig. 13.15   A typical layout of a decision room

3. **Tele/computer conferencing:** If groups are composed of members or sub-groups that are geographically dispersed, tele/computer conferencing provides for interactive connection between two or more decision rooms. This interaction will involve transmission of the computerised and audiovisual information. Whereas decision networks can be viewed as the use of local area networks, for decision-making involving groups the decision room is an entirely new development.

The decision room is used by an organization to create an environment in which groups may enhance their decisions. The decision-making process is guided by a *facilitator*, The facilitator is usually not from within the organization but a trained professional in group dynamics brought in for the decision-making sessions. There will also usually be a computer controller whose responsibility is to maintain computer communications and software support within the room.

The decision room (an example of which can be seen in Fig. 13.15) consists of a table with networked workstations for the participants and workstations for the facilitator and controller. The screen of any node of the network can be projected on to the wall screen. The facilitator can also ensure that, if required, any participant's screen can replace some or all of the other nodes for demonstration or interactive purposes. Breakout rooms, used for smaller discussions, are also equipped with similar networked machines. A combination of overhead projector, flipchart, photocopier and other presentation devices are provided as well.

The software may take many forms but will always consist of tools that aid group decision-making, are easy to use and are interactive. Examples of software (as well as spreadsheet and statistical/graphical packages) are:

- **Brainstorming:** Brainstorming software may be used at any stage of the proceedings but is particularly valuable at early stages when members of the group need to think and converse freely on issues. A problem or statement can be entered for comment. This will appear on all screens. Each individual may then produce comments, which are anonymously consolidated and displayed. The tool increases creativity and lateral thinking.

- **Voting:** It is frequently important to obtain a swift view on the acceptability of proposals from a group perspective before proceeding. Voting software enables this to happen. It is not merely restricted to yes/no but will also enable different formats for expressing preferences, including multiple choice and 1-5 scales.

- **Policy formation:** Software can aid policy formation by allowing decision-makers to identify connections and relations between issues and communicate this to all present for comment.

The software will be used as part of a methodology followed by the facilitator in arriving at decisions. Much work is still to be done in the area of development of tools to support decision rooms.

Decision rooms are expensive to equip and all but the largest organizations would find it difficult to justify the expenditure—particularly so as the use of the decision room is not regarded as an everyday occurrence. It is becoming more common for establishments, especially academic institutions, to hire out these facilities to organizations when needed.

It is difficult to analyse the effectiveness of these group decision support systems although it appears that they are most likely to be beneficial (and to be regarded as beneficial by participants) for larger group size (size eight and above). Participants are aware of the need to impose some structure on groups of this size and welcome the direction given by the decision room and the facilitator.

The primary advantage of GDSS is that it fosters an environment that is conducive to decision-making. A second advantage of GDSS is that whereas in traditional meetings, extroverts or politically powerful people can dominate the shy and the introverted. GDSS allows all members of the group to participate. Another advantage of a GDSS is that it greatly enhances the efficiency of group meetings, since the system generates and processes ideas in parallel and there is no cross talk among group members. Further, the system has good 'organizational memory'. It captures all ideas instantaneously, which reduces the need for documentation and the risk of loosing or misinterpreting ideas.

13.4.7 Applications of a DSS

Applications of a DSS can be classified into following *three* categories:

1. **Independent problems:** The independent problems are 'standalone problems' whose solutions are independent of other problems. The goal is to find the best solution to the given problem. In the business world, independent problems are rare.

2. **Interrelated problems:** In interrelated problems, solutions are interrelated by each other to find the most effective solution to the group of interrelated problems. These type of problems usually require team effort. Suppose Thums Up's goal is to increase sale of its soft drink by 10% this summer. This requires the coordination of a set of interrelated tasks, such as developing

an effective advertising campaign, motivation of the sales force, developing pricing strategies, and offering incentives to distributors. To accomplish these tasks, talents of a group of experts are required.

3. **Organizational problems:** In organizational problems, all departments within an organization are included. Such problems require team effort. Total quality management is a good example of an organizational effort, because for it to be effective, it requires a joint effort from all departments/units in the organization.

A DSS is ideal for interrelated and inter-organization problems. For example, in a manufacturing environment, a DSS can help a production manager answer complex and data-intensive questions such as the number of machines to be operated, the amount of materials required to fill a new order, production scheduling, and labour scheduling.

Another application of DSS is forecasting, demand management, and supplier evaluation. A DSS can consolidate data from different sources to forecast demand, determine the appropriate quantity and mix the resources necessary to meet the demand, and balance supply and demand for a wide variety of products. It can also present managers with comprehensive data about different company projects, programs, and products so that they can make sound decisions. Other applications of DSS include corporate planning, developing effective advertising strategies and pricing policies, determining an optimal product mix, and handling investment portfolios. DSS are used all over the world by public, private and government agencies to solve complex and data-intensive problems. In India, DSS is being especially used to develop regional health care plans.

13.5 Electronic Commerce (EC)

Electronic commerce is the process of doing business electronically. It involves the automation of a variety of business-to-business and business-to-consumer transactions through reliable and secure connections. In short, it is the automation of the business process between buyers and sellers. The technologies and services can include, but are not limited to: electronic data interchange (EDI), e-mail, electronic funds transfer (EFT), electronic benefits transfer (EBT), electronic forms, digital cash, interoperable database access, bulletin boards, electronic catalogs, intranets, cable services, world wide web/Internet services, electronic banking, web broadcasting, push technologies, web site management tools, Extranets, Internet telephony, Bar coding-2D, Imaging, Internet-electronic forms, Internet publishing, voice recognition, security services such as firewalls, encryption, and gateway managers.

Thus, EC is not a single technology, but rather a sophisticated combination of technologies and consumer-based services integrated to form a new paradigm in business transaction processing. The future of EC is bright and viable—the application, however, has not yet reached full integration into the business mainstream. Several significant hurdles remain, which must be cleared before electronic commerce will become a mainstay business strategy.

Electronic Commerce impacts a broad number of business activities such as:

• Marketing, sales and sales promotion.
• Pre-sales, sub-contracts, supply.
• Financing and insurance.
• Commercial transactions: ordering, delivery, payment.
• Product service and maintenance.
• Co-operative product development.
• Distributed co-operative working.
• Use of public and private services.
• Business-to-administrations (concessions, permissions, tax, customs, etc.).

- Transport and logistics.
- Public procurement.
- Automatic trading of digital goods.
- Accounting.

13.5.1 Role of Internet in Electronic Commerce

There are *six* reasons for the Internet's dramatic impact on the scope of business networking applications and for the emergence of Internet as the foundation for the world's new information infrastructure:

1. **Universality:** Any business using the Internet can interact with any other business using the Internet. This is by no means true of earlier networking technologies that allowed businesses to ship goods to only those companies connected to the same network.

2. **Reach:** The Internet is everywhere: large cities and small towns throughout the modern and developing world.

3. **Performance:** Unlike many other public networks, the Internet can handle visual images, audio clips, and other large electronic objects, It provides its users with a high-function window to the world, in addition to handling everyday networking tasks such as electronic mail.

4. **Reliability:** The design concepts for the Internet came out of U.S. Department of Defense. Hence, Internet technology is highly robust and reliable in spite of significant differences in the extent to which various Internet service providers actually implement and ensure this reliability.

5. **Cost:** Compared with alternative networking technologies, Internet costs are surprisingly low.

6. **Momentum:** Tens of millions of individuals are already connected to the Internet, and business use is increasing at a dramatic rate.

13.5.2 E-Commerce Applications

There are *three* distinct classes of e-commerce applications:

- Customer-to-business.
- Intra-organizational.
- Inter-organizational.

Customer-to-business

Customer-to-business e-commerce applications include:

- **Social portals:** Electronic applications enable consumers to find online information about existing new products and services. This also includes applications that enable consumers to communicate with each other through electronic mail, video-conferencing, and newsgroups.

- **Transaction portals:** These include applications that enable and facilitate the completion of transactions between buyers and sellers. In electronically facilitated consumer-to-business transactions, customers learn about products through electronic publishing, buy products with electronic cash and other secure payment systems, and even have information goods delivered over the network.

The objective of this class of e-commerce is to provide consumers with greater convenience and lower prices. E-commerce provides consumers with convenient shopping methods, from online catalog ordering to phone banking, both of which eliminate the costs of expensive retail branches. E-commerce facilitates factory orders by eliminating many intermediary steps, thereby lowering manufacturers' inventory and distribution costs, and indirectly providing consumers with lower prices.

Intra-organization

Intra-organizational e-commerce applications include:

- **Workgroup communications:** These applications enable managers to communicate with employees using electronic mail, video-conferencing, and bulletin boards. The goal is to use technology to increase the dissemination of information, resulting in better-informed employees.

- **Collaborative publishing:** These applications enable companies to organise, publish, and disseminate human resources manuals, product specifications, and meeting minutes using tools such as the World Wide Web. The goal is to provide the information to enable better strategic and tactical decision-making throughout the firm. Also, online publishing shows immediate and clear benefits: reduced costs for printing and distributing documentation, faster delivery of information, and reduction of outdated information.

- **Sales force productivity:** These applications improve the flow of information between the production and sales forces, and between firms and customers. By better integrating the sales forces with other parts of the organization, companies can have greater access to market intelligence and competitor information, which can be funneled into better strategy. The goal is to allow firms to collect market intelligence quickly and to analyze it more thoroughly.

  Within intra-organizational electronic commerce, the largest area of growth can be seen in the development of "Corporate Intranets," which are primarily set up to publish and access vital corporate information. Some of the most common types of information are: human resources information, employee communications, product development and project management data, internal catalogs, sales support data, equipment and shipment tracking, and accessing corporate databases.

Inter-organization

Inter-organizational e-commerce applications include:

- **Supplier management:** Electronic applications help companies reduce the number of suppliers and facilitate business partnerships by reducing purchase order (PO) processing costs and cycle times, and by increasing the number of POs processed with fewer people.

- **Inventory management:** Electronic applications shorten the order-ship-bill cycle. If the majority of a business's partners are electronically linked, information once sent by fax or mail can now be instantly transmitted. Businesses can also track their documents to ensure that they were received there by improving auditing capabilities. This also helps to reduce inventory levels, improve inventory turns, and eliminate out-of-stock occurrences.

- **Distribution management:** Electronic applications facilitate the transmission of shipping documents such as bills of lading, purchase orders, advanced ship notices, and claims, and enable better resource management by ensuring that the documents themselves contain more accurate data.

- **Channel management:** Electronic applications quickly disseminate information about changing operational conditions to trading partners. Technical, product, and pricing information that once required repeated telephone calls and countless hours can now be posted to electronic bulletin boards. By electronically linking production-related information with international distributor and reseller networks, companies can eliminate thousands of hours of labour and ensure accurate information sharing.

13.5.3 Advantages of EC Applications

Following are the advantages to individual organizations, consumers, and society:

1. Reduced costs to buyers from increased competition in procurement as more suppliers are able to compete in an electronically open marketplace.

2. Reduced errors, time and overhead costs in information processing by eliminating requirements for re-entering data.
3. Reduced costs to suppliers by electronically accessing on-line databases of bid opportunities, on-line abilities to submit bids, and on-line review of rewards.
4. Reduced time to complete business transactions, particularly from delivery to payment.
5. Creation of new markets through the ability to easily and cheaply reach potential customers.
6. Easier entry into new markets, especially geographically remote markets, for companies of all sizes and locations.
7. Better quality of goods as specifications are standardized and competition is increased, and improved variety of goods through expanded markets and the ability to produce customized goods.
8. Faster time to market as business processes are linked, enabling seamless processing and eliminating time delays.
9. Optimization of resource selection as businesses form operative teams to increase the chances of economic successes, and to provide the customer products and capabilities more exactly meeting his or her requirements.
10. Reduced inventories and reduction of risk of obsolete inventories as the demand for goods and services is electronically linked through just-in-time inventory and integrated manufacturing techniques.
11. Ability to undertake major global programs in which the cost and personnel needed to manage a non-automated system would be unreasonable or prohibitive.
12. Reduced overhead costs through uniformity, automation, and large-scale integration of management processes.
13. Reduced use of ecologically damaging materials through electronic coordination of activities and the movement of information rather than physical objects.
14. Reduced advertising costs.
15. Reduced delivery cost, notably for goods that can also be delivered electronically.
16. Reduced design and manufacturing cost.
17. Improved market intelligence and strategic planning.
18. More opportunity for niche marketing.
19. Equal access to markets (i.e., for small-to-medium enterprises (SMEs) *vis-a-vis* larger corporations).

13.6 Electronic Business (E-Business)

E-business is about using Internet technologies to transform the way key business processes are performed. Its most visible form is online purchasing, both wholesale and retail. The pace is quickening. It is estimated that the value of goods that will be ordered/purchased by 2007 will be one trillion US dollars.

13.6.1 Opportunities and Benefits

There is a range of e-business opportunities that depend on the nature of the business and the customers it serves. Here are some opportunities of online business:

- Retail sellers on the Internet can sell high quality, specialized products that appeal to an audience of affluent, well-educated, and well-informed people.
- Companies that sell their goods through catalogs and expand their reach to additional global customers at a low marginal cost.
- Wholesalers, distributors, or service providers can sell to businesses that have embraced e-business and that demand the convenience and efficiencies of buying from a Web site.

- Companies holding comprehensive sets of digital assets (logos, image libraries, inventory information, and so forth) can sell and distribute their products electronically.
- Business-to-business sellers, the majority of whose customer base is already on the Internet, can build a closer relationship electronically.
- Companies having a corporate Web site and an efficient network operation can establish subsidiary sites for related, ancillary, or consumable products.
- Businesses selling products can readily be distributed over the Internet (for example, software, market research, industry and financial reports, news about local events, sports, travel and so on) and expand their customer bases.
- Businesses selling products can be sampled on the Web (for example, books, magazines, and recorded music) can promote them economically.
- Businesses selling products are subject to frequent changes (for example, airline tickets, financial instruments) can reduce production and obsolescence costs because they offer only current products on the site. They can also adjust pricing in real time in response to fluctuations in demand.
- Businesses that configure products to customer measurements or specifications (for example, custom-tailored garments, configured PCs, food shopping and delivery services or other just-in-time products) can expand made-to-order services to new markets.

The primary benefits of e-business are global accessibility and sales reach, the prospect of increased profits from new markets and electronic channels, improved customer service and loyalty, shorter time-to-market, and supply chain integration.

13.7 Mobile Commerce

Mobile commerce, commonly referred to as M-commerce, means to pay for merchandise services or information through a mobile phone. Wireless application protocol (WAP) is enabling technology to bring the Internet content and services to mobile phones and other wireless terminals. Today, mobile is a obiquitous, always reachable, highly convenient and supremely secure device for any kind of transaction. Coupled with localisation of services and applications, the enhanced services, the increasing availability of bandwidth, the *always on* Internet connectivity, it is not hard to see while mobiles are redefining communication scope for ever. Experience to date suggests that mobile banking and brokerage services are relatively high on most users wish list. Some of the important aspects of M-commerce are:

WAP: WAP provides a much-needed medium to connect in a secure, fast, nimble, online, interactive way with services, information and other users.

WAP applications: Wireless applications have a major role to play in easing business processes in every situation where information exchange is a critical need. WAP is being used to develop enhanced forms of existing applications and view versions of today's emerging applications.

13.8 E-Governance

The advent of new information and communication technologies have made electronic governance as tool to enhance the following relationship:

- Government to Government
- Government to citizen
- Citizen to Government
- Government to private and other sectors
- Private and NGOs to Government.

While e-government is defined as a mere delivery of government services and information to the public using electronic means, e-governance allows citizens to communicate with government, participate in the government's policy-making and citizens to communicate each other. It truly allows citizens to participate in the government decision-making process.

13.8.1 Models of E-Governance

There are *four* models of e-governance. The models are explained as follows:

Broadcasting/Wider Dissemination Model

This model is based on dissemination of governmental information, already available in public domain, into the wider public domain through the use of ICT and convergent media. This model could be applied in the following possible ways:

- Placing government laws and legislations online.
- To make available online the names, addresses, fax numbers, e-mails, etc. of local/regional/state/national government officials.
- To make available online information relating to government plans, budgets, expenditures, and performances.
- Placing key judicial decisions online, which are of value to general citizens and create a precedence for future actions.

Critical Value Information—Flow Model

This model is based on the principle of dissemination/channelising of information of critical value to target audience or in wider public domain through the use of ICT and convergent media. Possible applications of this model are:

- To make available online corruption-related data about a particular ministry/division/officials.
- To make available online research studies, enquiry reports, reports of the various commissions.
- To make available online human rights violations of the government or allied authorities for access to judiciary, NGOs and concerned citizens.
- To make available critical environmental information to local inhabitants.

Comparative Analysis Model

This model can harness the potential and capacity offered by latest communication technologies and aims it towards better governance. This model could be applied in the following possible ways:

- To learn from historic policies and actions and derive learning lessons for future policy-making.
- To evaluate effectiveness of current policies and identify key learnings in terms of strengths, flaws in policies.
- To effectively establish conditions of precedence, especially in case of judicial or legal decision-making, and use it to influence/advocate future decision-making.

Interactive Service Model

This model opens up avenues for direct participation of individuals in the governance processes. The model could be applied in the following possible ways:

- To establish an interactive communication channel with key policy-makers and members of Planning Commission.
- To conduct electronic ballots for the election of government officials and other office bearers.
- To conduct public debates/opinion polls on issues of wider concern before formulation of policies and legislative frameworks.
- Establish decentralised form of governance.
- Performing governance functions online such as revenue collection, governmental procurement, payment transfer, etc.

13.9 Enterprise Resource Planning

Enterprise Resource Planning (ERP) is a software architecture facilitating the flow of information among different functions of an organization. It is an area which has revolutionised the business environment. Many organizations have re-engineered the processes and adopted ERP. It encompasses a broad set of activities supported by multi-module application software, and includes product planning, purchasing, maintenance inventories, vendor/customer service, and tracking orders. ERP uses a client/server environment, supported by GUI (Graphic User Interface) technology. It is an integrated system of commonly designed applications and consolidating all business operations into uniform system environment. Following are the main features of ERP:

- A software architecture integrating all functions of a business.
- Integration is seamless. This is achieved through (a) common database; (b) instant sharing of information which is common and simultaneous; and (c) one time entry being sufficient for the whole enterprise to get updated.
- Powerful, user-friendly GUI technology.
- Supported by client-server architecture for communication at different levels of the system.
- Uniform system environment.

13.9.1 Enterprise Modelling

Enterprise-modelling is the most important prerequisite before the selection/implementation of an ERP system. It encompasses complete understanding and detailed mapping of the firm's business functions and decision-making process, both independently and interactively. Enterprise integration leads to:

- More agile enterprise.
- Helps in eliminating redundant or non-value added activities.
- More efficient system after being enabled by information technology.
- Streamlines *five* important flows in an enterprise:
    - (a) Information;
    - (b) Material;
    - (c) Money;
    - (d) Control; and
    - (e) Intangibles, such as customer satisfaction and quality improvement.
- Empowerment of employees to take action.

Based on Hansen (1991), there are *five* reasons which help in building employees motivation due to integration:

- When people understand the vision, or larger task of an enterprise, and are given the right information, the resources, and the responsibility, "they will do the right thing."
- Empowered people—and with good leadership, empowered groups—will have not only the ability but also the desire to participate in the decision process.
- The existence of a comprehensive and effective communications network must distribute knowledge and information widely, embracing the openness and trust that allow the individual to feel empowered to affect the "real" problems.
- The democratisation and dissemination of information throughout the network in all directions, irrespective of organizational position, ensures that the integrated enterprise is truly integrated.
- Information freely shared with empowered people, who are motivated to make decisions, will naturally distribute the decision-making process throughout the entire organization.

The integration of the enterprise helps in building an efficient and effective information network across the enterprise. Hoffman (1992) identified following reasons for integration:

- Identification of the major functions to be included in a program management organization.
- Defining the scope and content of the information systems' architecture and related metrics as a management guide.
- Providing guide and/or road map through the process of developing such an organisation to manage a large-scale integration program.

13.9.2 Role of Information Technology in Enterprise Modelling

Advancement in information technology (IT) has transformed the business process in an extended enterprise system by enabling seamless integration at the interfaces of functions and hierarchies. Table 13.4 gives the indication of shifting paradigms during recent years which have been triggered and supported by integration of enterprise and support of information technology.

Table 13.4 Role of IT in Changing the Enterprise System

Old System	Intervening Trend	Emerging Paradigm
Role of Information is very limited	Information system designs, computerisation of major activities, automation	Seamless integration of enterprise through IT support
Manual analysis of data MRP	Computerisation and networking MRP II	Integrated network of systems Open-loop MRP ERP
Information appears at and accessed from only one place, at one time.	Shared databases, electronic mail, client server architecture	Simultaneously one can access same information at any place and whenever needed
Only an expert can perform complex work	Expert systems, neutral computing	Novices can perform complex work
Business must be either centralized or decentralized	Telecommunication and networks: client/server	Business can be both centralised and decentralised
Managers make all decisions	Decision support systems, enterprise expert systems, support systems	Decision-making is part of everyone's job
Field personnel need offices to receive, send, store, and process information	Wireless communication and portable computers, information highways, electronic mail	Field personnel can manage information from any location
Personal contact is the best contact with potential buyers	Interactive video disk, desktop teleconferencing, electronic mail	The best contact is the one that is most cost-effective
One has to locate items manually	Tracking technology, groupware, workflow software, client/server	Items are located automatically
Overall plans get revised periodically	High performance computing systems	Plans get revised instantaneously whenever needed
All must come to one place to work together	Groupware and group support systems, telecommunicatons, electronic mail, client/server	People can work together while at different locations
Customized products and services are expensive and take a long time to develop	CAD-CAM, CASE tools, on-line systems for JIT decision-making, expert systems	Customized products can be made fast and inexpensively (mass customization)

Old System	Intervening Trend	Emerging Paradigm
A long period of time is spanned between the inception of an idea and its implementation (time-to-market)	CAD-CAM, electronic data interchange, groupware, imaging (document processing)	Time-to-market can be reduced by 90 per cent.
Information-based organizations and processes	Artificial intelligence, expert systems	Knowledge-based organizations and processes
Move labour to countries where labour is inexpensive (off-shore production)	Robots, imaging technologies, object oriented programming, expert systems, geographical information systems (GIS)	Work can be done in countries with high wages and salaries.

13.9.3 Guidelines for ERP Implementation

Based on experiences from the successful ERP projects, following useful guidelines are available in literature:

1. Understand the needs of the enterprise and feeling for corporate culture in the context of readiness for change.
2. The message should come from the top regarding adoption of the project.
3. Continuous and frequent communication from top regarding usefulness and mindset for the project.
4. Initiate with a feasibility report.
5. Start with changes in the business processes in the early stages of the project. Make everybody aware of this. Keep them informed: it will reduce resistance for change.
6. Decide phases of project implementation. Hold consultative meetings. Try for consensus.
7. Top executive should play the role of champion and set the project as the ultimate goal in all efforts. A total dedication and mission is needed at this stage.
8. Hire experienced consultants.
9. Visit sites of your vendors. See how the ERP solution is functioning. Extract useful tips from the existing users.
10. Carefully study the documentation of the vendor.
11. Make a balanced implementation team, which should include IT, HRD, works, financial and top executives. Other experienced functional managers should also be included.
12. Hold regular training and appraisal sessions in the organization.
13. Ensure that the problems arising out of changes are handled carefully. Such problems are inevitable.
14. Ensure good feedback mechanism to evaluate the results due to implementation.
15. Decide whether to go for modular or complete ERP solution.
16. Look into the future capabilities of the enterprise when it is armed with ERP. Take radical decisions for transformation, if need arises.

13.9.4 Post-implementation

To start with, many post-implementation problems can be traced to wrong expectations and fear. Expectations and fear that corporate management have from an ERP are outlined.

A few of the popular expectations are:

- Improvement in process.
- Enhanced productivity in all fronts.
- Total automation and disbanding of all manual processes.

- Improvement of key performance indicators.
- Elimination of manual record keeping.
- Actual information system available to concerned people on requirement basis.
- Integration of all operations.

A host of fears in respect of ERP implementation are:
- Job redundancy.
- Loss of importance as information is no longer an individual prerogative.
- Change in job profile.
- Loss of proper control and authorization.
- Increased stress due to greater transparency.
- Fear of loss of authority by individuals.

Hence, it is almost essential to balance the expectations and fear in the implementation process. Some realities that any organization must keep in mind are:
- For organizational change, strategic, business process and change and consequential organizational change are involved.
- Change in mindset is essential for organizational change.
- Measuring key performance indicators is necessary to bring a new culture in the organization. However, it is seen that this aspect is not taken care of by most companies in India because either the company did not feel it necessary or lacked the tools to do so.
- Some of the processes are better to be done manually.

In essence, a successful ERP implementation is not the end of the road. Continuous improvements are required to derive the maximum benefit.

13.9.5 Tasks after ERP Implementation

The effective use of ERP is the process at communication in all forms—written, oral workshops, meetings, etc. The process should start early by educating all layers of the management on the particular ERP product, its relevance, functionality, limitations and benefits.

At the start of the project, critical success factors (CSFs) or the organization as a whole should be listed. These should be drilled down to CSFs for respective functionalities of each department/section of the organization. From these CSFs, performance measures required to address these CSFs should be culled out. Numeric figures against these performance measures can be classified as key performance indicators (KPls). The process of firming up is usually done through workshops.

Envisioning the processes to be configured on an ERP is the critical portion to ensure user buy-in during the post implementation phase. The end-users should be involved in evolving the process. This should be done keeping the ERP functionality, KPls derived from the organizational goals and CSFs in mind.

Having evolved the processes during configuration, construction and implementation stage, some of the tasks required to be performed in past-implementation period are:
- Develop new job descriptions and organization structure to suit the post-ERP scenario.
- Determine the skill gap between existing and envisioned jobs.
- Assess training requirements, plan and implement the training for the required staff.
- Develop and amend human resources, financial and operational policies to suit the future ERP environment.
- Develop a plan for workforce logistics adjustment.

13.9.6 Post-Implementation Blues

It is generally seen that in most Indian organizations, monitoring KPIs and taking corrective business decisions to improve them do not exist. Therefore, it is necessary to follow a stretched target to be achieved in phases. Certain KPls, although exist in the system, are better monitored and controlled after the ERP system attains maturity.

During post-implementation phase, it is necessary to change the system requirements many times. It may be because of the following reasons:

- A change in the business environment requires a change in CSFs, resulting in a new or changed set of KPls necessitating re-configuration.
- A review indicates the need for change in some processes.
- Vision changes in the ERP and improvements in hardware and communication technology necessitate changes.
- New additions in the business require extra functionality.

At present, trend is to outsource the activity of maintenance and upgradation to enable the organization to concentrate on its core business activity. ERP audit, an emerging trend, is to correct its course as and when required. It could be general in nature or very specific. One of the specialised areas is to evaluate the security, authorisation and controls. Hence, a periodic independent audit is essential for an organization to ensure that it gets the best return on investment.

13.9.7   Causes of Failure in ERP Implementation

The ERP implementation fails to succeed due to following reasons:

1. **Absence of an executive sponsor:** Since ERP crosses functions within a company, the implementation needs someone with an authority to bring various functional executives together. There should be people directed and devoted towards the project.
2. When the project is viewed as an IT effort or as an effort towards automatmg finance/manufacturing/supply-chain, etc.
3. When there is no full-time project manager for ERP implementation.
4. *When the IT people start taking decisions in ERP implementation due to dominant role in handling hardware/software/communication, etc.:* As a matter of fact, they generally lack understanding of the functional requirements.
5. Lack of documentation of implementation procedure.
6. Lack of internal communication by top executive regarding project implications.
7. Lack of vendor support and team work.
8. Lack of re-engineering effort and insistence on continuation of current practices.
9. Massive change and unmanageable transformation without proper grasping by employees.

13.9.8   ERP Software Package (SAP)

SAP AG has developed an ERP package called SAP. It is a unique system that supports nearly all areas of business on a global scale. SAP has a number of application modules in the package. Some of these modules are:

- Financial
- Controlling
- Investment management
- Treasury
- Integrated enterprise management
- Sales and distribution
- Production, planning and control

- Materials management
- Human resources management
- Internet and intranet.

Each of these modules has a number of components, each taking care of specific functionalities of any normal business.

13.10 E-Enterprises

In the pre-industrial revolution, managing business and ownership were not separated. In the nineteenth century, there was a separation of ownership and control. This resulted in recruiting managers to monitor day-to-day operations of the enterprise and owners (shareholders) gave risk capital. During the industrial era, the enterprise started to adopt mass production which led to focus on productivity and led to turn to task-based specialisation. In the late twentieth century, all earlier factors have changed such as reducing task-based specialisation, fewer levels of hierarchy, and moving from managing physical resources to managing knowledge.

Nature of the enterprise has been changing due to digital development. New coordinating technologies led to the decline of centralised decision-making and bureaucracy. Though the new technologies return to the pre-industrial organizational model, but with a difference that electronic networks help microbusinesses to tap into the global reservoirs of information, expertise and finance. This means future business enterprises are not stable and permanent but temporary.

Earlier, economic eras had long periods of stability followed by short periods of change. This is known as *punctuated equilibrium*. The digital information creates a business environment of constant change known as *punctuated chaos*. Business decisions have to keep pace with electronic markets.

13.10.1 The Information Age

There has been evolution of the infotech usage in e-Enterprise. The phases of development have been Brochureware (1995), e-commerce (1997), e-Business (1999) and e-Enterprise (2000). In e-Enterprise, entire value chain both from the supply side and demand side is integrated.

This is a complex combination of tradition and infotech, a competitive virtual organization and an extension of BPR movement of late 1980s and early 1990s. E-enterprise applications consist of not only customers, suppliers and internal processes, employees, and back-office functions, but also external partners.

In 1995, scientists considered as *physical value chain* changes to *virtual value chain*. The physical value chain comprises:

Inbound logistics → Operations → Outbound logistics → Marketing and Sales
→ Service = Value.

Contrarily, virtual value chain comprises:

Gather → Organise → Select → Synthesize → Distribute → Value

In the latter case, information is captured at all stages of the physical value chain, and the same is used to increase performance. It was viewed that every business is information business. Without information, business cannot succeed.

There is a difference betwen information system (IS) and information technology (IT). It is concerned with **how** (the technology infrastructure or platform) while IS focuses on **what** (identification and prioritisation of systems). Information management has many domains in addition to how and what. They are **who** (information management strategy), **why** (organization strategy) and **where** (information resource strategy). A movement from data to knowledge, distinguishing between data, information and knowledge, is shown in Table 13.5.

Table 13.5   Movement from Data to Knowledge

	Data	*Information*	*Knowledge*
Content	Events	Trends	Expertise
Form	Transactions	Patterns	Learnings
Information task	Representation	Manipulation	Codification
Human element	Observation	Judgement	Experience
Organizational Intent	Automation	Decision-making	Action
Value test	Building block	Uncertainty reduction	New understanding

Enterprises are required to maximize their know-how. This means a new culture of information discovery, distribution, and application. However, networks are more valuable. There are interdependencies, organizational collaboration, and industrial convergences.

13.10.2 The Network-centric Era

The network-centric era has produced two distinct type of E-enterprises. Old economy companies have followed the evolutionary changes, while new type companies, based on information technology, have come to be known as dotcom enterprises. The evolution of the era started in 1984 with the introduction of collaborative network-based software and moved to the PCs revolution. Then 'File Server' or 'host' mainframe computer was introduced and connected to LAN, linking any number of PCs or workstations. In the 1980s and 1990s the relational database technology started to emerge. Back-office systems were most structured information, while front-office systems dealt with unstructured information.

There was an emergence of collaborative network solutions by groupware which supported the exchange of information among workgroups (whether physical or virtual, formal or informal). The tools were e-mail, electronic calendars, and on-line document repositories. Then there was a development of on-line discussion groups via intranets within the organization. The e-mail became a tool for managing workflow. In the networking era, the labour intensive system was replaced by the 'applicant tracking system' (ATS).

The nature of management improved along four dimensions: asynchronous communications, authentication, information dissemination, and mobility. Asynchronous communications technologies allowed for both voice mail and e-mail connections. These can be saved and official authentication provided. Technologies facilitated rapid information dissemination and increased mobility (time and place irrelevant for messages receiving or answering).

Inside the enterprise: Four layers are distinguished:

• Empowered individual means knowledge access and workflow integration. The former consists of specialized knowledge and expertise of individuals, while the latter consists of using information and knowledge tools in work processes.

• Second layer is automated workgroups. This consists of group collaborations such as team facilitation solutions, electronic discussion solutions, departmental reference system solutions, departmental scheduling solutions and document authorising solutions.

• Third layer is the integrated enterprise. This comprises enterprise data systems, enterprise-wide communication, enterprise knowledge management, and enterprise process innovation.

• Fourth layer in the extended enterprise consists of extranet and electronic commerce. This also consists of customer and supplier transactions, marketing and communications, ecosystem development, and market-facing systems.

The market-facing enterprise depends on computers for defining and managing business environments. There have been *three* stages of enterprise development. The basic stage came during 1980s to mid-1990s. The intermediate stage was achieved by 1998. The advanced stage came when

IT users integrated and developed competitive advantages internally (managing knowledge assets), externally (market-facing systems), and innovatively (process innovation).

There is a trend of IT industry convergence of four Cs—computers, communications, consumer electronics, and content. All these have one thing in common, that is, digital foundation. The hardware development will have the convergence of PCs and consumer electronics. The communications will have both voice and data. The content will have multiple media—text, image, audio, and video. The industry will have *five* main elements—hardware, communications, software, content, and services.

Success factors: There are *five* success factors:

- Application agility/flexibility.
- Creation/improvement/integration.
- Overcoming political obstacles.
- Application and data integration.
- Putting the CEO in charge.

13.10.3 Architecture

Net led to the transition from e-commerce to e-business to e-enterprise. This transformation affected all aspects of the business. Changes are significant in several aspects such as culture, management processes, technology, etc. as given in Table 13.6. Implications of these aspects and its varying inpact or the type of enterprise are also indicated.

E-enterprise architecture aims at bringing technology and business together. Architecture has to have an interactive approach. Different issues and focus are given in Table 13.6.

Table 13.6   E-enterprises—Issues and Focus

Issues	*Focus*
e-Business models	Target market analysis, financial modelling, inter-enterprise touch point, ownership, and resource analysis
e-Process models	Business entities, use-cases, inter-organizational processes, reusable business process, and business components
e-Application models	User-interface mockups, application specification and business rules
e-Application rules	A rules engine, application framework, component software
e-Distibution/integration	Distributed object architecture, technology components, middleware, and Enterprise application Integration (EAI) software
e-Data	Data management systems, data warehouses, legacy data, and ERP /MRP data repositories
e-Network	Network security solutions, encryption, connectivity tools, a Network Operating System (NOS) and systems analysis and management tools.

13.10.4 Role of Managers

The role of managers is to facilitate the smooth functioning of processes not just by giving orders. It also has the implication that a Chief Executive Officer (CEO) can give up control but stay in command.

E-CEO has to operate in real time business where nothing can wait for tomorrow. As the e-world moves fast, the e-CEO has to be of a different breed. The difference between tradition and e-CEO is given in Table 13.7.

Table 13.7   E-CEOs—A New Breed

Traditional CEO	*e-CEO*
Encouraging	Evanglizing
Alert	Paranoid
Cordial	Brutally frank
Infotech semi-literate (at best)	Infotech literate (at least)
Clearly focused	Intensely focused
Fast moving	Faster moving
Hates ambiguity	Likes ambiguity
Suffers from technology	Suffers from brandwidth
Confrontation anxiety	Separation anxiety
A paragon of good judgement	A paragaon of good judgement
Age: 57	Age: 38
Rich	Really rich

e-CEO runs companies built on faith which means evangelizing. He has to have the ability as a real-time decision-maker. He has to spend a lot of time in recruiting since their companies are growing fast and depends on brainpower. He is paranoid and proud.

13.10.5 Digital Strategies

The emergence of the Web has given the opportunity for developing a market-facing system. Technology-enabled enterprises are moving towards integration. An enterprise's connection to the outside world is its World Wide Web site. These are the new-breed enterprises.

The merging of technologies is making the marketplace to move into the cyberspace Now, strategic planning is replaced with digital strategy. Internet is eliminating conventional intermediaries, but creating infomediaries. With the advent of the web, it is important to know which countries are already selling to whom, and which countries are sufficiently online to attract clients.

13.10.6 Network-based Businesses

Some of the businesses such as banks, telephone companies, airlines, and railroads use networks. The distinction is that these networks transport people, goods, or information for customers and do not do mere own distribution. There are three usage patterns:

- **Zero concentration:** When customers use a network randomly.
- **Zone concentration:** When customers concentrate their usage on some portion of the network.
- **Lane concentration:** Customers use heavily the individual links in a network.

Organizations should handle the natural business unit and make profit-and-loss assessments at that level. In case it is zero concentration, then the company should use the entire network. The concentration usage patterns allow the company to have either the zone or the lane instead of the entire network.

Bill Gates' book *Business @ the Speed of Thought* gave 12 rules to make the digital information flow an intrinsic part of the company. They are:

For Knowledge Work

- Insist that communication flows through e-mail.
- Study sales data online to share insights easily.
- Shift knowledge workers into high-level thinking.

- Use digital tools to create virtual teams.
- Convert every paper process into a digital process.

For Business Operations

- Use digital tools to eliminate single-task jobs.
- Create a digital feedback loop.
- Use digital systems to route customer complaints immediately.
- Use digital communications to redefine the boundaries.

For Commerce

- Transform every business process into just-in-time delivery.
- Use digital delivery to eliminate the middle man.
- Use digital tools to help customers solve problems for themselves.

While Gates gave twelve rules, Brown tried to find success factors through the examples of successful companies.

13.10.7 Nine Ways

E-enterprises have been classified into *nine* groups. They are the patterns for success in dot.coms. They are:

1. Selling to business, direct-sales practices
2. Corporate intranet
3. Streamlining the supply chain
4. Recruiting online
5. Winning and keeping web surfers
6. Direct marketing
7. Selling to consumers
8. Customer service
9. Coordinating finance.

The difference between the Web success and Web failure is how people sift through details and fine-tune plans.

13.11 Some Important IT Applications

The impact of IT is all pervasive in modern society. Organizations and countries are leveraging IT to gain significant competitive advantage in the international trade arena. Important IT applications are:

- Business data processing
- Financial information system
- Medical applications
- Scientific applications
- Educational applications
- Entertainment applications
- Multilingual applications.

13.11.1 Business Data Processing

Business data processing constitutes the largest segment of computer use. Computers are used for at least *three* basic organizational tasks:

- Management transaction processing

- Control operations
- Decision-making

13.11.2 Financial Information System

Financial information system is a sub-system of any business that provides information to persons and groups, both inside and outside the firm, concerning the firm's financial matters. Information is provided in the form of periodic and special reports. Important areas of coverage are:

- Accounting information system
- Payroll system
- Inventory level
- Maintenance costs
- Purchasing costs
- Economic order quantity
- Electronic commerce

13.11.3 Medical Applications

Computers are used in medical research, medical education, and aiding people with limitations. Important areas are:

- Hospital administration
  - Accounting
  - Payroll
  - Bed allocation
  - Drug and equipment details
- Patient monitoring
  - Using scanning instruments
- Patient data
  - Medical information of patient
  - Clinical reports
  - Details of tests
  - Summary charts
- Medical records
  - History of patients for reference and research
- Diagnosis
  - Matching conditions of patient against case studies
  - Testing hypothesis analysis programs
- Research
  - Using medical statistics and record
  - Through modelling
  - Training medical students

13.11.4 Scientific Applications

Applications involving mathematical, statistical and model processing form a large class of computer usage, *e.g.*, space technology, weather forecasting.

13.11.5 Educational Applications

Computers can be used as a resource in teaching and learning at all levels of education. Computer-based tutorial, computer-aided instruction, and automatic examination and evaluation system are some of the applications of information technology.

13.11.6 Entertainment Applications

Multimedia represents the convergence of computers, digital video, digital audio, and sound synthesis technologies. It can be referred to as a means of entertainment because of its applications in interactive games and leisure telecommunications, audio CD player and CD-ROM player.

13.11.7 Multilingual Applications

To provide computer support to non-English language users, multilingual applications and systems are needed. Multilingual system and application development is one of the latest developments in the field of computers.

Self-assessment Questions

1. 'The twenty-first century witnessed advances from an age of automation to an era of digitisation.' Justify the statement with reasons.

2. Explain the cascade model, suggested by Feraud, of the evolution of information management.

3. 'Information' is an important resource. Discuss its special characteristics and show through a block diagram, how information is processed.

4. 'Information technology is an enabler of change and a catalyst.' Elaborate the statement in detail with *two* live examples.

5. Define the terms 'data' and 'information'. Discuss the difference between data and information, and give examples.

6. Classify the information requirements of decision-makers for planning.

7. (*a*) Compare and contrast-formal and informal information. Give *three* examples of each.

   (*b*) 'Formal information cannot do much to help top level decision-makers'. Discuss.

8. Why does management need information? Is it possible for the management of an organization to make effective decisions without the aid of an information system? Discuss.

9. Classify the information obtained and used in the organizations.

10. Explain the value of information for a successful functioning of any organization.

11. Illustrate how a data life cycle works. Take any situation in an organization.

12. Define management information system and discuss its objectives.

13. Discuss the various categories of MIS and their role in decision-making.

14. Explain the role of MIS in the organizational structure.

15. What impact would (*a*) the technological revolution, (*b*) R&D, (*c*) product changes, and (*d*) information explosion have on the need for information, by management of an engineering industry, and R&D organization in electronic components.

16. Write a short note on the importance of MIS and its different levels of management.

17. Mention the steps involved in designing an MIS for an organization. What should be done to create 'acceptance' of the system in the organization?

18. What considerations must influence the selection of a computer system for an MIS?

19. What are the approaches for designing the strategies for implementing an MIS? Illustrate with a flow diagram.

20. Mention the disadvantages of information systems.

21. Discuss different approaches of MIS development in an organization. Explain in detail *any two*.

22. List the constraints in developing an effective MIS.

23. What are the limitations of MIS? How can these be overcome for successful implementation?

24. What do you mean by the term 'Decision Support System'? How did Gorry and Morton initially view the DSS?

25. 'DSS are especially useful for semi-structured problems'. Comment on this statement with at least *two* examples.

26. Explain *three* objectives of DSS.

27. Explain Alter's classification of DSS with type of operation and an example in each class.

28. Identify and explain *any three* characteristics of a decision support system.

29. Discuss *three* main components of a DSS.

30. Name and explain the *five* functions of a DSS.

31. If you are preparing a weekly report for a departmental head, showing the hours that each employee worked each day, would you use a graph or a tabular display? Support your answer with reasons.

32. When are graphs required to be used?

33. How is development of DSS determined?

34. What are the *three* methods for developing a DSS? Explain each of them in detail with examples.

35. What is a GDSS and how does it facilitate group decision-making?

36. What are the *three* types of computer-based support available in a GDSS?

37. What is the role of *facilitator* and *brainstorming* in a GDSS?

38. Write *any three* applications of DSS.

39. What is Electronic Commerce? Mention the business activities involving Electronic Commerce.

40. Explain *six* reasons of using Internet in Electronic Commerce.

41. Discuss practical applications of E-commerce in banks and engineering industries in India.

42. Mention *three* distinct E-commerce applications. Explain any *one* of them in detail.

43. Outline the various advantages of E-commerce applications to organizations, consumers, and society.

44. What do you understand by electronic business? What are the characteristics of e-business applications? Discuss them with reference to an e-business application of your choice.

45. What is mobile commerce? How is it useful in business? Discuss some important aspects of mobile commerce.

46. Explain the term 'E-Governance'. Discuss its different models and applications thereof.

47. Define enterprise resource planning in its right perspective. What are its component subsystems?

48. Explain the purpose of modelling an enterprise. How does ERP fit in the enterprise modelling endeavour?

49. Discuss the role of information technology in enterprise modelling.

50. What are the factors involved in ERP implementation? What should be done to avoid failure in ERP implementation?

51. Outline the expectations of an organizations during post-implementation of ERP package.

52. 'ERP package ends up with job redundancy, change in job profile and increased stress due to greater transparency.' Comment on this statement with reasons.

53. Explain in detail why is it necessary to change the system requirements many times during post-implementation phase.

54. Mention different application modules of ERP software package. Explain *any three* of them in detail.

55. What are e-enterprises? Discuss the nature of work these enterprises are expected to perform.

56. Explain *five* basic elements of the evolving information technology for a homogeneous front-office.

57. Outline the differences between the global technologies and applications of the PC era to the web-based era.

58. What is the difference between information system and information technology? Distinguish between data, information and knowledge.

59. Explain the *four* layers inside the enterprise.

60. Discuss the technology components for building e-enterprises.

61. Define virtual office and the range of alternative work arrangements.

62. What is digital strategy? Explain in detail network-based business.

63. How are e-enterprises classified? Discuss in brief.

64. 'The impact of information technology is all pervasive in modern society.' Elaborate this statement with important IT applications in scientific and educational planning.

65. 'ERP is a business solution'. Justify the statement.

Selected References

1. Abell, D F and J S Hammand. *Strategic Market Planning, Problems and Analytical Approaches*. Prentice-Hall, Inc., Englewood-Cliffs, 1979.

2. Adhikary, M. *Managerial Economics*. Khosla Educational Publishers, Delhi, 1987.

3. Allen, R G D. *Mathematical Analysis for Economists*. ELBS and Macmillan.

4. Anthony, R N, et al. *Management Control Systems*. Homewood, RD Irwin, 1984.

5. Apte, S S. *Maintenance Management*. National Productivity Council, New Delhi.

6. Bell, D J. *Planning Corporate Manpower*. Longman, London, 1974.

7. Bennis, W G. *Organisation Development: Its Nature, Origins and Prospects*. Addison-Wesley, Reading, 1969

8. Buffa, E S. *Modern Production/Operations Management*. John Wiley & Sons, New York, 1983.

9. Claude, Jr S. G. *The Hisotory of Management Thought*. Prentice-Hall, Englewood-Cliffs, NJ, 1968.

10. Chamber, John C, et al. *How to Choose the Right Forecasting Technique*. Harvard Business Review, 1971.

11. Chamberlain, N W and J W Kuhn. *Collective Bargaining*, McGraw-Hill, New York, 1965.

12. Dalela, S and Mansoor Ali. *Industrial Engineering and Management Systems*. Standard Publishers Distributors, Delhi, 2000.

13. Datta, A K. *Integrated Materials Management-A Functional Approach*. Prentice-Hall of India (P) Ltd., New Delhi, 1986.

14. Davar, R S. *Modern Marketing Management*. Progressive Corporation (P) Ltd., Mumbai, 1969.

15. Drucker, P F. *Management Tasks, Responsibilities and Practices*. Allied Publishers (P) Ltd., New Delhi, 1975.

16. Gordon, F. *Maintenance Engineering*. Applied Science Publishers Ltd., London, 1973.

17. Gupta, A K and J K Sharma. *Management of Systems*. Macmillan India Ltd., New Delhi, 1999.

18. Gupta, A K. *Reliability Engineering and Terotechnology*. Macmillan India Ltd., New Delhi, 1996.

19. Gupta, A K. *Management Information Systems*. S. Chand & Co. Ltd., New Delhi, 2006.

20. Hersey, P and K H Blanchard. *Management of Organisation Behaviour*. Prentice-Hall of India (P) Ltd., New Delhi, 1983.

21. Hannagan, Tim. *Management: Concepts and Practices*. Macmillan India Ltd., New Delhi, 1997.

22. International Labour Organisation. Employers Organisations in Industrial Relations in Asia, ILO, Geneva, 1975.

23. Jain, K C and L N Aggarwal. *Production Management*. Khanna Publishers, Delhi, 1995.

24. Kelly, A. *Maintenance Planning and Cotrol*. Butterworths Company Ltd., London, 1984.

25. Khanna, O P. *Industrial Engineering and Management*. Dhanpat Rai, Delhi, 1983.

26. Kotler, P. *Marketing Management—Analysis, Planning and Control*. Prentice-Hall of India (P) Ltd., New Delhi, 1986.

27. Koontz, D and C Donnell. *A System and Contingency Analysis of Management Functions*. McGraw-Hall Kogakusha Ltd., Tokyo, 1985.

28. Mascarenhas, S J, O A J. *New Product Development: Its Marketing Research and Management*. Oxford & IBH Publishing Co. (P) Ltd., New Delhi, 1987.

29. Moder, J J, et al. *Project Management with CPM and PERT.* Van Nostrand Reinhold, New York, 1983.

30. Murdick, R G, et al. *Information Systems for Modern Management.* Prenice-Hall of India (P) Ltd., New Delhi, 1990.

31. Nagarajan, K. *Project Management.* New Age International Publishers, New Delhi, 2004.

32. Pareek, U and T V Rao. *Designing and Managing Human Resource Systems.* Oxford & IBH Publishing Co. (P) Ltd., New Delhi, 1981.

33. Panneerselvam, R. *Production and Operations Management.* Prentice-Hall of India (P) Ltd., New Delhi, 1999.

34. Robertson, S A. *Engineering Management.* Blackie & Son Ltd., Glasgow, 1964.

35. Salvendy, G (ed). *Handbook of Industrial Engineering.* John Wiley & Sons, New York, 1982.

36. Singh, J P. *Organisation Development: Concepts and Strategeis.* Indian Institute of Management, Ahmedabad, 1984.

37. Sharma, S D. *Operations Research.* Kedar Nath Ram Nath & Co., Meerut, 2002.

38. Tricker and Boland. *Management Information and Control Systems.* John Wiley & Sons., London, 1982.

39. Verma, P and S Mookerjee. *Trade Unions in India.* Oxford & IBH Publishing Co. (P) Ltd., New Delhi, 1982.

40. White, E N. *Miantenance Planning, Control and Documentation.* Gower Press, London, 1979.

41. Yeates, D. *Systems Project Management* ELBS Pitman, London, 1986.

Control Charts and Acceptance Sampling

Introduction

A quality control chart is the basic analytical tool used to control quality and maintain at the desired level. It requires adequate knowledge of (a) possible causes of variations in product quality characteristics, and (b) purpose and logic of construction and application of control charts. Mainly there are two types of causes leading to variations in quality characteristics: (a) chance cause; and (b) assignable causes. The *chance causes* operate randomly and influence the quality characteristics only marginally and imperceptibly. Their effect is extremely difficult to identify and trace them. They are inherent in the manufacturing process itself. Small variations in the quality of raw materials and process conditions, atmospheric and climatic influences, or the skill of manual operators are some of the examples of these causes. *Assignable causes* bring about relatively large variations in product quality and require to be promptly identified, located and removed. Inexperienced workmen, mechanical faults in the plant, defective or low quality raw materials, machines requiring adjustments, etc. are some examples of assignable causes. Being small in number, non-random by nature, and amenable to identification and removal, these are rightly described as assignable causes. Thus, the basic purpose is to distinguish between chance variations and assignable variations in quality.

Logic of Control Charts

A quality control chart helps identify whether a given production process is statistically under control or not. It is based on the assumption that the sampling distribution of sample mean $\bar{X}$ is approximately normal with population mean μ and standard error $\sigma_{\bar{x}} = \sigma/\sqrt{n}$.

Applying this to quality control with respect to same measurable quality characteristic such as the diameter of a pipe, the sampling distribution of sample mean $\bar{X}$ is approximately normal when the process is under control. In that case, mean $\mu_{\bar{x}} = \mu$ and standard error $\sigma_{\bar{x}} = \sigma/\sqrt{n}$, where σ is the process standard deviation and n, the sample size.

It provides that only one in 20 samples drawn from the population will have a mean that will fall outside the limits

$$\mu_{\bar{x}} \pm 1.96 \frac{\sigma}{\sqrt{n}}.$$

Similarly, $\mu_{\bar{x}} \pm 3 \dfrac{\sigma}{\sqrt{n}}$ provides the two limits about which it can be asserted that only rarely (about 27 times in 10,000) a sample mean crosses these limits only due to chance. This provides the essential logic how control charts work as a device for separating assignable variations from random variations.

Construction of Control Charts

The construction of control charts and their application to a given production process consists of the following *two* steps:

(a) Estimating the process average μ and the process dispersion σ for determining the central line and the control limits, respectively. Both μ and σ are estimated by drawing a number of samples and obtaining the two estimates on the basis thereof. The control limits are then set

$$\text{at } \mu' \pm 3 \left(\frac{\sigma'}{\sqrt{n}} \right),$$

where μ' is an unbiased estimate of μ and σ' of σ.

(b) Selecting product samples of size n and observing the selected items with reference to the desired quality characteristic, first to estimate the process average μ and process dispersion σ, and then to remain constantly informed whether the sample mean points continue to lie within the control limits during the cause of future production.

For both purposes, samples are drawn randomly from the assembly line as the production process is on. The sample size, n, may vary from being as small as 2 units to as large as 20 units. In practice, a sample of size 4 to 6 units is considered satisfactory. For a sample size $n = 5$, the number of samples to be drawn for estimating μ and σ should at least be 20. The sample size and the number of samples drawn should vary inversely so that the total number of product units inspected in all the samples is at least 100. Then only reasonable estimates of μ and σ can be expected.

Types of Control Charts

There are *two* types of control charts—control charts for variables and control charts for attributes. When the quality characteristics can be measured, it is called *control charts for variables*. When quality is judged in terms of the product items possessing or not possessing a certain attribute, it is called *control charts for attributes*.

Control Charts for Variables

Control charts for variables consist of (a) $\overline{X}$ charts, and (b) R charts. X charts are again of *two* types: (i) $\overline{X}$ and σ charts; and (ii) $\overline{X}$ and R charts. The main difference between the two refers to whether σ', an estimate of the process dispersion σ, is estimated on the basis of sample standard deviation or on the basis of sample range R.

$\overline{X}$ Charts

An estimate μ' of the process average μ, in case of both $\overline{X}$ charts, is obtained by computing the mean $\overline{\overline{X}}$ of the sample mean $\overline{X}$. The process dispersion σ is estimated by using sample standard deviations S in the case of $\overline{X}$ and σ charts, and sample range R in the case of $\overline{X}$ and R charts. The construction of $\overline{X}$ charts for both the types are given in Table A.1.

Table A.1   Measurements of a Critical Dimension of 15 Samples of 4 Items
(Unit: 0.001 gm in excess of 0.500 gm)

Sample No.	Measurements of Individual Items									
	X_1	X_2	X_3	X_4	ΣX_i	$\overline{X}$	ΣX^2	s^2	S	R
1	20	22	16	21	79	19.75	1581	5.187	2.277	6
2	24	18	20	22	84	21.00	1784	5.000	2.236	6
3	19	15	21	22	77	19.25	1511	7.187	2.681	7
4	15	20	22	16	73	18.25	1365	8.187	2.861	7
5	21	19	23	15	78	19.50	1556	8.750	2.958	8
6	14	16	21	23	74	18.50	1422	13.250	3.640	9
7	23	14	15	20	72	18.00	1350	13.500	3.674	9
8	17	19	22	24	82	20.50	1710	7.250	2.693	7
9	18	20	23	21	82	20.50	1694	3.250	1.803	5
10	24	18	15	22	79	19.75	1609	12.187	3.490	8

Sample No.	Measurements of Individual Items									
	X_1	X_2	X_3	X_4	ΣX_i	$\bar{X}$	ΣX^2	S^2	S	R
11	22	17	16	20	75	18.75	1429	5.687	2.385	6
12	24	18	19	20	81	20.25	1661	5.187	2.278	6
13	22	17	21	15	75	18.75	1439	8.187	2.861	7
14	14	20	24	16	74	18.50	1428	14.750	3.841	10
15	21	24	16	21	82	20.50	1714	8.250	2.872	8

$$\Sigma \bar{X} = 291.75 \qquad \Sigma S^2 = 125.809 \qquad \Sigma S = 42.550 \qquad \Sigma R = 108$$
$$\bar{\bar{X}} = \Sigma \bar{X}/M \qquad S_m^2 = \Sigma S^2/M \qquad \bar{S} = \Sigma S/M \qquad \bar{R} = \Sigma R/M$$
$$= 291.75/15 \qquad\qquad = 125.809/15 \qquad = 42.55/15 \qquad = 108/15$$
$$= 19.45 \qquad\qquad\qquad = 8.387 \qquad\qquad = 2.836 \qquad = 7.20$$

$\bar{X}$ and σ Charts

Setting the process average and control limits

For sample size $n = 4$, the mean of $M = 15$ sample means is $\bar{\bar{X}} = 19.45$, which is an estimate of the process average μ. Since the standard error of estimate of the distribution of sample mean $\sigma_{\bar{x}} = \sigma/\sqrt{n}$, the two control limits are set at

$$\bar{\bar{X}} \pm 3\sigma_{\bar{x}} \qquad\qquad ...(1)$$

or

$$\bar{\bar{X}} \pm 3\left(\frac{\sigma}{\sqrt{n}}\right) \qquad\qquad ...(2)$$

Substituting A for the factor $3/\sqrt{n}$, the two control limits may be stated as

$$\bar{\bar{X}} \pm A\sigma. \qquad\qquad ...(3)$$

Estimate of σ in terms of sample variance S^2

The determination of control limits in equations (2) and (3) requires estimation of σ as a measure of process dispersion. An estimate σ' of the process dispersion σ may be obtained either in terms of sample variance S^2 or in terms of sample standard deviation S. Computed either way, the resultant estimate σ' will not be an unbiased estimate of σ as the sample size is small.

When obtained in terms of S^2, compute S^2 for each sample, sum it up for all the M samples, and find their mean by dividing the sum by the number of samples. Thus, the mean of $M = 15$ sample variances, *denoted as* S_m^2, as per details given in Table A.1 is

$$S_m^2 = \frac{125.809}{15} = 8.387$$

Since the under-root of S_m^2 is not an unbiased estimate of σ, the bias can be removed by multiplying S_m^2 by the ratio $[n/(n-1)]$. Thus, the unbiased estimate of σ is given by

$$\sigma' = \sqrt{S_m^2\left(\frac{n}{n-1}\right)}. \qquad\qquad ...(4)$$

For $n = 4$ and $S_m^2 = 8.387$,

$$\sigma' = \sqrt{S_m^2\left(\frac{n}{n-1}\right)} = \sqrt{(8.387)\left(\frac{4}{3}\right)} = 3.34.$$

Accordingly, the two control limits in terms of (3) are set at

$$\bar{\bar{X}} \pm A\sigma'$$

or

$$\bar{\bar{X}} \pm A \sqrt{S_m^2 \left(\frac{n}{n-1}\right)}, \qquad \qquad ...(5)$$

in which $A = 3/\sqrt{n}$.

Substituting the values in (5), the control limits are

Upper Control Limit $(U.C.L_{\bar{X}}) = 19.45 + \left(\frac{3}{2}\right)(3.34) = 24 : 46$

and Lower Control Limit $(L.C.L_{\bar{X}}) = 19.45 - \left(\frac{3}{2}\right)(3.34) = 14.44.$

Obtaining the estimate of σ in terms of sample standard deviation S

Alternatively, the estimate of process dispersion σ' can be arrived at by computing the sample standard deviation S for each sample, and then obtaining their mean $\bar{S}$. Since $\bar{S}$ is not an unbiased estimate of σ, the bias is removed by dividing $\bar{S}$ by the factor C_2, where

$$C_2 = \sqrt{\frac{2}{n}} \cdot \frac{\left(\frac{n-2}{2}\right)!}{\left(\frac{n-3}{2}\right)!} \qquad \qquad ...(6)$$

While the values of C_2 will vary depending on the sample size n, in the present case

$$C_2 = \sqrt{\frac{2}{4}} \cdot \frac{\left(\frac{4-2}{2}\right)!}{\left(\frac{4-3}{2}\right)!} = \sqrt{(0.5)} \frac{1!}{0.5!} = 0.7979$$

that is, the unbiased estimate σ' of the process dispersion σ in terms of $\bar{S}$ is

$$\sigma' = \frac{\bar{S}}{C_2} \qquad \qquad ...(7)$$

According to computations made in Table A.1,

$$\bar{S} = \frac{\Sigma S}{M} = \frac{42.55}{15} = 2.836$$

Then in terms of equation (7),

$$\sigma' = \frac{2.836}{0.7979} = 3.555,$$

which is approximately the same as obtained by using equation (4).

Using $\sigma' = \dfrac{\bar{S}}{C_2}$ for σ in $\sigma_{\bar{X}} = \dfrac{\sigma}{\sqrt{n}}$,

$$\sigma_{\bar{X}} = \frac{\bar{S}}{C_2 \sqrt{n}}. \qquad \qquad ...(8)$$

Then in terms of equation (8), the two control limits are set at

$$\bar{\bar{X}} \pm 3 \frac{\bar{S}}{C_2 \sqrt{n}} \qquad \qquad ...(9)$$

Writing A_1 for $3/C_2 \sqrt{n}$, these may be restated as

$$\bar{\bar{X}} \pm A_1 \bar{S} \qquad \qquad ...(10)$$

Table A.2 gives the values of C_2 and A_1 for sample sizes ranging from 2 to 15. It may be observed that as n tends to be large, C_2 approaches unity and, consequently, $\bar{S}$ tends to become an unbiased estimate of σ.

Table A.2   Values of C_2 and A_1 for Samples of Sizes 2 to 15

n	C_2	A_1
2	0.5642	3.760
3	0.7236	2.394
4	0.7979	1.880
5	0.8407	1.596
6	0.8686	1.410
7	0.8882	1.277
8	0.9027	1.175
9	0.9139	1.094
10	0.9227	1.028
11	0.9300	0.973
12	0.9359	0.925
13	0.9410	0.884
14	0.9453	0.848
15	0.9490	0.816

Using $A_1 = 1.880$, $\bar{S} = 2.84$ and $n = 4$, the two control limits, in terms of equation (10), are

$$\text{U.C.L}_{\bar{X}} = 19.45 + (1.880)\,(2.84) = 24.79$$
$$\text{L.C.L}_{\bar{X}} = 19.45 - (1.880)\,(2.84) = 14.11$$

$\bar{X}$ and R Charts

Setting the process average and control limits

The estimate σ' of process dispersion σ in the case of $\bar{X}$ and R charts is obtained by using the sample range R. Use of R is particularly useful where control charts are required to be constructed with reference to two or more quality characteristics of a single product, or a single characteristic of two or more related products.

In any such situation, saving on time needed for determining the control limits is an important consideration. Since sample range takes much less time to compute, σ' based on R can be obtained more efficiently than the one based on sample standard deviation S.

Accordingly, the mean of sample ranges $\bar{R}$ is used as an estimate of process dispersion σ. Like S_m^2 and $\bar{S}$, $\bar{R}$ is also not an unbiased estimate of σ. In order to obtain the unbiased estimate σ', $\bar{R}$ is divided by a factor d_2 whose values for samples of size 2 to 15 are listed in Table A.3. Then σ' is obtained as

$$\sigma' = \bar{R}/d_2. \qquad \qquad \text{...(11)}$$

Table A.3   Value of d_2 and $A_2 \ (= 3/d_2 \sqrt{n})$ for sample of sizes 2 to 15

n	d_2	A_2
2	1.128	1.880
3	1.693	1.023
4	2.059	0.729
5	2.326	0.577
6	2.534	0.483
7	2.704	0.419
8	2.847	0.373

n	d_2	A_2
9	2.970	0.337
10	3.078	0.308
11	3.173	0.285
12	3.258	0.266
13	3.336	0.249
14	3.407	0.235
15	3.472	0.223

In terms of Table A.1, $\bar{R}$ based on 15 sample ranges is 7.20. The value of d_2 for $n = 4$ read from Table A.3 being 2.059,

$$\sigma' = \frac{\bar{R}}{d_2} = \frac{7.20}{2.059} = 3.50$$

Substituting $\bar{R}/d_2$ for σ in $\sigma_{\bar{x}} = \sigma/\sqrt{n}$,

$$\sigma_{\bar{X}} = \frac{\bar{R}}{d_2\sqrt{n}}, \qquad \qquad ...(12)$$

and the two control limits are thus defined as

$$\bar{\bar{X}} \pm 3\frac{\bar{R}}{d_2\sqrt{n}} \qquad \qquad ...(13)$$

Let

$$A_2 = \frac{3}{d_2\sqrt{n}}, \qquad \qquad ...(14)$$

the control limits in equation (13) may be restated as

$$\bar{\bar{X}} \pm A_2\bar{R} \qquad \qquad ...(15)$$

Using the value of $\bar{R} = 7.20$ and of $A_2 = 0.729$ according to Table A.3, the two control limits are

$$\text{U.C.L}_{\bar{X}} = 19.45 + (0.729)\,(7.20) = 24.70$$

and

$$\text{L.C.L}_{\bar{X}} = 19.45 - (0.729)\,(7.20) = 14.20$$

These are approximately the same as those derived from expression (10).

A comparison of the control charts defined in expressions (10) and (15) will show that while the two control limits are more accurate in the case of $\bar{X}$ and σ charts, these are merely satisfactory in the case $\bar{X}$ and R charts when the sample size n is rather small. Since both are essentially $\bar{X}$ charts, the resultant control limits get placed at the same level when applied to the same data.

Drawing the Control Chart

After obtaining the estimate $\bar{\bar{X}}$ of the process average μ and σ' of the process dispersion σ, using either of the methods stated above, drawing a control chart is a simple task. Using the process average

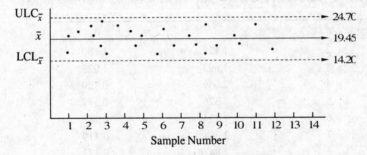

Fig. A.1 $\bar{X}$ and R control chart

($\bar{\bar{X}}$ = 19.45) as the central line, the two control limits fall equi-distant from the central line as in Fig. A.1. For example, the control limits drawn here are those of an $\bar{X}$ and R charts which, as computed above, are U.C.L$_{\bar{X}}$ = 24.70, and L.C.L$_{\bar{X}}$ = 14.20.

R Charts

The construction of R charts follows the same basic principle as for the $\bar{X}$ charts. The central line in the case of these charts is drawn at $\bar{R}$, which is the mean of the sample ranges. The control limits are determined in terms of standard deviation of the sample ranges, *denoted as* σ_R. Thus, the control limits of $\bar{R}$ chart are set as

$$\bar{R} \pm 3\sigma_R \quad \text{or} \quad \left(1 \pm \frac{3\sigma_R}{\bar{R}}\right)\bar{R} \qquad \qquad ...(16)$$

Let $$D_3 = 1 - \frac{3\sigma_R}{\bar{R}} \quad \text{and} \quad D_4 = 1 + \frac{3\sigma_R}{\bar{R}},$$

the two control limits in equation (16) above are restated as

and
$$\begin{aligned} \text{L.C.L}_R &= D_3\bar{R} \\ \text{U.C.L}_R &= D_4\bar{R}. \end{aligned} \qquad \qquad ...(17)$$

The use of D_3 and D_4 factors, as defined, is only to facilitate obtaining the two control limits. For sample sizes ranging from 2 to 15, the tabulated values of D_3 and D_4 are given in Table A.4.

Table A.4 Values of D_3 and D_4 for sample sizes of 2 to 15

n	D_3	D_4
2	0.000	3.267
3	0.000	2.575
4	0.000	2.282
5	0.000	2.115
6.	0.000	2.004
7	0.076	1.924
8	0.136	1.864
9	0.184	1.816
10	0.223	1.777
11	0.256	1.744
12	0.284	1.716
13	0.308	1.692
14	0.329	1.671
15	0.348	1.652

Drawing upon necessary computations made in Table A.1, the value of $\bar{R} \doteq 7.20$, while $D_3 = 0$ and $D_4 = 2.282$ according to Table A.4. Substituting these values in equation (17),

$$\text{U.C.L}_R = (2.282)(7.20) = 16.43$$

$$\text{L.C.L}_R = (0)(7.20) = 0$$

The lower control limit for R charts coming to zero should not surprise. In fact, the lower control limit for these charts in many cases may even turn out to be negative. This is particularly so where n is small. Since sample ranges cannot have negative values, the lower control limit in such cases is invariably set at zero.

The use of R charts need clear understanding as to the following:

(a) The sampling distribution of R based on all possible samples of small size is not normal even when the population is normal. This implies that a larger number of R points falls beyond the upper control limit in the case of R charts than $\bar{X}$ points may do in the case of $\bar{X}$ charts. But this does not undermine the utility of R charts because the control limits set at $(\bar{R} \pm 3\sigma_R)$ still indicate the need to look for an assignable cause in the event of unusual variations in the quality characteristic of interest; and

(b) When the lower control limit for R chart is zero, it means the control chart has no such limit. In that case, the decision, whether or not the process is under control, is taken only on the basis of the positioning of sample R points vis-à-vis the upper control limit. The process is considered to have gone out of control as and when a sample R point comes to lie above the upper control limit.

Whereas one or more sample R point(s) may fall above the upper control limit of an R chart, the corresponding sample mean point(s) may not fall outside any of the two control limits of an $\bar{X}$ chart. This happens because a large part of the variations in the sample values is smoothed during the process of averaging in the case of $\bar{X}$ charts. The same does not happen in the case of R charts.

Regarding the use of R charts, it is important to bear the following points in mind:

(a) The R charts hardly serve any useful purpose particularly when an assignable cause increases the variations to the extent that it disturbs even the process average;

(b) The R chart serves as a warning for an assignable cause interfering with the normal functioning of the production process well before it gets depicted on the $\bar{X}$ chart; and

(c) The R charts are often used alongwith the $\bar{X}$ charts for their special role referred to in (b) above, and for the fact that they are more expeditiously constructed.

Control Charts for Use

For $\bar{X}$ chart (Figure A.1), the central line and control limits must be based on samples selected randomly from the assembly line of an ongoing production process. Before a control chart is in use during the future course of production, it is essential to finalise the central line and control limits. In case one or more sample mean points fall outside the two control limits, central line and control limits should recomputed after excluding all such out-of-line sample data. This process should be repeated till all remaining sample mean points fall within the revised control limits. Until such time, control limits remain mere *trail units*. As and when the chart attains this stage, the process is considered to be under control. In Figure A.1, control chart has acquired the final use position. Thereafter, repeated samples of same size should be selected and observed, by plotting on the control chart. As long as sample mean or range points fall within the control limits, the process is said to be under control. Any sample mean/range point falling outside the control limits is an indication of the presence of some assignable cause, calling for immediate action to locate and remove it.

Selection of samples during the course of production must meet the requirements such as (a) samples are taken off the assembly line one after the other observing a constant time interval, (b) every sample consists of equal number of items, all produced as nearly as possible at one time, (c) units comprising all individual samples are as homogeneous as possible so that the chance variations are the minimum within each sample, and maximum among different samples.

Process Out of Control

The possible indications of the process getting out of control are:

- When any single sample point, based on a sample taken from the assembly line, falls beyond any of the two control limits.
- When a series of sample points fall close to the two control limits.

- When a series of sample points fall on either side of the central line.
- When a series of sample points form a trend either in upward or downward direction.

Lack of process control, as revealed by any of the above indicators, is seen both on $\bar{X}$ and R charts. As a measure of abundant caution, control charts require to have two sets of control limits. While the usual limits set at $\pm 3\sigma$ may remain as action limits, the other two set at $\pm 2\sigma$ may be designated at warning limits.

Control Charts for Attributes

These charts are used when a product is viewed on the whole as meeting or not meeting certain specifications/requirements. In all such cases, following two issues are taken into consideration: (a) The decision about acceptance/rejection of a product is taken on the basis of conforming/non-conforming to a test with reference to some requirement(s) that cannot be measured. In such an event, the attributes of the product, instead of variables, are considered; (b) Inspection of the product with regard to desired attribute(s) is required irrespective of conforming them or not. This resulted that the product is classified as rejected or accepted.

Control Charts for Defectives

The charts for defectives are of *two* types:

1. Charts for fraction defectives, known as *p charts*.
2. Charts for total number of defective, known as *np charts*.

This choice as to which one of the two should be used in a given problem situation depends on whether or not the lot size remains constant. If the lot size remains constant, it is better to construct *np charts*, as these are easy to understand and take much less time to construct. If lot size varies, *p charts* are constructed. For constant lot size, both np and p charts can be used without any difference in interpretation. Being identical in all respects, both provide the same information regarding the process being under control or out of control.

Control limits for p and np charts

It is held that when sample n is large, the sampling distribution of the number of defectives (or fraction defective) is approximately normal with mean np (or p) and standard deviation $\sqrt{npq}$ (or $\sqrt{pq/n}$), where $q = 1 - p$.

Let $\bar{p}$ be the mean of the fraction defective p_i in different samples. Using $\bar{p}$ as an estimate of p, the control limits are set as usual at

$$n\bar{p} \pm 3\sqrt{n\bar{p}(1-\bar{p})} \quad \text{or} \quad n\bar{p} \pm 3\sqrt{n\bar{p}\bar{q}} \qquad \text{...(18)}$$

for *np* charts, and at

$$\bar{p} \pm 3\sqrt{\frac{\bar{p}(1-\bar{p})}{n}} \quad \text{or} \quad \bar{p} \pm 3\sqrt{\frac{\bar{p}\bar{q}}{n}} \qquad \text{...(19)}$$

for *p* charts, where $\bar{q} = 1 - \bar{p}$.

Table A.5, gives the computation to obtain central line $(n\bar{p}$ or $\bar{p})$ and the two control limits for two types of control charts. It gives the values of *np* (number of defective items) and *p* (the proportion of defective items) for 20 samples of size 100 each. The average of *np* and *p* values in columns (3) and (4), respectively results in $n\bar{p} = 10$ and $\bar{p} = 0.10$.

Substituting the required value is equations (18) and (19)

U.C.L$_{np}$: $\quad n\bar{p} + 3\sqrt{n\bar{p}(1-\bar{p})} = 19$

Central Line : $\quad n\bar{p} = 10$

L.C.L$_{np}$: $\quad n\bar{p} - 3\sqrt{n\bar{p}(1-\bar{p})} = 1$

for the *np* chart, and

Table A.5   Number of Defective Fan Regulators in 20 Lots of Sample Size $n = 100$

Lot/Sample No.	Lot/Sample size, n	No. of Defective Fan Regulators in Each Lot, np	Fraction Defectives, p_i
1	100	10	0.10
2	100	12	0.12
3	100	14	0.14
4	100	9	0.09
5	100	8	0.08
6	100	11	0.11
7	100	6	0.06
8	100	16	0.16
9	100	15	0.15
10	100	10	0.10
11	100	8	0.08
12	100	8	0.08
13	100	12	0.12
14	100	15	0.15
15	100	4	0.04
16	100	8	0.08
17	100	7	0.07
18	100	11	0.11
19	100	7	0.07
20	100	9	0.09
		200	2.00

$$n\bar{p} = 200/20 = 10 \qquad \bar{p} = 2.00/20 = 0.10$$

U.C.L.$_p$	:	$\bar{p} + 3\sqrt{\bar{p}\bar{q}/n} = 0.19$
Central Line	:	$\bar{p} = 0.10$
L.C.L.$_p$	:	$\bar{p} - 3\sqrt{\bar{p}\bar{q}/n} = 1$

for the p chart.

With reference to p charts, the above control limits may be understood to mean as under:

- The mean per cent defective is 0.10 or 10 per cent.
- About 99.7 per cent of the times the lot per cent defective p will be between 1 per cent (L.C.L.) and 19 per cent (U.C.L.) defective items.
- Only in about 3 out of 1,000 samples of size 100 each, per cent defective p either exceeds 19 per cent or is below 1 per cent.

It may be remembered that as long as the lot size remains constant, the two control limits vis-à-vis the central line are at the same level in the case of both the p chart and the np chart. When the to size varies, all the three lines will differ with the lot size in the case of np charts, and only the two control limits (not the central line) in the case of p charts. Interestingly, the larger the lot size, the closer are the two control limits to the central line.

Varying lot size presents a few additional problems in drawing the p charts. These are as follows.

(a) It may be appreciated that p charts require computation of new control limits for each lot of a different size. This makes the task of showing the two control limits in relation to a single central line quite tedious;

(b) To save oneself the hassle of computing control limits again and again, one may estimate the average lot size and compute the control limits based thereon. However, the use of average lot size also necessitates review of control limits from time to time; and

(c) When individual lot size differs substantially from the average lot size, it is advisable to have the control limits for each lot shown on the chart. In that case, using three sets of control limits is more desirable. While one set of control limits may be corresponding to the expected average lot size, the second can be close to the expected minimum lot size. The third may be computed close to the expected maximum lot size.

The construction and use of *np* and *p* charts is otherwise subject to all such considerations as are applicable to control charts for variables. An important difference, however, is that the control limits of these charts require more frequent revision than those for the $\bar{X}$ and R charts.

However, these charts have the following distinct advantages too:

• Both can be constructed for, and applied to, quality characteristics which are measurable.

• Either of them (np or p) may be used for any number of quality characteristics. This is contrary to $\bar{X}$ and R charts which are required to be drawn separately for each single quality characteristic.

• Construction and use of both these charts need much less time and cost than any other chart for variables.

Control Charts for Number of Defects

Popularly known as *C* charts, these charts deal with number of defects per unit of a product, denoted as *C*. *Defectives* represent the number of items not acceptable for failure to meet a certain test/specifications. *Defects*, on the other hand, refer to the number of instances of lack of conformity of a single item to given specifications. *C* charts are used extensively in automobile industry, production of aircraft, electronic computer assembly, TV and radio manufacturing. *C* charts show graphically how many defects figure in a unit of production, and whether the production process is under control with respect to the number of defects that may contain in a single product unit.

Defects may occur in a given manufactured product owing to various reasons. However, the probability that a particular defect occurs at a given point or in a given form is negligible. This accounts for the distribution of the number of defects *C* in a single product item to follow the Poisson distribution with mean μ and standard deviation $\sqrt{\mu}$.

Accordingly, the construction of *C* charts is based on an estimate of μ, which can be obtained by computing $\bar{C}$, the average number of defects per unit. This requires classification of units inspected according to the number of defects contained in each, and obtaining $\bar{C}$ as the total number of defects divided by the total number of units inspected.

The central line of the *C* charts is then set at $\bar{C}$ and the two control limits at

$$\bar{C} \pm 3\sqrt{\bar{C}}, \qquad \qquad ...(20)$$

so that
$$U.C.L_C = \bar{C} + 3\sqrt{\bar{C}}$$
and
$$L.C.L_C = \bar{C} - 3\sqrt{\bar{C}}.$$

As soon as the control chart is finally readied for further use in the manner described for the $\bar{X}$ chart, testing future production is done by (a) selecting a single unit one after the other after a constant time interval, (b) counting the number of defects *C* contained in each, and (c) observing whether *C* falls within or outside the control limits. As before, a particular point falling outside the two control limits indicates the process having gone out of control at that point of time.

It may be noted that C cannot be negative. This means that even when equation (20) results in a negative lower control limit, it should be taken as zero. As in the case of *np* and *p* charts, C charts also need frequent revision of control limits. Even otherwise, the control limits for C charts require more frequent revision during early stages of production, when machine operators and foremen are not quite conversant with the machines and other mechanical operations. As the necessary familiarisation takes place, a C chart will need frequent revision that usual.

Acceptance Sampling

Acceptance sampling is another area of quality control where statistical techniques have been used to the best advantage of buyers and sellers for greater efficiency in results at much less cost. Its primary function is to help promptly decide whether to accept or reject the material offered for sale.

In an overall view, acceptance sampling consists of (*i*) drawing a random sample of size *n* from the product lot of size *N* offered for sale, (*ii*) observing the sample for the number of defective items *d*, (*iii*) deciding an acceptance number C, and (*iv*) taking a decision by comparing the observed number of defective items *d* with the acceptance number C.

The general approach is based on the belief that the proportion of defective items in the sample is a measure of the average lot quality. The lot ought to be rejected if the sample indicates that it contains too large a proportion of defectives. By doing this, the buyer protects himself against the trouble of 100 per cent inspection. Similarly, if the sample inspection reveals a smaller proportion of defective items in the lot, it should be accepted, for it saves the supplier the cost of 100 per cent inspection before he offers the lot for sale.

Sampling Plans

Depending on how the buyer and the seller (or supplier) reach an agreement, the decision to accept or reject a lot is taken on the basis of the result of a single sample or more. This suggests the need for different acceptance sampling plans.

A sampling plan is specified by the sample size *n* and the acceptance number C. Accordingly, acceptance sampling may be a single, double, or sequential sampling plan, depending on the number of samples used for deciding the lot.

Under each of these sampling plans, the decision to accept or reject a lot is taken by evaluating in terms of the laws of probability the risk of committing the two types of errors, that is, the risks of

   (*a*) accepting a lot as of satisfactory quality when it ought to have been rejected for being below the desired quality level; and

   (*b*) rejecting a lot as of unsatisfactory quality when it ought to have been accepted for being of satisfactory quality level.

Single sampling plan

Under the single sampling plan, a random sample of size *n* is taken from a randomly operating process (from the assembly line) or an isolated lot offered for sale. The sample is inspected for the number of defective items *d* contained in it. If *d* does not exceed a specific pre-determined number of defective items C, known as acceptance number, the lot is accepted, otherwise it is rejected, that is,

$$\text{if } d > C, \text{ the lot is rejected,}$$

and $$\text{if } d \leq C, \text{ the lot is accepted}$$

The requirements of a single sampling plan are met as soon as *n* and C are stated. For example, for a single sampling plan defined by $n = 100$ and $C = 2$, the lot is rejected if $d > 2$, and accepted if $d \leq 2$.

Double sampling plan

The double sampling plan provides for a decision to accept or reject a lot on the basis of a second sample, if the first sample fails to offer conclusive evidence for taking a final decision either way. First, a sample of size n is selected from the lot. The lot is accepted if the number of defective items d in the sample is C_1 or less, and rejected if d is more than C_2.

When the number of defective items d in the sample is between C_1 and C_2, the lot is placed in a doubtful category and a second sample of the same size is drawn from the lot. The lot is accepted if the total number of defective items in both the samples is C_2 or less. The lot is rejected if the total number of defective items in both the samples is more than C_2.

Sequential sampling plan

Sequential or multiple sampling plan allows selection of as many samples as are needed to reach a final decision. After inspecting each sample, the lot is either accepted, rejected, or placed in a doubtful category. It means sampling continues as long as the lot remains in a doubtful category. Theoretically, a sequential sampling plan permits a continuous process of sample selection and inspection. In actual practice, final decision to accept or reject the lot is usually taken after a maximum of 8 or 9 samples have been drawn.

The double sampling plan is used more often than either of the other two sampling plans. If a given lot has a small percentage of defective items, the chances that it is accepted on the basis of the result of the first sample are naturally high. This reduces the cost of sampling as the second sample need not be taken and inspected thereafter. When a lot comes to be put into a doubtful category on the basis of the results of the first sample, it is quite appealing to give the lot a second chance of evaluation before being finally rejected.

Example A 1. The mean life of battery cells, manufactured in a certain plant estimated on the basis of a large sample, was found as 1500 hours, with standard deviation of 180 hours. Considering these values as the process average and process dispersion, compute the 3-sigma control limits for $\bar{X}$ chart for sample of size $n = 9$.

Solution. Given $\bar{X} = 1500$ hours, $\sigma' = 180$ hours, and $n = 9$.

Since the given estimate of process average and process dispersion are based on a large sample, the desired control limits are

$$\bar{\bar{X}} \pm 3 \frac{\sigma'}{\sqrt{n}}$$

Substituting the values, $\text{L.C.L}_{\bar{X}} = \bar{\bar{X}} - 3 \frac{\sigma'}{\sqrt{n}} = 1500 - 3\,(180/\sqrt{9}) = 1320$

and $\text{U.C.L}_{\bar{X}} = \bar{\bar{X}} + 3 \frac{\sigma'}{\sqrt{n}} = 1500 + 3\,(180/\sqrt{9}) = 1680$

Example A 2. Twenty-five samples of six items each were selected from the assembly line of a machine. On measurement of a critical dimension, the mean of 25 sample means was reported as 0.81 inch and $\bar{R}$ as 0.0025 inch. Compute the control limits for $\bar{X}$ and R charts.

Solution. With $\bar{X} = 0.81$ inch, $\bar{R} = 0.0025$ inch, and $n = 6$, the control limits for $\bar{X}$ chart are obtained as $\bar{\bar{X}} \pm A_2 \bar{R}$. The value of A_2 is 0.483 (Table A 3). Substituting the values,

$$\text{L.C.L}_{\bar{X}} = \bar{\bar{X}} - A_2 \bar{R} = 0.81 - (0.483)\,(0.0025) = 0.8088$$

and $\text{U.C.L}_{\bar{X}} = \bar{\bar{X}} + A_2 \bar{R} = 0.81 - (0.483)\,(0.0025) = 0.8112$

The control limits for R charts are

$$\text{L.C.L}_R = D_3 \bar{R}$$

and $\text{U.C.L}_R = D_4 \bar{R}$

According to Table A.4, the value of $D_3 = 0$ and of $D_4 = 2.004$. Substituting the values,

$$\text{L.C.L}_R = 0$$

and $\text{U.C.L}_R = (2.004)\,(0.0025) = 0.0050.$

Example A 3. Twenty samples of four gas cylinders each were selected from the assembly line of an automatic gas filling plant. The mean weight of gas contained in each cylinder based on means of 20 samples was found to be 22 kg, mean of 20 sample variances as 0.81 kg, and mean of their standard deviations as 0.475 kg. Obtain (*a*) the estimate of process dispersion by using sample variances and sample standard deviations, and (*b*) the control limits for $\bar{X}$ chart based on two estimates.

Solution. Given $\bar{\bar{X}} = 22$ kg, $S_m^2 = 0.81$ kg, $\bar{S} = 0.475$ kg, and $n = 4$.

(*a*) The estimate of process dispersion by using S_m^2 is

$$\sigma' = \sqrt{S_m^2 \left(\frac{n}{n-1}\right)} = \sqrt{0.81 \left(\frac{4}{3}\right)} = 1.039$$

The value of C_2 according to Table A 2 being 0.7979, the estimate of process dispersion using $\bar{S}$ is

$$\sigma' = \frac{\bar{S}}{C_2} = \frac{0.475}{0.7979} = 0.5953$$

(*b*) Using $\sigma' = 1.039$, the two control limits are

$$\text{L.C.L}_{\bar{X}} = \bar{\bar{X}} - 3\frac{\sigma'}{\sqrt{n}} = 22 - 3\left(\frac{1.039}{\sqrt{4}}\right) = 20.44$$

and

$$\text{U.C.L}_{\bar{X}} = \bar{\bar{X}} + 3\frac{\sigma'}{\sqrt{n}} = 22 + 3\left(\frac{1.039}{\sqrt{4}}\right) = 23.56$$

Using $\sigma' = 0.5953$, the two control limits are

$$\text{L.C.L}_{\bar{X}} = \bar{\bar{X}} - 3\frac{\sigma'}{\sqrt{n}} = 22 - 3\left(\frac{0.5953}{\sqrt{4}}\right) = 21.11$$

and

$$\text{U.C.L}_{\bar{X}} = \bar{\bar{X}} + 3\frac{\sigma'}{\sqrt{n}} = 22 + 3\left(\frac{0.5953}{\sqrt{4}}\right) = 22.89.$$

Example A 4. Inspection of a large sample of a product revealed a fraction defective of 0.25. Compute the upper and lower control limits for the lot size $N = 200$.

Solution. With $\bar{p} = 0.25$, $\bar{q} = (1 - \bar{p}) = 0.75$, the control limits are obtained as

$$\bar{p} \pm 3\sqrt{\frac{pq}{n}}$$

Substituting the values, $\text{L.C.L}_{\bar{p}} = \bar{p} - 3\sqrt{\frac{pq}{n}} = 0.25 - 3\sqrt{\frac{(0.25)(0.75)}{200}} = 0.1582$

and

$$\text{U.C.L}_{\bar{p}} = \bar{p} + 3\sqrt{\frac{pq}{n}} = 0.25 + 3\sqrt{\frac{(0.25)(0.75)}{200}} = 0.3418.$$

Example A 5. The quality control manager of a production unit is in the process of setting up quality control chart for one of its newly introduced products with respect to its diameter. He has randomly picked up as many as 25 samples of 4 units each. The sum of the sample means was found as 625 and that of their variances as 112.5. Compute the trial control limits for the $\bar{X}$ and σ control charts.

Solution. Given are the sums $\Sigma \bar{X} = 625$ and $\Sigma S^2 = 1125$, so that

$$\bar{\bar{X}} = \Sigma \bar{X}/M = 25$$

and
$$S_m^2 = \Sigma S^2/M = 4.5$$

While $\overline{\overline{X}} = 25$ is an unbiased estimate of the process average, that of process dispersion

$$\sigma' = \sqrt{S_m^2 \left(\frac{n}{n-1}\right)} = \sqrt{4.5\left(\frac{4}{3}\right)} = 2.45$$

Thus, the two trial limits are

$$\text{L.C.L}_{\overline{X}} = \overline{\overline{X}} - \frac{3}{\sqrt{n}} \, \sigma' = 25 - \frac{3}{2}(2.45) = 21.325$$

and

$$\text{U.C.L}_{\overline{X}} = \overline{\overline{X}} + \frac{3}{\sqrt{n}} \, \sigma' = 25 + \frac{3}{2}(2.45) = 28.675.$$

Example A 6. On your advice as a statistician, the production engineer working in a plant has generated the following data on the weight measurements for 10 samples of 10 items each randomly picked up from the assembly line:

Sample mean weight: 120   122   124   123   122   121   120   123   120   121

Standard deviation of   2.2   2.4   2.3   2.5   2.4   2.1   2.0   2.3   2.22   2.1
sample weights:

(a) Establish the control limits as a gesture of help to the production engineer, (b) Do you consider that the resultant control limits are final for checking the future production in relation to product weight characteristic?

Solution. (a) Given 10 sample means, an estimate of the process average $\overline{\overline{X}} = \Sigma \overline{X}/M = 1216/10 = 121.6$. Similarly, for 10 sample standard deviations, their mean $\overline{S} = \Sigma \overline{S}/M = 22.5/10 = 2.25$. Since $\overline{S}$ is not an unbiased estimate of σ, multiply $\overline{S}$ by the factor

$$C_2 = \sqrt{\frac{2}{n}} \cdot \frac{\left(\frac{n-2}{2}\right)!}{\left(\frac{n-3}{2}\right)!},$$

to get the unbiased estimate of process dispersion σ as $\sigma' = \overline{S}/C_2$. According to Table A.2, the value of C_2 for $n = 10$ is 0.9227. Thus, the two control limits are

$$\text{L.C.L}_{\overline{X}} = \overline{\overline{X}} - 3\frac{\overline{S}}{C_2\sqrt{n}} = 121.6 - \frac{3}{\sqrt{10}}\left(\frac{2.25}{0.9227}\right) = 119.29$$

and

$$\text{U.C.L}_{\overline{X}} = \overline{\overline{X}} + 3\frac{\overline{S}}{C_2\sqrt{n}} = 121.6 + \frac{3}{\sqrt{10}}\left(\frac{2.25}{0.9227}\right) = 123.91.$$

(b) Since one of the sample means ($\overline{X} = 124$) falls beyond the upper control limit, the resultant control limits are only trial limits. These are not yet final for being used to check the future process of production as to control of quality for the product weight characteristic.

Example A 7. A production control engineer lifted 25 samples of 4 items each from the assembly line on random basis. He measured a critical dimension of the product and, for 25 samples, he found mean of sample means as 120, mean of sample ranges as 6.2, and mean of standard deviations as 4.5. Help the production control engineer by (a) computing the control limits for $\overline{X}$ and σ control chart, (b) obtaining the control limits of $\overline{X}$ and R control chart, and (c) comparing the two sets of control charts for comments.

Solution. Given $\overline{\overline{X}} = 120$, $\overline{S} = 4.5$, $\overline{R} = 6.2$, and $n = 4$.

(a) With $\overline{\overline{X}} = 120$ as an estimate of the process average, the unbiased estimate of process dispersion is $\sigma' = \overline{S}/C_2$, where $C_2 = 0.7979$ according to Table A 2. Thus, the two control limit $\overline{X}$ and σ chart are

$$\text{L.C.L}_{\bar{X}} = \bar{\bar{X}} - \frac{3}{\sqrt{n}}\left(\frac{S}{C_2}\right) = 120 - \frac{3}{\sqrt{2}}\left(\frac{4.5}{0.7979}\right) = 111.54$$

and

$$\text{U.C.L}_{\bar{X}} = \bar{\bar{X}} + \frac{3}{\sqrt{n}}\left(\frac{S}{C_2}\right) = 120 + \frac{3}{\sqrt{2}}\left(\frac{4.5}{0.7979}\right) = 128.46.$$

(b) With $\bar{\bar{X}} = 120$ as an estimate of the process average, the unbiased estimate of process dispersion $\sigma' = \bar{R}/d_2$, where $d_2 = 2.059$ according to Table A 3. Thus, the two control limits $\bar{X}$ and R chart are

$$\text{L.C.L}_{\bar{X}} = \bar{\bar{X}} - \frac{3}{\sqrt{n}}\left(\frac{\bar{R}}{d_2}\right) = 120 - \frac{3}{\sqrt{2}}\left(\frac{6.2}{2.059}\right) = 111.54$$

and

$$\text{U.C.L}_{\bar{X}} = \bar{\bar{X}} + \frac{3}{\sqrt{n}}\left(\frac{\bar{R}}{d_2}\right) = 120 + \frac{3}{\sqrt{2}}\left(\frac{6.2}{2.059}\right) = 128.50.$$

(c) The control limits for the $\bar{X}$ and R chart are marginally wider. This provides the possibility, howsoever small, that a particular sample mean point which falls within the two control limits for $\bar{X}$ and σ chart may not do so in the case of $\bar{X}$ and R chart.

Example A 8. A quality control assistant was asked to obtain the control limits for R quality control chart. He randomly picked up 10 samples of size 10 each from the assembly line and generated the following range values of a given product quality characteristic:

Range values: 2.5   3.7   4.6   3.8   4.0   3.9   4.2   3.9   4.3

Compute for him the two control limits for the R control chart and advise him with your comments.

Solution. Given 10 range values, the mean range

$$\bar{R} = \Sigma R/M = 38.7/10 = 3.87$$

Then the two R control chart limits are

$$\bar{R} \pm 3\sigma_R \quad \text{or} \quad \left(1 \pm \frac{3\sigma_R}{\bar{R}}\right)\bar{R}$$

Given that

$$D_3 = \left(1 - \frac{3\sigma_R}{\bar{R}}\right) \quad \text{and} \quad D_4 = \left(1 + \frac{3\sigma_R}{\bar{R}}\right)$$

for sample size $n = 10$, $D_3 = 0.223$ and $D_4 = 1.777$ according to Table A 4.

Thus, the two control limits are

$$\text{L.C.L}_{\bar{R}} = D_3\bar{R} = (0.223)\,(3.87) = 0.86$$

and

$$\text{U.C.L}_{\bar{R}} = D_4\bar{R} = (1.777)\,(3.87) = 6.88.$$

Comments. As the sample size $n = 10$, the lower control limit is not zero. Had n been smaller, the lower control limit could as well be zero.

Example A 9. One hundred randomly selected lady dress pieces of a certain make were got carefully examined by a group of girls. Thorough inspection for the number of defects resulted in the following data:

No. of defects, d_i:	0	1	2	3	4	5	6	7
No. of dress pieces, f_i:	35	22	15	10	7	5	4	2

(a) Construct the control limits for the number of defects C for the said dress pieces; and

(b) Also, comment on the resultant lower control limit.

Solution. (a) Given the distribution of 100 dress pieces according to the number of defects, the average number of defects $\bar{C} = \Sigma d_i\, f_i/N = 208/100 = 2.08$. Thus, the two control limits are

$$\text{L.C.L}_C = \bar{C} - 3\sqrt{\bar{C}} = 2.08 - 3\sqrt{2.08} = 0 \text{ (for } -1.25)$$

and
$$\text{U.C.L}_C = \bar{C} + 3\sqrt{\bar{C}} = 2.08 + 3\sqrt{2.08} = 6.41.$$

(b) Since C cannot be negative, the lower control limit too cannot be negative. Even if it comes negative, it has to be taken as zero as in the present case.

Example A 10. A buyer has decided that he will accept a product lot offered for sale if a sample of 50 products contains 3 or less defective items, and reject it if the defective items are found more than 5. He further asserts that in case the sample outcome places the lot in a doubtful category, he will draw a second sample of 50 items and will accept the lot if the number of defective items in the two samples is 5 or less, otherwise he will reject the lot. It the first sample shows 4 defective items and the second 2 defective items, what should the buyer do about the lot?

Solution. Given are the defective items $C_1 = 3$ and $C_2 = 5$. Since the number of defective items in the first sample is $d_1 = 4$, it is more than $C_1 = 3$ and less than $C_2 = 5$. The lot is placed in a doubtful category.

In the second sample, the defective items are $d_2 = 2$. As the total number of defective times in the two samples $(d_1 + d_2) = 6$, it is again more than $C_2 = 5$. Thus, the buyer will reject the lot.

Example A 11. The ABC company produces incandescent light bulbs. Following data on the number of lumens for 40W light bulbs were collected when the process was in control:

Sample	Observations	
	1	2
1	600	610
2	590	600
3	580	570
4	620	600
5	570	620

Construct $\bar{X}$ chart [value of A_2 for $n = 2$ is 1.88].

Hint : Calculation of $\bar{X}$-chart is given as follows :

S.No.	Observations		$\bar{X}$	Range
1	600	610	605	1
2	590	600	595	10
3	580	570	575	10
4	620	600	610	20
5	570	620	595	50

$\bar{\bar{X}} = 596$; $\bar{R} = 20$; $\text{U.C.L.}_{\bar{x}} = 6.33.6$; $\text{L.C.L.}_{\bar{x}} = 558.4$.

MULTIPLE CHOICE/SHORT QUESTIONS

Chapter 1

1. The management function 'organizing' focuses on the
   (a) process by which the structure and allocation of jobs are determined.
   (b) course of actions that can be chosen from available alternatives.
   (c) process by which manager anticipates the future.
   (d) process by which manager select, train, promote, and retire sub-ordinates.

2. According to International Labour Organisation, management is the
   (a) process of planning, organising, staffing, leading and influencing people, and controlling.
   (b) getting things done by other people.
   (c) art of co-ordinating men, machine, material, money, market, information and knowledge.
   (d) complex of continuously co-ordinated activity by means of which any undertaking obliguesing administration public or private service conducts its business.

3. What are the three major schools of management thought?
   (a) Quantitative school, management process school, and behavioural school.
   (b) Quality school, management control, and management thought school.
   (c) Management system school, management thought school and communication management school.
   (d) Organisation of management school, management proces school, and behavioural school.

4. One of the decisional roles of the manager is
   (a) monitor   (b) disseminator
   (c) knowledge team builder   (d) disturbance handler

5. One of the informational roles of the manager is
   (a) disseminator   (b) entrepreneur
   (c) leader   (d) liaison.

6. What are the **three** modes of change in the organisation?

7. What is re-engineering?

8. What are the **three** interpersonal role of management.

9. Mention **any two** knowledge leadership role of management.

10. Write **four** managerial functions in the management process.

Chapter 2

1. Military organisation is known as
   (a) line organisation   (b) line and staff organisation
   (c) fundamental organisation   (d) matrix organisation

2. Functional organisation was developed by
   (a) Frank Gilbreth
   (b) F.W. Taylor
   (c) ASME
   (d) Gantt
3. What are **two** main techniques of organisation planning?
4. Define the principle of functional task.
5. Functional organisation is
   (a) less differentiated and more diffused.
   (b) more differentiated and longer-term.
   (c) more differentiated and focused.
   (d) goal orientation.
6. Mention **five** basic parts of an organisation.
7. Divisional organisation is
   (a) less differentiated and shorter-term.
   (b) formality of structure.
   (c) time-orientation.
   (d) more differentiated with less formality.
8. Matrix organisation induces
   (a) focusing of undivided human effort on two (or more) essential organisational tasks simultaneously.
   (b) formality of structure.
   (c) time orientation.
   (d) confrontation.
9. Three popular models of organisation development are
   (a) Lewin's unfreezing, changing and freezing model, Taylor's model, French model
   (b) Turner model, Leavitt's system model, Maslow model
   (c) Peter Drucker model, Alfred Candler model, Larry Griener's sequential process model
   (d) Leavitt's system model, Lewin's unfreezing, changing and freezing model, Lary Griener's sequential process model
10. What is the main characteristic of successful organisation development programme?

Chapter 3

1. The founder of scientific management was
   (a) F.W. Taylor
   (b) F. Gilbreth
   (c) H. Gantt
   (d) H. Simon
2. Standing orders, which are statutory, are applicable to
   (a) all industries.
   (b) all process industries.
   (c) only major industries.
   (d) all industries employing more than 100 workers.
3. The classical management principle in terms of human factors was proposed by
   (a) Elton Mayo
   (b) M.P. Follett
   (c) F.W. Taylor
   (d) Kurt Lewin.

4. Taylor's philosophy of scientific management pays attention to
   (a) convert inputs to desired outputs
   (b) plan appropriate manpower
   (c) time management
   (d) develop a scientific method for each element of work so as to replace rule of thumb.

5. Manufacturing a number of identical parts/products in lots either to meet a specific order or to meet continuous demand is known as
   (a) job production
   (b) batch production
   (c) continuous production
   (d) flow production.

6. Strategic management is primarily carried out by
   (a) top management
   (b) middle management
   (c) knowledge management
   (d) operational management.

7. What is SWOT analysis?

8. Functional responsibility of systems management is
   (a) Organsiational analysis
   (b) Development of written policies and procedures
   (c) Work measurement
   (d) All of the above.

9. Mention three essential management functions.

10. What do you understand by SMART.

Chapter 4

1. The appellate authority for any industrial dispute is
   (a) Management
   (b) Labour Court
   (c) High Court/Supreme Court
   (d) Board of Directors

2. Induction and orientation are part of the following human resource management functions:
   (a) Recruitment
   (b) Training
   (c) Re-training
   (d) Skill development

3. Managers who displays Theory X behaviour are
   (a) autocratic
   (b) democratic
   (c) participative
   (d) situational

4. Anthropology is one of the disciplines of human resource management which deals with
   (a) measurement and analysis of physical factors in achieving efficiency.
   (b) development of a socio-technical model for employees' health and safety improvement.
   (c) cultural variations and discoverable patterns of behaviour from history and environment.
   (d) allocation of scarce resources with orientation to future.

5. The process of human resource planning consists of demand forecasting, supply forecasting, determining human resource requirements, productivity and cost analysis, action planning, and
   (a) human asset accounting
   (b) internal supply analysis

      (*c*) analysis of manpower utilisation

      (*d*) human resource budgeting and control

6. Long-term manpower forecasts are made usually for

      (*a*) about 2 to 5 years   (*b*) about 3 to 5 years

      (*c*) over five years   (*d*) less than five years

7. What are four Cs of human resources management?

8. Benchmarking is used to develop objectives by

      (*a*) obtaining reports from the Government

      (*b*) using SMART objectives

      (*c*) making comparisons with excellent/best-practice companies

      (*d*) listening to suggestions from employees.

9. What is the overall aim of recruitment and selection process?

10. Mention **five** on-the-job training methods.

Chapter 5

1. Should one consider transportation facilities as an important factor for evaluating location alternatives of organisations?

2. Are process layouts meant to handle a high-variety, low-volume mix?

3. What are the criteria for selection of a site?

4. Mention **two** new concepts developed by Sargant Florance for industrial location.

5. The objectives of plant layout are

      (*a*) optimum utilization of resources   (*b*) better inventory control

      (*c*) economics of material handling   (*d*) All of the above

6. What are the tools and techniques of plant layout?

7. State **two** computerised layout design procedures.

8. What is full abbreviation of CRAFT.

9. Define ALDEP.

10. What is CORELAP?

Chapter 6

1. Why is preventive maintenance better than the breakdown maintenance in a shop-floor?

2. How is generalized relationship of failure depicted?

3. What are the **four** important functions of maintenance?

4. Define condition-based maintenance?

5. When is shutdown maintenance carried out?

6. In your opinion, when maintenance work of public utilities be carried out?

7. In order to formulate a maintenance strategy and evolve a maintenance plan, the maintenance engineer must find

      (*a*) important items for repair

      (*b*) whether work can be done without loss of production/facilities/service.

      (*c*) what is required to be done

      (*d*) All of the above

8. Work measurement techniques are

      (*a*) direct standards, work sheets, work content comparison

      (*b*) work sheets, indirect standards, breakdown analysis

(c) critical analysis, work content comparison, non-repetitive work

(d) direct standards, non-repetitive work, breakdown analysis

9. What are the **two** main divisions of maintenance standards?

10. How is downtime index calculated?

Chapter 7

1. The method of classification of items to be adopted for spare part inventory is
   - (a) ABC analysis
   - (b) VED analysis
   - (c) XYZ analysis
   - (d) SDI analysis.

2. A simple EOQ model consists of the following costs:
   - (a) Carrying and stockout
   - (b) Ordering and stockout
   - (c) Carrying and ordering
   - (d) Carrying and back order.

3. Regardless of approach used, the key element necessary in determining the level of safety stock which should be carried is the
   - (a) demand for items being inventoried
   - (b) length of lead time
   - (c) lead time demand for items
   - (d) cost of stockout per unit of time

4. The time elapsed between the placing of an order and its arrival is called as
   - (a) cycle time
   - (b) lead time
   - (c) work station process time
   - (d) None of the above.

5. EOQ is influenced too much by
   - (a) lead time
   - (b) inventory carrying cost
   - (c) variable demand rate
   - (d) production rate.

6. The following is **not** a basic component of an inventory control system:
   - (a) Planning what inventory to stock and how to acquire it.
   - (b) Forecasting the demand for parts and products
   - (c) Organising the internal inventory users and explain how they can help control inventory costs
   - (d) Controlling inventory levels.

7. A company requires 9000 units of a certain item annually. It costs Rs. 3.00 per unit. The cost per purchase order is Rs 300.00 and the inventory carrying cost per unit per year is 20 per cent of the unit cost. The economic order quantity for the company is
   - (a) 4000 units
   - (b) 3500 units
   - (c) 3000 units
   - (d) 5000 units

8. In EOQ model, if the unit ordering cost is doubled, what happens to the EOQ?

9. Are MRP techniques applicable only for manufacturing situations?

10. What are the **four** main heads under which systems and procedures in stores can be classified?

Chapter 8

1. Break-even analysis shows profit when
   - (a) sales revenue > fixed cost
   - (b) sales revenue > variable cost
   - (c) sales revenue > total cost
   - (d) sales revenus = fixed cost

2. All financial decisions on any project appraisal are based on the
   - (a) future value of money
   - (b) present value of money
   - (c) opportunity cost of money
   - (d) Any one of above.

3. In a balance-sheet, bills receivable is a part of
   - (a) current - liabilities
   - (b) long-term liabilities
   - (c) fixed assets
   - (d) current assets

4. Functions of finance includes
   - (a) investment decision
   - (b) wage and incentive distribution
   - (c) sales distribution
   - (d) costing the products

5. If the cost of manufacturing (direct material and direct labour) is 60% of sales and profit is 10% of sales, what would be the improvement in profit, if the cost of manufacturing is reduced from 60% to 50% keeping other expenses constant?
   - (a) 50%
   - (b) 200%
   - (c) 75%
   - (d) 100%

6. The objective of financial management is to
   - (a) minimize wastage
   - (b) maximize profit and return
   - (c) maximize wealth
   - (d) (b) and (c) above

7. External reporting of balance-sheet and profit and loss account includes
   - (a) shareholders
   - (b) financial institutions/banks
   - (c) taxation authorities and govt. & semi-govt. authorities
   - (d) All of the above.

8. Sources of funds include
   - (a) funds from operations
   - (b) sale of investments and other fixed assets
   - (c) increase in fixed assets
   - (d) decrease in working capital.

9. To analyse a financial ratio, two main ways are
   - (a) increase in liabilities
   - (b) dividend received
   - (c) trend analysis and comparative analysis
   - (d) depreciation and amortization

10. How is return on investment ratio calculated?

Chapter 9

1. The elasticity of total cost of the function, $C = 2x^2 + 4x + 3$, is
   - (a) $(4x^2 + 4x)/(2x^2 + 4x + 3)$
   - (b) $(2x^2 + 4x + 3)/(4x^2 + 4x)$
   - (c) $(4x^2 + 4x)(2x^2 + 4x + 3)$
   - (d) None of the above.

2. The general mathematical form of the production function is

    (a) $Q = f(L, K, R, S, V, Y)$

    (b) $Q = f(L, K, V, Y)$

    (c) $Q = f(K, R, S, Y)$

    (d) $Q = f(L, R, S, V)$

where Q = specific output of various inputs as labour (L), capital (K), raw material (R), land (S), returns to scale (V), and efficiency parameter (Y).

3. If the production function of a firm is $Q = 4L^{3/4} K^{1/4}$, $L > 0$, $K > 0$, the marginal product of capital is

    (a) $MPK = 3L^{-1/4} K^{-3/4}$

    (b) $MPK = L^{3/4} K^{-3/4}$

    (c) $MPK = 4L^{3/4} K^{1/4}$

    (d) None of the above

4. The production function derived by Cobb and Douglas, using the annual data for production, is

    (a) $Q = AL^{\alpha} K^{\beta}$

    (b) $Q = \lambda^{\alpha+\beta} f(L, K)$

    (c) $Q = 1.01 L^{0.75} K^{0.25}$

    (d) $Q = \lambda^{\alpha} f(L, K)$

5. What is average fixed cost?

6. When a product, that sells for Rs 600, has a contribution of 70% of the selling price, what is its variable cost?

7. Management of a processing plant is considering to add Rs 90,000 conveyor belt that engineers estimate will last for 10 years and generate savings of Rs 20,000 per year. Assuming no salvage value, what is the approximate internal rate of return expected on the conveyor.

8. When is the firm in short-term equilibrium?

9. If the total cost function of a firm is $C = \dfrac{1}{3}x^3 - 5x^2 + 30x + 10$, where C is the total cost and x, the output under perfect competition given as 6. At what values of x will the profit be maximized?

10. What is cost elasticity?

Chapter 10

1. What are the three phases of activities suggested by Juran for continuous quality improvement?

    (a) Quality planning, quality control, and quality improvement

    (b) Total quality management, quality assurance, quality planning

    (c) Quality control, quality assurance, and quality improvement

    (d) Quality planning, quality assurance, and total quality management.

2. What are the four factors in Deming's cycle?

3. What was the main contribution in quality improvement by Philip B Crosby?

4. Define in brief ISO 9002.

5. Define quality circle.

6. What is the shortest formula for reliability?

7. Mention 4 Ps in cause-effect diagram.

8. The **seven** control tools for quality improvement are scatter diagram, histogram, graphs and charts, Pareto diagram, cause-effect to diagram, control chart, and _____.

9. Checksheets are forms specially prepared enable data to be collected simply by making _____.

10. ISO 9003 is a model for _____.

Chapter 11

1. Mention **four** important reasons for an organisation to start the development of a new product.

2. Describe essential 4 Ps for marketing activities.

3. According to Philip Kotler, a well known author in marketing, marketing is a human activity directed at satisfying.

4. What are **five** most common accepted characteristics of marketing of services?

5. At the growth stage of a product, the price of the product is
   - (a) highest
   - (c) moderate
   - (b) lowest
   - (d) high

6. Brand of an engineering product means
   - (a) word
   - (c) symbol and device
   - (b) mark
   - (d) All of the above

7. Advantages of a matrix organisation are
   - (a) permits task/project focus with loosing benefits of specialisation.
   - (b) prove costly because of large volume of information processing.
   - (c) provide a flexible structure.
   - (d) Both (a) and (c) above.

8. In Howard-Sheth model of buyer behaviour, **four** major sets of variables are inputs, outputs, exogenous/external, and _____.

9. In pricing strategy of Pricing and Promotion decisions, four types of competition are perfect competition, monopoly, _____ and _____.

10. In sales promotion schemes, the objective of price-off offers means to
   - (a) encourage immediate sales, attract non-users, induce trial of a new product, counter competition, inventory clearance at the retail level, inventory build-up at the trade level.
   - (b) encourage purchase, off-season sales promotion
   - (c) add speed to slow moving products.
   - (d) encourage regular users, reinforce brand image, and counter competition.

Chapter 12

1. PERT never uses
   - (a) activities with probabilistic times
   - (c) activity variance estimates
   - (b) dummy activities
   - (d) None of the above

2. In a PERT network, expected time estimate (t_e) is calculated as $t_e = (a + 4m + b)/6$ based on the assumption of
   (a) normal distribution of time estimates
   (b) exponential distribution of time estimates
   (c) beta distribution of time estimates
   (d) gamma distribution of time estimates

3. In a project network, there could be following number of critical paths:
   (a) 0   (b) exactly one
   (c) exactly two   (d) one or many.

4. In PERT analysis, one usually takes the following number of time estimates for each activity:
   (a) 1   (b) 2
   (c) 3   (d) 4

5. Slack represents the difference between
   (a) latest allowed time and normal expected time.
   (b) latest allowed time and earliest expected time.
   (c) proposed allowable time and earliest expected time.
   (d) project limitation time and actual starting project.

6. What are **three** major classified industrial projects?

7. Which one of the following is **not** the project monitoring and progressing techniques?
   (a) Progress measurement technique
   (b) Performance monitoring technique
   (c) Updating, reviewing and reporting technique
   (d) Network techniques (PERT/CPM/GERT)

8. According to Planning Commission's Memorandum Feasibility Studies for Public Sector projects, the main factor covered in a feasibility report includes
   (a) raw material survey   (b) demand study
   (c) investment study, and profitability and cash-flow analysis
   (d) All of the above

9. Which one of the following is **not** the project cost and productivity control techniques?
   (a) Computerized information systems
   (b) Productivity budgeting technique
   (c) Value engineering
   (d) COST/WBS

10. The profitability analysis of a project may focus on cost of production, working results, and _____.

Chapter 13

1. The availability of information to management at various levels has improved due to development of telecommunication; processing of data with computer; and _____.

2. A decision support system usually supports which level of management?
   (a) Operational management
   (b) Knowledge level management

(*c*) Middle level management

(*d*) None of the above.

3. Specify the nature of information required by top management to take decision.

   (*a*) Sporadic and one-shot

   (*b*) Operational, instantaneous, on-line

   (*c*) Operational

   (*d*) None of the above.

4. What are the **five** objectives of an effective MIS?

5. Information providing system is meant for processing information, making a summary of information, and providing _____.

6. The management activities at middle level management are _____ and _____.

7. What are the information needs and sources for purchasing?

8. Top down approach for MIS development develops/permits

   (*a*) individual functional applications.

   (*b*) managers at all levels to influence the design of MIS.

   (*c*) activities in sequence.

   (*d*) a corporate plan as a guide for designing the information system.

9. A decision support system is an _____.

10. Enterprise resource planning is a software achitecture facilitating the _____.

Appendix–I

1. A control chart that plots the fractive defective or percent defective items from samples is a

   (*a*) $\bar{X}$ bar chart   (*b*) R chart

   (*c*) P chart   (*d*) C chart

2. Show mathematically how upper and lower control limits are calculated in a $\bar{X}$-bar-*R*-chart.

3. Mention **two** types of control charts.

4. What are **two** types of control charts for variables?

5. There are two types of $\bar{X}$ charts, i.e., $\bar{X}$ and σ charts, and _____.

6. Charts for fraction defectives are known as charts. _____

7. Charts for total number of defectives are known as charts _____.

8. *np* charts are better used when lot size is

   (*a*) more   (*b*) less

   (*c*) remains constant   (*d*) None of the above

9. If lot size varies, it is always better to use

   (*a*) *np* chart   (*b*) $\bar{X}$ chart

   (*c*) R chart   (*d*) P chart

10. A sampling plan is specified by the _____ and _____.

Answers to Multiple Choice/Short Questions

Chapter 1
1. *a*   2. *d*   3. *a*
4. *d*   5. *a*
6. Continuous improvement, benchmarking and re-engineering
7. Total, radical redesign of the system
8. Figurehead, leader, liaison
9. Knowledge team builder, sustaining and maintaining knowledge
10. Planning, organising, directing, and controlling

Chapter 2
1. *a*   2. *b*
3. Organisation analysis and organisation design
4. Each employee must be assigned specific task, role, relationship, and job-related activities
5. *c*
6. Operating core, strategic apex, middle line, technostructure, support staff
7. *d*   8. *a*   9. *d*
10. Successful organisation develop capable people who keep the organisation flexible and responsive to changing needs and goals.

Chapter 3
1. *a*   2. *d*   3. *b*
4. *d*   5. *b*   6. *a*
7. SWOT analysis is strengths, weaknesses, opportunities, and threats facing the organisation
8. *d*
9. Directing, implementing, evaluating
10. S–Specific about what to be accomplished; M–Measurable difference must be identified; A–Attainable targets should be established; R–Result output-oriented change is desirable; T–Time limits should be established

Chapter 4
1. *c*   2. *b*   3. *a*
4. *c*   5. *d*   6. *c*
7. commitment, competence, congruence, cost-effectiveness
8. *c*
9. Define requirement, attracting candidates, and selecting candidates.
10. (*a*) On-the-job training; (*b*) Vestibule training; (*c*) Simulation; (*d*) Demonstration and examples; (*e*) Apprenticeship

Chapter 5
1. Yes, transportation facilities, *e.g.*, rail, air and road facilities form an important factor for evaluating location alternatives of organizations
2. Yes
3. Price of land, disposal of waste
4. Location factor, coefficient of location
5. *d*
6. Process charts, process flow diagrams, machine data cards, visualization of layout
7. Improvement-type algorithm, construction type algorithm
8. Computerised Relative Allocation of Facilities Technique
9. It is a automated layout design program (ALDEP) using basic data on facilities and builds a design by successively placing the departments in the layout
10. CORELAP is a computerized relationship layout planning

Chapter 6
1. Breakdown leads to sudden halt of production and poor health of machines. Preventive maintenance on the contrary could be judiciously planned
2. Bath-tub-curve

3. Inspection/check-ups, lubrication, storage of spare parts, training to maintenance staff

4. It is corrective maintenance based on condition monitoring, where continuous checks are made to determine the 'health' of an item and to expose incipient faults

5. It is carried out when the item is out of service

6. Public holidays, evenings and weekends

7. *d*   8. *a*

9. Quality standards, service standards

10. Downtime index = (Downtime hours × 100)/Production hours

Chapter 7

1. *b*   2. *c*   3. *b*

4. *b*   5. *c*   6. *c*

7. *c*

8. Decrease 1.414 times

9. No

10. Identification system, receipt system, storage system, issue system

Chapter 8

1. *c*   2. *b*   3. *d*

4. *a*   5. *d*   6. *d*

7. *d*   8. *c*   9. *d*

10. (Profit before taxes × sales)/(sales × equity capital)

Chapter 9

1. *a*   2. *a*   3. *b*

4. *c*

5. Average fixed cost = Total fixed cost/output

6. Rs. 180

7. 18%

8. When it intends to maximize its profit by producing and selling units of a commodity

9. $x = 4, 6$

10. The relative change in total cost in response to the proportionate change in output

Chapter 10

1. *a*

2. Plan, do, check, act

3. Awareness, zero defects, do it right first time

4. It specifies a model for quality assurance in production and installation

5. A group who meet voluntarily and regularly to identify and solve their non-work-related problems and implement their solutions with management approval

6. Reliability = Quality now + Quality later

7. Promotion, place, price, and product

8. Check sheets

9. Check marks

10. Quality assurance in final inspection testing

Chapter 11

1. Targetting specific customer segment; improve sales; reduce cost of production; simplification and standardisation

2. Product, price, promotion, and place

3. Human needs and wants through exchange processes

4. Intangibility, inseparability, heterogeneity, perishability, ownership

5. *d*   6. *d*   7. *d*

8. Perceptual and learning constructs

9. Oligopoly and monopolistic

10. *a*

Chapter 12

1. *d*   2. *c*   3. *d*

4. *c*   5. *b*

6. Normal project, crash project, and disaster project

7. *d*   8. *d*   9. *a*

10. Break-even level

Chapter 13

1. Video technology
2. *c*   3. *a*
4. Facilitate, provide, help, support, a system of people, computers, required documents, etc
5. Exception reports
6. Tactical planning, decision making
7. Comparison of prices, quality, lead time with predetermined standards
8. *d*
9. Interactive data processing and display system for decision making
10. Flow of information among different functions of an organisation

Appendix–I

1. *c*
2. $\text{UCL} = \overline{\overline{X}} - K\sigma_{\overline{X}}$, $\text{LCL} = \overline{\overline{X}} - K\sigma_{\overline{x}}$

   where $\overline{\overline{X}}$ = average of sample averages and $\sigma_{\overline{X}}$ = standard deviation of sample averages
3. Control charts for variables and control charts for attributes
4. $\overline{X}$ charts and R charts
5. $\overline{X}$ and R charts
6. *p*   7. *np*   8. *c*
9. *d*
10. Sample size *n*, acceptance number *c*

NOTES

NOTES

NOTES

NOTES